GROUP THEORY

AND ITS APPLICATION TO THE
QUANTUM MECHANICS OF ATOMIC SPECTRA

PURE AND APPLIED PHYSICS

A SERIES OF MONOGRAPHS AND TEXTBOOKS

CONSULTING EDITOR

H. S. W. MASSEY

University College, London, England

Volume 1. F. H. FIELD and J. L. FRANKLIN, Electron Impact Phenomena and the Properties of Gaseous Ions. 1957

Volume 2. H. KOPFERMANN, Nuclear Moments. English Version Prepared from the Second German Edition by E. E. SCHNEIDER. 1958

Volume 3. WALTER E. THIRRING, Principles of Quantum Electrodynamics. Translated from the German by J. BERNSTEIN. With Additions and Corrections by WALTER E. THIRRING. 1958

Volume 4. U. FANO and G. RACAH, Irreducible Tensorial Sets. 1959

Volume 5. E. P. WIGNER, Group Theory and Its Application to the Quantum Mechanics of Atomic Spectra. With Additions and Corrections by E. P. WIGNER. Translated from the German by J. J. GRIFFIN. 1959

Volume 6. J. IRVING and N. MULLINEUX, Mathematics in Physics and Engineering. 1959

Volume 7. KARL F. HERZFELD and THEODORE A. LITOVITZ, Absorption and Dispersion of Ultrasonic Waves. 1959

IN PREPARATION

FAY AJZENBERG-SELOVE (ed.). Nuclear Spectroscopy.

ACADEMIC PRESS *New York and London*

GROUP THEORY

AND ITS APPLICATION TO THE QUANTUM MECHANICS OF ATOMIC SPECTRA

EUGENE P. WIGNER
Palmer Physical Laboratory, Princeton University
Princeton, New Jersey

TRANSLATED FROM THE GERMAN BY

J. J. GRIFFIN
University of California, Los Alamos Scientific Laboratory
Los Alamos, New Mexico

EXPANDED AND IMPROVED EDITION

1959

ACADEMIC PRESS NEW YORK AND LONDON

ACADEMIC PRESS INC.
111 FIFTH AVENUE
NEW YORK 3, N. Y.

United Kingdom Edition
Published by
ACADEMIC PRESS INC. (LONDON) LTD.
40 PALL MALL, LONDON SW 1

Library of Congress Catalog Card Number 59–10741

PRINTED IN THE UNITED STATES OF AMERICA

Author's Preface

The purpose of this book is to describe the application of group theoretical methods to problems of quantum mechanics with specific reference to atomic spectra. The actual solution of quantum mechanical equations is, in general, so difficult that one obtains by direct calculations only crude approximations to the real solutions. It is gratifying, therefore, that a large part of the relevant results can be deduced by considering the fundamental symmetry operations.

When the original German version was first published, in 1931, there was a great reluctance among physicists toward accepting group theoretical arguments and the group theoretical point of view. It pleases the author that this reluctance has virtually vanished in the meantime and that, in fact, the younger generation does not understand the causes and the basis for this reluctance. Of the older generation it was probably M. von Laue who first recognized the significance of group theory as the natural tool with which to obtain a first orientation in problems of quantum mechanics. Von Laue's encouragement of both publisher and author contributed significantly to bringing this book into existence. I like to recall his question as to which results derived in the present volume I considered most important. My answer was that the explanation of Laporte's rule (the concept of parity) and the quantum theory of the vector addition model appeared to me most significant. Since that time, I have come to agree with his answer that the recognition that almost all rules of spectroscopy follow from the symmetry of the problem is the most remarkable result.

Three new chapters have been added in translation. The second half of Chapter 24 reports on the work of Racah and of his followers. Chapter 24 of the German edition now appears as Chapter 25. Chapter 26 deals with time inversion, a symmetry operation which had not yet been recognized at the time the German edition was written. The contents of the last part of this chapter, as well as that of Chapter 27, have not appeared before in print. While Chapter 27 appears at the end of the book for editorial reasons, the reader may be well advised to glance at it when studying, in Chapters 17 and 24, the relevant concepts. The other chapters represent the translation of Dr. J. J. Griffin, to whom the author is greatly indebted for his ready acceptance of several suggestions and his generally cooperative attitude. He also converted the left-handed coordinate system originally used to a right-handed system and added an Appendix on notations.

The character of the book—its explicitness and its restriction to one subject only, viz. the quantum mechanics of atomic spectra—has not been changed. Its principal results were contained in articles first published in the *Zeitschrift für Physik* in 1926 and early 1927. The initial stimulus for these articles was given by the investigations of Heisenberg and Dirac on the quantum theory of assemblies of identical particles. Weyl delivered lectures in Zürich on related subjects during the academic year 1927–1928. These were later expanded into his well-known book.

When it became known that the German edition was being translated, many additions were suggested. It is regrettable that most of these could not be followed without substantially changing the outlook and also the size of the volume. Author and translator nevertheless are grateful for these suggestions which were very encouraging. The author also wishes to thank his colleagues for many stimulating discussions on the role of group theory in quantum mechanics as well as on more specific subjects. He wishes to record his deep indebtedness to Drs. Bargmann, Michel, Wightman, and, last but not least, J. von Neumann.

E. P. Wigner

Princeton, New Jersey
February, 1959

Translator's Preface

This translation was initiated while the translator was a graduate student at Princeton University. It was motivated by the lack of a good English work on the subject of group theory from the physicist's point of view. Since that time, several books have been published in English which deal with group theory in quantum mechanics. Still, it is perhaps a reasonable hope that this translation will facilitate the introduction of English-speaking physicists to the use of group theory in modern physics.

The book is an interlacing of physics and mathematics. The first three chapters discuss the elements of linear vector theory. The second three deal more specifically with the rudiments of quantum mechanics itself. Chapters 7 through 16 are again mathematical, although much of the material covered should be familiar from an elementary course in quantum theory. Chapters 17 through 23 are specifically concerned with atomic spectra, as is Chapter 25. The remaining chapters are additions to the German text; they discuss topics which have been developed since the original publication of this book: the recoupling (Racah) coefficients, the time inversion operation, and the classical interpretations of the coefficients.

Various readers may wish to utilize the book differently. Those who are interested specifically in the mathematics of group theory might skim over the chapters dealing with quantum physics. Others might choose to de-emphasize the mathematics, touching Chapters 7, 9, 10, 13, and 14 lightly for background and devoting more attention to the subsequent chapters. Students of quantum mechanics and physicists who prefer familiar material interwoven with the less familiar will probably apply a more even distribution of emphasis.

The translator would like to express his gratitude to Professor E. P. Wigner for encouraging and guiding the task, to Drs. Robert Johnston and John McHale who suggested various improvements in the text, and to Mrs. Marjorie Dresback whose secretarial assistance was most valuable.

J. J. GRIFFIN

Los Alamos, New Mexico
February, 1959

Contents

1. Vectors and Matrices

Linear Transformations

An aggregate of n numbers $(\mathfrak{v}_1, \mathfrak{v}_2, \mathfrak{v}_3, \cdots, \mathfrak{v}_n)$ is called an n-dimensional vector, or a vector in n-dimensional space; the numbers themselves are the components of this vector. The coordinates of a point in n-dimensional space can also be interpreted as a vector which connects the origin of the coordinate system with the point considered. Vectors will be denoted by bold face German letters; their components will carry a roman index which specifies the coordinate axis. Thus $\mathfrak{v}_k$ is a vector component (a number), and $\boldsymbol{\mathfrak{v}}$ is a vector, a set of n numbers.

Two vectors are said to be equal if their corresponding components are equal. Thus

$$\boldsymbol{\mathfrak{v}} = \boldsymbol{\mathfrak{w}} \tag{1.1}$$

is equivalent to the n equations

$$\mathfrak{v}_1 = \mathfrak{w}_1; \qquad \mathfrak{v}_2 = \mathfrak{w}_2; \qquad \cdots; \qquad \mathfrak{v}_n = \mathfrak{w}_n .$$

A vector is a null vector if all its components vanish. The product $c\boldsymbol{\mathfrak{v}}$ of a number c with a vector $\boldsymbol{\mathfrak{v}}$ is a vector whose components are c times the components of $\boldsymbol{\mathfrak{v}}$, or $(c\boldsymbol{\mathfrak{v}})_k = c\mathfrak{v}_k$. Addition of vectors is defined by the rule that the components of the sum are equal to the sums of the corresponding components. Formally

$$(\boldsymbol{\mathfrak{v}} + \boldsymbol{\mathfrak{w}})_k = \mathfrak{v}_k + \mathfrak{w}_k . \tag{1.2}$$

In mathemtaical problems it is often advantageous to introduce new variables in place of the original ones. In the simplest case the new variables $x_1', x_2', \cdots, x_n'$ are linear functions of the old ones, $x_1, x_2, \cdots, x_n$. That is

$$\begin{aligned} x_1' &= \boldsymbol{\alpha}_{11}x_1 + \cdots + \boldsymbol{\alpha}_{1n}x_n \\ x_2' &= \boldsymbol{\alpha}_{21}x_1 + \cdots + \boldsymbol{\alpha}_{2n}x_n \\ &\cdot \\ &\cdot \\ &\cdot \\ x_n' &= \boldsymbol{\alpha}_{n1}x_1 + \cdots + \boldsymbol{\alpha}_{nn}x_n \end{aligned} \tag{1.3}$$

or

$$x_i' = \sum_{k=1}^{n} \boldsymbol{\alpha}_{ik} x_k . \tag{1.3a}$$

The introduction of new variables in this way is called *linear transformation*.

The transformation is completely determined by the coefficients $\boldsymbol{\alpha}_{11}, \cdots, \boldsymbol{\alpha}_{nn}$, and the aggregate of these n^2 numbers arranged in a square array is called the *matrix* of the linear transformation (1.3):

$$\begin{pmatrix} \boldsymbol{\alpha}_{11} & \boldsymbol{\alpha}_{12} & \cdots & \boldsymbol{\alpha}_{1n} \\ \boldsymbol{\alpha}_{21} & \boldsymbol{\alpha}_{22} & \cdots & \boldsymbol{\alpha}_{2n} \\ \cdot & \cdot & & \cdot \\ \cdot & \cdot & & \cdot \\ \cdot & \cdot & & \cdot \\ \boldsymbol{\alpha}_{n1} & \boldsymbol{\alpha}_{n2} & \cdots & \boldsymbol{\alpha}_{nn} \end{pmatrix} \tag{1.4}$$

We shall write such a matrix more concisely as $(\boldsymbol{\alpha}_{ik})$ or simply $\boldsymbol{\alpha}$.

For Eq. (1.3) actually to represent an introduction of new variables, it is necessary not only that the x' be expressible in terms of the x, but also that the x can be expressed in terms of the x'. That is, if we view the x_i as unknowns in Eq. (1.3), a unique solution to these equations must exist giving the x in terms of the x'. The necessary and sufficient condition for this is that the determinant formed from the coefficients $\boldsymbol{\alpha}_{ik}$ be nonzero:

$$\begin{vmatrix} \boldsymbol{\alpha}_{11} & \cdots & \boldsymbol{\alpha}_{1n} \\ \cdot & & \cdot \\ \cdot & & \cdot \\ \cdot & & \cdot \\ \boldsymbol{\alpha}_{n1} & \cdots & \boldsymbol{\alpha}_{nn} \end{vmatrix} \neq 0. \tag{1.4a}$$

Transformations whose matrices have nonvanishing determinants are referred to as *proper* transformations, but an array of coefficients like (1.4) is always called a matrix, whether or not it induces a proper transformation. Boldface letters are used to represent matrices; matrix coefficients are indicated by affixing indices specifying the corresponding axes. Thus $\boldsymbol{\alpha}$ is a matrix, an array of n^2 numbers; $\boldsymbol{\alpha}_{jk}$ is a matrix element (a number).

Two matrices are equal if all their corresponding coefficients are equal. Thus

$$\boldsymbol{\alpha} = \boldsymbol{\beta} \tag{1.5}$$

is equivalent to the n^2 equations

$$\boldsymbol{\alpha}_{jk} = \boldsymbol{\beta}_{jk} \qquad (j, k = 1, 2, \cdots, n).$$

Another interpretation can be placed on the equation

$$x_i' = \sum_{k=1}^{n} \boldsymbol{\alpha}_{ik} x_k \tag{1.3a}$$

by considering the x_j', not as components of the original vector in a new coordinate system, but as the components of a *new vector in the original coordinate system.* We then say that the matrix $\boldsymbol{\alpha}$ transforms the vector $\mathfrak{x}$ into the vector $\mathfrak{x}'$, or that $\boldsymbol{\alpha}$ applied to $\mathfrak{x}$ gives $\mathfrak{x}'$

$$\mathfrak{x}' = \boldsymbol{\alpha}\mathfrak{x}. \tag{1.3b}$$

This equation is completely equivalent to (1.3a).

An n-dimensional matrix is a *linear operator* on n-dimensional vectors. It is an *operator* because it transforms one vector into another vector; it is *linear* since for arbitrary numbers a and b, and arbitrary vectors $\mathfrak{r}$ and $\mathfrak{v}$, the relation

$$\boldsymbol{\alpha}(a\mathfrak{r} + b\mathfrak{v}) = a\boldsymbol{\alpha}\mathfrak{r} + b\boldsymbol{\alpha}\mathfrak{v} \tag{1.6}$$

is true. To prove (1.6) one need only write out the left and right sides explicitly. The kth component of $a\mathfrak{r} + b\mathfrak{v}$ is $a\mathfrak{r}_k + b\mathfrak{v}_k$, so that the ith component of the vector on the left is:

$$\sum_{k=1}^{n} \boldsymbol{\alpha}_{ik}(a\mathfrak{r}_k + b\mathfrak{v}_k).$$

But this is identical with the ith component of the vector on the right side of (1.6)

$$a\sum_{k=1}^{n} \boldsymbol{\alpha}_{ik}\mathfrak{r}_k + b\sum_{k=1}^{n} \boldsymbol{\alpha}_{ik}\mathfrak{v}_k\,.$$

This establishes the linearity of matrix operators.

An n-dimensional matrix is the *most general* linear operator in n-dimensional vector space. That is, every linear operator in this space is equivalent to a matrix. To prove this, consider the arbitrary linear operator O which transforms the vector $\mathfrak{e}_1 = (1, 0, 0, \cdots, 0)$ into the vector $\mathfrak{r}_{\cdot 1}$, the vector $\mathfrak{e}_2 = (0, 1, 0, \cdots, 0)$ into the vector $\mathfrak{r}_{\cdot 2}$, and finally, the vector $\mathfrak{e}_n = (0, 0, 0, \cdots, 1)$ into $\mathfrak{r}_{\cdot n}$, where the components of the vector $\mathfrak{r}_{\cdot k}$ are $\mathfrak{r}_{1k}, \mathfrak{r}_{2k}, \cdots, \mathfrak{r}_{nk}$. Now the matrix $(\mathfrak{r}_{ik})$ transforms each of the vectors $\mathfrak{e}_1, \mathfrak{e}_2, \cdots, \mathfrak{e}_n$ into the same vectors, $\mathfrak{r}_{\cdot 1}, \mathfrak{r}_{\cdot 2}, \cdots, \mathfrak{r}_{\cdot n}$ as does the operator O. Moreover, any n-dimensional vector $\mathfrak{a}$ is a linear combination of the vectors $\mathfrak{e}_1, \mathfrak{e}_2, \cdots, \mathfrak{e}_n$. Thus, both O and $(\mathfrak{r}_{ik})$ (since they are linear) transform any arbitrary vector $\mathfrak{a}$ into the same vector $a_1\mathfrak{r}_{\cdot 1} + \cdots + a_n\mathfrak{r}_{\cdot n}$. The matrix $(\mathfrak{r}_{ik})$ is therefore equivalent to the operator O.

The most important property of linear transformations is that two of them, applied successively, can be combined into a single linear transformation. Suppose, for example, we introduce the variables x' in place of the original x via the linear transformation (1.3), and subsequently introduce variables x'' via *a second linear transformation,*

$$\begin{array}{l} x_1'' = \boldsymbol{\beta}_{11}x_1' + \boldsymbol{\beta}_{12}x_2' + \cdots + \boldsymbol{\beta}_{1n}x_n' \\ \quad\vdots \\ x_n'' = \boldsymbol{\beta}_{n1}x_1' + \boldsymbol{\beta}_{n2}x_2' + \cdots + \boldsymbol{\beta}_{nn}x_n'. \end{array} \tag{1.7}$$

Both processes can be *combined into a single one*, so that the x'' are introduced directly in place of the x by one linear transformation. Substituting (1.3) into (1.7), one finds

$$
\begin{aligned}
x_1'' &= \beta_{11}(\alpha_{11}x_1 + \cdots + \alpha_{1n}x_n) + \cdots + \beta_{1n}(\alpha_{n1}x_1 + \cdots + \alpha_{nn}x_n)\\
x_2'' &= \beta_{21}(\alpha_{11}x_1 + \cdots + \alpha_{1n}x_n) + \cdots + \beta_{2n}(\alpha_{n1}x_1 + \cdots + \alpha_{nn}x_n)\\
&\;\;\vdots\\
x_n'' &= \beta_{n1}(\alpha_{11}x_1 + \cdots + \alpha_{1n}x_n) + \cdots + \beta_{nn}(\alpha_{n1}x_1 + \cdots + \alpha_{nn}x_n).
\end{aligned}
\tag{1.8}
$$

Thus, the x'' are linear functions of the x. We can write (1.8) more concisely by condensing (1.3) and (1.7)

$$x_j' = \sum_{k=1}^{n} \alpha_{jk}x_k \qquad (j = 1, 2, \cdots, n) \tag{1.3c}$$

$$x_i'' = \sum_{j}^{n} \beta_{ij}x_j' \qquad (i = 1, 2, \cdots, n). \tag{1.7a}$$

Then (1.8) becomes

$$x_i'' = \sum_{j=1}^{n} \sum_{k=1}^{n} \beta_{ij}\alpha_{jk}x_k. \tag{1.8a}$$

Furthermore, by defining γ through

$$\gamma_{ik} = \sum_{j=1}^{n} \beta_{ij}\alpha_{jk} \tag{1.9}$$

one obtains simply

$$x_i'' = \sum_{k=1}^{n} \gamma_{ik}x_k. \tag{1.8b}$$

This demonstrates that the combination of two linear transformations (1.7) and (1.3), with matrices (β_{ik}) and (α_{ik}) is a single linear transformation which has the matrix (γ_{ik}).

The matrix (γ_{ik}), defined in terms of the matrices (α_{ik}) and (β_{ik}) according to Eq. (1.9), is called the *product* of the matrices (β_{ik}) and (α_{ik}). Since (α_{ik}) transforms the vector $\mathfrak{r}$ into $\mathfrak{r}' = \alpha\mathfrak{r}$, and (β_{ik}) transforms the vector $\mathfrak{r}'$ into $\mathfrak{r}'' = \beta\mathfrak{r}'$, the product matrix (γ_{ik}) by its definition, transforms $\mathfrak{r}$ directly into $\mathfrak{r}'' = \gamma\mathfrak{r}$. This method of combining transformations is called "matrix multiplication," and exhibits a number of simple properties, which we now enumerate as theorems.

First of all we observe that the formal rule for matrix multiplication is the same as the rule for the multiplication of determinants.

1. *The determinant of a product of two matrices is equal to the product of the determinants of the two factors.*

In the multiplication of matrices, it is not necessarily true that

$$\boldsymbol{\alpha\beta} = \boldsymbol{\beta\alpha}. \tag{1.E.1}$$

For example, consider the two matrices

$$\begin{pmatrix} 1 & 1 \\ 0 & 1 \end{pmatrix} \text{ and } \begin{pmatrix} 1 & 0 \\ 1 & 1 \end{pmatrix}.$$

Then

$$\begin{pmatrix} 1 & 1 \\ 0 & 1 \end{pmatrix}\begin{pmatrix} 1 & 0 \\ 1 & 1 \end{pmatrix} = \begin{pmatrix} 2 & 1 \\ 1 & 1 \end{pmatrix}$$

and

$$\begin{pmatrix} 1 & 0 \\ 1 & 1 \end{pmatrix}\begin{pmatrix} 1 & 1 \\ 0 & 1 \end{pmatrix} = \begin{pmatrix} 1 & 1 \\ 1 & 2 \end{pmatrix}.$$

This establishes a second property of matrix multiplication.

2. *The product of two matrices depends in general upon the order of the factors.*

In the very special situation when Eq. (1.E.1) is true, the matrices $\boldsymbol{\alpha}$ and $\boldsymbol{\beta}$ are said to *commute.*

In contrast to the commutative law,

3. *The associative law of multiplication is valid in matrix multiplication.*

That is,

$$\boldsymbol{\gamma}(\boldsymbol{\beta\alpha}) = (\boldsymbol{\gamma\beta})\boldsymbol{\alpha}. \tag{1.10}$$

Thus, it makes no difference whether one multiplies $\boldsymbol{\gamma}$ with the product of $\boldsymbol{\beta}$ and $\boldsymbol{\alpha}$, or the product of $\boldsymbol{\gamma}$ and $\boldsymbol{\beta}$ with $\boldsymbol{\alpha}$. To prove this, denote the i–kth element of the matrix on the left side of (1.10) by $\boldsymbol{\epsilon}_{ik}$. Then

$$\boldsymbol{\epsilon}_{ik} = \sum_{j=1}^{n} \boldsymbol{\gamma}_{ij}(\boldsymbol{\beta\alpha})_{jk} = \sum_{j=1}^{n}\sum_{l=1}^{n} \boldsymbol{\gamma}_{ij}\boldsymbol{\beta}_{jl}\boldsymbol{\alpha}_{lk}\,. \tag{1.10a}$$

The i–kth element on the right side of (1.10) is

$$\boldsymbol{\epsilon}'_{ik} = \sum_{l=1}^{n} (\boldsymbol{\gamma\beta})_{il}\boldsymbol{\alpha}_{lk} = \sum_{l=1}^{n}\sum_{j=1}^{n} \boldsymbol{\gamma}_{ij}\boldsymbol{\beta}_{jl}\boldsymbol{\alpha}_{lk}\,. \tag{1.10b}$$

Then $\boldsymbol{\epsilon}_{ik} = \boldsymbol{\epsilon}'_{ik}$, and (1.10) is established. One can therefore write simply $\boldsymbol{\gamma\beta\alpha}$ for both sides of (1.10).

The validity of the associative law is immediately obvious if the matrices are considered as linear operators. Let $\boldsymbol{\alpha}$ transform the vector $\mathfrak{r}$ into $\mathfrak{r}' = \boldsymbol{\alpha}\mathfrak{r}$, $\boldsymbol{\beta}$ the vector $\mathfrak{r}'$ into $\mathfrak{r}'' = \boldsymbol{\beta}\mathfrak{r}'$, and $\boldsymbol{\gamma}$ the vector $\mathfrak{r}''$ into $\mathfrak{r}''' = \boldsymbol{\gamma}\mathfrak{r}''$. Then the combination of two matrices into a single one by matrix multiplication signifies simply the combination of two operations. The product $\boldsymbol{\beta\alpha}$ transforms $\mathfrak{r}$ directly into $\mathfrak{r}''$, and $\boldsymbol{\gamma\beta}$ transforms $\mathfrak{r}'$ directly into $\mathfrak{r}'''$. Thus both $(\boldsymbol{\gamma\beta})\boldsymbol{\alpha}$ and $\boldsymbol{\gamma}(\boldsymbol{\beta\alpha})$ transform $\mathfrak{r}$ into $\mathfrak{r}'''$, and the two operations are equivalent.

4. *The unit matrix*

$$\mathbf{1} = \begin{pmatrix} 1 & 0 & 0 & \cdots & 0 \\ 0 & 1 & 0 & \cdots & 0 \\ 0 & 0 & 1 & \cdots & 0 \\ \cdot & \cdot & \cdot & & \cdot \\ \cdot & \cdot & \cdot & & \cdot \\ \cdot & \cdot & \cdot & & \cdot \\ 0 & 0 & 0 & \cdots & 1 \end{pmatrix} \tag{1.11}$$

plays a special role in matrix multiplication, just as the number 1 does in ordinary multiplication. For every matrix $\boldsymbol{\alpha}$,

$$\boldsymbol{\alpha} \cdot \mathbf{1} = \mathbf{1} \cdot \boldsymbol{\alpha}.$$

That is, $\mathbf{1}$ commutes with all matrices, and its product with any matrix is just that matrix again. The elements of the unit matrix are denoted by the symbol δ_{ik}, so that

$$\delta_{ik} = 0 \qquad (i \neq k)$$

$$\delta_{ik} = 1 \qquad (i = k). \tag{1.12}$$

The δ_{ik} defined in this way is called the Kronecker delta-symbol. The matrix $(\delta_{ik}) = \mathbf{1}$ induces the *identity* transformation, which leaves the variables unchanged.

If for a given matrix $\boldsymbol{\alpha}$, there exists a matrix $\boldsymbol{\beta}$ such that

$$\boldsymbol{\beta\alpha} = \mathbf{1}, \tag{1.13}$$

then $\boldsymbol{\beta}$ is called the *inverse*, or *reciprocal*, of the matrix $\boldsymbol{\alpha}$. Equation (1.13) states that a transformation via the matrix $\boldsymbol{\beta}$ exists which combines with $\boldsymbol{\alpha}$ to give the identity transformation. If the determinant of $\boldsymbol{\alpha}$ is not equal to zero ($|\boldsymbol{\alpha}_{ik}| \neq 0$), then an inverse transformation always exists (as has been mentioned on page 2). To prove this we write out the n^2 equations (1.13) more explicitly

$$\sum_{j=1}^{n} \beta_{ij}\alpha_{jk} = \delta_{ik} \qquad (i, k = 1, 2, \cdots, n). \tag{1.14}$$

Consider now the n equations in which i has one value, say l. These are n linear equations for n unknowns $\boldsymbol{\beta}_{l1}, \boldsymbol{\beta}_{l2}, \cdots, \boldsymbol{\beta}_{ln}$. They have, therefore, one and only one solution, provided the determinant $|\boldsymbol{\alpha}_{j\lambda}|$ does not vanish. The same holds for the other $n - 1$ systems of equations. This establishes the fifth property we wish to mention.

5. *If the determinant* $|\boldsymbol{\alpha}_{jk}| \neq 0$, *there exists one and only one matrix* $\boldsymbol{\beta}$ *such that* $\boldsymbol{\beta\alpha} = \mathbf{1}$.

Moreover, the determinant $|\boldsymbol{\beta}_{jk}|$ is the reciprocal of $|\boldsymbol{\alpha}_{jk}|$, since, according to Theorem 1,

$$|\boldsymbol{\beta}_{jk}| \cdot |\boldsymbol{\alpha}_{jk}| = |\delta_{jk}| = \mathbf{1}. \tag{1.15}$$

From this it follows that $\boldsymbol{\alpha}$ *has no inverse if* $|\boldsymbol{\alpha}_{ik}| = 0$, and that $\boldsymbol{\beta}$, the inverse of $\boldsymbol{\alpha}$, must also have an inverse.

We now show that if (1.13) is true, then

$$\boldsymbol{\alpha\beta} = \mathbf{1} \tag{1.16}$$

is true as well. That is, if $\boldsymbol{\beta}$ is the inverse of $\boldsymbol{\alpha}$, then $\boldsymbol{\alpha}$ is also the inverse of $\boldsymbol{\beta}$. This can be seen most simply by multiplying (1.13) from the right with $\boldsymbol{\beta}$,

$$\boldsymbol{\beta\alpha\beta} = \boldsymbol{\beta}, \tag{1.17}$$

and this from the left with the inverse of $\boldsymbol{\beta}$, which we call $\boldsymbol{\gamma}$. Then

$$\boldsymbol{\gamma\beta\alpha\beta} = \boldsymbol{\gamma\beta}$$

and since, by hypothesis $\boldsymbol{\gamma\beta} = \mathbf{1}$, this is identical with (1.16). Conversely, (1.13) follows easily from (1.16). This proves Theorem 6 (the inverse of $\boldsymbol{\alpha}$ is denoted by $\boldsymbol{\alpha}^{-1}$).

6. *If* $\boldsymbol{\alpha}^{-1}$ *is the inverse of* $\boldsymbol{\alpha}$, *then* $\boldsymbol{\alpha}$ *is also the inverse of* $\boldsymbol{\alpha}^{-1}$.

It is clear that *inverse matrices commute* with one another.

Rule: The inverse of a product $\boldsymbol{\alpha\beta\gamma\delta}$ is obtained by multiplying the inverses of the individual factors in reverse order ($\boldsymbol{\delta}^{-1}\boldsymbol{\gamma}^{-1}\boldsymbol{\beta}^{-1}\boldsymbol{\alpha}^{-1}$). That is

$$(\boldsymbol{\delta}^{-1}\boldsymbol{\gamma}^{-1}\boldsymbol{\beta}^{-1}\boldsymbol{\alpha}^{-1}) \cdot (\boldsymbol{\alpha\beta\gamma\delta}) = \mathbf{1}.$$

Another important matrix is

7. *The null matrix, every element of which is zero.*

$$\mathbf{0} = \begin{pmatrix} 0 & 0 & 0 & \cdots & 0 \\ 0 & 0 & 0 & \cdots & 0 \\ . & . & . & \cdots & . \\ 0 & 0 & 0 & \cdots & 0 \end{pmatrix}. \tag{1.18}$$

Obviously one has

$$\boldsymbol{\alpha} \cdot \mathbf{0} = \mathbf{0} \cdot \boldsymbol{\alpha} = \mathbf{0}$$

for any matrix $\boldsymbol{\alpha}$.

The null matrix plays an important role in another combination process for matrices, namely, addition. The sum $\boldsymbol{\gamma}$ of two matrices $\boldsymbol{\alpha}$ and $\boldsymbol{\beta}$ is the matrix whose elements are

$$\boldsymbol{\gamma}_{ik} = \boldsymbol{\alpha}_{ik} + \boldsymbol{\beta}_{ik}. \tag{1.19}$$

The n^2 equations (1.19) are equivalent to the equation

$$\boldsymbol{\gamma} = \boldsymbol{\alpha} + \boldsymbol{\beta} \quad \text{or} \quad \boldsymbol{\gamma} - \boldsymbol{\alpha} - \boldsymbol{\beta} = \mathbf{0}.$$

Addition of matrices is clearly commutative.

$$\boldsymbol{\alpha} + \boldsymbol{\beta} = \boldsymbol{\beta} + \boldsymbol{\alpha}. \tag{1.20}$$

Moreover, multiplication by sums is distributive.

$$\boldsymbol{\gamma}(\boldsymbol{\alpha} + \boldsymbol{\beta}) = \boldsymbol{\gamma\alpha} + \boldsymbol{\gamma\beta}$$
$$(\boldsymbol{\alpha} + \boldsymbol{\beta})\boldsymbol{\gamma} = \boldsymbol{\alpha\gamma} + \boldsymbol{\beta\gamma}.$$

Furthermore, the product of a matrix $\boldsymbol{\alpha}$ and a number a is defined to be that matrix $\boldsymbol{\gamma}$ each element of which is a times the corresponding elements of $\boldsymbol{\alpha}$.

$$\boldsymbol{\gamma}_{ik} = a\boldsymbol{\alpha}_{ik}\,. \tag{1.21}$$

The formulas

$$(ab)\boldsymbol{\alpha} = a(b\boldsymbol{\alpha}); \qquad \boldsymbol{\alpha}a\boldsymbol{\beta} = a\boldsymbol{\alpha\beta}; \qquad a(\boldsymbol{\alpha} + \boldsymbol{\beta}) = a\boldsymbol{\alpha} + a\boldsymbol{\beta}$$

then follow directly.

Since integral powers of a matrix $\boldsymbol{\alpha}$ can easily be defined by successive multiplication

$$\begin{aligned} \boldsymbol{\alpha}^2 &= \boldsymbol{\alpha}\cdot\boldsymbol{\alpha}; & \boldsymbol{\alpha}^3 &= \boldsymbol{\alpha}\cdot\boldsymbol{\alpha}\cdot\boldsymbol{\alpha}; \ldots \\ \boldsymbol{\alpha}^{-2} &= \boldsymbol{\alpha}^{-1}\cdot\boldsymbol{\alpha}^{-1}; & \boldsymbol{\alpha}^{-3} &= \boldsymbol{\alpha}^{-1}\cdot\boldsymbol{\alpha}^{-1}\cdot\boldsymbol{\alpha}^{-1}; \ldots \end{aligned} \tag{1.22}$$

polynomials with positive and negative integral exponents can also be defined

$$\cdots + a_{-n}\boldsymbol{\alpha}^{-n} + \cdots + a_{-1}\boldsymbol{\alpha}^{-1} + a_0\mathbf{1} + a_1\boldsymbol{\alpha} + \cdots + a_n\boldsymbol{\alpha}^n + \cdots. \tag{1.23}$$

The coefficients a in the above expression are not matrices, but numbers. *A function of* $\boldsymbol{\alpha}$ *like* (1.23) *commutes with any other function of* $\boldsymbol{\alpha}$ *(and, in particular, with* $\boldsymbol{\alpha}$ *itself).*

Still another important type of matrix which appears frequently is the diagonal matrix.

8. *A diagonal matrix is a matrix the elements of which are all zero except for those on the main diagonal.*

$$\mathbf{D} = \begin{pmatrix} D_1 & 0 & \cdots & 0 \\ 0 & D_2 & \cdots & 0 \\ \cdot & \cdot & \cdot & \cdot \\ \cdot & \cdot & \cdot & \cdot \\ \cdot & \cdot & \cdot & \cdot \\ 0 & 0 & \cdots & D_n \end{pmatrix}. \tag{1.24}$$

The general element of this diagonal matrix can be written

$$\mathbf{D}_{ik} = D_i\delta_{ik}\,. \tag{1.25}$$

All diagonal matrices commute, and the product of two diagonal matrices is again diagonal. This can be seen directly from the definition of the product.

$$(\mathbf{DD}')_{ik} = \sum_j \mathbf{D}_{ij}\mathbf{D}' = \sum_j D_i\delta_{ij}D_j'\delta_{jk} = D_iD_i'\delta_{ik}\,. \tag{1.26}$$

Conversely, if a matrix $\boldsymbol{\alpha}$ commutes with a diagonal matrix $\mathbf{D}$, the diagonal elements of which are all different, then $\boldsymbol{\alpha}$ must itself be a diagonal matrix. Writing out the product

$$\boldsymbol{\alpha}\mathbf{D} = \mathbf{D}\boldsymbol{\alpha}$$

$$(\boldsymbol{\alpha}\mathbf{D})_{ik} = \boldsymbol{\alpha}_{ik} D_k = (\mathbf{D}\boldsymbol{\alpha})_{ik} = D_i \boldsymbol{\alpha}_{ik} . \tag{1.27}$$

That is

$$(D_i - D_k)\boldsymbol{\alpha}_{ik} = 0 \tag{1.27a}$$

and for a nondiagonal element ($i \neq k$), $D_i \neq D_k$ requires that $\boldsymbol{\alpha}_{ik}$ be zero. Then $\boldsymbol{\alpha}$ is diagonal.

The sum of the diagonal elements of a matrix is called the spur or trace of the matrix.

$$\text{Tr}\,\boldsymbol{\alpha} = \sum_j \boldsymbol{\alpha}_{jj} = \boldsymbol{\alpha}_{11} + \boldsymbol{\alpha}_{22} + \cdots + \boldsymbol{\alpha}_{nn} . \tag{1.28}$$

The trace of a product $\boldsymbol{\alpha\beta}$ is therefore

$$\text{Tr}\,\boldsymbol{\alpha\beta} = \sum_i (\boldsymbol{\alpha\beta})_{ii} = \sum_{jk} \boldsymbol{\alpha}_{jk}\boldsymbol{\beta}_{kj} = \text{Tr}\,\boldsymbol{\beta\alpha}. \tag{1.29}$$

This establishes another property of matrices.

9. *The trace of a product of two matrices does not depend on the order of the two factors.*

This rule finds its most important application in connection with *similarity transformations* of matrices. A similarity transformation is one in which the transformed matrix $\boldsymbol{\alpha}$ is multiplied by the transforming matrix $\boldsymbol{\beta}$ from the right and by its reciprocal from the left. The matrix $\boldsymbol{\alpha}$ is thus transformed into $\boldsymbol{\beta}^{-1}\boldsymbol{\alpha\beta}$. *A similarity transformation leaves the trace of the matrix unchanged,* since the rule above states that $\boldsymbol{\beta}^{-1}\boldsymbol{\alpha\beta}$ has the same trace as $\boldsymbol{\alpha\beta\beta}^{-1} = \boldsymbol{\alpha}$.

The importance of similarity transformations arises from the fact that

10. *A matrix equation remains true if every matrix in it is subjected to the same similarity transformation.*

For example, transformation of a product of matrices $\boldsymbol{\alpha\beta} = \boldsymbol{\gamma}$ yields

$$\boldsymbol{\sigma}^{-1}\boldsymbol{\alpha\sigma\sigma}^{-1}\boldsymbol{\beta\sigma} = \boldsymbol{\sigma}^{-1}\boldsymbol{\gamma\sigma}$$

and if

$$\boldsymbol{\alpha\beta} = \mathbf{1},$$

$$\boldsymbol{\sigma}^{-1}\boldsymbol{\alpha\sigma\sigma}^{-1}\boldsymbol{\beta\sigma} = \boldsymbol{\sigma}^{-1}\mathbf{1}\cdot\boldsymbol{\sigma} = \mathbf{1}.$$

We can also see that relationships among sums of matrices and products of matrices and numbers are also preserved under similarity transformation. Thus, from

$$\boldsymbol{\gamma} = \boldsymbol{\alpha} + \boldsymbol{\beta}$$

it follows that

$$\boldsymbol{\sigma}^{-1}\boldsymbol{\gamma} = \boldsymbol{\sigma}^{-1}(\boldsymbol{\alpha} + \boldsymbol{\beta}) = \boldsymbol{\sigma}^{-1}\boldsymbol{\alpha} + \boldsymbol{\sigma}^{-1}\boldsymbol{\beta}$$

and

$$\boldsymbol{\sigma}^{-1}\boldsymbol{\gamma}\boldsymbol{\sigma} = \boldsymbol{\sigma}^{-1}\boldsymbol{\alpha}\boldsymbol{\sigma} + \boldsymbol{\sigma}^{-1}\boldsymbol{\beta}\boldsymbol{\sigma}.$$

Likewise

$$\boldsymbol{\beta} = a \cdot \boldsymbol{\alpha}$$

implies

$$\boldsymbol{\sigma}^{-1}\boldsymbol{\beta}\boldsymbol{\sigma} = a\boldsymbol{\sigma}^{-1}\boldsymbol{\alpha}\boldsymbol{\sigma}.$$

Theorem 10 therefore applies to every matrix equation involving products of matrices and numbers or other matrices, integral (positive or negative) powers of matrices, and sums of matrices.

These ten theorems for matrix manipulation were presented in the very first papers on quantum mechanics by Born and Jordan,[1] and are undoubtedly already familiar to many readers. They are reiterated here since a firm command of these basic rules is indispensable for what follows and for practically every quantum mechanical calculation. Besides, they must very often be used implicitly, or else even the simplest proofs become excessively tedious.[2]

Linear Independence of Vectors

The vectors $\mathfrak{v}_1, \mathfrak{v}_2, \cdots, \mathfrak{v}_k$ are said to be linearly independent if no relationship of the form

$$a_1\mathfrak{v}_1 + a_2\mathfrak{v}_2 + \cdots + a_n\mathfrak{v}_k = 0 \tag{1.30}$$

exists except that in which every $a_1, a_2, \cdots, a_k$ is zero. Thus no vector in a linearly independent set can be expressed as a linear combination of the other vectors in the set. In the case where one of the vectors, say $\mathfrak{v}_1$, is a null vector, the set can no longer be linearly independent, since the relationship

$$1 \cdot \mathfrak{v}_1 + 0 \cdot \mathfrak{v}_2 + \cdots + 0 \cdot \mathfrak{v}_k = 0$$

is surely satisfied, in violation of the condition for linear independence.

As an example of linear dependence, consider the four-dimensional vectors: $\mathfrak{v}_1 = (1, 2, -1, 3)$, $\mathfrak{v}_2 = (0, -2, 1, -1)$, and $\mathfrak{v}_3 = (2, 2, -1, 5)$. These are linearly dependent since

$$2\mathfrak{v}_1 + \mathfrak{v}_2 - \mathfrak{v}_3 = 0.$$

On the other hand, $\mathfrak{v}_1$ and $\mathfrak{v}_2$ are linearly independent.

[1] M. Born and P. Jordan, *Z. Physik* **34,** 858 (1925).

[2] For example, the associative law of multiplication (Theorem 3) is used implicitly three times in the deduction of the commutability of inverses (Theorem 6). (Try writing out all the parentheses!)

If k vectors $\mathfrak{v}_1, \mathfrak{v}_2, \cdots, \mathfrak{v}_k$ are linearly dependent, then there can be found among them k' vectors ($k' < k$) which are linearly independent. Moreover, all k vectors can be expressed as linear combinations of these k' vectors.

In seeking k' vectors which are linearly independent we omit all null vectors, since, as we have already seen, a null vector can never be a member of a linearly independent set. We then go through the remaining vectors one after another, rejecting any one which can be expressed as a linear combination of those already retained. The k' vectors retained in this way are linearly independent, since if none of them can be expressed as a linear combination of the others, no relationship of the type (1.30) can exist among them. Moreover, each of the rejected vectors (and thus all of the k original vectors) can be expressed in terms of them, since this was the criterion for rejection.

The linear dependence or independence of k vectors $\mathfrak{v}_1, \mathfrak{v}_2, \cdots, \mathfrak{v}_k$ is also a property of the vectors $\boldsymbol{\alpha}\mathfrak{v}_1, \cdots, \boldsymbol{\alpha}\mathfrak{v}_k$ which result from them by a *proper* transformation $\boldsymbol{\alpha}$. That is,

$$a_1\mathfrak{v}_1 + a_2\mathfrak{v}_2 + \cdots + a_k\mathfrak{v}_k = 0 \tag{1.31}$$

implies

$$a_1\boldsymbol{\alpha}\mathfrak{v}_1 + a_2\boldsymbol{\alpha}\mathfrak{v}_2 + \cdots + a_k\boldsymbol{\alpha}\mathfrak{v}_k = 0 \tag{1.31a}$$

as can be seen by applying $\boldsymbol{\alpha}$ to both sides of (1.31) and using the linearity property to obtain (1.31a). Conversely, (1.31a) implies (1.31). It also follows that any specific linear relationship which exists among the $\mathfrak{v}_i$ exists among the $\boldsymbol{\alpha}\mathfrak{v}_i$, and conversely.

No more than n n-dimensional vectors can be linearly independent. To prove this, note that the relation implying linear dependence

$$a_1\mathfrak{v}_1 + \cdots + a_{n+1}\mathfrak{v}_{n+1} = 0 \tag{1.32}$$

is equivalent to n linear homogeneous equations for the components of the vectors.

$$\begin{aligned} &a_1(\mathfrak{v}_1)_1 + \cdots + a_n(\mathfrak{v}_n)_1 + a_{n+1}(\mathfrak{v}_{n+1})_1 = 0 \\ &\cdot \\ &\cdot \\ &\cdot \\ &a_1(\mathfrak{v}_1)_n + \cdots + a_n(\mathfrak{v}_n)_n + a_{n+1}(\mathfrak{v}_{n+1})_n = 0. \end{aligned} \tag{1.32a}$$

If the coefficients $a_1, a_2, \cdots, a_n, a_{n+1}$ in these equations are viewed as unknowns, the fact that n linear homogeneous equations in $n + 1$ unknowns always have nontrivial solutions implies at once that the relationship (1.32) always exists. Thus, $n + 1$ n-dimensional vectors are always linearly dependent.

An immediate corollary to the above theorem is the statement that any *n linearly independent n-dimensional vectors form a complete vector system;* that is, an arbitrary n-dimensional vector $\mathfrak{w}$ can be expressed as a linear combination of them. Indeed, the theorem states that some relationship

$$a_1\mathfrak{v}_1 + \cdots + a_n\mathfrak{v}_n + b\mathfrak{w} = 0$$

must exist among the n vectors and the arbitrary vector. Moreover, if $\mathfrak{v}_1, \mathfrak{v}_2, \cdots, \mathfrak{v}_n$ are linearly independent, the coefficient b cannot be zero. Thus any vector $\mathfrak{w}$ can be written as a linear combination of the $\mathfrak{v}_i$, so that these form a complete vector system.

A row or a column of an n-dimensional matrix can be looked upon as a vector. For example, the components of the vector $\boldsymbol{\alpha}_{\cdot k}$ which forms the kth column are $\boldsymbol{\alpha}_{1k}, \boldsymbol{\alpha}_{2k}, \cdots, \boldsymbol{\alpha}_{nk}$, and those of the vector $\boldsymbol{\alpha}_{i\cdot}$ which forms the ith row are $\boldsymbol{\alpha}_{i1}, \cdots, \boldsymbol{\alpha}_{in}$. A nontrivial linear relationship among the column vectors $\boldsymbol{\alpha}_{\cdot 1}, \cdots, \boldsymbol{\alpha}_{\cdot n}$

$$a_1\boldsymbol{\alpha}_{\cdot 1} + \cdots + a_n\boldsymbol{\alpha}_{\cdot n} = 0$$

is simply a nonzero solution of the set of linear homogeneous equations for the $a_1, a_2, \cdots, a_n$.

$$\begin{aligned} a_1\boldsymbol{\alpha}_{11} + \cdots + a_n\boldsymbol{\alpha}_{1n} &= 0 \\ &\cdot \\ &\cdot \\ &\cdot \\ a_1\boldsymbol{\alpha}_{n1} + \cdots + a_n\boldsymbol{\alpha}_{nn} &= 0. \end{aligned}$$

The vanishing of the determinant $|\boldsymbol{\alpha}_{ik}|$ is the necessary and sufficient condition that such a solution exist. Therefore, if this determinant does not vanish ($|\boldsymbol{\alpha}_{ik}| \neq 0$), then the vectors $\boldsymbol{\alpha}_{\cdot 1}, \cdots, \boldsymbol{\alpha}_{\cdot n}$ are linearly independent and form a complete vector system. Conversely, if the vectors $\mathfrak{v}_1, \cdots, \mathfrak{v}_n$ are linearly independent, the matrix which is formed by taking them as its columns must have a nonzero determinant. Of course, this whole discussion applies equally well to the row-vectors of a matrix.

2. Generalizations

1. We now generalize the results of the previous chapter. The first generalization is entirely formal, the second one is of a more essential nature. To denote the components of vectors and the elements of matrices, we have affixed the appropriate coordinate axes as indices. So far, the coordinate axes have been denoted by $1, 2, 3, \cdots, n$. From now on we will name the coordinate axes after the elements of an arbitrary set. If G is a set of objects $g, h, i, \cdots$, then the vector $\mathfrak{v}$ in the space of the set G is the set of numbers $\mathfrak{v}_g, \mathfrak{v}_h, \mathfrak{v}_i, \cdots$. Of course only vectors which are defined in the same space can be equated (or added, etc.) since only then do the components correspond to the same set.

A similar system will be used for matrices. Thus for a matrix $\boldsymbol{\alpha}$ to be applied to a vector $\mathfrak{v}$ with components $\mathfrak{v}_g, \mathfrak{v}_h, \mathfrak{v}_i, \cdots$, the columns of $\boldsymbol{\alpha}$ must be labeled by the elements of the same set G as that specifying the components of $\mathfrak{v}$. In the simplest case the rows are also named after the elements $g, h, i, \cdots$ of this set, and $\boldsymbol{\alpha}$ transforms a vector $\mathfrak{v}$ in the space of G into a vector $\boldsymbol{\alpha}\mathfrak{v}$ in the same space. That is

$$\mathfrak{v}'_j = \sum_{l \in G} \boldsymbol{\alpha}_{jl} \mathfrak{v}_l \tag{2.1}$$

where j is an element of the set G, and l runs over all the elements of this set.

For example, the coordinate axes can be labeled by three letters x, y, z. Then $\mathfrak{v}$, with components $\mathfrak{v}_x = 1, \mathfrak{v}_y = 0, \mathfrak{v}_z = -2$, is a vector, and

$$\begin{array}{cc} & \begin{array}{ccc} x & y & z \end{array} \\ \boldsymbol{\alpha} = & \begin{pmatrix} 1 & 2 & 3 \\ 0 & 5 & -1 \\ -4 & -2 & 4 \end{pmatrix} \begin{array}{c} x \\ y \\ z \end{array} \end{array}$$

is a matrix. (The symbols for the rows and columns are indicated.) In this example $\boldsymbol{\alpha}_{xx} = 1$, $\boldsymbol{\alpha}_{xy} = 2$, $\boldsymbol{\alpha}_{xz} = 3$. Eq. (2.1) states that the x-component of $\mathfrak{v}' = \boldsymbol{\alpha}\mathfrak{v}$ is given by

$$\begin{aligned} \mathfrak{v}'_x &= \boldsymbol{\alpha}_{xx}\mathfrak{v}_x + \boldsymbol{\alpha}_{xy}\mathfrak{v}_y + \boldsymbol{\alpha}_{xz}\mathfrak{v}_z \\ &= 1 \cdot 1 + 2 \cdot 0 + 3(-2) = -5. \end{aligned}$$

The simple generalization above is purely formal; it involves merely another system of labeling the coordinate axes and the components of vectors and matrices. Two matrices which operate on vectors in the same space can be multiplied with one another, just like the matrices in the previous chapter. The expression

$$\boldsymbol{\gamma} = \boldsymbol{\beta}\boldsymbol{\alpha} \tag{2.2}$$

is equivalent to

$$\gamma_{jk} = \sum_{l \epsilon G} \beta_{jl}\alpha_{lk},$$

where j and k are two elements of the set G, and l runs over all the elements of this set.

2. A further generalization is that in which the rows and columns of matrices are labeled by elements of *different sets*, F and G. Then from (2.1),

$$\mathfrak{w}_j = \sum_{l \epsilon G} \alpha_{jl}\mathfrak{v}_l, \tag{2.1a}$$

where j is an element of the set F, and l runs over all the elements of the set G. Such a matrix, whose rows and columns are labeled by different sets is called a *rectangular* matrix, in contrast with the square matrices of the previous chapter; it transforms a vector $\mathfrak{v}$ in the space of G into a vector $\mathfrak{w}$ in the space of F. In general the set F need not contain the same number of elements as the set G. If it does contain the same number of elements, then the matrix has an equal number of rows and columns and is said to be "square in the broader sense."

Let the set G contain the symbols $*$, $\triangle$, $\square$, and the set F the numbers 1 and 2. Then

$$\begin{matrix} & * & \triangle & \square & \\ \boldsymbol{\alpha} = & \left(\begin{matrix} 5 \\ 0 \end{matrix}\right. & \begin{matrix} 7 \\ -1 \end{matrix} & \left.\begin{matrix} 3 \\ -2 \end{matrix}\right) & \begin{matrix} 1 \\ 2 \end{matrix} \end{matrix}$$

is a rectangular matrix. (The labels of the rows and columns are again indicated.) It transforms a vector $\mathfrak{v}_* = 1, \mathfrak{v}_\triangle = 0, \mathfrak{v}_\square = -2$ into the vector

$$\mathfrak{w} = \boldsymbol{\alpha}\mathfrak{v}.$$

The components $\mathfrak{w}_1$ and $\mathfrak{w}_2$ are then

$$\mathfrak{w}_1 = \alpha_{1*}\mathfrak{v}_* + \alpha_{1\triangle}\mathfrak{v}_\triangle + \alpha_{1\square}\mathfrak{v}_\square = 5 \cdot 1 + 7 \cdot 0 + 3(-2) = -1$$

$$\mathfrak{w}_2 = \alpha_{2*}\mathfrak{v}_* + \alpha_{2\triangle}\mathfrak{v}_\triangle + \alpha_{2\square}\mathfrak{v}_\square = 0 \cdot 1 + (-1)(0) + (-2)(-2) = 4.$$

Two rectangular matrices $\boldsymbol{\beta}$ and $\boldsymbol{\alpha}$ can be multiplied only if the columns of the first factor and the rows of the second factor are labeled by the same set F; i.e., only if the rows of the second factor and the columns of the first "match." On the other hand, the rows of the first and the columns of the second factor can correspond to elements of completely different sets, E and G. Then

$$\boldsymbol{\gamma} = \boldsymbol{\beta}\boldsymbol{\alpha} \tag{2.2a}$$

is equivalent to

$$\gamma_{jk} = \sum_{l \epsilon F} \beta_{jl}\alpha_{lk}$$

where j is an element of E, k an element of G, and l runs over all the elements of F. The rectangular matrix $\boldsymbol{\alpha}$ transforms a vector in the space of G into one in the space of F; the matrix $\boldsymbol{\beta}$ then transforms this vector into one in the space of E. The matrix $\boldsymbol{\gamma}$ therefore transforms a vector in the space of G into one in the space of E.

Let G be the set $*, \triangle, \square$ again, let F contain the letters x and y, and E the numbers 1 and 2. Then if

$$\boldsymbol{\beta} = \begin{array}{c} \begin{matrix} x & y \end{matrix} \\ \begin{pmatrix} 7 & 8 \\ 9 & 3 \end{pmatrix} \end{array} \begin{matrix} 1 \\ 2 \end{matrix} \quad \text{and} \quad \boldsymbol{\alpha} = \begin{array}{c} \begin{matrix} * & \triangle & \square \end{matrix} \\ \begin{pmatrix} 2 & 3 & 4 \\ 5 & 6 & 7 \end{pmatrix} \end{array} \begin{matrix} x \\ y \end{matrix},$$

one has, for instance,

$$\begin{aligned} \gamma_{1*} &= \beta_{1x}\alpha_{x*} + \beta_{1y}\alpha_{y*} = 7 \cdot 2 + 8 \cdot 5 = 54 \\ \gamma_{2\triangle} &= \beta_{2x}\alpha_{x\triangle} + \beta_{2y}\alpha_{y\triangle} = 9 \cdot 3 + 3 \cdot 6 = 45 \end{aligned}$$

and

$$\boldsymbol{\gamma} = \begin{array}{c} \begin{matrix} * & \triangle & \square \end{matrix} \\ \begin{pmatrix} 54 & 69 & 84 \\ 33 & 45 & 57 \end{pmatrix} \end{array} \begin{matrix} 1 \\ 2 \end{matrix}.$$

3. We now investigate how the ten theorems of matrix calculus deduced in Chapter 1 must be modified for rectangular matrices. We see immediately that they remain true for the generalized square matrix discussed at the beginning of this chapter, since the specific *numerical nature* of the indices has not been used anywhere in the first chapter.

Addition of two rectangular matrices—just as that of two vectors—presupposes that they are defined in the same coordinate system, that is, that *the rows match the rows and the columns match the columns*. In the equation

$$\boldsymbol{\alpha} + \boldsymbol{\beta} = \boldsymbol{\gamma}$$

the labeling of the rows of the three matrices $\boldsymbol{\alpha}$, $\boldsymbol{\beta}$, $\boldsymbol{\gamma}$ must be the same, as well as the labeling of their columns. On the other hand, for multiplication the columns of the first factor and the rows of the second factor must match; only then (and always then) can the product be constructed. The resulting product has the row labeling of the first, and the column labeling of the second factor.

THEOREM 1. We can speak of the determinant of a rectangular matrix if it has the same number of rows and columns, although these may be labeled differently. For matrices "square in the broader sense" the rule that the determinant of the product equals the product of the determinants is still valid.

THEOREMS 2 and 3. The associative law also holds for the multiplication of rectangular matrices

$$(\boldsymbol{\alpha}\boldsymbol{\beta})\boldsymbol{\gamma} = \boldsymbol{\alpha}(\boldsymbol{\beta}\boldsymbol{\gamma}). \tag{2.3}$$

Clearly all multiplication on the right side can actually be carried out provided it can be done on the left side, and conversely.

THEOREMS 4, 5, and 6. The matrix $\mathbf{1}$ will always be understood to be a square matrix with rows and columns labeled by the same set. Multiplication by it can always be omitted.

Matrices which are square in the broader sense have a reciprocal only if their determinant is nonvanishing. For rectangular matrices with a different number of rows and columns, the inverse is not defined at all. If $\boldsymbol{\alpha}$ is a matrix which is square only in the broader sense, the equation

$$\boldsymbol{\beta\alpha} = \mathbf{1}$$

implies that the columns of $\boldsymbol{\beta}$ match the rows of $\boldsymbol{\alpha}$. Furthermore, the rows of $\mathbf{1}$ must match the rows of $\boldsymbol{\beta}$, and its columns must match the columns of $\boldsymbol{\alpha}$. Since $\mathbf{1}$ is square in the restricted sense, the columns of $\boldsymbol{\alpha}$ must also match the rows of $\boldsymbol{\beta}$.

The rows of the matrix $\boldsymbol{\beta}$ *inverse to the matrix* $\boldsymbol{\alpha}$ *are labeled by the same set as the elements of the columns of* $\boldsymbol{\alpha}$; *its columns by the same elements as the rows of* $\boldsymbol{\alpha}$. There exists for any matrix $\boldsymbol{\alpha}$ which is square in the broader sense and has a nonvanishing determinant, an inverse $\boldsymbol{\beta}$ such that

$$\boldsymbol{\beta\alpha} = \mathbf{1}. \tag{2.4}$$

Moreover,

$$\boldsymbol{\alpha\beta} = \mathbf{1}. \tag{2.4a}$$

However, it should be noted that the rows and columns of $\mathbf{1}$ in (2.4) are labeled differently from those of $\mathbf{1}$ in (2.4a).

THEOREM 7. With respect to addition and the null matrix, the same rules hold for rectangular matrices as for square matrices. However, the *powers of rectangular matrices cannot be constructed* since the multiplication of $\boldsymbol{\alpha}$ with $\boldsymbol{\alpha}$ presupposes that the columns of $\boldsymbol{\alpha}$ and the rows of $\boldsymbol{\alpha}$ match, i.e., that $\boldsymbol{\alpha}$ is square.

THEOREMS 8, 9, and 10. For rectangular matrices the concepts of diagonal matrix and trace are meaningless; also, the similarity transformation is undefined. Consider the equation

$$\boldsymbol{\sigma\alpha\sigma}^{-1} = \boldsymbol{\beta}.$$

This implies that the labeling of the rows of $\boldsymbol{\beta}$ and $\boldsymbol{\sigma}$ are the same. But this is the same as the labeling of the columns of $\boldsymbol{\sigma}^{-1}$, and thus of the columns of $\boldsymbol{\beta}$. It follows that the matrix $\boldsymbol{\beta}$ is square in the restricted sense; likewise, $\boldsymbol{\alpha}$, whose rows must match the columns of $\boldsymbol{\sigma}$ and whose columns must match the rows of $\boldsymbol{\sigma}^{-1}$, must be square in the restricted sense.

On the other hand, $\boldsymbol{\sigma}$ *itself can be square in the broad sense: the columns and rows of* $\boldsymbol{\alpha}$ *are then different from those of* $\boldsymbol{\beta}$. Similarity transformations which change the labeling of rows and columns are especially important. The so-called transformation theory of quantum mechanics is an example of such transformations.

The introduction of rectangular matrices is very advantageous in spite of the apparent complication which is involved, since substantial simplifications can be achieved with them. The outline above is designed not as a rigid scheme but rather to accustom the reader to thinking in terms of these entities. The use of such more complicated matrices will always be explained specifically unless the enumeration of rows and columns is so very clear by the form and definition of the elements that further explanation is scarcely desirable.

4. Quite frequently it occurs that the rows are named not with just one number but with two or more numbers, for example

$$\boldsymbol{\gamma} = \begin{pmatrix} a_1b_1c_1d_1 & a_1b_1c_1d_2 & a_1b_1c_2d_1 & a_1b_1c_2d_2 \\ a_1b_2c_1d_1 & a_1b_2c_1d_2 & a_1b_2c_2d_1 & a_1b_2c_2d_2 \\ a_2b_1c_1d_1 & a_2b_1c_1d_2 & a_2b_1c_2d_1 & a_2b_1c_2d_2 \\ a_2b_2c_1d_1 & a_2b_2c_1d_2 & a_2b_2c_2d_1 & a_2b_2c_2d_2 \end{pmatrix}. \tag{2.E.1}$$

The first column is called the "1,1 column;" the second, the "1,2 column;" the third, the "2,1 column;" the fourth, the "2,2 column;" the rows are designated in the same way. The elements of (2.E.1) are

$$\gamma_{ij;kl} = a_i b_j c_k d_l \,.$$

For clarity, a semicolon is used to separate the labels of the rows from those of columns.

Among such matrices, the direct product $\boldsymbol{\gamma}$ of two matrices $(\boldsymbol{\alpha}_{ik})$ and $(\boldsymbol{\beta}_{jl})$ is especially important

$$\boldsymbol{\gamma} = \boldsymbol{\alpha} \times \boldsymbol{\beta}. \tag{2.5}$$

Equation (2.5) is equivalent to[1]

$$\gamma_{ij;kl} = \alpha_{ik}\beta_{jl} \,. \tag{2.6}$$

If the number of rows in $\boldsymbol{\alpha}$ is n_1 and the number of columns, n_2, and the corresponding numbers for $\boldsymbol{\beta}$ are n_1' and n_2', then $\boldsymbol{\gamma}$ has exactly n_1n_1' rows and n_2n_2' columns. In particular, if $\boldsymbol{\alpha}$ and $\boldsymbol{\beta}$ are both square matrices then $\boldsymbol{\alpha} \times \boldsymbol{\beta}$ is also square.

[1] The factors $\boldsymbol{\alpha}$ and $\bar{\boldsymbol{\alpha}}$ of the ordinary matrix product are merely written next to one another, $\bar{\boldsymbol{\alpha}}\boldsymbol{\alpha}$. The matrix (2.E.1) is the direct product of the two matrices

$$\begin{pmatrix} a_1c_1 & a_1c_2 \\ a_2c_1 & a_2c_2 \end{pmatrix} \times \begin{pmatrix} b_1d_1 & b_1d_2 \\ b_2d_1 & b_2d_2 \end{pmatrix} = \boldsymbol{\gamma}.$$

THEOREM 1. If $\alpha\bar{\alpha} = \bar{\bar{\alpha}}$ and $\beta\bar{\beta} = \bar{\bar{\beta}}$, and if $\alpha \times \beta = \gamma$ and $\bar{\alpha} \times \bar{\beta} = \bar{\gamma}$ then $\gamma\bar{\gamma} = \bar{\bar{\alpha}} \times \bar{\bar{\beta}}$.

$$(\alpha \times \beta)(\bar{\alpha} \times \bar{\beta}) = \alpha\bar{\alpha} \times \beta\bar{\beta} \tag{2.7}$$

That is, the matrix product of two direct products is the direct product of the two matrix products. To show this, consider

$$(\alpha \times \beta)_{ik;i'k'} = \alpha_{ii'}\beta_{kk'}\;;\quad (\bar{\alpha} \times \bar{\beta})_{i'k';i''k''} = \bar{\alpha}_{i'i''}\bar{\beta}_{k'k''}$$

and

$$(\alpha \times \beta)(\bar{\alpha} \times \bar{\beta})_{ik;i''k''} = \sum_{i'k'} \alpha_{ii'}\beta_{kk'}\bar{\alpha}_{i'i''}\bar{\beta}_{k'k''}\,. \tag{2.8}$$

But

$$(\alpha\bar{\alpha})_{ii''} = \sum_{i'} \alpha_{ii'}\bar{\alpha}_{i'i''}\;;\quad (\beta\bar{\beta})_{kk''} = \sum_{k'} \beta_{kk'}\bar{\beta}_{k'k''}$$

and

$$(\alpha\bar{\alpha} \times \beta\bar{\beta})_{ik;i''k''} = \sum_{i'} \alpha_{ii'}\bar{\alpha}_{i'i''} \sum_{k'} \beta_{kk'}\bar{\beta}_{k'k''}\,, \tag{2.9}$$

Therefore, from (2.8) and (2.9), one obtains Theorem 1, namely

$$(\alpha \times \beta)\,(\bar{\alpha} \times \bar{\beta}) = \alpha\bar{\alpha} \times \beta\bar{\beta}. \tag{2.7}$$

THEOREM 2. *The direct product of two diagonal matrices is again a diagonal matrix; the direct product of two unit matrices is a unit matrix.* This is easily seen directly from the definition of direct products.

In formal calculations with matrices it must be verified that the multiplication indicated is actually possible. In the first chapter where we had square matrices with n rows and columns throughout, this was, of course, always the case. In general, however, it must be established that the *rows* of the first factor in matrix multiplication match the *columns* of the second factor, i.e., that they both have the same names or labels. The direct product of two matrices can always be constructed by (2.6).

A generalized type of matrix with several indices is referred to by M. Born and P. Jordan as a "*super-matrix*." They interpret the matrix $(\alpha_{ij;kl})$ as *a matrix* $(\mathbf{A}_{ik})$ *whose elements* $\mathbf{A}_{ik}$ *are themselves matrices.* $\mathbf{A}_{ik}$ is that matrix in which the number $\alpha_{ij;kl}$ occurs in the jth row and the lth column.

$$(\alpha_{ij;kl}) = \alpha = (\mathbf{A}_{ik}),\quad \text{where}\quad (\mathbf{A}_{ik})_{jl} = \alpha_{ij;kl}\,. \tag{2.10}$$

THEOREM 3. *If* $\alpha = (\mathbf{A}_{ii'})$ *and* $\beta = (\mathbf{B}_{i'i''})$, *then* $\alpha\beta = \gamma = (\mathbf{C}_{ii''})$ *where*

$$\mathbf{C}_{ii''} = \sum_{i'} \mathbf{A}_{ii'}\mathbf{B}_{i'i''}\,. \tag{2.11}$$

The right-hand side of (2.11) consists of a sum of products of *matrix multiplications.* We have

$$(\boldsymbol{\alpha\beta})_{ik;i''k''} = \sum_{i',k'} \boldsymbol{\alpha}_{ik;i'k'}\boldsymbol{\beta}_{i'k';i''k''}.$$

On the other hand

$$\boldsymbol{\gamma}_{ik;i''k''} = (\mathbf{C}_{ii''})_{kk''} = \sum_{i'} (\mathbf{A}_{ii'}\mathbf{B}_{i'i''})_{kk''}$$

and

$$(\mathbf{A}_{ii'}\,\mathbf{B}_{i'i''})_{kk''} = \sum_{k'} (\mathbf{A}_{ii'})_{kk'}\,(\mathbf{B}_{i'i''})_{k'k''} = \sum_{k'} \boldsymbol{\alpha}_{ik;i'k'}\boldsymbol{\beta}_{i'k';i''k''}.$$

Therefore,

$$(\boldsymbol{\alpha\beta})_{ik;i''k''} = \boldsymbol{\gamma}_{ik;i''k''};$$

which proves Theorem 3. Of course, on the right side of (2.11) care must be taken with regard to the order of the factors, whereas in the corresponding equation for the multiplication of simple matrices this was not necessary. With this single restriction, super-matrices can be multiplied according to the rules which hold for simple matrices.

In the simplest case we might have two square matrices

$$\left[\begin{array}{cc:ccc} \alpha_{11} & \alpha_{12} & \alpha_{13} & \alpha_{14} & \alpha_{15} \\ \alpha_{21} & \alpha_{22} & \alpha_{23} & \alpha_{24} & \alpha_{25} \\ \hdashline \alpha_{31} & \alpha_{32} & \alpha_{33} & \alpha_{34} & \alpha_{35} \\ \alpha_{41} & \alpha_{42} & \alpha_{43} & \alpha_{44} & \alpha_{45} \\ \alpha_{51} & \alpha_{52} & \alpha_{53} & \alpha_{54} & \alpha_{55} \end{array}\right] \quad \text{and} \quad \left[\begin{array}{ccc:cc} \beta_{11} & \beta_{12} & \beta_{13} & \beta_{14} & \beta_{15} \\ \beta_{21} & \beta_{22} & \beta_{23} & \beta_{24} & \beta_{25} \\ \hdashline \beta_{31} & \beta_{32} & \beta_{33} & \beta_{34} & \beta_{35} \\ \beta_{41} & \beta_{42} & \beta_{43} & \beta_{44} & \beta_{45} \\ \beta_{51} & \beta_{52} & \beta_{53} & \beta_{54} & \beta_{55} \end{array}\right] \qquad (2.12)$$

We can divide these into submatrices along the dotted lines, taking care that the division of columns in the first (2:3) coincides with the division of rows in the second. We then write for the two matrices (2.12) the abbreviated forms

$$\begin{pmatrix} \mathbf{A}_{11} & \mathbf{A}_{12} \\ \mathbf{A}_{21} & \mathbf{A}_{22} \end{pmatrix} \quad \text{and} \quad \begin{pmatrix} \mathbf{B}_{11} & \mathbf{B}_{12} \\ \mathbf{B}_{21} & \mathbf{B}_{22} \end{pmatrix}.$$

The *product of the two matrices* (2.12) can be written

$$\begin{pmatrix} \mathbf{A}_{11}\mathbf{B}_{11} + \mathbf{A}_{12}\mathbf{B}_{21} & \mathbf{A}_{11}\mathbf{B}_{12} + \mathbf{A}_{12}\mathbf{B}_{22} \\ \mathbf{A}_{21}\mathbf{B}_{11} + \mathbf{A}_{22}\mathbf{B}_{21} & \mathbf{A}_{21}\mathbf{B}_{12} + \mathbf{A}_{22}\mathbf{B}_{22} \end{pmatrix} = \begin{pmatrix} \mathbf{C}_{11} & \mathbf{C}_{12} \\ \mathbf{C}_{21} & \mathbf{C}_{22} \end{pmatrix}.$$

On the other hand, the expression

$$\begin{pmatrix} \mathbf{B}_{11} & \mathbf{B}_{12} \\ \mathbf{B}_{21} & \mathbf{B}_{22} \end{pmatrix} \begin{pmatrix} \mathbf{A}_{11} & \mathbf{A}_{12} \\ \mathbf{A}_{21} & \mathbf{A}_{22} \end{pmatrix} = \begin{pmatrix} \mathbf{B}_{11}\mathbf{A}_{11} + \mathbf{B}_{12}\mathbf{A}_{21} & \mathbf{B}_{11}\mathbf{A}_{12} + \mathbf{B}_{12}\mathbf{A}_{22} \\ \mathbf{B}_{21}\mathbf{A}_{11} + \mathbf{B}_{22}\mathbf{A}_{21} & \mathbf{B}_{21}\mathbf{A}_{12} + \mathbf{B}_{22}\mathbf{A}_{22} \end{pmatrix}$$

is meaningless, since the number of columns of $\mathbf{B}_{11}$, for example, differs from the number of rows of $\mathbf{A}_{11}$.

3. The Principal Axis Transformation

In the first chapter we established a very important property of similarity transformations. They leave the trace of a matrix unchanged;[1] the matrix $\boldsymbol{\alpha}$ has the same trace as $\boldsymbol{\sigma}^{-1}\boldsymbol{\alpha}\boldsymbol{\sigma}$. Is the trace of a matrix the only invariant under similarity transformation? Clearly not, since, for example, the determinant $|\boldsymbol{\sigma}^{-1}\boldsymbol{\alpha}\boldsymbol{\sigma}|$ is also equal to the determinant $|\boldsymbol{\alpha}|$. In order to obtain further invariants, we consider the determinantal equation of the nth order for λ.

$$\begin{vmatrix} \alpha_{11}-\lambda & \alpha_{12} & \cdots & \alpha_{1n} \\ \alpha_{21} & \alpha_{22}-\lambda & \cdots & \alpha_{2n} \\ \cdot & \cdot & \cdots & \cdot \\ \cdot & \cdot & \cdots & \cdot \\ \cdot & \cdot & \cdots & \cdot \\ \alpha_{n1} & \alpha_{n2} & \cdots & \alpha_{nn}-\lambda \end{vmatrix} = 0 \tag{3.1}$$

or, in shorter form,

$$|\boldsymbol{\alpha} - \lambda \mathbf{1}| = 0. \tag{3.2}$$

We call this the *secular equation* of $\boldsymbol{\alpha}$. The secular equation of $\boldsymbol{\beta} = \boldsymbol{\sigma}^{-1}\boldsymbol{\alpha}\boldsymbol{\sigma}$ is

$$|\boldsymbol{\beta} - \lambda \mathbf{1}| = |\boldsymbol{\sigma}^{-1}\boldsymbol{\alpha}\boldsymbol{\sigma} - \lambda \mathbf{1}| = 0. \tag{3.3}$$

Clearly the determinant $|\boldsymbol{\sigma}^{-1}(\boldsymbol{\alpha} - \lambda\mathbf{1})\boldsymbol{\sigma}|$ is also equal to zero; this can be written

$$|\boldsymbol{\sigma}^{-1}| \cdot |\boldsymbol{\alpha} - \lambda \mathbf{1}| \cdot |\boldsymbol{\sigma}| = 0. \tag{3.4}$$

Equation (3.4) shows that the n roots of the secular equation $|\boldsymbol{\beta} - \lambda\mathbf{1}| = 0$ are identical[2] with the n roots of the secular equation $|\boldsymbol{\alpha} - \lambda\mathbf{1}| = 0$. *The roots of the secular equation, the so-called eigenvalues of the matrix, are invariant under similarity transformations.* We shall see later that in general a matrix has no other invariants. Also, the *trace is the sum*, and *the determinant is the product* of the eigenvalues, so that their invariance is included in the theorem stated above.

[1] The matrix which undergoes a similarity transformation must always be a square matrix. For this reason we again denote the rows and columns with the numbers, $1, 2, \cdots, n$.

[2] $|\boldsymbol{\sigma}^{-1}|$ and $|\boldsymbol{\sigma}|$ are numbers!

We now consider one eigenvalue, λ_1. The determinant of the matrix $(\boldsymbol{\alpha} - \lambda_1\mathbf{1})$ is zero, so that the linear homogeneous equations

$$\left.\begin{aligned} \boldsymbol{\alpha}_{11}\mathfrak{r}_1 + \boldsymbol{\alpha}_{12}\mathfrak{r}_2 + \cdots + \boldsymbol{\alpha}_{1n}\mathfrak{r}_n &= \lambda_1\mathfrak{r}_1 , \\ \boldsymbol{\alpha}_{21}\mathfrak{r}_1 + \boldsymbol{\alpha}_{22}\mathfrak{r}_2 + \cdots + \boldsymbol{\alpha}_{2n}\mathfrak{r}_n &= \lambda_1\mathfrak{r}_2 , \\ \cdots\cdots\cdots\cdots\cdots\cdots \\ \boldsymbol{\alpha}_{n1}\mathfrak{r}_1 + \boldsymbol{\alpha}_{n2}\mathfrak{r}_2 + \cdots + \boldsymbol{\alpha}_{nn}\mathfrak{r}_n &= \lambda_1\mathfrak{r}_n \end{aligned}\right\} \tag{3.5}$$

have a solution. A linear homogeneous system of equations like (3.5) can be written for each of the n eigenvalues λ_k. We denote the solutions of this system, which are determined only up to a common constant factor, by $\mathfrak{r}_{1k}, \mathfrak{r}_{2k}, \cdots, \mathfrak{r}_{nk}$; then we have

$$\sum_j \boldsymbol{\alpha}_{ij}\mathfrak{r}_{jk} = \lambda_k\mathfrak{r}_{ik} . \tag{3.5a}$$

The set of n numbers $\mathfrak{r}_{1k}, \mathfrak{r}_{2k}, \cdots, \mathfrak{r}_{nk}$ is called an *eigenvector* $\mathfrak{r}_{\cdot k}$ of the matrix $\boldsymbol{\alpha}$; the eigenvector $\mathfrak{r}_{\cdot k}$ belongs to the eigenvalue λ_k. Equation (3.5a) can then be written

$$\boldsymbol{\alpha}\mathfrak{r}_{\cdot k} = \lambda_k\mathfrak{r}_{\cdot k} . \tag{3.5b}$$

The matrix transforms an eigenvector into a vector which differs from the eigenvector only by a constant factor; this factor is the eigenvalue itself.

The eigenvectors $\mathfrak{r}_{\cdot 1}, \mathfrak{r}_{\cdot 2}, \cdots, \mathfrak{r}_{\cdot n}$ can be combined into a matrix $\boldsymbol{\rho}$ in such a way that $\mathfrak{r}_{\cdot k}$ is the kth column of this matrix.

$$\boldsymbol{\rho}_{ik} = (\mathfrak{r}_{\cdot k})_i = \mathfrak{r}_{ik} .$$

Then the left side of (3.5a) consists of the (ik) element of $\boldsymbol{\alpha}\boldsymbol{\rho}$. The right side also can be interpreted as the (ik) element of a matrix, the matrix $\boldsymbol{\rho}\boldsymbol{\Lambda}$, where $\boldsymbol{\Lambda}$ is a diagonal matrix with diagonal elements $\lambda_1, \lambda_2, \cdots, \lambda_n$

$$\boldsymbol{\Lambda}_{jk} = \delta_{jk}\lambda_k .$$

Then (3.5a) reads

$$(\boldsymbol{\alpha}\boldsymbol{\rho})_{ik} = \sum_j \boldsymbol{\rho}_{ij}\delta_{jk}\lambda_k = (\boldsymbol{\rho}\boldsymbol{\Lambda})_{ik}$$

then the n^2 equations (3.5a) can be summarized as

$$\boldsymbol{\alpha}\boldsymbol{\rho} = \boldsymbol{\rho}\boldsymbol{\Lambda}, \tag{3.6}$$

or

$$\boldsymbol{\rho}^{-1}\boldsymbol{\alpha}\boldsymbol{\rho} = \boldsymbol{\Lambda} \tag{3.6a}$$

if $\boldsymbol{\rho}$ *has a reciprocal.*

A similarity transformation by a matrix whose columns are the n eigenvectors transforms the original matrix into the diagonal form; the diagonal elements are the eigenvalues of the matrix. Two matrices which have the same eigenvalues can always be transformed into one another since they can both be transformed into the same matrix. The eigenvalues are the only invariants under a similarity transformation.

This is true, of course, only if $\boldsymbol{\rho}$ has a reciprocal, that is, if the n vectors $\mathbf{r}_{\cdot 1}\, \mathbf{r}_{\cdot 2} \cdots, \mathbf{r}_{\cdot n}$ are linearly independent. This is generally the case, and is always true if the eigenvalues are all different. Nevertheless, there are exceptions, as is shown, for example, by the matrices

$$\begin{pmatrix} 1 & 1 \\ 0 & 1 \end{pmatrix} \quad \text{or} \quad \begin{pmatrix} 1 & i \\ i & -1 \end{pmatrix}.$$

These cannot be brought into diagonal form by any kind of similarity transformation. The theory of elementary divisors deals with such matrices; however, we need not go into this, since we shall have always to deal with matrices which can be brought into the diagonal form (3.6a) (e.g., with unitary and/or Hermitian matrices).

The conditions for the commutability of two matrices can be reviewed very well from the viewpoint developed above. If two matrices can be brought into diagonal form by the same transformation, i.e., if they have the same eigenvectors, then they commute.[3] As diagonal matrices they certainly commute after the similarity transformation; therefore they must also commute in their original form.

In the first chapter we defined the rational function of a matrix

$$f(\boldsymbol{\alpha}) = \cdots a_{-3}\boldsymbol{\alpha}^{-3} + a_{-2}\boldsymbol{\alpha}^{-2} + a_{-1}\boldsymbol{\alpha}^{-1} + a_0\mathbf{1} + a_1\boldsymbol{\alpha} + a_2\boldsymbol{\alpha}^2 + a_3\boldsymbol{\alpha}^3 + \cdots.$$

To bring $f(\boldsymbol{\alpha})$ into diagonal form it is sufficient to transform $\boldsymbol{\alpha}$ to the diagonal form $\boldsymbol{\Lambda} = \boldsymbol{\sigma}^{-1}\boldsymbol{\alpha}\boldsymbol{\sigma}$. Then, according to Theorem 10 of Chapter 1,

$$\begin{aligned} \boldsymbol{\sigma}^{-1}f(\boldsymbol{\alpha})\boldsymbol{\sigma} &= \boldsymbol{\sigma}^{-1}(\cdots a_{-2}\boldsymbol{\alpha}^{-2} + a_{-1}\boldsymbol{\alpha}^{-1} + a_0\mathbf{1} + a_1\boldsymbol{\alpha} + a_2\boldsymbol{\alpha}^2 + \cdots)\boldsymbol{\sigma}, \\ &= \cdots a_{-2}\boldsymbol{\Lambda}^{-2} + a_{-1}\boldsymbol{\Lambda}^{-1} + a_0\mathbf{1} + a_1\boldsymbol{\Lambda} + a_2\boldsymbol{\Lambda}^2 + \cdots = f(\boldsymbol{\Lambda}) \end{aligned}$$

and this is itself a diagonal matrix. If λ_k is the kth diagonal element in $\boldsymbol{\Lambda} = (\boldsymbol{\Lambda}_{ik}) = (\delta_{ik}\lambda_k)$, then $(\lambda_k)^\rho$ is the kth diagonal element in $(\boldsymbol{\Lambda})^\rho$, and

$$\cdots a_{-2}\lambda_k^{-2} + a_{-1}\lambda_k^{-1} + a_0 + a_1\lambda_k + a_2\lambda_k^2 + \cdots = f(\lambda_k)$$

is the kth diagonal element in $f(\boldsymbol{\Lambda})$.

A rational function $f(\boldsymbol{\alpha})$ of a matrix $\boldsymbol{\alpha}$ can be brought into diagonal form by the same transformation which brings $\boldsymbol{\alpha}$ into diagonal form. The diagonal elements, the eigenvalues of $f(\boldsymbol{\alpha})$, are the corresponding functions $f(\lambda_1), f(\lambda_2), \cdots, f(\lambda_n)$ of the diagonal elements $\lambda_1, \lambda_2, \cdots, \lambda_n$ of $\boldsymbol{\alpha}$. We assume that this law holds not only for rational functions but also for arbitrary functions $F(\boldsymbol{\alpha})$ of $\boldsymbol{\alpha}$ and consider this as the *definition* of general matrix functions.

[3] Note that the eigenvalues can differ arbitrarily.

Special Matrices

One can obtain from a square matrix $\boldsymbol{\alpha}$ a new matrix $\boldsymbol{\alpha}'$, in which the roles of rows and columns are interchanged. The matrix $\boldsymbol{\alpha}'$ so formed is called the *transpose* of $\boldsymbol{\alpha}$, and the transposition is indicated by the prime. Then

$$\alpha'_{ik} = \alpha_{ki}\,. \tag{3.7}$$

Rule: The transpose of a product $\boldsymbol{\alpha\beta\gamma\delta}\cdots$ is the product of the transposes in reverse order:

$$(\boldsymbol{\alpha\beta\gamma}\cdots\boldsymbol{\epsilon})' = \boldsymbol{\epsilon}'\cdots\boldsymbol{\gamma}'\boldsymbol{\beta}'\boldsymbol{\alpha}'. \tag{3.7a}$$

To see this, consider the left-hand side alone

$$(\boldsymbol{\alpha\beta\gamma}\cdots\boldsymbol{\epsilon})'_{ki} = (\boldsymbol{\alpha\beta\gamma}\cdots\boldsymbol{\epsilon})_{ik} = \sum_{\varkappa\lambda\mu\cdots\zeta} \alpha_{i\varkappa}\beta_{\varkappa\lambda}\gamma_{\lambda\mu}\cdots\epsilon_{\zeta k}\,.$$

On the other hand, the right side is

$$(\boldsymbol{\epsilon}'\cdots\boldsymbol{\gamma}'\boldsymbol{\beta}'\boldsymbol{\alpha}')_{ki} = \sum_{\zeta\cdots\mu\lambda\varkappa} \epsilon'_{k\zeta}\cdots\gamma'_{\mu\lambda}\beta'_{\lambda\varkappa}\alpha'_{\varkappa i}$$

which verifies (3.7a).

The matrix which is formed by replacing each of the n^2 elements with its complex conjugate is denoted by $\boldsymbol{\alpha}^*$, the complex conjugate of $\boldsymbol{\alpha}$. If $\boldsymbol{\alpha} = \boldsymbol{\alpha}^*$ all the elements are real.

By interchanging the rows and columns and taking the complex conjugate as well, one obtains from $\boldsymbol{\alpha}$ the matrix $\boldsymbol{\alpha}^{*\prime} = \boldsymbol{\alpha}'^*$. This matrix is called the *adjoint* $\boldsymbol{\alpha}^\dagger$ of $\boldsymbol{\alpha}$:

$$\boldsymbol{\alpha}^{*\prime} = \boldsymbol{\alpha}^\dagger = \boldsymbol{\alpha}'^*. \tag{3.8}$$

The complex conjugate of a product is clearly the product of the complex conjugates.

$$(\boldsymbol{\alpha\beta\gamma}\cdots\boldsymbol{\epsilon})^* = \boldsymbol{\alpha}^*\boldsymbol{\beta}^*\boldsymbol{\gamma}^*\cdots\boldsymbol{\epsilon}^*.$$

For the adjoint, the order must be reversed.

$$\begin{aligned}(\boldsymbol{\alpha\beta\gamma}\cdots\boldsymbol{\epsilon})^\dagger &= (\boldsymbol{\alpha\beta\gamma}\cdots\boldsymbol{\epsilon})^{*\prime} = (\boldsymbol{\alpha}^*\boldsymbol{\beta}^*\boldsymbol{\gamma}^*\cdots\boldsymbol{\epsilon}^*)' \\ &= (\boldsymbol{\epsilon}^{*\prime}\cdots\boldsymbol{\gamma}^{*\prime}\boldsymbol{\beta}^{*\prime}\boldsymbol{\alpha}^{*\prime}) = \boldsymbol{\epsilon}^\dagger\cdots\boldsymbol{\gamma}^\dagger\boldsymbol{\beta}^\dagger\boldsymbol{\alpha}^\dagger.\end{aligned} \tag{3.8a}$$

By assuming various relationships between a matrix $\boldsymbol{\alpha}$ and its adjoint, transpose, and reciprocal, special kinds of matrices can be obtained. Since their names appear frequently in the literature we will mention them all; in what follows, we shall use only *unitary*, *Hermitian*, and *real orthogonal* matrices.

If $\boldsymbol{\alpha} = \boldsymbol{\alpha}^*$ (i.e., $\alpha_{ik} = \alpha^*_{ik}$), the matrix is said to be *real*, and all n^2 elements α_{ik} are real. If $\boldsymbol{\alpha} = -\boldsymbol{\alpha}^*$ ($\alpha_{ik} = -\alpha^*_{ik}$), then the matrix is purely imaginary.

If $\mathbf{S} = \mathbf{S}'$ ($\mathbf{S}_{ik} = \mathbf{S}_{ki}$), the matrix is *symmetric*; if $\mathbf{S} = -\mathbf{S}'$ ($\mathbf{S}_{ik} = -\mathbf{S}_{ki}$), it is skew- or anti-symmetric.

If $\mathbf{H} = \mathbf{H}^\dagger$ ($\mathbf{H}_{ik} = \mathbf{H}^*_{ki}$), the matrix is said to be *Hermitian*; if $\mathbf{A} = -\mathbf{A}^\dagger$, *skew- or anti-Hermitian*.

If $\boldsymbol{\alpha}$ is *real as well as symmetric*, then $\boldsymbol{\alpha}$ is *Hermitian* also, etc.

If $\mathbf{O}' = \mathbf{O}^{-1}$, then $\mathbf{O}$ is *complex orthogonal*. A matrix $\mathbf{U}$, for which $\mathbf{U}^\dagger = \mathbf{U}^{-1}$, is said to be a unitary matrix. If $\mathbf{R}^\dagger = \mathbf{R}^{-1}$, and $\mathbf{R} = \mathbf{R}^*$ (real), then $\mathbf{R}' = \mathbf{R}^{*\prime} = \mathbf{R}^\dagger = \mathbf{R}^{-1}$ and $\mathbf{R}' = \mathbf{R}^{-1}$; $\mathbf{R}$ is said to be real orthogonal, or simply *orthogonal*.

Unitary Matrices and the Scalar Product

Before discussing unitary matrices, we must introduce one more new concept. In the very first chapter we defined the sum of two vectors and a constant multiple of a vector. Another important elementary concept is the *scalar product* of two vectors. The scalar product of a vector $\mathfrak{a}$ with a vector $\mathfrak{b}$ is a number. We shall distinguish between the Hermitian scalar product

$$\mathfrak{a}_1^*\mathfrak{b}_1 + \mathfrak{a}_2^*\mathfrak{b}_2 + \cdots + \mathfrak{a}_n^*\mathfrak{b}_n = (\mathfrak{a}, \mathfrak{b}) \tag{3.9}$$

and the simple scalar product

$$\mathfrak{a}_1\mathfrak{b}_1 + \mathfrak{a}_2\mathfrak{b}_2 + \cdots + \mathfrak{a}_n\mathfrak{b}_n = ((\mathfrak{a}, \mathfrak{b})). \tag{3.9a}$$

Unless we specify otherwise, we always refer to the *Hermitian* scalar product rather than the simple scalar product. If the vector components $\mathfrak{a}_1, \mathfrak{a}_2, \cdots, \mathfrak{a}_n$ are real, both products are identical.

If $(\mathfrak{a}, \mathfrak{b}) = 0 = (\mathfrak{b}, \mathfrak{a})$, then $\mathfrak{a}$ and $\mathfrak{b}$ are said to be orthogonal to one another. If $(\mathfrak{a}, \mathfrak{a}) = 1$, it is said that $\mathfrak{a}$ is a *unit vector*, or that it is normalized. The product $(\mathfrak{a}, \mathfrak{a})$ is always real and positive, and vanishes only when all the components of $\mathfrak{a}$ vanish. This holds only for the Hermitian scalar product, in contrast to the simple scalar product; for example, suppose $\mathfrak{a}$ is the two-dimensional vector $(1, i)$. Then $((\mathfrak{a}, \mathfrak{a})) = 0$, but $(\mathfrak{a}, \mathfrak{a}) = 2$. In fact $(\mathfrak{a}, \mathfrak{a}) = 0$ implies that $\mathfrak{a} = 0$; but this does not follow from $((\mathfrak{a}, \mathfrak{a})) = 0$.

Simple Rules for Scalar Products:

1. Upon interchange of the vectors

$$(\mathfrak{a}, \mathfrak{b}) = (\mathfrak{b}, \mathfrak{a})^* \tag{3.10}$$

whereas

$$((\mathfrak{a}, \mathfrak{b})) = ((\mathfrak{b}, \mathfrak{a})). \tag{3.10a}$$

2. If c is a number,

$$(\mathfrak{a}, c\mathfrak{b}) = c(\mathfrak{a}, \mathfrak{b}) \quad \text{and} \quad ((\mathfrak{a}, c\mathfrak{b})) = c((\mathfrak{a}, \mathfrak{b})). \tag{3.11}$$

On the other hand

$$(c\mathfrak{a}, \mathfrak{b}) = c^*(\mathfrak{a}, \mathfrak{b}) \quad \text{whereas} \quad ((c\mathfrak{a}, \mathfrak{b})) = c((\mathfrak{a}, \mathfrak{b})).$$

3. *The scalar product is linear in the second factor*, since

$$(\mathfrak{a}, b\mathfrak{b} + c\mathfrak{c}) = b(\mathfrak{a}, \mathfrak{b}) + c(\mathfrak{a}, \mathfrak{c}). \tag{3.12}$$

It is, however, "antilinear" in the first factor

$$(a\mathfrak{a} + b\mathfrak{b}, \mathfrak{c}) = a^*(\mathfrak{a}, \mathfrak{c}) + b^*(\mathfrak{b}, \mathfrak{c}). \tag{3.12a}$$

4. Furthermore, the important rule

$$(\mathfrak{a}, \boldsymbol{\alpha}\mathfrak{b}) = (\boldsymbol{\alpha}^\dagger\mathfrak{a}, \mathfrak{b}) \quad \text{or} \quad (\boldsymbol{\beta}\mathfrak{a}, \mathfrak{b}) = (\mathfrak{a}, \boldsymbol{\beta}^\dagger\mathfrak{b}) \tag{3.13}$$

is valid for arbitrary vectors $\mathfrak{a}$ and $\mathfrak{b}$, and every matrix $\boldsymbol{\alpha}$. To see this, write out

$$(\mathfrak{a}, \boldsymbol{\alpha}\mathfrak{b}) = \sum_{k=1}^{n} \mathfrak{a}_k^*(\boldsymbol{\alpha}\mathfrak{b})_k = \sum_{k=1}^{n} \mathfrak{a}_k^* \sum_{\lambda=1}^{n} \boldsymbol{\alpha}_{k\lambda}\mathfrak{b}_\lambda$$

and

$$(\boldsymbol{\alpha}^\dagger\mathfrak{a}, \mathfrak{b}) = \sum_{\lambda=1}^{n} (\boldsymbol{\alpha}^\dagger\mathfrak{a})_\lambda^*\mathfrak{b}_\lambda = \sum_{\lambda=1}^{n} \sum_{k=1}^{n} (\boldsymbol{\alpha}_{k\lambda}^*\mathfrak{a}_k)^*\mathfrak{b}_\lambda = \sum_{\lambda=1}^{n} \sum_{k=1}^{n} \boldsymbol{\alpha}_{k\lambda}\mathfrak{a}_k^*\mathfrak{b}_\lambda.$$

Instead of applying the matrix $\boldsymbol{\alpha}$ *to one factor of a scalar product, its adjoint* $\boldsymbol{\alpha}^\dagger$ *can be applied to the other factor.*

For the simple scalar product the same rule holds for the transposed matrix; that is

$$((\mathfrak{a}, \boldsymbol{\alpha}\mathfrak{b})) = ((\boldsymbol{\alpha}'\mathfrak{a}, \mathfrak{b})).$$

5. We now write the condition $\mathbf{U}^\dagger = \mathbf{U}^{-1}$ for the unitarity of a matrix somewhat more explicitly: $\mathbf{U}^\dagger\mathbf{U} = \mathbf{1}$ implies that

$$\sum_{j=1}^{n} (\mathbf{U}^\dagger)_{ij}\mathbf{U}_{jk} = \sum_{j=1}^{n} \mathbf{U}_{ji}^*\mathbf{U}_{jk} = \delta_{ik}; \qquad (\mathbf{U}_{\cdot i}, \mathbf{U}_{\cdot k}) = \delta_{ik}. \tag{3.14}$$

If the n columns of a unitary matrix are looked upon as vectors, they comprise n orthogonal unit vectors. Similarly, from $\mathbf{U}\mathbf{U}^\dagger = \mathbf{1}$, it follows that

$$\sum_{j} \mathbf{U}_{ij}\mathbf{U}_{kj}^* = \delta_{ik}; \qquad (\mathbf{U}_{k\cdot}, \mathbf{U}_{i\cdot}) = \delta_{ik}. \tag{3.14a}$$

The n rows of a unitary matrix also form n unit vectors which are mutually orthogonal.

6. A unitary transformation leaves the Hermitian scalar product unchanged; in other words, for *arbitrary* vectors $\mathfrak{a}$ and $\mathfrak{b}$,

$$(\mathbf{U}\mathfrak{a}, \mathbf{U}\mathfrak{b}) = (\mathfrak{a}, \mathbf{U}^\dagger\mathbf{U}\mathfrak{b}) = (\mathfrak{a}, \mathfrak{b}). \tag{3.15}$$

Conversely, if (3.15) holds for a matrix $\mathbf{U}$ for every pair of arbitrary vectors

$\mathfrak{a}$ and $\mathfrak{b}$, then $\mathbf{U}$ is unitary, since then Eq. (3.15) holds also for $\mathfrak{a} = \mathfrak{e}_i$, and $\mathfrak{b} = \mathfrak{e}_k$ (where $(\mathfrak{e}_k)_l = \delta_{kl}$). But in this special case (3.15) becomes

$$\delta_{ik} = (\mathfrak{e}_i, \mathfrak{e}_k) = (\mathbf{U}\mathfrak{e}_i, \mathbf{U}\mathfrak{e}_k) = \sum_j (\mathbf{U}\mathfrak{e}_i)_j^*(\mathbf{U}\mathfrak{e}_k)_j$$
$$= \sum_j (\sum_l \mathbf{U}_{jl}\delta_{il})^* \cdot \sum_l \mathbf{U}_{jl}\delta_{kl} = \sum_j \mathbf{U}_{ji}^*\mathbf{U}_{jk}$$

which is just Eq. (3.14). Thus (3.15) is the necessary and sufficient condition that $\mathbf{U}$ be unitary.

The same rule applies to *complex orthogonal* matrices, with respect to the *simple scalar product.*

7. The product $\mathbf{UV}$ of two unitary matrices $\mathbf{U}$ and $\mathbf{V}$ is unitary.

$$(\mathbf{UV})^\dagger = \mathbf{V}^\dagger\mathbf{U}^\dagger = \mathbf{V}^{-1}\mathbf{U}^{-1} = (\mathbf{UV})^{-1}. \tag{3.16}$$

The reciprocal $\mathbf{U}^{-1}$ of a unitary matrix is also unitary.

$$(\mathbf{U}^{-1})^\dagger = (\mathbf{U}^\dagger)^\dagger = \mathbf{U} = (\mathbf{U}^{-1})^{-1}. \tag{3.17}$$

The Principal Axis Transformation for Unitary and Hermitian Matrices

Every unitary matrix $\mathbf{V}$ *and every Hermitian matrix* $\mathbf{H}$ *can be brought into diagonal form by a similarity transformation with a unitary matrix* $\mathbf{U}$. For such matrices, the exceptional case mentioned on page 22 cannot occur. First of all, we point out that a unitary (or Hermitian) matrix remains unitary (or Hermitian) after a unitary transformation. Since it is a product of three unitary matrices, $\mathbf{U}^{-1}\mathbf{VU}$ is itself unitary. $\mathbf{U}^{-1}\mathbf{HU}$ is also Hermitian, if only $\mathbf{H}$ is Hermitian, since by (3.17)

$$(\mathbf{U}^{-1}\mathbf{HU})^\dagger = \mathbf{U}^\dagger\mathbf{HU}^{-1\dagger} = \mathbf{U}^\dagger\mathbf{HU} = \mathbf{U}^{-1}\mathbf{HU}. \tag{3.18}$$

To bring $\mathbf{V}$ or $\mathbf{H}$ to the diagonal form, we determine an eigenvalue of $\mathbf{V}$ or $\mathbf{H}$. Let this be λ_1; the corresponding eigenvector, $\mathbf{U}_{\cdot 1} = (\mathbf{U}_{11} \cdots \mathbf{U}_{n1})$ is determined only up to a constant factor. We choose the constant factor so that

$$(\mathbf{U}_{\cdot 1}, \mathbf{U}_{\cdot 1}) = 1.$$

This is always possible since $(\mathbf{U}_{\cdot 1}, \mathbf{U}_{\cdot 1})$ can never vanish. We now construct a unitary matrix $\mathbf{U}$ of which the first column is $\mathbf{U}_{\cdot 1}$.[4] With this unitary matrix we now transform $\mathbf{V}$ or $\mathbf{H}$ into $\mathbf{U}^{-1}\mathbf{VU}$ or $\mathbf{U}^{-1}\mathbf{HU}$. For example, in $\mathbf{U}^{-1}\mathbf{VU}$, we have for the first column

$$\mathbf{X}_{r1} = (\mathbf{U}^{-1}\mathbf{VU})_{r1} = (\mathbf{U}^\dagger\mathbf{VU})_{r1} = \sum_\nu \mathbf{U}_{\nu r}^* \sum_\mu \mathbf{V}_{\nu\mu}\mathbf{U}_{\mu 1} = \sum_\nu \mathbf{U}_{\nu r}^*\lambda_1\mathbf{U}_{\nu 1} = \delta_{r1}\lambda_1,$$

since $\mathbf{U}_{\cdot 1}$ is already an eigenvector of $\mathbf{V}$. We see that λ_1 *occurs in the first row of the first column, and all the other elements of the first column are zero.*

Obviously, this holds true not only for $\mathbf{U}^{-1}\mathbf{VU}$, but also for $\mathbf{U}^{-1}\mathbf{HU}$. Since

[4] See the lemma at the end of the proof.

$\mathbf{U}^{-1}\mathbf{HU}$ is Hermitian, the first row is also zero, except for the very first element; thus $\mathbf{U}^{-1}\mathbf{HU}$ has the form

$$\begin{pmatrix} \lambda_1 & 0 & \cdots & 0 \\ 0 & & & \\ \cdot & & & \\ \cdot & & & \\ \cdot & & & \\ 0 & & & \end{pmatrix} \tag{3.E.1}$$

But $\mathbf{U}^{-1}\mathbf{VU}$ must have exactly the same form! Since $\mathbf{X}$ is a unitary matrix, its first column $\mathbf{X}_{\cdot 1}$ is a unit vector, and from this it follows that

$$|\mathbf{X}_{11}|^2 + |\mathbf{X}_{21}|^2 + \cdots + |\mathbf{X}_{n1}|^2 = |\lambda_1|^2 = 1. \tag{3.E.2}$$

The same argument applies to the first row, $\mathbf{X}_{1\cdot}$ of $\mathbf{X}$. The sum of the squares is given by

$$|\mathbf{X}_{11}|^2 + |\mathbf{X}_{12}|^2 + \cdots + |\mathbf{X}_{1n}|^2 = |\lambda_1|^2 + |\mathbf{X}_{12}|^2 + |\mathbf{X}_{13}|^2 + \cdots + |\mathbf{X}_{1n}|^2 = 1,$$

which implies that $\mathbf{X}_{12}, \mathbf{X}_{13}, \cdots, \mathbf{X}_{1n}$ all vanish.

Therefore, every unitary or Hermitian matrix cna be transformed into the form (3.E.1) by a unitary matrix. The matrix (3.E.1) is not yet a diagonal matrix, as it cannot be, since we have used the existence of only one eigenvalue. It is however more like a diagonal matrix than the original matrix $\mathbf{V}$, or $\mathbf{H}$. It is natural to write (3.E.1) as a super-matrix

$$\begin{pmatrix} \lambda_1 & \mathbf{0} \\ \mathbf{0} & \mathbf{V}_1 \end{pmatrix} \quad \text{or} \quad \begin{pmatrix} \lambda_1 & \mathbf{0} \\ \mathbf{0} & \mathbf{H}_1 \end{pmatrix}, \tag{3.E.3}$$

where the matrix $\mathbf{V}_1$ or $\mathbf{H}_1$ has only $n - 1$ rows and columns. We can then transform (3.E.3) by another unitary matrix

$$\begin{pmatrix} 1 & \mathbf{0} \\ \mathbf{0} & \mathbf{U}_1 \end{pmatrix}$$

where $\mathbf{U}_1$ has only $n - 1$ rows and columns.

Undcr this process (3.E.1) assumes the form

$$\begin{pmatrix} \lambda_1 & \mathbf{0} \\ \mathbf{0} & \mathbf{U}_1^\dagger \mathbf{V}\mathbf{U}_1 \end{pmatrix} \quad \text{or} \quad \begin{pmatrix} \lambda_1 & \mathbf{0} \\ \mathbf{0} & \mathbf{U}_1^\dagger \mathbf{H}_1\mathbf{U} \end{pmatrix} \tag{3.E.4}$$

The procedure above can be applied again and $\mathbf{U}_1$ can be chosen so that $\mathbf{U}_1^\dagger\mathbf{V}_1\mathbf{U}_1$ or $\mathbf{U}_1^\dagger\mathbf{H}_1\mathbf{U}_1$ has the form

$$\begin{pmatrix} \lambda_2 & \mathbf{0} \\ \mathbf{0} & \mathbf{V}_2 \end{pmatrix} \quad \text{or} \quad \begin{pmatrix} \lambda_2 & \mathbf{0} \\ \mathbf{0} & \mathbf{H}_2 \end{pmatrix}$$

where $\mathbf{V}_2$ or $\mathbf{H}_2$ are only $n - 2$ dimensional. Then $\mathbf{U}_1^\dagger\mathbf{U}^\dagger\mathbf{VUU}_1$ has the form

$$\begin{pmatrix} \mathbf{\Lambda}_1 & \mathbf{0} \\ \mathbf{0} & \mathbf{V}_2 \end{pmatrix}, \quad \text{where} \quad \mathbf{\Lambda}_1 = \begin{pmatrix} \lambda_1 & 0 \\ 0 & \lambda_2 \end{pmatrix}.$$

Clearly, repetition of this procedure will bring $\mathbf{V}$ or $\mathbf{H}$ *entirely into diagonal form*, so that the theorem is proven.

This theorem is not valid for symmetric or complex orthogonal matrices, as the second example on page 22 shows (the second matrix is symmetric and complex orthogonal). However, it is valid for real symmetric or real orthogonal matrices, which are just special cases of Hermitian or unitary matrices.

Lemma. If $(\mathfrak{u}_{\cdot 1}, \mathfrak{u}_{\cdot 1}) = 1$, then a unitary matrix can be constructed (in many different ways), whose first column is $\mathfrak{u}_{\cdot 1} = (\mathfrak{u}_{11}, \mathfrak{u}_{21}, \cdots, \mathfrak{u}_{n1})$.

We first construct in general a matrix the first column of which is $\mathfrak{u}_{\cdot 1}$ and which has a nonvanishing determinant. Let the second column of this matrix be $\mathfrak{v}_{\cdot 2} = (\mathfrak{v}_{12}, \mathfrak{v}_{22}, \cdots, \mathfrak{v}_{n2})$, the third $\mathfrak{v}_{\cdot 3}$, etc.

$$\begin{pmatrix} \mathfrak{u}_{11} & \mathfrak{v}_{12} & \mathfrak{v}_{13} & \cdots & \mathfrak{v}_{1n} \\ \mathfrak{u}_{21} & \mathfrak{v}_{22} & \mathfrak{v}_{23} & \cdots & \mathfrak{v}_{2n} \\ \mathfrak{u}_{31} & \mathfrak{v}_{32} & \mathfrak{v}_{33} & \cdots & \mathfrak{v}_{3n} \\ \cdot & \cdot & \cdot & & \cdot \\ \cdot & \cdot & \cdot & & \cdot \\ \cdot & \cdot & \cdot & & \cdot \\ \mathfrak{u}_{n1} & \mathfrak{v}_{n2} & \mathfrak{v}_{n3} & \cdots & \mathfrak{v}_{nn} \end{pmatrix}$$

The vectors $\mathfrak{u}_{\cdot 1}, \mathfrak{v}_{\cdot 2}, \mathfrak{v}_{\cdot 3}, \cdots$ are then linearly independent since the determinant does not vanish. Since we also wish them to be orthogonal, we use the Schmidt procedure to "orthogonalize" them. First substitute $\mathfrak{u}_{\cdot 2} = a_{21}\mathfrak{u}_{\cdot 1} + \mathfrak{v}_{\cdot 2}$ for $\mathfrak{v}_{\cdot 2}$; this leaves the determinant unaltered. Then set

$$(\mathfrak{u}_{\cdot 1}, \mathfrak{u}_{\cdot 2}) = 0 = a_{21}(\mathfrak{u}_{\cdot 1}, \mathfrak{u}_{\cdot 1}) + (\mathfrak{u}_{\cdot 1}, \mathfrak{v}_{\cdot 2}) = a_{21} + (\mathfrak{u}_{\cdot 1}, \mathfrak{v}_{\cdot 2})$$

and determine a_{21} from this. Next write $\mathfrak{u}_{\cdot 3}$ in place of $\mathfrak{v}_{\cdot 3}$ with $\mathfrak{u}_{\cdot 3} = a_{31}\mathfrak{u}_{\cdot 1} + a_{32}\mathfrak{u}_{\cdot 2} + \mathfrak{v}_{\cdot 3}$ and determine a_{31} and a_{32} so that

$$0 = (\mathfrak{u}_{\cdot 1}, \mathfrak{u}_{\cdot 3}) = a_{31}(\mathfrak{u}_{\cdot 1}, \mathfrak{u}_{\cdot 1}) + (\mathfrak{u}_{\cdot 1}, \mathfrak{v}_{\cdot 3})$$

$$0 = (\mathfrak{u}_{\cdot 2}, \mathfrak{u}_{\cdot 3}) = a_{32}(\mathfrak{u}_{\cdot 2}, \mathfrak{u}_{\cdot 2}) + (\mathfrak{u}_{\cdot 2}, \mathfrak{v}_{\cdot 3}).$$

Proceeding in this way, we finally write $\mathfrak{u}_{\cdot n}$ in place of $\mathfrak{v}_{\cdot n}$, with $\mathfrak{u}_{\cdot n} = a_{n1}\mathfrak{u}_{\cdot 1} + a_{n2}\mathfrak{u}_{\cdot 2} + \cdots + a_{n,n-1}\mathfrak{u}_{\cdot n-1} + \mathfrak{v}_{\cdot n}$, and determine $a_{n1}, a_{n2}, a_{n3}, \cdots, a_{n,n-1}$, so that

$$0 = (\mathfrak{u}_{\cdot 1}, \mathfrak{u}_{\cdot n}) = a_{n1}(\mathfrak{u}_{\cdot 1}, \mathfrak{u}_{\cdot 1}) + (\mathfrak{u}_{\cdot 1}, \mathfrak{v}_{\cdot n}),$$

$$0 = (\mathfrak{u}_{\cdot 2}, \mathfrak{u}_{\cdot n}) = a_{n2}(\mathfrak{u}_{\cdot 2}, \mathfrak{u}_{\cdot 2}) + (\mathfrak{u}_{\cdot 2}, \mathfrak{v}_{\cdot n}),$$

$$\cdots\cdots\cdots\cdots\cdots\cdots\cdots\cdots\cdots\cdots\cdots\cdots\cdots\cdots$$

$$0 = (\mathfrak{u}_{\cdot n-1}, \mathfrak{u}_{\cdot n}) = a_{n,n-1}(\mathfrak{u}_{\cdot n-1}, \mathfrak{u}_{\cdot n-1}) + (\mathfrak{u}_{\cdot n-1}, \mathfrak{v}_{\cdot n}).$$

In this way, with the help of the $\frac{1}{2}n(n-1)$ numbers a we succeed in substituting the vectors $\mathfrak{u}$ for the vectors $\mathfrak{v}$. The $\mathfrak{u}$ are orthogonal and non-null by virtue of the linear independence of the $\mathfrak{v}$. Assume, for example, that $\mathfrak{u}_{\cdot n} = 0$. This implies

$$a_{n1}\mathfrak{u}_{\cdot 1} + a_{n2}\mathfrak{u}_{\cdot 2} + \cdots + a_{n,n-1}\mathfrak{u}_{\cdot n-1} + \mathfrak{v}_{\cdot n} = 0$$

and since the $\mathfrak{u}_{\cdot 1}, \mathfrak{u}_{\cdot 2}, \cdots, \mathfrak{u}_{\cdot n}$ are linear combinations of the $\mathfrak{u}_{\cdot 1}, \mathfrak{v}_{\cdot 2}, \cdots, \mathfrak{v}_{\cdot n-1}$, one could write $\mathfrak{v}_{\cdot n}$ in terms of these $n-1$ vectors, in contradiction to their linear independence.

Finally, we normalize the $\mathfrak{u}_{\cdot 2}, \mathfrak{u}_{\cdot 3}, \cdots, \mathfrak{u}_{\cdot n}$, thereby constructing a unitary matrix whose first column is $\mathfrak{u}_{\cdot 1}$.

This "*Schmidt Orthogonalization Procedure*" shows how to construct from any set of linearly independent vectors an orthogonal normalized set in which the kth unit vector is a linear combination of just the first k of the original vectors. If one starts with n n-dimensional vectors which form a complete set of vectors, one obtains a complete *orthogonal* system.

If a unitary matrix $\mathbf{V}$ or a Hermitian matrix $\mathbf{H}$ is brought to the diagonal form this way, then the resulting matrix $\mathbf{\Lambda}_v$ or $\mathbf{\Lambda}_h$ is also unitary or Hermitian. It follows that

$$\mathbf{\Lambda}_v\mathbf{\Lambda}_v^* = \mathbf{1}, \quad \text{or} \quad \mathbf{\Lambda}_h = \mathbf{\Lambda}_h^\dagger. \tag{3.19}$$

The absolute value of each eigenvalue of a unitary matrix[5] *is 1; the eigenvalues of a Hermitian matrix are real.* This follows directly from (3.19), which states that for the eigenvalues λ_v of the unitary matrix, $\lambda_v\lambda_v^* = 1$; for those of a Hermitian matrix, $\lambda_h = \lambda_h^*$. The eigenvectors of $\mathbf{V}$, and of $\mathbf{H}$, as columns of the unitary matrix $\mathbf{U}$, can be assumed to be orthogonal.

Real Orthogonal and Symmetric Matrices

Finally, we investigate the implications of the requirement that $\mathbf{V}$, or $\mathbf{H}$, be complex orthogonal (or symmetric), as well as unitary (or Hermitian). In this case, both $\mathbf{V}$ and $\mathbf{H}$ are real.

From $\mathbf{U}^\dagger\mathbf{V}\mathbf{U} = \mathbf{\Lambda}_v$, we obtain the complex conjugate $\mathbf{U}^{*\dagger}\mathbf{V}^*\mathbf{U}^* = (\mathbf{U}^*)^\dagger\mathbf{V}\mathbf{U}^* = \mathbf{\Lambda}_v^*$. Since the eigenvalues, as roots of the secular equation, are independent of how the matrix is diagonalized (i.e., whether by $\mathbf{U}$ or $\mathbf{U}^*$), the diagonal form $\mathbf{\Lambda}_v$ can also be written as $\mathbf{\Lambda}_v^*$. Thus the numbers $\lambda_1, \lambda_2, \cdots, \lambda_n$ are the same as the numbers $\lambda_1^*, \lambda_2^*, \cdots, \lambda_n^*$. This implies that *the complex eigenvalues* of a real orthogonal matrix $\mathbf{V}$ *occur in conjugate pairs.* Moreover since $\mathbf{V}\mathbf{V}' = \mathbf{1}$, they all have absolute value 1; the real eigenvalues are therefore ± 1. In an odd-dimensional matrix at least one eigenvalue must be real.

[5] As equation (3.E.2) already shows.

If $\mathfrak{v}$ is an eigenvector for the eigenvalue λ, then $\mathfrak{v}^*$ is an eigenvector for the complex conjugate value λ^*. To see this write $\mathbf{V}\mathfrak{v} = \lambda\mathfrak{v}$; then $\mathbf{V}^*\mathfrak{v}^* = \lambda^*\mathfrak{v}^* = \mathbf{V}\mathfrak{v}^*$. Moreover, if λ^* is different from λ, then $(\mathfrak{v}^*, \mathfrak{v}) = 0 = ((\mathfrak{v}, \mathfrak{v}))$; the simple scalar product of an eigenvector with itself vanishes if the corresponding eigenvalue is not real (not ± 1). Conversely, real eigenvectors (for which the simple scalar product does not vanish) correspond to the eigenvalues ± 1. Also, let $\mathfrak{v}$ be the eigenvector for λ_1, let $\mathfrak{v}^*$ be that for λ_1^*, and $\mathfrak{z}$ that for λ_2. Then if $\lambda_1 \neq \lambda_2$, it follows that

$$0 = (\mathfrak{v}^*, \mathfrak{z}) = ((\mathfrak{v}, \mathfrak{z})).$$

The simple scalar product of two eigenvectors of a real orthogonal matrix is always zero if the corresponding eigenvalues are not complex conjugates; when the eigenvalues are complex conjugates, the corresponding eigenvectors are themselves complex conjugates.

The determinant of an orthogonal matrix is ± 1. To see this, consider $\mathbf{V}\mathbf{V}' = \mathbf{1}$; it follows that the determinant of $\mathbf{V}$ multiplied with that of $\mathbf{V}'$ must give 1. The determinant of $\mathbf{V}$, however, is equal to that of $\mathbf{V}'$, so that both must be either $+1$ or -1.

If $\mathbf{H}$ is real, the Eq. (3.5) is real, since the λ_h are real. *The eigenvectors of a real Hermitian matrix can be assumed real.* (Since they are only determined up to a constant factor, they can also be multiplied by a complex factor.) Thus, the unitary matrix $\mathbf{U}$ in $\mathbf{U}^{-1}\mathbf{H}\mathbf{U} = \mathbf{\Lambda}_h$ can be assumed real.

4. The Elements of Quantum Mechanics

1. In the years before 1925 the development of the then new "Quantum Mechanics" was directed primarily toward the determination of the energy of stationary states, i.e., toward the calculation of the energy levels. The older "Separation Theory" of Epstein–Schwarzschild gave a prescription for the determination of the energy levels, or terms, only for systems whose classical mechanical motions had the very special property of being periodic, or at least quasi-periodic.

An idea of W. Heisenberg, which attempted a precise statement of the Bohr correspondence principle, corrected this deficiency. It was proposed independently by M. Born and P. Jordan, and by P. A. M. Dirac. Its essence is the requirement that only motions which later would be seen as quantum mechanically allowed motions should occur in the calculation. In carrying through this idea these authors were led to introduce matrices with infinite numbers of rows and columns as a formal representation of position and momentum coordinates, and formal calculations with "q-numbers" obeying the associative but not the commutative law.

Thus, for example, the equation for the energy $\mathbf{H}$ of the linear oscillator[1]

$$\mathbf{H} = \frac{1}{2m}\mathfrak{p}^2 + \frac{K}{2}\mathfrak{q}^2 \tag{4.1}$$

is obtained by formally substituting the matrices $\mathfrak{p}$ and $\mathfrak{q}$ for *the momentum and position coordinates* p and q in the *Hamiltonian formulation* of the classical expression for the energy. It is required that $\mathbf{H}$ be a diagonal matrix. The diagonal terms $\mathbf{H}_{nn}$ then give the possible energy values, the stationary levels of the system. On the other hand, the absolute squares of elements $\mathfrak{q}_{nk}$ of the matrix $\mathfrak{q}$ are proportional to the probability of a spontaneous transition from a state with energy $\mathbf{H}_{nn}$ to one with energy $\mathbf{H}_{kk}$. They give, therefore, the intensity of the line with frequency $\omega = \dfrac{\mathbf{H}_{nn} - \mathbf{H}_{kk}}{\hbar}$. All of this follows from the same considerations which suggest the introduction of matrices for $\mathfrak{p}$ and $\mathfrak{q}$.

In order to specify the problem completely, one had still to introduce a

[1] The m is the mass of the oscillating particle, and K the force constant; q and p are the position and momentum coordinates.

"commutation relation" between $\mathbf{p}$ and $\mathbf{q}$. This was assumed to be

$$\mathbf{pq} - \mathbf{qp} = \frac{\hbar}{i}\mathbf{1} \tag{4.2}$$

where $\hbar$ is *Planck's constant* divided by 2π.

Calculations with these quantities, although often fairly tedious, led very rapidly to beautiful and important results of a far-reaching nature. Thus, the "selection rules" for angular momentum and certain "sum rules" which determine the relative intensity of the Zeeman components of a line could be calculated in agreement with experiment, an achievement for which the Separation Theory was inadequate.

E. Schrödinger, by an approach which was independent of Heisenberg's point of view, arrived at results which were mathematically equivalent to those mentioned above. His method bears deep resemblance to the ideas of L. DeBroglie. The discussion to follow is based on Schrödinger's approach.

Consider a many-dimensional space with as many coordinates as the system considered has position coordinates. Every arrangement of the positions of the particles of the system corresponds to a point in this multidimensional "configuration space." This point will move in the course of time, tracing out a curve by which the motion of the system can be completely described classically. There exists a fundamental correspondence between the classical motion of this point, the system point in configuration space, and the motion of a wave-packet, also considered in configuration space,[2] if only we assume that the index of refraction for these waves is $[2m(E - V)]^{1/2}/E$. E is the total energy of the system; V, the potential energy as a function of the configuration.

The correspondence consists in the fact that the smaller the ratio between the wavelengths in the wave-packet and the radius of curvature of the path in configuration space, the more accurately the wave-packet will follow that path. On the other hand if the wave-packet contains wavelengths as large as the classical radius of curvature of the path in configuration space then important differences between the two motions exist, due to interference among the waves.

Schrödinger assumes that the motion of the configuration point corresponds to the motion of the waves, and not to the classically calculated motion.

If we denote the scalar amplitude of the waves by ψ, the wave equation reads

$$\frac{E-V}{E^2}\frac{\partial^2\psi}{\partial t^2} = \frac{1}{2m_1}\frac{\partial^2\psi}{\partial x_1^2} + \frac{1}{2m_2}\frac{\partial^2\psi}{\partial x_2^2} + \cdots + \frac{1}{2m_f}\frac{\partial^2\psi}{\partial x_f^2}, \tag{4.3}$$

[2] The development of the text follows Schrödinger's ideas more closely than is customary at present (remark of translator).

where $x_1, x_2, \cdots, x_f$ are the position coordinates of the particles in the system considered, $m_1, m_2, \cdots, m_f$, the corresponding masses, and $V(x_1, x_2, \cdots, x_f)$ is the potential energy in terms of the coordinates of the individual particles $x_1, x_2, \cdots, x_f$.

The total energy of the system appears explicitly in (4.3). On the other hand the frequency, or the period of the waves, is still unspecified. Schrödinger assumes that the frequency of a wave which is associated with the motion of a system with total energy E is given by $\hbar\omega = E$. He therefore substitutes into (4.3)

$$\psi = \psi_E \exp\left(-i\frac{E}{\hbar}t\right), \tag{4.4}$$

where ψ_E is independent of t. He thus obtains the eigenvalue equation

$$\frac{1}{\hbar^2}(V - E)\psi_E = \frac{1}{2m_1}\frac{\partial^2\psi_E}{\partial x_1^2} + \frac{1}{2m_2}\frac{\partial^2\psi_E}{\partial x_2^2} + \cdots + \frac{1}{2m_f}\frac{\partial^2\psi_E}{\partial x_f^2} \tag{4.5}$$

where ψ_E is a function of the particle position coordinates $x_1, x_2, \cdots, x_f$. It is necessary to require that ψ_E be square-integrable, i.e., the integral

$$\int_{-\infty}^{\infty}\cdots\int_{-\infty}^{\infty}|\psi_E(x_1, x_2, \cdots, x_f)|^2\, dx_1\, dx_2 \cdots dx_f$$

over all configuration space must be finite. In particular, ψ must vanish at infinity. The values of E for which the determination of such a function, ψ_E, is possible are called the "*eigenvalues*" of (4.5); *they give the possible energy values of the system.* The corresponding square integrable solution of (4.5) is called the *eigenfunction* belonging to the eigenvalue E.

Equation (4.5) is also written in the form

$$\mathbf{H}\psi_E = E\psi_E \tag{4.5a}$$

where $\mathbf{H}$ is a linear *operator* (The Hamiltonian, or energy operator).

$$\mathbf{H} = -\hbar^2\left(\frac{1}{2m_1}\frac{\partial^2}{\partial x_1^2} + \frac{1}{2m_2}\frac{\partial^2}{\partial x_2^2} + \cdots + \frac{1}{2m_f}\frac{\partial^2}{\partial x_f^2}\right) + V(x_1, x_2, \cdots, x_f). \tag{4.5b}$$

The last term means multiplication by $V(x_1, x_2, \cdots, x_f)$.
It transforms one function of $x_1, x_2, \cdots, x_f$ into another function. The function ψ of (4.4) fulfills the relationship

$$i\hbar\frac{\partial\psi}{\partial t} = \mathbf{H}\psi. \tag{4.6}$$

The total energy of the system does not appear explicitly in (4.6), so that it applies generally to all motions, independent of the energy of the system; it is called the *time-dependent Schrödinger equation.*

The two Eqs. (4.5) (or (4.5a), (4.5b)) and (4.6) are the basic equations of quantum mechanics. The latter specifies the change of a configuration wave in the course of time—to which, as we will see, a far-reaching physical reality is attributed; (4.5), (or (4.5a), (4.5b)) is the equation for the frequency $\omega = E/\hbar$, the energy E, and the periodic time-dependence of the wave function ψ. Indeed, (4.5a) results from (4.6) and the assumption that

$$\psi = \psi_E \exp\left(-i \frac{E}{\hbar} t\right).$$

2. We now summarize the most important properties of the eigenvalues and eigenfunctions of (4.5b). For this purpose we first define the scalar product of two functions φ and g by

$$(\varphi, g) = \int_{-\infty}^{\infty} \cdots \int \varphi(x_1 \cdots x_f)^* \, g(x_1 \cdots x_f) \, dx_1 \cdots dx_f = \int \varphi^* g. \tag{4.7}$$

All the simple calculational rules of Chapter 3 apply to this scalar product. Thus, if a_1 and a_2 are numerical constants,

$$(\varphi, a_1 g_1 + a_2 g_2) = a_1(\varphi, g_1) + a_2(\varphi, g_2),$$

and

$$(\varphi, g) = (g, \varphi)^*.$$

(φ, φ) is real and positive and vanishes only if $\varphi = 0$. If $(\varphi, \varphi) = 1$, then φ is said to be normalized. If the integral

$$(\varphi, \varphi) = \int_{-\infty}^{\infty} \cdots \int |\varphi(x_1 \cdots x_f)|^2 \, dx_1 \cdots dx_f = c^2$$

is finite, then φ can always be normalized by multiplication by a constant $\left(1/c \text{ in the case above, since } \left(\frac{\varphi}{c}, \frac{\varphi}{c}\right) = 1\right)$. Two *functions* are orthogonal if their scalar product is zero.

The scalar product given in the Eq. (4.7) is constructed by considering the functions $\varphi(x_1 \cdots x_f)$, $g(x_1 \cdots x_f)$ of $x_1, x_2, \cdots, x_f$ as vectors, whose components are labeled by f continuous indices. The function vector $\varphi(x_1 \cdots x_f)$ is defined in an f-fold infinite-dimensional space. Each system of values of $x_1 \cdots x_f$, i.e., each configuration, corresponds to one dimension. Then the scalar product of φ and g, in vector language, is

$$(\varphi, g) = \sum_{x_1 \cdots x_f} \varphi(x_1 \cdots x_f)^* g(x_1 \cdots x_f)$$

for which the integral (4.7) was substituted.

The definition of the linear dependence or independence of functions is also in harmony with concepts from the discussion of vectors. A linear relationship

$$a_1\varphi_1 + a_2\varphi_2 + \cdots + a_k\varphi_k = 0$$

exists among $\varphi_1, \varphi_2, \cdots, \varphi_k$ if this equation is true for all the vector components, i.e., for all sets of values of $x_1 \cdots x_f$, with given constants $a_1, a_2, \cdots, a_k$. Furthermore an operator $\mathbf{H}$ is said to be linear if

$$\mathbf{H}(a\varphi + bg) = a\mathbf{H}\varphi + b\mathbf{H}g \tag{4.8}$$

is true for all functions φ and g. In general we will be concerned only with linear operators. Linear operators for function-vectors correspond to matrices for ordinary vectors. Both transform the vectors to which they are applied into other vectors. The linearity condition, Eq. (4.8), holds for all matrices. We have seen that every operator which can be applied to a finite-dimensional vector is equivalent to a matrix.[3] The infinite-dimensional operators also have a matrix form, but it is often strongly singular.

As an example, the elements of the matrix $\mathfrak{q}_1$ which corresponds to the operation "multiplication by x_1" are

$$(\mathfrak{q}_1)_{x_1x_2\cdots x_f;\, x_1'x_2'\cdots x_f'} = x_1\,\delta_{x_1x_1'}\,\delta_{x_2x_2'}\cdots\delta_{x_fx_f'}. \tag{4.E.1}$$

It transforms the vector ψ into the vector $\mathfrak{q}_1\psi$, with components

$$\mathfrak{q}_1\psi(x_1x_2\cdots x_f) = \sum_{x_1'\cdots x_f'} (\mathfrak{q}_1)_{x_1\cdots x_f;\, x_1'\cdots x_f'}\,\psi(x_1'\cdots x_f')$$

$$= \sum_{x_1'\cdots x_f'} x_1\,\delta_{x_1x_1'}\,\delta_{x_2x_2'}\cdots\delta_{x_fx_f'}\,\psi(x_1'\cdots x_f') = x_1\psi(x_1\cdots x_f).$$

This vector is exactly the function $x_1\psi$ into which ψ is transformed by the operation "multiplication by x_1."

The matrix which corresponds to the operator "differentiation with respect to x_1" is denoted by $(i/\hbar)\mathfrak{p}_1$ since $(\hbar/i)\partial/\partial x_1$ corresponds to p_1

$$\left(\frac{i}{\hbar}\,\mathfrak{p}_1\right)_{x_1\cdots x_f;\, x_1'\cdots x_f'} = \lim_{\Delta\to 0}\frac{1}{\Delta}\,(\delta_{x_1+\frac{1}{2}\Delta,\, x_1'} - \delta_{x_1-\frac{1}{2}\Delta,\, x_1'})\,\delta_{x_2x_2'}\cdots\delta_{x_fx_f'}. \tag{4.E.2}$$

It transforms the vector ψ into

$$\sum_{x_1'\cdots x_f'}\lim_{\Delta\to 0}\frac{1}{\Delta}\,(\delta_{x_1+\frac{1}{2}\Delta,\, x_1'} - \delta_{x_1-\frac{1}{2}\Delta,\, x_1'})\,\delta_{x_2x_2'}\cdots\delta_{x_fx_f'}\,\psi(x_1', x_2', \cdots, x_f')$$

$$= \lim_{\Delta\to 0}\frac{1}{\Delta}\,(\psi(x_1 + \tfrac{1}{2}\Delta, x_2, \cdots, x_f) - \psi(x_1 - \tfrac{1}{2}\Delta, x_2, \cdots, x_f))$$

and this is precisely the derivative of ψ with respect to x_1.

A matrix $\mathbf{H}$ is said to be Hermitian if $\mathbf{H} = \mathbf{H}^\dagger$, that is, if one has

$$(\mathfrak{v}, \mathbf{H}\mathfrak{w}) = (\mathbf{H}^\dagger\mathfrak{v}, \mathfrak{w}) = (\mathbf{H}\mathfrak{v}, \mathfrak{w})$$

for arbitrary vectors $\mathfrak{v}$ and $\mathfrak{w}$. In other words, $\mathbf{H}$ is Hermitian if it can be transferred from one to the other of the factors in a scalar product. The Hermitian nature of operators is *defined* by this requirement.

[3] See Chapter 1, page 3.

An operator $\mathbf{H}$ is Hermitian if for all functions φ, g, satisfying certain conditions (e.g., square integrability, which implies that the function vanishes at infinity), one has

$$(\varphi, \mathbf{H}g) = (\mathbf{H}\varphi, g). \tag{4.9}$$

Sums and real multiples of Hermitian operators are again linear and Hermitian. The same holds for their powers, reciprocals, etc.

The Hamiltonian operator (4.5b) is Hermitian. To demonstrate this, note first that multiplication by a real function $V(x_1, x_2, \cdots, x_f)$ is Hermitian.

$$\left.\begin{aligned}(\varphi, Vg) &= \int_{-\infty}^{\infty}\cdots\int \varphi(x_1 \cdots x_f)^* V(x_1 \cdots x_f) g(x_1 \cdots x_f)\, dx_1 \cdots dx_f \\ &= \int_{-\infty}^{\infty}\cdots\int (V(x_1 \cdots x_f)\varphi(x_1 \cdots x_f))^* g(x_1 \cdots x_f)\, dx_1 \cdots dx_f \\ &= (V\varphi, g).\end{aligned}\right\} \tag{4.9a}$$

The operator $(\hbar/i)\, \partial/\partial x_k$ is also Hermitian. By partial integration

$$\left.\begin{aligned}\left(\varphi, \frac{\hbar}{i}\frac{\partial}{\partial x_k} g\right) &= \int_{-\infty}^{\infty}\cdots\int \varphi(x_1 \cdots x_f)^* \frac{\hbar}{i}\frac{\partial}{\partial x_k} g(x_1 \cdots x_f)\, dx_1 \cdots dx_f \\ &= \int_{-\infty}^{\infty}\cdots\int -\frac{\hbar}{i}\left(\frac{\partial}{\partial x_k}\varphi(x_1 \cdots x_f)\right)^* g(x_1 \cdots x_f)\, dx_1 \cdots dx_f \\ &= \left(\frac{\hbar}{i}\frac{\partial}{\partial x_k}\varphi, g\right)\end{aligned}\right\} \tag{4.10}$$

since ψ vanishes for $x_k = \pm\infty$, and $i^* = -i$. Therefore its square $-(\hbar^2)\, \partial^2/\partial x_k^2$ is also Hermitian, as can be shown also directly by two partial integrations. Then all the summands of $\mathbf{H}$ are Hermitian, so that $\mathbf{H}$, itself, is Hermitian.

The equation

$$\mathbf{H}\psi = E\psi$$

for ψ is well known to have nonvanishing square integrable solutions only for certain values of E. The values for which such a solution exists are called *eigenvalues*; the set of all of them is called the *spectrum* of $\mathbf{H}$.

The eigenvalues of a Hermitian operator are all real. If $\mathbf{H}\psi_E = E\psi_E$, the scalar product with ψ_E is

$$(\psi_E, \mathbf{H}\psi_E) = (\psi_E, E\psi_E) = E(\psi_E, \psi_E). \tag{4.11}$$

But in (4.11) $(\psi_E, \mathbf{H}\psi_E) = (\mathbf{H}\psi_E, \psi_E) = (\psi_E, \mathbf{H}\psi_E)^*$. Then, since (ψ_E, ψ_E) is real, E must also be real.

A Hermitian operator may have a *discrete* and also a *continuous* spectrum. The eigenvalues of the discrete spectrum are discrete numbers (there may be a finite number or a denumerably infinite number); the corresponding eigenfunctions can be normalized (in our case this means that the square integral (ψ_E, ψ_E) is finite) and it will be assumed from now on that they have already been normalized. The eigenfunctions are distinguished from one another by indices $\psi_E, \psi_F, \cdots$. Ordinarily the discrete eigenvalues comprise the interesting portion of the spectrum. Where we have so far referred simply to "eigenvalues" we have meant discrete eigenvalues.

A solution of the eigenvalue equation which belongs to the *continuous spectrum* $\psi(x_1, x_2, \cdots, x_f, E)$ does not have a finite square integral. It might be thought, therefore, that it does not belong to the spectrum at all. However, if we construct the so-called "eigendifferential"

$$\int_E^{E+\Delta} \psi(x_1, x_2, \cdots, x_f;\ E)\, dE = \psi(x_1, x_2, \cdots, x_f;\ E, E + \Delta), \tag{4.E.3}$$

it becomes square integrable, so that it can be normalized. This would not be the case if E actually did not belong to the spectrum. The eigendifferential (4.E.3) belongs to the interval between E and $E + \Delta$. This shows that the continuous spectrum consists not of points but of continuous regions. The solutions $\psi(x_1, x_2, \cdots, x_f;\ E)$ of the eigenvalue equation are called the eigenfunctions of the continuous spectrum, although they cannot be normalized. They depend on the eigenvalue E in a continuous fashion; we usually introduce E as a variable rather than as an index to differentiate the various continuum eigenfunctions. If we divide the continuous spectrum into definite small regions of length Δ, then an eigendifferential can be defined for each, which—after they have been normalized—assume properties more and more similar to the eigenfunctions of the discrete spectrum as Δ becomes smaller and smaller.

The eigenfunctions belonging to different eigenvalues of the discrete spectrum are orthogonal to one another. To establish this, note that from $\mathbf{H}\psi_E = E\psi_E$, it follows that

$$(\psi_F, \mathbf{H}\psi_E) = (\psi_F, E\psi_E); \qquad (\mathbf{H}\psi_F, \psi_E) = E(\psi_F, \psi_E).$$

Similarly $\mathbf{H}\psi_F = F\psi_F$, together with the reality of the eigenvalues, implies

$$(\mathbf{H}\psi_F, \psi_E) = (F\psi_F, \psi_E) = F^*(\psi_F, \psi_E) = F(\psi_F, \psi_E).$$

Subtracting, we see that if $E \neq F$, (ψ_E, ψ_F) must be zero. Likewise, the discrete eigenfunctions are orthogonal to all the eigendifferentials, and the eigendifferentials are orthogonal to one another, provided the regions to which they belong do not overlap.

More than one linearly independent eigenfunction may belong to one eigenvalue of, say, the discrete spectrum. If this is the case, the eigenvalue is said to be "degenerate." Every possible linear combination of degenerate eigenfunctions is also an eigenfunction with the same eigenvalue. From the linear set of eigenfunctions, one can choose a linearly independent set; then all eigenfunctions of the eigenvalue in question can be expressed as linear combinations of this linearly independent set. This set can be orthogonalized, e.g., by the Schmidt procedure. Of course, the selection process is necessarily an arbitrary one; it is clear that the Schmidt procedure can give many different orthogonal systems, depending on the order in which the eigenfunctions are taken. However, this need not concern us for the present.

From now on we will always assume that an orthogonal set has been selected in some way from the degenerate eigenfunctions. Then all the eigenfunctions and eigendifferentials form an *orthogonal system.* If ψ and ψ' are two arbitrary different functions of this system, then

$$(\psi, \psi') = 0 \tag{4.12}$$

and

$$(\psi, \psi) = 1. \tag{4.12a}$$

This orthogonal system is also complete, if only the division of the continuous spectrum is sufficiently fine (i.e., if Δ is sufficiently small). In other words, every function $\varphi(x_1 \cdots x_f)$ for which the integral (φ, φ) converges, can be developed in a series

$$\varphi = \sum_{\varkappa} g_\varkappa \psi_\varkappa + \sum_{E} g(E, \Delta)\psi(E, E + \Delta), \tag{4.13}$$

where the index $\varkappa$ runs over all discrete eigenvalues, and E runs from the lower bound over all the eigendifferentials. This series expansion actually applies only for an infinitely small Δ; hence the second sum should be replaced by an integral

$$\varphi = \sum_{\varkappa} g_\varkappa \psi_\varkappa + \int g(E)\psi(E)\, dE, \tag{4.13a}$$

where the integration is taken over the entire region of the continuous spectrum. If several linearly independent eigenfunctions belong to an eigenvalue of the continuous spectrum, then in (4.13a) several integrals occur, or even—if the number of eigenfunctions is infinite—one or more double or multiple integrals. On the other hand, if the problem considered has no continuous spectrum, then the second term in (4.13) and the integral in

(4.13a) are omitted. By construction of the scalar product of $\psi_\varkappa$ with (4.13), the coefficient $g_\varkappa$ is seen to be given by

$$(\psi_\varkappa, \varphi) = g_\varkappa . \tag{4.14}$$

And similarly,

$$(\psi(E, E + \Delta), \varphi) = g(E, \Delta). \tag{4.14a}$$

In formal calculations, the continuous spectrum is frequently suppressed, the calculations being done as though only a discrete spectrum existed. It is clear just what change the existence of a continuous spectrum effects: Terms with integrals are added to the sums.

The developments of this chapter—especially in so far as they concern the continuous spectrum—are not rigorous. Rigorous eigenvalue theory first disposed of the arbitrary Hermitian operator[4] just a short time before this book was first written. We have summarized here only a portion of its results. The rigorous theory is rather complicated. However, the theory is almost invariably used in the form given above.[5]

[4] J. V. Neumann, *Math. Ann.* **102,** 49 (1924).

[5] The theory of the spectral decomposition of Hermitian (more precisely, "self adjoint") operators is given by M. H. Stone in his Linear Transformations in Hilbert Space (Am. Math. Soc. publication, New York, 1932). A somewhat shorter treatment is contained in F. Riesz and B. Sz-Nagy's "Functional Analysis," F. Ungar Publ., New York, 1955.

5. Perturbation Theory

1. It often happens that the eigenvalues and eigenfunctions of a given problem are known, and there is interest in those for a similar problem whose energy operator differs from the energy operator of the given problem by a relatively slight change, "a perturbation." Perturbation theory deals with the methods of solution of problems of this kind. One perturbation theory has been developed via matrix theory by M. Born, W. Heisenberg, and P. Jordan; however, we follow the Rayleigh–Schrödinger method in the discussion which follows.

We calculate as though the initial system had no continuous spectrum and assume that the perturbed system also has a pure point spectrum. The slight complications introduced by a continuous spectrum will be discussed at the end; at first, the theory is explained in its simplest form.

Consider a Hermitian operator $\mathbf{H}$ with eigenvalues $E_1, E_2, \cdots$ and eigenfunctions $\psi_1, \psi_2, \cdots$

$$\mathbf{H}\psi_k = E_k\psi_k . \tag{5.1}$$

One wants to determine the eigenvalues F and the eigenfunctions φ of the operator $\mathbf{H} + \lambda\mathbf{V}$, where $\mathbf{V}$ is also Hermitian and λ is a small number

$$(\mathbf{H} + \lambda\mathbf{V})\varphi_k = F_k\varphi_k . \tag{5.2}$$

We first expand F and φ as power series in λ, which we cut off at the second term

$$F_k = E_k + \lambda E_k' + \lambda^2 E_k'' \cdots \tag{5.3a}$$

$$\varphi_k = \psi_k + \lambda\psi_k' + \lambda^2\psi_k'' \cdots = \psi_k + \lambda \sum_l a_{kl}\psi_l + \lambda^2 \sum_l b_{kl}\psi_l \cdots . \tag{5.3b}$$

In (5.3a) and (5.3b) it is assumed that F_k and φ_k go over into E_k and ψ_k for $\lambda = 0$; also, ψ_k' and ψ_k'' are expanded as a series in the functions ψ (as discussed in the previous chapter) with coefficients a_{kl} and b_{kl}.

We substitute (5.3a) and (5.3b) into (5.2) and obtain

$$\mathbf{H}[\psi_k + \lambda \sum_l a_{kl}\psi_l + \lambda^2 \sum b_{kl}\psi_l] + \lambda\mathbf{V}[\psi_k + \lambda \sum_l a_{kl}\psi_l]$$
$$= (E_k + \lambda E_k' + \lambda^2 E_k'')(\psi_k + \lambda \sum_l a_{kl}\psi_l + \lambda^2 \sum_l b_{kl}\psi_l). \tag{5.4}$$

The coefficients of equal powers of λ on both sides of (5.4) must be equal.

The terms not involving λ cancel because of (5.1). The equality of the coefficients of λ and λ^2 give

$$\sum_l a_{kl} E_l \psi_l + \mathbf{V}\psi_k = E'_k \psi_k + E_k \sum_l a_{kl}\psi_l \,, \tag{5.5a}$$

$$\sum_l b_{kl} E_l \psi_l + \sum_l a_{kl} \mathbf{V}\psi_l = E''_k \psi_k + E'_k \sum_l a_{kl}\psi_l + E_k \sum_l b_{kl}\psi_l \,. \tag{5.5b}$$

Equation (5.5a) allows the determination of E'_k and a_{kl} for $l \neq k$. By forming the scalar product with ψ_k or ψ_l, and using the orthogonality relationship we obtain

$$a_{kk}E_k + (\psi_k, \mathbf{V}\psi_k) = E'_k + a_{kk}E_k \,, \tag{5.6}$$

$$a_{kl}E_l + (\psi_l, \mathbf{V}\psi_k) = E_k a_{kl} \; (l \neq k). \tag{5.7}$$

If we introduce here the abbreviation

$$\mathbf{V}_{\alpha\beta} = (\psi_\alpha, \mathbf{V}\psi_\beta) = (\mathbf{V}\psi_\alpha, \psi_\beta) = (\psi_\beta, \mathbf{V}\psi_\alpha)^* = \mathbf{V}^*_{\beta\alpha} \tag{5.8}$$

($\mathbf{V}_{\alpha\beta}$ are called *matrix elements* of the operator $\mathbf{V}$) these become

$$E'_k = (\psi_k, \mathbf{V}\psi_k) = \mathbf{V}_{kk} \,, \tag{5.6a}$$

$$a_{kl} = \frac{(\psi_l, \mathbf{V}\psi_k)}{E_k - E_l} = \frac{\mathbf{V}_{lk}}{E_k - E_l} \qquad (l \neq k). \tag{5.7a}$$

Similarly, by multiplication with ψ^*_k and integration over all configuration space, we obtain from (5.5b)

$$b_{kk}E_k + \sum_l a_{kl}(\psi_k, \mathbf{V}\psi_l) = E''_k + E'_k a_{kk} + E_k b_{kk} \,. \tag{5.9}$$

We break the sum over l on the left side into two parts by writing the term with $l = k$ separately. We then substitute the value for E'_k from (5.6a), and that for a_{kl} from (5.7a), obtaining

$$E''_k = \sum_{l\neq k} \frac{(\psi_l, \mathbf{V}\psi_k)(\psi_k, \mathbf{V}\psi_l)}{E_k - E_l} = \sum_{l \neq k} \frac{|\mathbf{V}_{lk}|^2}{E_k - E_l} \,.$$

This yields a new eigenvalue F_k to terms of order λ^2

$$F_k = E_k + \lambda \mathbf{V}_{kk} + \lambda^2 \mathop{}_{l \neq k} \frac{|\mathbf{V}_{lk}|^2}{E_k - E_l} \,. \tag{5.10}$$

The new eigenfunction φ_k is given by

$$\varphi_k = \psi_k + \lambda \sum_{l \neq k} \frac{\mathbf{V}_{lk}}{E_k - E_l} \psi_l + \lambda a_{kk}\psi_k$$

to terms of order λ. We note that a_{kk} always dropped out of the foregoing equations. This corresponds to the circumstance that the normalization constant of φ_k is unspecified. If we set $(\varphi_k, \varphi_k) = 1$, we obtain $a_{kk} = 0$, and

$$\varphi_k = \psi_k + \lambda \sum_{l \neq k} \frac{\mathbf{V}_{lk}}{E_k - E_l} \psi_l \tag{5.11}$$

is normalized to terms in λ^2.

One should note that when the eigenvalues E_k and E_l of two eigenfunctions ψ_l and ψ_k happen to coincide in the initial problem, infinitely large terms can appear in the sums in (5.10) and (5.11). We shall see immediately that such terms can be eliminated, so that their appearance poses no serious difficulty. After this has been done, the summations which appear can be carried out in most practical cases.

However, nothing has yet been said about the convergence of the entire procedure, i.e., of the series (5.3a) and (5.3b). These might very well diverge; in many examples the third term alone is already infinitely large! Moreover it is known that a discrete eigenvalue, especially when it was already overlapped in the initial problem by the continuous spectrum, can dissolve under a perturbation, that is, can go over entirely into the continuous spectrum.

Nevertheless, (5.11) retains a well-defined meaning: it describes a state which for small λ, if not absolutely stationary, is nonetheless nearly so, decaying only after a very long time. The eigenvalue F_k of (5.10) provides the approximate energy, and upon division by $\hbar$, it provides the approximate frequency for this state. If $a = (\mathbf{H} + \lambda\mathbf{V} - F_k)\varphi_k$ is constructed via (5.10) and (5.11), it is found to be of second order in λ. Thus if it is assumed that the wave function $\varphi(t)$ of this system coincides with φ_k at $t = 0$ ($\varphi(0) = \varphi_k$), then one can write

$$\varphi(t) = \varphi_k \exp\left(-i\frac{F_k t}{\hbar}\right) + \chi(t). \tag{5.12}$$

Substituting this into the time-dependent Schrödinger equation

$$\begin{aligned} i\hbar\frac{\partial\varphi}{\partial t} &= F_k\varphi_k \exp\left(-i\frac{F_k}{\hbar}t\right) + i\hbar\frac{\partial\chi}{\partial t} = (\mathbf{H} + \lambda\mathbf{V})\varphi(t) \\ &= F_k\varphi_k \exp\left(-i\frac{F_k}{\hbar}t\right) + a\exp\left(-i\frac{F_k}{\hbar}t\right) + (\mathbf{H} + \lambda\mathbf{V})\chi, \end{aligned}$$

one obtains

$$i\hbar\frac{\partial\chi}{\partial t} = a\exp\left(-i\frac{F_k}{\hbar}t\right) + (\mathbf{H} + \lambda\mathbf{V})\chi, \tag{5.13}$$

from which $\frac{\partial}{\partial t}(\chi, \chi)$ can be calculated:

$$\frac{\partial}{\partial t}(\chi, \chi) = -\frac{i}{\hbar}\left[\exp\left(-i\frac{F_k}{\hbar}t\right)(\chi, a) - \exp\left(+i\frac{F_k}{\hbar}t\right)(a, \chi)\right].$$

By using *Schwarz' Inequality* $|(\chi, a)|^2 \leqslant (\chi, \chi) \cdot (a, a)$ we can set an upper bound on the time derivative.

$$\frac{\partial}{\partial t}(\chi, \chi) \leqslant \frac{2}{\hbar}\sqrt{(\chi, \chi)(a, a)}$$

or, since a is time-independent,

$$\frac{\partial}{\partial t}\sqrt{(\chi, \chi)} \leqslant \frac{1}{\hbar}\sqrt{(a, a)}; \qquad \sqrt{(\chi, \chi)} \leqslant \frac{1}{\hbar}\sqrt{(a, a)}\,t + c. \tag{5.14}$$

For $t = 0$, we have assumed that $\chi = 0$; therefore, the constant c is also zero. Then

$$(\chi, \chi) \leqslant (a, a)\frac{t^2}{\hbar^2}.$$

That is, the difference between $\varphi(t)$ *and* $\varphi_k \exp\left(-i\frac{F_k}{\hbar}t\right)$ *is always very small for times which are small compared with* $\hbar/\sqrt{(a, a)}$. Since (a, a) is proportional to λ^4 the function φ_k behaves like a genuine eigenfunction for relatively long times, provided only that λ is small.

2. As we have mentioned, a modification of this development is necessary when a degeneracy occurs in the initial problem, that is, when several linearly independent eigenfunctions belong to the same eigenvalue. The summations in (5.10) and (5.11) are taken over *all the eigenfunctions*, including every eigenfunction whose eigenvalue E_l is equal to E_k. Therefore, this sum can be constructed only if $(\psi_l, \mathbf{V}\psi_k)$ vanishes for all eigenfunctions ψ_l with eigenvalue $E_l = E_k$.

Let the eigenfunctions $\psi_{k1}, \psi_{k2}, \cdots, \psi_{ks}$ have the same eigenvalue E_k. We have already assumed that these are mutually orthogonal. Now there exists a certain arbitrariness in the choice of the initial eigenfunctions for our approximation procedure, since in place of $\psi_{k1}, \psi_{k2}, \cdots, \psi_{ks}$ other sets could be chosen, e.g.,

$$\left.\begin{aligned} \psi'_{k1} &= \boldsymbol{\alpha}_{11}\psi_{k1} + \boldsymbol{\alpha}_{12}\psi_{k2} + \cdots + \boldsymbol{\alpha}_{1s}\psi_{ks} \\ \psi'_{k2} &= \boldsymbol{\alpha}_{21}\psi_{k1} + \boldsymbol{\alpha}_{22}\psi_{k2} + \cdots + \boldsymbol{\alpha}_{2s}\psi_{ks} \\ &\cdots\cdots\cdots\cdots\cdots\cdots \\ \psi'_{ks} &= \boldsymbol{\alpha}_{s1}\psi_{k1} + \boldsymbol{\alpha}_{s2}\psi_{k2} + \cdots + \boldsymbol{\alpha}_{ss}\psi_{ks} \end{aligned}\right\} \tag{5.15}$$

Consequently, there is no longer any reason to assume that the first approximation to φ_k is simply ψ_k. *If* $(\boldsymbol{\alpha}_{\mu\mu'})$ *is a unitary matrix, the* $\psi'_{k\nu}$ *are also mutually orthogonal* (and, of course, orthogonal to other eigenfunctions, with eigenvalues different from E_k).

$$\left.\begin{aligned}(\psi'_{k\nu}, \psi'_{k\mu}) &= (\sum_{\nu'} \boldsymbol{\alpha}_{\nu\nu'}\, \psi_{k\nu'}, \sum_{\mu'} \boldsymbol{\alpha}_{\mu\mu'}\, \psi\ \ \cdot) \\ &= \sum_{\nu'\mu'} \boldsymbol{\alpha}^*_{\nu\nu'}\, \boldsymbol{\alpha}_{\mu\mu'}\, (\psi_{k\nu'}, \psi_{k\mu'}) = \sum_{\nu'\mu'} \boldsymbol{\alpha}^*_{\nu\nu'}\, \boldsymbol{\alpha}_{\mu\mu'}\, \delta_{\nu'\mu'} = \delta_{\nu\mu}.\end{aligned}\right\} \tag{5.16}$$

Thus, *the* $\psi'_{k\nu}$ *are as suitable a basis for the approximation procedure as the original* $\psi_{k\nu}$.

This raises the question whether all matrix elements $(\psi'_{k\nu}, \mathbf{V}\psi'_{k\mu})$ (with $\nu \neq \mu$) could not be made to vanish by suitable choice of the matrix $\boldsymbol{\alpha}$. This can in fact be done. Consider

$$(\psi'_{k\nu}, \mathbf{V}\psi'_{k\mu}) = \sum_{\nu',\mu'=1}^{s} \boldsymbol{\alpha}^*_{\nu\nu'}\, \boldsymbol{\alpha}_{\mu\mu'}\, (\psi_{k\nu'}, \mathbf{V}\psi_{k\mu'}). \tag{5.17}$$

If we denote the Hermitian matrix formed from the quantities $(\psi_{k\nu'}, \mathbf{V}\psi_{k\mu'}) = \mathbf{V}_{k\nu';\, k\mu'}, = \mathbf{v}_{\nu'\mu'}$ by $\mathbf{v}$, the matrix $\boldsymbol{\alpha}$ must be determined so that $\boldsymbol{\alpha}^*\mathbf{v}\boldsymbol{\alpha}'$ is a diagonal matrix. If $\boldsymbol{\alpha}$ is chosen in this way, then $(\psi'_{k\nu}, \mathbf{V}\psi'_{k\mu})$ in (5.17) vanishes unless $\nu = \mu$: *use of the set* $\psi'_{k\nu}$ *(which is in every respect equivalent to the* $\psi_{k\nu'}$*) as the initial system for the perturbation calculation insures that none of the terms with zero denominators appears in the Eqs. (5.10) and (5.11).*

The entire problem then consists in selecting $\boldsymbol{\alpha}$ so that it transforms $\mathbf{v}$ into the diagonal form. Since $\boldsymbol{\alpha}$ is unitary, so is $\boldsymbol{\alpha}^*$, and $\boldsymbol{\alpha}^* = \boldsymbol{\alpha}'^{-1}$. The equation specifying $\boldsymbol{\alpha}_{\mu\mu'}$ is then

$$\sum_{\mu'} \mathbf{v}_{\nu\mu'}\, \boldsymbol{\alpha}_{\mu\mu'} = \boldsymbol{\alpha}_{\mu\nu}\, v'_{\mu}, \tag{5.18}$$

where the v'_μ are the eigenvalues of the matrix $\mathbf{v}$.

Again we will calculate the eigenvalues to terms in λ^2, and the eigenfunctions to terms in the first power of λ. On the basis of the preceding paragraph, we assume the eigenfunctions $\psi_{k1}, \psi_{k2}, \cdots, \psi_{ks}$ of the eigenvalue E whose shift we wish to calculate to be such that

$$(\psi_{k\nu}, \mathbf{V}\psi_{k\mu}) = \mathbf{V}_{k\nu;k\mu} = \mathbf{V}_{k\nu;k\nu}\, \delta_{\mu\nu} = v'_\nu\, \delta_{\nu\mu}\,. \tag{5.19}$$

In other words we use the ψ' from the outset. The remaining eigenfunctions need no double label: ψ_l belongs to E_l but the E_l are not necessarily all distinct. We denote the eigenvalue of the operator $\mathbf{H} + \lambda\mathbf{V}$ to which the eigenfunction $\varphi_{k\nu}$ belongs, by $F_{k\nu}$; this will indicate the fact that the s-fold degenerate eigenvalue[1] E_k splits in general into s new eigenvalues.

[1] So-called because it has s linearly independent eigenfunctions.

Let

$$F_{k\nu} = E_k + \lambda E'_{k\nu} + \lambda^2 E''_{k\nu} \cdots \tag{5.20}$$

and

$$\varphi_{k\nu} = \psi_{k\nu} + \lambda \sum_{\mu=1}^{s} \beta_{k\nu;k\mu}\psi_{k\mu} + \lambda \sum_{l\neq k} a_{k\nu;l}\psi_l + \lambda^2 \sum_{\mu=1}^{s} \gamma_{k\nu;k\mu}\psi_{k\mu} + \lambda^2 \sum_{l\neq k} b_{k\nu;l}\psi_l . \tag{5.20a}$$

If we insert (5.20) and (5.20a) into the equation $(\mathbf{H} + \lambda\mathbf{V})\varphi_{k\nu} = F_{k\nu}\varphi_{k\nu}$, and again equate the coefficients of equal powers of λ, the terms in the 0th power vanish, and the terms in λ and λ^2 give

$$\sum_{\mu} E_k\beta_{k\nu;k\mu}\psi_{k\mu} + \sum_{l\neq k} E_l a_{k\nu;l}\psi_l + \mathbf{V}\psi_{k\nu} = \sum_{\mu} E_k\beta_{k\nu;k\mu}\psi_{k\mu} + \sum_{l\neq k} E_k a_{k\nu;l}\psi_l + E'_{k\nu}\psi_{k\nu} , \tag{5.21}$$

and

$$\left.\begin{aligned} &\sum_{\mu} E_k\gamma_{k\nu;k\mu}\psi_{k\mu} + \sum_{l\neq k} E_l b_{k\nu;l}\psi_l + \sum_{\mu} \beta_{k\nu;k\mu}\mathbf{V}\psi_{k\mu} \\ &+ \sum_{l\neq k} a_{k\nu;l}\mathbf{V}\psi_l = \sum_{\mu} E_k\gamma_{k\nu;k\mu}\psi_{k\mu} + \sum_{l\neq k} E_k b_{k\nu;l}\psi_l \\ &+ \sum_{\mu} E'_{k\nu}\beta_{k\nu;k\mu}\psi_{k\mu} + \sum_{l\neq k} E'_{k\nu}a_{k\nu;l}\psi_l + E''_{k\nu}\psi_{k\nu} . \end{aligned}\right\} \tag{5.21a}$$

From these equations, the unknowns $E'_{k\nu}$, $E''_{k\nu}$, $a_{k\nu;l}$ and $\beta_{k\nu;k\mu}$ can be determined just as in the nondegenerate case. For the energy $F_{k\nu}$ we obtain

$$F_{k\nu} = E_k + \lambda \mathbf{V}_{k\nu;k\nu} + \lambda^2 \sum_{l\neq k} \frac{|\mathbf{V}_{l;k\nu}|^2}{E_k - E_l} \tag{5.22}$$

and the corresponding eigenfunction is

$$\left.\begin{aligned} \varphi_{k\nu} = \psi_{k\nu} &+ \lambda \sum_{\mu\neq\nu} \sum_{l\neq k} \frac{\mathbf{V}_{k\mu;l}\mathbf{V}_{l;k\nu}}{(E_k - E_l)(\mathbf{V}_{k\nu;k\nu} - \mathbf{V}_{k\mu;k\mu})} \psi_{k\mu} \\ &+ \lambda \sum_{l\neq k} \frac{\mathbf{V}_{l;k\nu}}{E_k - E_l} \psi_l . \end{aligned}\right\} \tag{5.23}$$

In these expressions, we have used the fact that the $\psi_{k1}, \psi_{k2}, \cdots, \psi_{ks}$ have already been chosen so that the $\mathbf{V}_{k\nu;k\mu} = 0$ for $\nu \neq \mu$.

If the $\mathbf{V}_{k\nu;k\nu} = v'_\nu$ for $\nu = 1, 2, \cdots, s$ are all different, the eigenvalue E_k divides in the first approximation into s new eigenvalues. Then all the $\varphi_{k\nu}$ can also be constructed at once since no vanishing denominators appear in (5.23).

However, if some of the eigenvalues of $\mathbf{v}$, $v'_\nu = \mathbf{V}_{k\nu;k\nu}$, are equal, the perturbed eigenvalues are still degenerate to first order in λ. The corresponding zero-order wave functions $\psi_{k\nu}$ are therefore subject to still another unitary transformation. To obtain the $\varphi_{k\mu}$ to first-order in λ, these functions must be chosen so that the Hermitian matrix

$$\mathbf{w}_{\mu\nu} = \sum_{l \neq k} \frac{\mathbf{V}_{k\mu;l}\mathbf{V}_{l;k\nu}}{E_k - E_l} \tag{5.24}$$

is diagonal. Then the terms with zero denominators in (5.23) vanish, and the summation can be carried out. All this occurs automatically if the correct eigenfunctions for the first approximation (5.15) are known from other considerations and used from the beginning.

With this modification, the perturbation procedure is therefore still applicable when several eigenfunctions (although not an infinite number) correspond to the same discrete eigenvalue. This situation will concern us in much of the work to follow, and the developments of this chapter form the basis for most quantum mechanical calculations. In fact, such calculations are often limited to the linear term in (5.22), that is, to the term involving $\mathbf{V}_{k\nu;k\nu} = v'_\nu$. This can be calculated by solving the secular equation of (5.18) or, more directly, by a simple quadrature, provided one knows the "correct linear combination," for which both

$$\mathbf{v}_{\nu\mu} = (\psi_{k\nu}, \mathbf{V}\psi_{k\mu}) = 0 \qquad (\nu \neq \mu)$$

and

$$\mathbf{w}_{\nu\nu'} = 0 \qquad (\nu \neq \nu' \text{ and } v'_\nu = v'_{\nu'})$$

are true. This "correct linear combination" can often be determined directly from group-theoretical considerations without the solution of the secular equation. Such determinations are one important application of group theory to quantum mechanical problems.

6. Transformation Theory and the Bases for the Statistical Interpretation of Quantum Mechanics

1. During the early stages of quantum mechanics, attention was devoted to the determination of energy eigenvalues, spontaneous transition probabilities, etc; later it turned more and more to questions of principle and sought for a physical interpretation of the matrices, operators, and eigenfunctions. This is given by the *statistical interpretation of quantum mechanics*, in the development of which M. Born, P. A. M. Dirac, W. Heisenberg, P. Jordan, and W. Pauli Jr. were leaders.

While in classical mechanics $2f$ numbers were necessary for the description of a system with f degrees of freedom (f position coordinates and f velocity coordinates), quantum mechanics describes this state by a normalized wave function $\varphi(x_1, \cdots x_f)$ ($(\varphi, \varphi) = 1$), the arguments of which are the position coordinates. Just as the classical theory defines a state by $2f$ *arbitrary* numbers, *quantum theory defines a state by any wave function which satisfies the one restriction*

$$\int_{-\infty}^{\infty} \cdots \int |\varphi(x_1, x_2, \cdots, x_f)|^2 \, dx_1 \cdots dx_f = 1.$$

This state may be an eigenfunction of the Schrödinger equation, or a linear combination of such eigenfunctions. The manifold of states is thus much larger in quantum mechanics than in the classical theory.

The development in time of a system in classical mechanics is determined by Newton's equations of motion; in quantum mechanics, by the time-dependent Schrödinger equation

$$i\hbar \frac{\partial \varphi}{\partial t} = \mathbf{H}\varphi, \tag{6.1}$$

where $\mathbf{H}$ is the Hamiltonian operator. In the simplest case $\mathbf{H}$ has the form

$$\mathbf{H} = -\sum_{k=1}^{f} \frac{\hbar^2}{2m_k} \frac{\partial^2}{\partial x_k^2} + V(x_1 \cdots x_f). \tag{6.2}$$

Indeed, the exact determination of $\mathbf{H}$ is the most important problem of quantum mechanics.

In classical mechanics the $2f$ numbers which serve to describe the state give the coordinates and velocities of the individual particles directly, and from these, arbitrary functions of these quantities could be calculated with no difficulty. In quantum mechanics, the question of the position of a particle has no meaning in general. Only the question of the probability with which a particle is to be found in a certain place is meaningful. The same holds for the momentum, and for functions of these quantities, as for example, the energy.

Quantum mechanical Hermitian operators correspond to all the physically significant quantities. Thus, for example, the operator which corresponds to the x_k coordinate is "multiplication with x_k"; to the momentum, $-i\hbar\,(\partial/\partial x_k)$; to the energy, $\mathbf{H}$ of (6.2); etc. This last operator is the one which is unique among them all, since its appearance in the time-dependent Schrödinger equation gives it a special role.

In general, these operators are obtained by taking the classical quantity expressed in terms of position and momentum coordinates, and replacing the position coordinate x_k by the operator "multiplication by x_k" and the momentum coordinate p_k by the operator $-i\hbar\,(\partial/\partial x_k)$. For example, in a classical harmonic oscillator the energy is

$$\frac{1}{2m}(p_1^2 + p_2^2 + p_3^2) + \frac{K}{2}(x_1^2 + x_2^2 + x_3^2).$$

It will be replaced in quantum mechanics by the operator

$$-\frac{\hbar^2}{2m}\left(\frac{\partial^2}{\partial x_1^2} + \frac{\partial^2}{\partial x_2^2} + \frac{\partial^2}{\partial x_3^2}\right) + \frac{K}{2}(x_1 \cdot x_1 + x_2 \cdot x_2 + x_3 \cdot x_3).$$

The form of this operator is exactly that given in (6.2).

A measurement of a quantity (coordinate, energy) can in general give only a value which occurs as an eigenvalue of the corresponding operator. Thus, for example, the possible energy levels are the eigenvalues of the operator $\mathbf{H}$. What is the probability if a system is in the state $\varphi(x_1 \cdots x_f)$ that the quantity with the operator $\mathbf{G}$ has the value λ_k? This probability is certainly zero if λ_k is not an eigenvalue of $\mathbf{G}$; on the other hand, if it is an eigenvalue and if ψ_k is the corresponding normalized eigenfunction, then

$$|(\varphi, \psi_k)|^2 = |(\psi_k, \varphi)|^2 \tag{6.3}$$

gives the desired probability.

Under the statistical interpretation, only probabilities for the possible outcomes of measurements can be calculated; the result of a measurement or of an experiment cannot in general be predicted with certainty.

If φ is expanded in the complete orthogonal system of the eigenfunctions of $\mathbf{G}$

$$\varphi = a_1\psi_1 + a_2\psi_2 + \cdots, \tag{6.4}$$

and if

$$\mathbf{G}\psi_k = \lambda_k\psi_k, \tag{6.4a}$$

then (6.3) states that the probability that a measurement yields the value λ_k is just the absolute square $|a_k|^2$ of

$$(\psi_k, \varphi) = a_k. \tag{6.5}$$

Of course the sum of the probabilities for all the possible values $\lambda_1, \lambda_2, \cdots$ must total 1. That is,

$$|a_1|^2 + |a_2|^2 + \cdots = 1.$$

That this is, in fact, the case, follows from the normalization of φ:

$$\begin{aligned}(\varphi, \varphi) &= (\sum_k a_k\psi_k, \sum_l a_l\psi_l) = \sum_{k,l} a_k^* a_l(\psi_k, \psi_l) \\ &= \sum_{k,l} a_k^* a_l\, \delta_{kl} = \sum_k |a_k|^2 = 1.\end{aligned}$$

The wave function $c\varphi$ (with $|c| = 1$) corresponds to the same state as the wave function φ; therefore, *the wave function is determined by the physical state only up to a factor of absolute value one.* All probabilities which are calculated from the wave function φ are identical with those calculated from the wave function $c\varphi$, as one can see at once from

$$|(\psi_k, c\varphi)|^2 = |c(\psi_k, \varphi)|^2 = |c|^2\, |(\psi_k, \varphi)|^2 = |(\psi_k, \varphi)|^2.$$

Since these probabilities are the only physical realities for the state, the two states are physically identical.

If several linearly independent eigenfunctions $\psi_{k1}, \psi_{k2}, \psi_{k3}, \cdots$ (which are assumed mutually orthogonal) belong to one eigenvalue λ_k, then the probability for λ_k is equal to the sum of the squares of the expansion coefficients,

$$|(\psi_{k1}, \varphi)|^2 + |(\psi_{k2}, \varphi)|^2 + |(\psi_{k3}, \varphi)|^2 + \cdots.$$

The preceding discussion applies only to the probabilities of discrete eigenvalues. The probability for a completely determined eigenvalue of the continuous spectrum is always zero, since in the continuous spectrum only finite regions can have finite probabilities. Provided the region is sufficiently small, this probability is equal to the absolute square of the expansion coefficient of the normalized eigendifferential which belongs to this region.

2. Only in one case does the expression for the probability calculated from quantum mechanics degenerate into a completely determined statement; this case is that in which the state function φ is an eigenfunction of the operator $\mathbf{G}$ which corresponds to the physical quantity to be measured so that $\mathbf{G}\varphi = \lambda_k\varphi$. Then φ is orthogonal to all the eigenfunctions of $\mathbf{G}$ not belonging to λ_k, and the probability for these eigenvalues is zero. The probability for λ_k is therefore 1. In this case the measurement gives the value λ_k with certainty.

If we have measured a quantity and have found it to have a certain value, then we must obtain the same value if only we repeat this measurement sufficiently rapidly. Otherwise, the statement given by the measurement, that the quantity concerned has this or that value, would be meaningless. The probability for a repeated measurement and also *the wave function*, which exists only for the calculation of probabilities, *is changed during a measurement.*[1] Indeed, we see that the wave function after the measurement which has given the eigenvalue λ_k for $\mathbf{G}$, must be an eigenfunction of $\mathbf{G}$ belonging to λ_k. Only then can a repeated measurement of $\mathbf{G}$ be certain to give again the value λ_k. In the measurement of $\mathbf{G}$ the wave function is disturbed and goes over into an eigenfunction of $\mathbf{G}$; specifically, into ψ_k if the measurement gave the result λ_k. It is not generally possible to predict with certainty just which eigenfunction of $\mathbf{G}$ the state function of the system will become; quantum mechanics gives only the probability $|(\psi_k, \varphi)|^2$ for the individual eigenfunction ψ_k and eigenvalue λ_k. Since the likelihood of transition of the wave function φ into ψ_k under the measurement $\mathbf{G}$ can be calculated from the two functions φ and ψ_k by the expression $|(\psi_k, \varphi)|^2$, this quantity is referred to as the transition probability from the state φ into the state ψ_k. If the transition probability of a wave function into every function is known, then the probability for all conceivable experiments is given.

With regard to the above it is especially important to note that the transition probability has a physical meaning and that it must therefore have the same value in two equivalent descriptions of the same system.

3. *Transition to a new "coordinate system."* If $\mathbf{G}, \mathbf{G}', \mathbf{G}'', \cdots$ are operators for different physical quantities, such as energy, momentum, position, etc., and $\varphi_1, \varphi_2, \cdots$ are wave functions for different states, then the same results are obtained from this system of operators and wave functions as from the system in which the operators are replaced by

$$\overline{\mathbf{G}} = \mathbf{U}\mathbf{G}\mathbf{U}^{-1}; \qquad \overline{\mathbf{G}'} = \mathbf{U}\mathbf{G}'\mathbf{U}^{-1}; \qquad \overline{\mathbf{G}''} = \mathbf{U}\mathbf{G}''\mathbf{U}^{-1}; \cdots,$$

and the state functions by

$$\bar{\varphi}_1 = \mathbf{U}\varphi_1; \qquad \bar{\varphi}_2 = \mathbf{U}\varphi_2; \qquad \bar{\varphi}_3 = \mathbf{U}\varphi_3 \cdots,$$

where $\mathbf{U}$ is an arbitrary unitary[2] operator. First of all, the eigenvalues which

[1] The wave function thus changes in two very different ways. First, continuously in the course of time according to the differential equation (6.1), and secondly, during measurements which are applied discontinuously to the system according to the laws of probability. (See subsequent discussion.)

[2] The unitarity of an operator $\mathbf{U}$ is defined in analogy to hermiticity: it will be required that, for two arbitrary functions f and g,

$$(f, g) = (\mathbf{U}f, \mathbf{U}g).$$

If f and g are vectors, $\mathbf{U}$ is a matrix, and this reduces to the usual (necessary and sufficient) condition for unitarity.

define the possible results of the measurements $\mathbf{G}$ and $\overline{\mathbf{G}} = \mathbf{U}\mathbf{G}\mathbf{U}^{-1}$ are identical, since the eigenvalues are not changed by a similarity transformation. If λ_k is an eigenvalue of $\mathbf{G}$, and ψ_k is the corresponding eigenfunction, then λ_k is also an eigenvalue of $\overline{\mathbf{G}} = \mathbf{U}\mathbf{G}\mathbf{U}^{-1}$, and the corresponding eigenfunction is $\mathbf{U}\psi_k$. To see this, note that $\mathbf{G}\psi_k = \lambda_k\psi_k$ implies that

$$\overline{\mathbf{G}}\mathbf{U}\psi_k = \mathbf{U}\mathbf{G}\mathbf{U}^{-1}\mathbf{U}\psi_k = \mathbf{U}\mathbf{G}\psi_k = \mathbf{U}\lambda_k\psi_k = \lambda_k\mathbf{U}\psi_k .$$

Moreover, the probability of this eigenvalue λ_k for the quantity, which corresponds to $\mathbf{G}$ in the first "coordinate system," and to $\mathbf{G}$ in the second, is equal in the two cases. In the first case it is

$$|(\psi_k, \varphi)|^2.$$

In the second case φ is replaced by $\mathbf{U}\varphi$ and ψ_k by the eigenfunction of $\overline{\mathbf{G}}$ which corresponds to λ_k, that is, by $\mathbf{U}\psi_k$. We thus obtain for the probability in the second "coordinate system"

$$|(\mathbf{U}\psi_k, \mathbf{U}\varphi)|^2$$

which is identical with that obtained above, by virtue of the unitarity of $\mathbf{U}$. Similarly, the transition probability between pairs of corresponding states φ_1, φ_2 and $\mathbf{U}\varphi_1, \mathbf{U}\varphi_2$ are also the same in the two coordinate systems, since

$$(\mathbf{U}\varphi_1, \mathbf{U}\varphi_2) = (\varphi_1, \varphi_2) \quad \text{implies} \quad |(\mathbf{U}\varphi_1, \mathbf{U}\varphi_2)|^2 = |(\varphi_1, \varphi_2)|^2.$$

Such a transformation to another coordinate system by a similarity transformation of the operators and simultaneous replacement of the wave function φ by $\mathbf{U}\varphi$ is called a *canonical transformation. Two descriptions which result from one another by a canonical transformation are equivalent.* Conversely, it will be shown in Chapter 20 that two quantum mechanical descriptions which are equivalent can be transformed into one another by a canonical transformation (unless time reversal takes place as will be discussed in Chapter 26).

4. We shall follow through one example of the application of transformation theory and the statistical interpretation. We select for this purpose the demonstration by Schrödinger of the significance of the absolute square of the matrix element.

$$(x_1 + x_2 + \cdots + x_N)_{FE} = (\psi_F, (x_1 + x_2 + \cdots + x_N)\,\psi_E) = \mathbf{X}_{FE}\,, \qquad (6.6)$$

where $N = f/3$ is the number of electrons, and $x_1, x_2, \cdots, x_N$ are their x-coordinates. According to matrix theory, this determines the probability of a transition induced by radiation polarized along the x-axis, from the stationary state ψ_E to a stationary state ψ_F. The indices E and F denote the energies of the two stationary states:

$$\mathbf{H}\psi_E = E\psi_E; \qquad \mathbf{H}\psi_F = F\psi_F\,. \qquad (6.7)$$

The notion of a transition induced by radiation has nothing to do with transitions induced by experiment, as discussed above. The latter arise from the conceptual structure of the statistical interpretation and give rise to the somewhat paradoxically sounding probability for the existence of the state φ' if the state is φ. It is a dimensionless quantity. The discussion at hand gives the probability that in the subsequent second the atom will undergo a transition from the state ψ_E to the state ψ_F by absorption of a light quantum $\hbar\omega = F - E$. This probability has the dimension time^{-1} and is meaningful only for transitions between two stationary states (eigenfunctions of the Hamiltonian operator $\mathbf{H}$), while the other has been defined for arbitrary states φ, φ'. Since it refers to a process evolving in the course of time it must be within the scope of Schrödinger's time-dependent equation.

Actually, the implication of this last statement is not true in all respects, since the time-dependent Schrödinger equation is not capable of explaining spontaneous emission. According to it the atoms are stable for arbitrarily long periods of time, even in excited states (such as ψ_F), since $\varphi = \psi_F \exp\left(-i\frac{F}{\hbar}t\right)$ is a solution of Eq. (6.1). Nonetheless, the Schrödinger equation embraces the absorption process (as well as induced emission of radiation) so that we must obtain the correct result as long as spontaneous emission plays no important role, i.e., as long as the atom is found almost completely in the ground state ψ_E. This same assumption will be seen later to be necessary to complete the calculation; it is justified provided the atom was initially in the lowest state ψ_E, the consideration is limited to relatively short times, and the intensity of the impinging light waves is not extremely high (as it can hardly be in practice).

We now present the treatment of the absorption processes. We assume that for time $t = 0$, the state of the system was $\varphi(0) = \psi_E$; then it changes according to the equation

$$i\hbar\frac{\partial\varphi}{\partial t} = \mathbf{H}\varphi = (\mathbf{H}_0 + \mathbf{H}_1)\varphi, \tag{6.8}$$

where $\mathbf{H}_0$ would have been the Hamiltonian operator in the absence of impinging radiation, and $\mathbf{H}_1$ is a supplementary operator involving the radiation. Radiation is simply an electric wave field

$$\mathscr{E}_x = P\sin\omega t; \qquad \mathscr{E}_y = 0; \qquad \mathscr{E}_z = 0. \tag{6.9}$$

The dependence of the field strength on the coordinates can be disregarded because of the small size of the atom. The potential in (6.2) is thus to be replaced by

$$V + \mathbf{H}_1 = V + e(x_1 + x_2 + \cdots + x_N)P\sin\omega t. \tag{6.8a}$$

The time dependence of the wave function, which would have been

$$\varphi = \psi_E \exp\left(-i\frac{E}{\hbar}t\right) \tag{6.10}$$

if P were zero, is modified by the supplementary potential, which will be treated as a perturbation. The equation for φ is

$$i\hbar\frac{\partial\varphi}{\partial t} = \mathbf{H}_0\varphi + (eP\sin\omega t)(x_1 + x_2 + \cdots + x_N)\varphi. \tag{6.11}$$

To solve this equation we expand φ in the complete set of eigenfunctions of $\mathbf{H}_0$,

$$\varphi(t) = a_E(t)\psi_E + a_F(t)\psi_F + a_G(t)\psi_G + \cdots, \tag{6.12}$$

where the $a_E, a_F, a_G, \cdots$ do not depend on the coordinates $x_1, x_2, \cdots, x_N$ and the $\psi_E, \psi_F, \psi_G, \cdots$ do not depend on the time. Then a state can be characterized by the expansion coefficients $a_E, a_F, a_G, \cdots$ instead of by its wave function φ.

The absolute squares of these quantities, $|a_E|^2, |a_F|^2, |a_G|^2, \cdots$, *give the probabilities of different excited levels* of the atom. If the atom is not perturbed by the light wave, these probabilities remain constant in time, and since initially only $|a_E|^2 = 1$ was different from zero, it remains so for all time. On the other hand, if a light wave impinges upon the atom then the higher states will also become excited. We shall calculate the strength of this excitation. To do this we assume that at time $t = 0$,

$$a_E(0) = 1, \qquad a_F(0) = 0, \qquad a_G(0) = 0, \cdots$$

and that the frequency ω of the light is given approximately by frequency of the energy jump

$$(F - E) = \hbar\omega. \tag{6.E.1}$$

If we substitute the expression (6.12) for φ into (6.11) we obtain a differential equation for the time dependence of the $a_E, a_F, a_G, \cdots$. Since we are interested in the excitation of the first excited state ψ_F, we construct the scalar product of this equation with ψ_F; then on the left-hand side only the term in a_F remains because of the orthogonality of the eigenfunctions of $\mathbf{H}_0$ (Eq. (4.12), (4.12a)) and we obtain

$$i\hbar\frac{\partial a_F(t)}{\partial t} = Fa_F + (Pe\sin\omega t)(\mathbf{X}_{FE}\cdot a_E + \mathbf{X}_{FF}a_F + \mathbf{X}_{FG}a_G + \cdots) \tag{6.13}$$

where we have substituted (6.6):

$$(\psi_F, (x_1 + x_2 + \cdots + x_N)\,\psi_E) = \mathbf{X}_{FE}\,.$$

The two terms on the right in (6.13) are of very different orders of magnitude. The energy E is of the order of magnitude of a few volts. On the other hand, only in a very intense monochromatic light ray does the amplitude of the electric vector P reach 10^{-2} volt/cm. The matrix elements of $\mathbf{X}$ are about 10^{-8} cm so that $Pe\mathbf{X} \approx 10^{-10}$ volt. We can therefore write

$$a_E = \exp\left(-i\frac{E}{\hbar}t\right), \qquad a_F = 0, \qquad a_G = 0, \cdots$$

in the second term on the right of (6.13). Since this term is already small, we substitute in it the approximate wave function from Eq. (6.10). This in turn is based on neglecting the perturbation altogether on the right of (6.13). This gives

$$i\hbar\frac{\partial a_F(t)}{\partial t} = Fa_F(t) + Pe\mathbf{X}_{FE}\sin\omega t\exp\left(-i\frac{E}{\hbar}t\right). \tag{6.14}$$

To integrate this equation, we substitute

$$a_F(t) = b(t)\exp\left(-i\frac{F}{\hbar}t\right).$$

Then

$$\exp\left(-i\frac{F}{\hbar}t\right)i\hbar\frac{\partial b(t)}{\partial t}$$
$$= \frac{iPe}{2}\mathbf{X}_{FE}\left\{\exp\left[-i\left(\frac{E}{\hbar}+\omega\right)t\right] - \exp\left[-i\left(\frac{E}{\hbar}-\omega\right)t\right]\right\}$$

and from this we obtain, by multiplying by $\exp\left(i\frac{F}{\hbar}t\right)$ and integrating,

$$i\hbar b(t) = \frac{iPe}{2}\mathbf{X}_{FE}\left\{\frac{\exp\left[-i\left(\omega-\frac{F-E}{\hbar}\right)t\right]}{-i\left(\omega-\frac{F-E}{\hbar}\right)}\right.$$
$$\left. - \frac{\exp\left[-i\left(-\omega-\frac{F-E}{\hbar}\right)t\right]}{-i\left(-\omega-\frac{F-E}{\hbar}\right)} + C\right\}.$$

The constant of integration is determined by the condition $b(0) = 0$. Then the expression for $b(t)$ can be broken into two parts:

$$b(t) = \frac{iPe}{2}\mathbf{X}_{FE}\left\{\frac{\exp\left[-i\left(\omega - \frac{F-E}{\hbar}\right)t\right] - 1}{\hbar\omega - F + E} + \frac{\exp\left[-i\left(-\omega - \frac{F-E}{\hbar}\right)t\right] - 1}{\hbar\omega + F - E}\right\}. \tag{6.15}$$

This expression actually does vanish at $t = 0$, as it should; we see also that $b(t)$ is a sum of two periodic functions.

If we keep the intensity of the light P^2 constant and change the frequency, the first term of (6.15) becomes very large if $\hbar\omega$ is approximately equal to $F - E$. Generally, excitations of any noticeable proportions occur only when this condition is met. This supplies an explanation for Bohr's frequency condition: the frequency of light which will effect a given transition from a state with energy E into a state with energy F must meet the condition (6.E.1); namely, $\hbar\omega \approx (F - E)$.

Because of this condition, we can neglect the second term in (6.15) compared to the first from now on. For the probability $|a_F(t)|^2 = |b(t)|^2$ of the state F, we then obtain

$$|b(t)|^2 = \frac{P^2e^2}{2}|\mathbf{X}_{FE}|^2 \frac{1 - \cos\left(\omega - \frac{F-E}{\hbar}\right)t}{(\hbar\omega - F + E)^2}. \tag{6.15a}$$

5. So far we have assumed that the light wave which impinges upon the atom at the time $t = 0$ has the form of a pure sine wave. Actually light consists in most cases of a superposition of sine waves, with the frequencies covering an interval approximately symmetric about $\omega = (F - E)/\hbar$ and with randomly distributed phases. Because of the random phases, it can be assumed that the effects of these superposed waves combine additively; then the total probability that at time t the atom is in the state F is

$$|b(t)|^2 = \sum_{\omega}|\mathbf{X}_{FE}|^2 \frac{P_\omega^2 e^2}{2} \frac{1 - \cos\left(\omega - \frac{F-E}{\hbar}\right)t}{(\hbar\omega - F + E)^2}, \tag{6.16}$$

where ω ranges over all the frequencies in the impinging light, and P_ω is the amplitude of the oscillation with frequency ω.

If the frequencies in the impinging radiation are grouped densely in a small region symmetrical about $(F - E/\hbar) = \omega$, bounded, for example, by ω_2 above and ω_1 below, then one can write $P_\omega^2 = 4J\,d\omega$, where J is the intensity (energy density) of the light per unit frequency $\omega/2\pi$, and $d\omega$ is an infinitesimal interval of ω. Then (6.16) becomes an integral

$$|b(t)|^2 = 2e^2J|\mathbf{X}_{FE}|^2 \int_{\omega_1}^{\omega_2} \frac{1 - \cos\left(\omega - \dfrac{F-E}{\hbar}\right)t}{(\hbar\omega - F + E)^2}\, d\omega, \tag{6.16a}$$

or, by introducing a new variable of integration

$$x = t\left(\omega - \frac{F-E}{\hbar}\right),$$

$$|b(t)|^2 = \frac{2}{\hbar^2}\, e^2Jt|\mathbf{X}_{FE}|^2 \int_{x_1}^{x_2} \frac{1 - \cos x}{x^2}\, dx. \tag{6.16b}$$

The new limits of integration are then

$$x_1 = t\left(\omega_1 - \frac{F-E}{\hbar}\right), \qquad x_2 = t\left(\omega_2 - \frac{F-E}{\hbar}\right). \tag{6.E.2}$$

However, since the integrand of (6.16b) receives important contributions only from a narrow region about $x = 0$, the integration can be taken from $-\infty$ to $+\infty$. The probability of the state with energy F then becomes

$$|b(t)|^2 = \frac{2\pi e^2Jt}{\hbar^2}\, |\mathbf{X}_{FE}|^2. \tag{6.17}$$

The extension of the range of integration is valid only when x_1 and x_2 are large, which implies according to (6.E.2) that the incident light must cover a frequency region on both sides of $\omega = (F - E)/\hbar$ which is large compared to $1/t$. On the other hand our calculation can claim validity only for times short compared to the lifetime τ of the state F. This means that the width of the incident light must be assumed very large compared with the "natural line width" $\hbar/\tau$.

The probability that the atom be in the state with energy F is proportional, according to (6.17), to the intensity J of the incident light, to the square of the matrix element $|\mathbf{X}_{FE}|^2$—which confirms the matrix theoretical prediction—and to the duration t of the light wave, as would be expected. We note again that (6.17) holds only for times short compared to the lifetime of the excited state and long compared to the reciprocal frequency width of the incident light.

In spite of this and its approximate character, (6.17) provides a very beautiful verification of the assumption that $|a_F|^2$ is the excitation strength of the state with energy F. Together with the concept of wave packets in configuration space, the equation forms an extremely powerful support for the statistical interpretation of quantum mechanics. Moreover, (6.17) also shows that

$$|\mathbf{X}_{FE}|^2 = |(\psi_F, (x_1 + x_2 + \cdots + x_N)\, \psi_E)|^2$$

is proportional to the probability of a transition induced by light polarized along the x-axis from the stationary state ψ_E to the stationary state ψ_F. These results, which have also been derived under much more general conditions than those considered here, form the basis for calculation of the intensities, or intensity ratios, of spectral lines.

7. Abstract Group Theory

Take the six matrices[1]

$$\left.\begin{array}{c}
\underset{\mathbf{E}}{\begin{pmatrix} 1 & 0 \\ 0 & 1 \end{pmatrix}}, \quad
\underset{\mathbf{A}}{\begin{pmatrix} 1 & 0 \\ 0 & -1 \end{pmatrix}}, \quad
\underset{\mathbf{B}}{\begin{pmatrix} -\frac{1}{2} & \frac{1}{2}\sqrt{3} \\ \frac{1}{2}\sqrt{3} & \frac{1}{2} \end{pmatrix}}, \quad
\underset{\mathbf{C}}{\begin{pmatrix} -\frac{1}{2} & -\frac{1}{2}\sqrt{3} \\ -\frac{1}{2}\sqrt{3} & \frac{1}{2} \end{pmatrix}}, \\[2ex]
\underset{\mathbf{D}}{\begin{pmatrix} -\frac{1}{2} & \frac{1}{2}\sqrt{3} \\ -\frac{1}{2}\sqrt{3} & -\frac{1}{2} \end{pmatrix}}, \quad
\underset{\mathbf{F}}{\begin{pmatrix} -\frac{1}{2} & -\frac{1}{2}\sqrt{3} \\ \frac{1}{2}\sqrt{3} & -\frac{1}{2} \end{pmatrix}}
\end{array}\right\} \qquad (7.E.1)$$

and form the multiplication table of the 36 products which result from multiplying each matrix in (7.E.1) with every other matrix in (7.E.1) according to the rule for matrix multiplication! We see that all 36 resulting matrices are identical with one of the matrices already occurring in (7.E.1). Such a system of matrices is called a *group*. We can summarize this property of these matrices in a table, the *group table*.

	E	A	B	C	D	F
E	E	A	B	C	D	F
A	A	E	D	F	B	C
B	B	F	E	D	C	A
C	C	D	F	E	A	B
D	D	C	A	B	F	E
F	F	B	C	A	E	D

The first factor appears in the first column, the second factor in the first row, and the product appears at the intersection in the table. This table summarizes all the multiplication rules of the matrices (7.E.1).

The strict definition of a *group* is as follows: A *group* is a set of objects (the *elements* of the group), among which one kind of operation is defined, called *multiplication*. *This* multiplication *specifies, for every two elements of the group* (factors), *a third element of the group*, the product.[2] This *group multiplication*, which is considered to be an inherent property of group elements, must also exhibit the following characteristics.

1. *The associative law must hold.* If $AB = F$ and $BC = G$, then $FC = AG$.

[1] We use the symbol E (German: Einheit, the unit) to represent the identity of the group.

[2] In what follows we have in mind a system of n-rowed matrices.

If the group elements are matrices, and if we understand group multiplication to be matrix multiplication, then the associative law is always satisfied (by Theorem 3, Chapter 1). Groups in which the commutative law of multiplication also holds, i.e., in which $AB = BA$, are called Abelian groups.

2. Among the elements there is one (and only one) which is called the *identity*, or *unit element*, E and which has the property that the product of it with any other element gives just the other element, i.e., $EA = AE = A$.

3. Every element has a *reciprocal*. That is, for every element A there exists an element B such that $BA = E$. We can then also show (as in Theorem 5, Chapter 1) that $AB = E$ as follows; $BA = E$ implies $BAB = B$; then if C is the reciprocal of B, it follows that $CBAB = CB$, i.e., $AB = E$. The reciprocal of A is denoted by A^{-1}.

These three properties of group elements and of group multiplication are the definition of a group. When formulated in this (or some other) way, they are referred to as *group axioms* or *group postulates*.

Rule: The reciprocal of a product $ABCD \cdots$ is formed by taking the reciprocals of the individual factors in *reverse order* (as one does for matrices). Thus

$$(ABCD \cdots)^{-1} = \cdots D^{-1}C^{-1}B^{-1}A^{-1}.$$

This can be verified at once.

$$(\cdots D^{-1}C^{-1}B^{-1}A^{-1})(ABCD \cdots) = E.$$

It should be observed that $AX = B$ and $AY = B$ imply that $X = Y$, since both X and Y are clearly equal to $A^{-1}B$. Also, $XA = B$ and $YA = B$ imply $X = Y = BA^{-1}$. If the group has only a finite number h of elements, it is called a finite group, and h is known as the *order* of the group.

Theorems for Finite Groups[3]

We consider an element X. We can then form a sequence of the elements

$$E, X, X^2, X^3, X^4, X^5, \cdots \tag{7.E.2}$$

etc. Since the elements of (7.E.2) are all group elements, and the total number of all the elements is finite, one of the sequence (7.E.2) must occur a second time after a certain number of powers. Let the first recurring element be $X^n = X^k$ (with $k < n$). Then we must have $k = 0$, and $X^n = E$; otherwise, $X^{n-1} = X^{k-1}$ would already have appeared in the sequence (7.E.2) and X would not be the first element to appear in it for *the second time*. If n is

[3] All the theorems on finite groups should be verified for the group (7.E.1). For this, make use of the group table!

the smallest number for which $X^n = E$, then n is called the *order* of X. The sequence

$$E, X, X^2, X^3, \cdots, X^{n-1} \tag{7.E.3}$$

is called the *period* of X. For example, the period of D in the group (7.E.1) is E, D, $D^2 = F$ ($D^3 = FD = E$), and the order of D is thus 3. The period of F is E, F, $F^2 = D$ ($F^3 = DF = E$), and the order of F is also 3. On the other hand the order of A is 2, since $A^2 = E$ at once.

The period of X itself forms a group (in fact, an *Abelian* group). A set of elements of a group, which itself forms a group, is called a *subgroup*. Example (7.E.3) is an Abelian *subgroup*.

THEOREM 1. *If $\mathscr{H}$ is a group of order h with elements $E, A_2, A_3, \cdots, A_h$, and if A_k is an arbitrary element of this group, then every element occurs once and only once in the sequence $EA_k = A_k, A_2A_k, A_3A_k, \cdots, A_hA_k$.* Let X be any element, and let $XA_k^{-1} = A_r$; then $A_rA_k = X$, and X occurs in the sequence. On the other hand X cannot occur twice because $A_rA_k = X$ and $A_sA_k = X$ imply that $A_r = A_s$.

Of course, the same holds for the series $A_kE, A_kA_2, A_kA_3, \cdots, A_kA_h$. Theorem 1 expresses the fact that in every column in the group table (as well as in every row) each element appears once and only once. The simplest and most important application of this theorem is the following: If $J_E, J_{A_2}, J_{A_3}, \cdots, J_{A_h}$ are numbers such that every group element X corresponds to a number J ("J is a function in group space"), then

$$\sum_{\nu=1}^{h} J_{A_\nu} = \sum_{\nu=1}^{h} J_{A_\nu X} = \sum_{\nu=1}^{h} J_{XA_\nu}. \tag{7.1}$$

Clearly, each sum involves exactly the same numbers, except in different order.

Let $\mathscr{B}$ be a subgroup of $\mathscr{H}$ with elements $E, B_2, B_3, \cdots, B_g$. The set of the g elements $EX, B_2X, B_3X, \cdots, B_gX$, is called a *right coset* $\mathscr{B}X$, provided X does not occur in the subgroup.[4] (For if it did, the elements of $\mathscr{B}X$ would be exactly those of $\mathscr{B}$, as Theorem 1 shows.) *A coset is certainly not a group*, for it cannot contain the identity E nor any other element of $\mathscr{B}$. Suppose, for example, that $B_kX = B_l$, then $X = B_k^{-1}B_l$, i.e., X would be contained in the subgroup $\mathscr{B}$ and $\mathscr{B}X$ would be $\mathscr{B}$ itself. Similarly, the elements $XE = X$, $XB_2, XB_3, \cdots, XB_g$ form a *left coset* of $\mathscr{B}$.

THEOREM 2. *Two right cosets of a subgroup $\mathscr{B}$ either contain the same elements or they have no elements in common.* Let one coset be $\mathscr{B}X$, the other $\mathscr{B}Y$. Then, $B_kX = B_lY$ implies $YX^{-1} = B_l^{-1}B_k$, i.e., YX^{-1} would be contained in $\mathscr{B}$. Then by Theorem 1, applied to the subgroup $\mathscr{B}$, the sequence EYX^{-1}, $B_2YX^{-1}, \cdots, B_gYX^{-1}$ is identical with $E, B_2, B_3, \cdots, B_g$ except for order.

[4] X must, of course, be an element of $\mathscr{H}$.

Thus $EYX^{-1}X$, $B_2YX^{-1}X$, $B_3YX^{-1}X$, $\cdots$, $B_gYX^{-1}X$, would also be identical with EX, B_2X, B_3X, $\cdots$, B_gX except for order. But the former are simply the members of the coset $\mathscr{B}Y = EY, B_2Y, B_3Y, \cdots, B_gY$. The elements of $\mathscr{B}Y$ thus coincide with the elements of $\mathscr{B}X$ if only a single element coincides. *The criterion for this is that YX^{-1} be contained in $\mathscr{B}$.*

For example, one subgroup of (7.E.1) is the period of A, that is, the two elements E and A. A right coset of this group is obtained by multiplying every element by one other element, say B, from the right. We thus obtain the coset $EB = B$, $AB = D$. Cosets are also obtained by multiplying the elements E, A with each of the other elements C, D, F. The coset obtained by multiplying E, A

with B is B, D
with C is C, F
with D is D, B
with F is F, C.

Thus, in this case the cosets obtained by multiplication by B and D (or C and F) are identical. Note, also, that $BD^{-1} = BF = A$ (or $CF^{-1} = CD = A$) is contained in the subgroup E, A.

We now consider all the *distinct* cosets of $\mathscr{B}$! Let them be $\mathscr{B}X_2$, $\mathscr{B}X_3, \cdots, \mathscr{B}X_l$. Each element of $\mathscr{H}$ occurs either in $\mathscr{B}$ or in one of the $l - 1$ cosets. Thus we obtain, in all, lg elements. Since every element occurs at least once and none occurs twice, lg must be equal to h. This establishes Theorem 3.

THEOREM 3. *The order g of a subgroup is a whole number divisor of the order h of the whole group.* The quotient $h/g = l$ is referred to as the *index* of the subgroup $\mathscr{B}$ in the group $\mathscr{H}$.

Since the period of every element is a subgroup with as many elements as its order, it follows that *the order of every element is a divisor of the order of the group.*

Criterion for subgroups. If a complex of group elements contains all the products AB of all the elements A and B contained in it, then it forms a group, and is, therefore, a subgroup of the original group. The *associative law* of multiplication holds for all the elements of the group, and thus also for the complex of elements considered. Also, with every element A, all its powers occur in the complex, therefore the *identity* E also occurs. Finally, if n is the order of A, then $A^n = E$, and $A^{n-1} = A^{-1}$. The *reciprocal* of every element also occurs in the complex. Therefore, all three group postulates are satisfied.

Examples of Groups

1. The group which contains *only one* element consists of the identity E alone.

2. The group of order 2 has the group multiplication table

	E	A
E	E	A
A	A	E

It is an *Abelian* group. We call it the reflection group since it is made up of the identity and the reflection transformation $x' = -x$.

3. The group of order 3 can contain, besides the identity, only an element of order 3, since its order must be an integral divisor of 3 (other than 1). It consists of a single period. Its elements are

$$E, A, A^2 (A^3 = E).$$

It is thus Abelian.

The same holds for every group whose order is a prime number p. Their elements are

$$E, A, A^2, A^3, \cdots, A^{p-1}.$$

Groups of this form are called *cyclic groups*, even if p is not a prime number. If ω is an nth primitive root of unity (i.e., ω^n is the lowest power of ω which is equal to 1, as for example, $\omega = \cos 2\pi/n + i \sin 2\pi/n$), then the numbers

$$1, \omega, \omega^2, \cdots, \omega^{n-1} \tag{7.E.4}$$

form a cyclic group of order n, if group multiplication is understood to be ordinary numerical multiplication. The cyclic groups are *all Abelian*. The "same group" as (7.E.4) is also formed by the numbers

$$0, 1, 2, \cdots, n-1 \tag{7.E.5}$$

if group multiplication is defined to be *addition, modulo n*. (For example, if $n = 7$, then $5 \cdot 4 = 2$, since $5 + 4 = 9 = 7 + 2 = n + 2$.) The elements of the group (7.E.5) can be made to correspond to the elements of (7.E.4) in a one-to-one fashion by making k correspond to ω^k. This correspondence has the property that by it "*products transform into products*," i.e., $k_1 \cdot k_2 = k_3$ implies $\omega^{k_1} \cdot \omega^{k_2} = \omega^{k_3}$. Such a pair of groups is said to be isomorphic.[5]

[5] To show that the theorems derived so far are not at all trivial, let us mention an implication they have for number theory. If $n + 1$ is a prime number, then the numbers $1, 2, 3, \cdots, n$ form a group in still another way if we interpret group multiplication as numerical multiplication modulo $n + 1$. If, say, $n + 1 = 7$, then $3 \cdot 5 = 1$, since $3 \cdot 5 = 15 = 2 \cdot 7 + 1$. The identity is then 1. The period of every one of the elements is then a fraction of n, the order of the group. Thus, we certainly have $A^n = 1$, if A is an element of the group. But, this is tantamount to the statement that $a^n \equiv 1 \pmod{n+1}$ if a is a number $1, 2, 3, \cdots, n$. This is a special case of the Fermat theorem which, it will be conceded, is certainly nontrivial.

Two groups are *isomorphic* if the elements A of the one can be made to correspond to the elements $\bar{A}$ of the other uniquely and reciprocally in such a way that from $AB = C$ it can be inferred that $\bar{A}\bar{B} = \bar{C}$, i.e., $\bar{A}\bar{B} = \overline{AB}$. Isomorphic groups are essentially identical; the individual elements are merely labeled differently.

4. There exist two groups of order 4; i.e., two groups, neither of which is isomorphic to the other. All others are isomorphic with one of these two. The first group is the cyclic group, say, 1, i, -1, $-i$ with group multiplication defined as numerical multiplication. The second group is the so-called *four-group*. Its group table is:

	E	A	B	C
E	E	A	B	C
A	A	E	C	B
B	B	C	E	A
C	C	B	A	E

All its elements (except for E) are of order 2; it, too, is Abelian.

5. The four-group is the first example of a very comprehensive set of groups, the symmetry groups. Consider a regular polygon of n sides in the XY plane. Let the coordinates of the n vertices be $x_k = r \cos 2\pi k/n$, $y_k = r \sin 2\pi k/n$ $(k = 0, 1, 2, 3, \cdots, n-1)$, and consider all linear substitutions

$$x' = \alpha x + \beta y; \qquad y' = \gamma x + \delta y$$

which transform the regular n-polygon "into itself," i.e., for which the new coordinates of the vertices $x'_\varkappa$, $y'_\varkappa$ can still be written in the form

$$x'_\varkappa = r \cos 2\pi\varkappa/n, \qquad y'_\varkappa = r \sin 2\pi\varkappa/n$$

$(\varkappa = 0, 1, 2, 3, \cdots, n-1)$. The matrices for these linear substitutions *form a group*, since the product of any two substitutions, the reciprocal of any single substitution, and the identity E are all, themselves, substitutions meeting the requirement for group elements.

The substitutions which transform the n-polygon into itself are: (A) Rotations of the plane through the angles $2\pi k/n$ $(k = 0, 1, 2, \cdots, n-1)$; the corresponding matrices are

$$\begin{pmatrix} \cos \dfrac{2\pi k}{n}, & \sin \dfrac{2\pi k}{n} \\[2ex] -\sin \dfrac{2\pi k}{n}, & \cos \dfrac{2\pi k}{n} \end{pmatrix} = \mathbf{D}_k \qquad (7.E.6)$$

These form a cyclic group. (B) Reflection of the plane and subsequent rotation through an angle $2\pi k/n$. The corresponding matrices are

$$\begin{pmatrix} -\cos \dfrac{2\pi k}{n}, & \sin \dfrac{2\pi k}{n} \\[2ex] \sin \dfrac{2\pi k}{n}, & \cos \dfrac{2\pi k}{n} \end{pmatrix} = \mathbf{U}_k \qquad (7.E.7)$$

These $2n$ matrices form a group of order $2n$, known as the *dihedral* group. The matrices (7.E.6) form a subgroup of this group; those of (7.E.7), a coset to this subgroup. The 4-group, with $n = 2$, is the simplest example of a dihedral group; the n-polygon degenerates into two vertices, a straight line. While the 4-group is still Abelian, the other dihedral groups are *no longer Abelian*. The group (7.E.1) is the dihedral group of the regular triangle, and is the first *non-Abelian* group; the elements E, F, D belong to the subgroup; A, B, C, to the coset.

The substitutions which transform regular bodies into themselves, are important and interesting groups, and are known as symmetry groups. They are usually specified by the regular bodies which they transform into themselves. Thus there exists a tetrahedral group, an octahedral group, an icosahedral group, etc. They play an important role in crystal physics.

6. The *permutation groups* are also very important. Consider the numbers from 1 to n: $1, 2, 3, \cdots, n$. Every order $\alpha_1, \alpha_2, \cdots, \alpha_n$ of these n numbers forms a permutation. There thus exist $n!$ permutations of n things, usually denoted by the symbol

$$\begin{pmatrix} 1, & 2, & 3, & \cdots, & n \\ \alpha_1, & \alpha_2, & \alpha_3, & \cdots, & \alpha_n \end{pmatrix}.$$

The objects to be permuted are written in their natural order in the upper line, and in the second line in the order which results by the permutation in question. Multiplication of two permutations P_1 and P_2 is done so that those changes which P_2 would effect in the natural order are made to take place in the order of P_1. Thus, if

$$P_1 = \begin{pmatrix} 1 & 2 & 3 \\ 2 & 1 & 3 \end{pmatrix} \quad \text{and} \quad P_2 = \begin{pmatrix} 1 & 2 & 3 \\ 3 & 1 & 2 \end{pmatrix}.$$

Then

$$P_1P_2 = \begin{pmatrix} 1 & 2 & 3 \\ 2 & 1 & 3 \end{pmatrix}\begin{pmatrix} 1 & 2 & 3 \\ 3 & 1 & 2 \end{pmatrix} = \begin{pmatrix} 1 & 2 & 3 \\ 1 & 3 & 2 \end{pmatrix}.$$

That is, since P_2 transforms the 1 into the 3, the 3 appears in P_1P_2 where the 1 appears in P_1. Likewise, since P_2 transforms the 2 into the 1, the 1 appears in P_1P_2 where the 2 appears in P_1, etc.

If P_1 transforms the k into α_k; P_2, the α_k into β_k; and P_3 transforms the β_k into γ_k, then P_1P_2 transforms the k into β_k, and P_2P_3 the α_k into γ_k. Thus, $(P_1P_2) \cdot P_3$ as well as $P_1 \cdot (P_2P_3)$ transforms the k into γ_k; thus, multiplication of permutations is *associative*.

The set of all $n!$ permutations of n objects forms a group with the identity

$$\begin{pmatrix} 1, 2, 3, \cdots, n \\ 1, 2, 3, \cdots, n \end{pmatrix}$$

as the unit element. This group is the *symmetric group*[6] of degree n. The symmetric group of the third degree is of order 6; it is isomorphic to the group (7.E.1), and thus to the dihedral group with $n = 3$. The correspondence is as follows

$$\underset{E}{\begin{pmatrix}1 & 2 & 3\\1 & 2 & 3\end{pmatrix}} \quad \underset{A}{\begin{pmatrix}1 & 2 & 3\\2 & 1 & 3\end{pmatrix}} \quad \underset{B}{\begin{pmatrix}1 & 2 & 3\\1 & 3 & 2\end{pmatrix}} \quad \underset{C}{\begin{pmatrix}1 & 2 & 3\\3 & 2 & 1\end{pmatrix}} \quad \underset{D}{\begin{pmatrix}1 & 2 & 3\\3 & 1 & 2\end{pmatrix}} \quad \underset{F}{\begin{pmatrix}1 & 2 & 3\\2 & 3 & 1\end{pmatrix}}$$

The symmetric groups also play an important role in quantum mechanics.

Conjugate Elements and Classes

The element XAX^{-1} is said to be an element *conjugate* to A. If two elements A and B are conjugate to a third element C, they are also conjugate to one another: From $A = XCX^{-1}$ and $B = YCY^{-1}$ it follows that $X^{-1}AX = C$ and $B = YX^{-1}AXY^{-1} = (YX^{-1})A(YX^{-1})^{-1}$. Those elements of a group which are conjugate to one another form a *class*. A class is determined by stating a single one of its elements A; the entire class can then be obtained by forming the sequence

$$EAE^{-1} = A, \qquad A_2AA_2^{-1}, \qquad A_3AA_3^{-1}, \cdots, A_hAA_h^{-1}.$$

All elements of this sequence are conjugate to A and to one another; moreover, every element conjugate to A (and thus every one conjugate to any other element in the sequence) occurs (actually more than once) in the sequence. The elements of a group can, therefore, be divided into classes, and every element appears in one and only one class.

The identity of the group forms a class by itself, since it is not conjugate to any other element. $XEX^{-1} = E$ for all X. Except for the class which consists only of the element E, no class is a subgroup, since none can contain the identity E. In an Abelian group, each class consists of just one element, since $XAX^{-1} = A$ for all X.

All the elements of a class have the same order. If $A^n = E$, then $(XAX^{-1})^n$ is also equal to E, as one can see directly

$$(XAX^{-1})^n = (XAX^{-1}) \cdot (XAX^{-1}) \cdots (XAX^{-1}) = XA^nX^{-1} = XEX^{-1} = E.$$

In a substitution group (a group of matrices), all the matrices which belong to the same class have the same trace. To see this, let $\boldsymbol{\alpha}$ and $\boldsymbol{\beta}$ belong to the same class. Then there exists a group element, i.e., a matrix $\boldsymbol{\gamma}$, such that

$$\boldsymbol{\beta} = \boldsymbol{\gamma}\boldsymbol{\alpha}\boldsymbol{\gamma}^{-1}$$

Consequently, $\text{Tr}\,\boldsymbol{\beta} = \text{Tr}\,\boldsymbol{\gamma}\boldsymbol{\alpha}\boldsymbol{\gamma}^{-1} = \text{Tr}\,\boldsymbol{\alpha}$.

[6] It is also often called the permutation group, but *never* the symmetry group.

For example, we form the class of C in the group (7.E.1). It consists of

$$ECE^{-1} = C, \quad ACA^{-1} = B, \quad BCB^{-1} = A, \quad CCC^{-1} = C,$$
$$DCD^{-1} = A, \quad FCF^{-1} = B.$$

The class of C thus consists of the elements A, B, C; this is also the class of A or B. All three elements A, B, C, are of order 2, and the trace in the matrix representation (7.E.1) of the group is 0 for all three. The class of D is

$$EDE^{-1} = D, \quad ADA^{-1} = F, \quad BDB^{-1} = F, \quad CDC^{-1} = F$$
$$DDD^{-1} = D, \quad FDF^{-1} = D.$$

The class of D (or F) consists of the two elements D, F.

8. Invariant Subgroups

A subgroup which consists entirely of whole classes of the original group is called an *invariant subgroup*. Let $\mathcal{R} = E, N_2, \cdots, N_n$ be an invariant subgroup. Since it is a group, it must contain along with N_i and N_j their product, N_iN_j. Moreover, it contains XN_iX^{-1} where X is *any element of the full group*, since an invariant subgroup contains all the elements XN_iX^{-1} of a class if only it contains one element N_i of the class. An ordinary subgroup would have to contain XN_iX^{-1} only if it contained X as well as N_i.

In an ordinary subgroup, as in any group, the elements

$$N_jE = N_j, \qquad N_jN_2, \cdots, N_jN_n \tag{8.E.1}$$

are identical with the elements of the subgroup, except for order. The same is true of the sequence

$$EN_j^{-1} = N_j^{-1}, \qquad N_2N_j^{-1}, \cdots, N_nN_j^{-1} \tag{8.E.2}$$

and the sequence

$$N_jEN_j^{-1} = E, \qquad N_jN_2N_j^{-1}, \cdots, N_jN_nN_j^{-1} \tag{8.E.3}$$

which is formed from (8.E.2) when one substitutes the sequence (8.E.1) for the first factor in each member—this has no effect other than rearranging the members. All N_i here are elements of the subgroup.

On the other hand, when the elements $E, N_2, \cdots, N_n$ form an invariant subgroup, the sequence

$$XEX^{-1} = E, \qquad XN_2X^{-1}, \cdots, XN_nX^{-1} \tag{8.E.4}$$

where X is an *arbitrary* element of the *whole* group, is identical with the elements of the invariant subgroup, except for order. All the elements of (8.E.4) occur in the invariant subgroup, since they are conjugate to elements of the subgroup; all the elements of the invariant subgroup occur in (8.E.4), as we now demonstrate. To find a given element N_k in (8.E.4), we need only construct $X^{-1}N_kX$. This is an element among the elements $E, N_2, \cdots, N_n$. Let it be N_i. Then $N_k = XN_iX^{-1}$, and N_k occurs in (8.E.4) in the ith place.

Every subgroup of an Abelian group is an invariant subgroup. Every element is a class in itself; therefore, every subgroup must consist entirely of whole classes. The symmetric groups have one, and in general only one, invariant subgroup which is composed of all the even permutations. The even permutations form a subgroup, since the product of two even permutations is an even permutation. Moreover, the element conjugate to an even permutation must be an even permutation, and, therefore, occurs in the subgroup (see also Chapter 13).

In Example (7.E.1) the elements E, D, and F comprise the invariant subgroup. The theorems which follow should be verified by the reader for the special case of this group.

The determination of the invariant subgroups is very important in a study of the constitution of the group. Groups which have no invariant subgroups are called *simple* groups.

The Factor Group

Consider now the cosets of the invariant subgroup $\mathscr{R}$. The elements $EU = U, N_2U, \cdots, N_nU$ form a right coset of $\mathscr{R}$. They also form a left coset, since $U = UU^{-1}EU, N_2U = UU^{-1}N_2U, \cdots, N_nU = UU^{-1}N_nU$ are identical with the elements $U = UE, UN_2, \cdots, UN_n$ except for order. That is, the complex $\mathscr{R}U$ is identical with the complex $U\mathscr{R}$. One can thus speak simply of cosets of invariant subgroups, without specifying whether they are left or right cosets.[1]

Let us multiply all the elements of one coset $\mathscr{R}U$ with all the elements of another coset $\mathscr{R}V$! Then $N_jUN_lV = N_jUN_lU^{-1}UV = N_kUV$, since both N_j and UN_lU^{-1}, and therefore their product N_k are contained in $\mathscr{R}$. The multiplication process thus yields the elements of a single coset $\mathscr{R}UV$.

If one considers the cosets of an invariant subgroup as entities in themselves and defines the product of two cosets to be that coset whose elements are obtained as the products of multiplication of the elements of the two cosets, then *the cosets themselves form a group*. This group is called the *factor group* of the invariant subgroup. The unit element of the factor group is the invariant subgroup itself. Every element N_jU of a coset $\mathscr{R}U$ yields again an element of the coset $\mathscr{R}U$ when multiplied (from the right or left) with an element N_l of $\mathscr{R}$. Explicitly, $N_l \cdot N_jU = N_lN_j \cdot U = N_k \cdot U$, and $N_j \cdot UN_l = N_j \cdot UN_lU^{-1}U = N_kU$. Second, every coset $\mathscr{R}U$ has a reciprocal, the coset $\mathscr{R}U^{-1}$. That is,

$$N_jU \cdot N_lU^{-1} = N_j \cdot UN_lU^{-1} = N_k,$$

which is an element of the invariant subgroup itself. The product of $\mathscr{R}U$ and $\mathscr{R}U^{-1}$ therefore yields $\mathscr{R}$, the unit element of the factor group.

The order of the factor group of $\mathscr{R}$ is equal to the number of cosets of $\mathscr{R}$, i.e., to its index. One should not confuse the factor group with a subgroup; the elements of a subgroup are elements of the group, whereas *the elements of the factor group are cosets.*

[1] We can see this in another way. The condition that U and V be in the same right coset is (see page 61) that UV^{-1} be in $\mathscr{R}$. The condition that they be in the same left coset is that $V^{-1}U$ be in $\mathscr{R}$. But if $\mathscr{R}$ is an invariant subgroup and contains UV^{-1}, it must also contain $V^{-1} \cdot UV^{-1} \cdot V = V^{-1}U$. Therefore, two elements are in the same left coset, provided only they are in the same right coset, and conversely.

The theorems which were deduced above can be obtained more simply with the help of a symbolic method, in which a totality of elements, a complex, is denoted by a single character, say $\mathscr{C}$. The product of a complex $\mathscr{C}$ with an element A is again a complex $\mathscr{C}A$ whose elements are obtained by multiplying all elements of $\mathscr{C}$ on the right by A (or on the left to obtain $A\mathscr{C}$). The product of two complexes $\mathscr{C}$ and $\mathscr{D}$ is a complex $\mathscr{C}\mathscr{D}$ whose elements are obtained when all the elements of $\mathscr{C}$ are multiplied on the right by the elements of $\mathscr{D}$. It can easily be seen that the *associative law* holds for this type of multiplication.

If $\mathscr{C}$ and $\mathscr{D}$ contain n and n' elements, respectively, then $\mathscr{C}\mathscr{D}$ contains at the most nn' elements. Usually, however, it contains fewer distinct elements, since some elements can occur more than once among the nn' products.

The condition that $\mathscr{C}$ be a subgroup is $\mathscr{C} \cdot \mathscr{C} = \mathscr{C}^2 = \mathscr{C}$. This subgroup is an *invariant* subgroup if for every element U the equation $U^{-1}\mathscr{C}U = \mathscr{C}$ holds. The right cosets of $\mathscr{C}$ are all distinct complexes $\mathscr{C}U$. If $\mathscr{C}$ is an invariant subgroup, then $U^{-1}\mathscr{C}U = \mathscr{C}$, so that $\mathscr{C}U = U\mathscr{C}$; the right cosets are also left cosets. The elements of the factor group are the distinct complexes $\mathscr{C}U$. The product of two complexes $\mathscr{C}U$ and $\mathscr{C}V$, in the sense of multiplication of factor groups, is identical with the product in the sense of multiplication of complexes

$$\mathscr{C}U \cdot \mathscr{C}V = \mathscr{C} \cdot U\mathscr{C} \cdot V = \mathscr{C} \cdot \mathscr{C}U \cdot V = \mathscr{C}^2UV = \mathscr{C}UV$$

Isomorphism and Homomorphism

In the preceding chapter we have become acquainted with the concept of the *isomorphism* of two groups. Two groups are isomorphic when a unique, *one-to-one* correspondence exists between their elements in such a way that products correspond to products. To A, or B, of one group corresponds $\bar{A}$, or $\bar{B}$, of the isomorphic group, and to the product AB corresponds the product $\bar{A} \cdot \bar{B} = \overline{AB}$. Obviously, isomorphic groups must be of the same order.

A less sharp correspondence between two groups is that of simple *homomorphism*, which resembles isomorphism except that the correspondence is not required to be one-to-one. A group $\mathscr{G}$ is homomorphic onto another group $\mathscr{H}$ if one and only one element of $\mathscr{H}$ corresponds to every element of $\mathscr{G}$ and if at least one element of $\mathscr{G}$ corresponds to every element of $\mathscr{H}$, and if the correspondence is such that the product of A and B of $\mathscr{G}$ corresponds to the product $\bar{A} \cdot \bar{B} = \overline{AB}$ of the corresponding elements $\bar{A}$ and $\bar{B}$ of $\mathscr{H}$.[2] In a homomorphism, one element, $\bar{A}$, of $\mathscr{H}$ may correspond to several different elements, say A and A', of $\mathscr{G}$. Accordingly, homomorphism

[2] The relationship which is called here the homomorphism of $\mathscr{G}$ *onto* $\mathscr{H}$ is described by most German authors as the homomorphism of $\mathscr{H}$ to $\mathscr{G}$. Also, the expressions holomorphism and isomorphism are used synonymously in some texts.

is not a reciprocal property. If $\mathscr{G}$ is homomorphic to $\mathscr{H}$, then $\mathscr{H}$ is not necessarily homomorphic to $\mathscr{G}$. The number of elements of $\mathscr{G}$ must be *equal to or greater* than the number of elements of $\mathscr{H}$; if the number is equal, the homomorphism becomes an isomorphism, which is then reciprocal.

The identity, E, of $\mathscr{G}$ corresponds to the identity, $\bar{E}$, of $\mathscr{H}$, since $E \cdot E = E$ implies $\bar{E} \cdot \bar{E} = \bar{E}$, and this is true only for the identity of the group. Also, inverse elements of $\mathscr{G}$ correspond to inverse elements of $\mathscr{H}$.

Consider all the elements $E, E_2, \cdots, E_n$ of $\mathscr{G}$ which correspond to the identity, $\bar{E}$, of $\mathscr{H}$, and denote this complex by $\mathscr{C}$. Since $E_k \cdot E_l$ corresponds to $\bar{E} \cdot \bar{E} = \bar{E}$, the complex $\mathscr{C}$ also contains $E_k \cdot E_l$, so that $\mathscr{C}$ is a group. Moreover, any element $U^{-1}E_kU$ conjugate to E_k corresponds to $\bar{E}$, since $\overline{U^{-1}} \cdot \bar{E} \cdot \bar{U} = \bar{U}^{-1}\bar{E}\bar{U} = \bar{E}$; the group $\mathscr{C}$ therefore is an *invariant subgroup* of $\mathscr{G}$. Likewise, the elements of the complex $\mathscr{A}$ to which one and the same element, $\bar{A}$, of $\mathscr{H}$ corresponds, form a coset of $\mathscr{C}$. Let A_j and A_l be two elements of $\mathscr{A}$; then $\bar{A}_j = \bar{A}_l = \bar{A}$. To any element $A_jA_l^{-1}$ corresponds the element $\bar{A}_j\overline{A_l^{-1}} = \bar{A}_j\bar{A}_l^{-1} = \bar{A}\bar{A}^{-1} = \bar{E}$; that is, $A_jA_l^{-1}$ is contained in $\mathscr{C}$, which is the condition that A_j and A_l be in one and the same coset of $\mathscr{C}$. The cosets of $\mathscr{C}$ are in one-to-one correspondence to the elements of $\mathscr{H}$; hence, the product of two cosets, $\mathscr{C}U$ and $\mathscr{C}V$ corresponds to the product $\bar{U}\bar{V} = \overline{UV}$ of the two elements $\bar{U}$ and $\bar{V}$. Since the cosets form the elements of the factor group of $\mathscr{C}$, *this factor group is isomorphic to* $\mathscr{H}$.

If $\mathscr{G}$ is homomorphic onto $\mathscr{H}$, then a factor group of $\mathscr{G}$ is isomorphic to $\mathscr{H}$. The order of $\mathscr{G}$ is an integral multiple of the order of $\mathscr{H}$. If the homomorphism is actually an isomorphism, then the invariant subgroup in question, $\mathscr{C}$, degenerates into the single identity element E.

By appropriate relabeling of the group elements, one can construct the following correspondence between the elements of $\mathscr{G}$ and $\mathscr{H}$.

$$\underbrace{E, G_2, \cdots, G_n}_{\bar{E}},\ \underbrace{G_{n+1}, G_{n+2}, \cdots, G_{2n}}_{H_2}, \cdots, \underbrace{G_{(h-1)n+1}, \cdots, G_{hn}}_{H_h}.$$

We see that a unique element of $\mathscr{H}$ corresponds to each element of $\mathscr{G}$. Conversely, certain elements of $\mathscr{G}$ correspond to each element of $\mathscr{H}$; this correspondence is, however, not one-to-one but n-to-one, since each element of $\mathscr{H}$ corresponds to exactly n elements of $\mathscr{G}$. The elements $E, G_2, \cdots, G_n$ form an invariant subgroup $\mathscr{C}$ (these were previously written $E, E_2, E_3, \cdots, E_n$); each of the other bracketed complexes forms one of the cosets of this subgroup, each corresponding to one element of $\mathscr{H}$.

Multiplication of an element of $\mathscr{G}$ corresponding to H_i by one corresponding to H_j yields an element which corresponds to $H_i \cdot H_j$. Multiplication of all n elements corresponding to H_i with all n corresponding to H_j yields the n

elements which correspond to $H_i \cdot H_j$, each n times. The group $\mathscr{H}$ is essentially identical to the factor group of the invariant subgroup $E, G_2, \cdots, G_n$. It is isomorphic to this factor group.

Clearly, every group is isomorphic to itself. Every group is also homomorphic onto the group which consists only of the identity element $\bar{E}$. To an element A corresponds the identity $\bar{E}$, and to an element B, also the identity $\bar{E}$. Thus, the product AB corresponds also to $\bar{E}\bar{E} = \bar{E}$. In this case, the invariant subgroup embraces the entire group.

Every substitution group is homomorphic to an Abelian group. The homomorphism can be constructed by letting the substitution correspond to the value of its determinant. What does this give in the case of the Example (7.E.1) of the previous chapter?

This concludes the abstract theory of finite groups; we turn next to the theory of their representations. Later, we shall discuss continuous groups. Our discussion was confined to the rudiments of abstract group theory, which is marvelously simple in its reasoning. A detailed presentation can be found in the Theory of Groups of Finite Order, by A. Speiser, or in Weber's well known Algebra. We shall, however, omit further discussion of the subject, having considered only those parts which are essential for what is to follow, and for the attainment of a sense of security in working with groups.[3]

[3] A more recent English treatise is H. Zassenhaus' "Theory of Groups," Chelsea Publ., New York, 1958.

9. The General Theory of Representations

A representation[1] of a group is a matrix group[2] onto which the group to be represented is homomorphic. Thus, it consists of the assignment of a *matrix* $\mathbf{D}(A)$ or simply $\mathbf{A}$ *to each group element* A in such a way that

$$\mathbf{D}(A)\mathbf{D}(B) = \mathbf{D}(AB) \tag{9.1}$$

holds true for all matrices $\mathbf{D}$. If all the matrices assigned to different group elements are different, *the matrix group is isomorphic to the group it represents* and *the representation is said to be faithful.* On the other hand, if more than one group element corresponds to the same matrix, those elements which correspond to the same matrix as the identity element form an invariant subgroup (as was pointed out in the preceding chapter). Then the representation is actually a faithful representation of the factor group of this invariant subgroup, but is unfaithful as a representation of the whole group.

Conversely, an unfaithful representation of the whole group can be constructed from every representation of a factor group. The elements of a factor group are the cosets of an invariant subgroup. By assigning to all the elements in a given coset of the group the same matrix which represented that coset as an element of the factor group, an unfaithful representation of the entire group is obtained.

Each matrix group is clearly its own faithful representation. It is also clear that we can assign the matrix (1) to every group element, and obtain the trivial homomorphism of any group onto the group which contains only the identity. In Example (7.E.1) we have a faithful representation of the symmetric group of three objects. An additional, but unfaithful, representation of this same group is obtained by assigning to each group element the matrix written below it.

$$\begin{matrix} E & A & B & C & D & F \\ (1) & (-1) & (-1) & (-1) & (1) & (1). \end{matrix} \tag{9.E.1}$$

This is actually a faithful representation of the factor group of the invariant subgroup E, D, F. This factor group has two elements, the invariant subgroup E, D, F and its coset A, B, C. The matrix (1) is assigned to the first element of the factor group; the matrix (—1), to the second.

[1] Stated more precisely: "representation by linear substitutions."

[2] By "matrix group" we specifically mean here a group with square matrices, i.e., with matrices whose rows and columns are labeled in the same way; also, this labeling is common to all the matrices in a given representation. These rules will be observed in all representation matrices.

The number of rows and columns in a representation matrix is called the *dimension* of the representation. From a given representation, new ones can be produced by applying the same similarity transformation to all the matrices of the group. Since similarity transformations do not affect the multiplication properties of the matrices, the whole nature of the representation remains unchanged under them. Two representations which result from one another in this way, or, to word it differently, which can be transformed into one another, are said to be *equivalent*. Equivalent representations are regarded as essentially the same.

From two representations, a single new one can be formed in several ways. Perhaps the simplest is that in which the two representations are merely joined into one. From a representation $\mathbf{D}(A_1), \mathbf{D}(A_2), \cdots, \mathbf{D}(A_h)$ and a second representation $\mathbf{D}'(A_1), \mathbf{D}'(A_2), \cdots, \mathbf{D}'(A_h)$ we thereby obtain the new representation, consisting of the super-matrices

$$\begin{pmatrix} \mathbf{D}(A_1), & \mathbf{0} \\ \mathbf{0}, & \mathbf{D}'(A_1) \end{pmatrix}; \begin{pmatrix} \mathbf{D}(A_2), & \mathbf{0} \\ \mathbf{0}, & \mathbf{D}'(A_2) \end{pmatrix}; \cdots; \begin{pmatrix} \mathbf{D}(A_h), & \mathbf{0} \\ \mathbf{0}, & \mathbf{D}'(A_h) \end{pmatrix}. \tag{9.E.2}$$

A similarity transformation of this new representation may obscure the fact that it was originally formed from two representations. A representation which arises from a representation (9.E.2) by such similarity transformation is said to be *reducible*. Clearly, reducible representations can always be brought into the form (9.E.2) by a similarity transformation; that is, reducible representations are equivalent to representations of the form (9.E.2). Representations for which this is not possible are said to be *irreducible*.

A representation which can be brought into the form (9.E.2) merely by a simultaneous relabeling of the rows and columns of all its matrices is, of course, reducible. In fact, such a renumbering can be carried out by a similarity transformation. To convert the $\bar{j}$th row and column into the jth row and column, we choose for $\mathbf{S}$ the matrix $\mathbf{S}_{ki} = \delta_{k\bar{i}}$; then $(\mathbf{S}^{-1})_{jm} = \delta_{\bar{j}m}$, and

$$\sum_i \mathbf{S}_{ki}(\mathbf{S}^{-1})_{ij} = \sum_i \delta_{k\bar{i}}\,\delta_{\bar{i}j} = \delta_{kj},$$

and transformation with S actually does achieve the desired renumbering:

$$\bar{\mathbf{A}} = \mathbf{S}^{-1}\mathbf{A}\mathbf{S}; \qquad \bar{\mathbf{A}}_{ji} = \sum_{mk} \delta_{\bar{j}m}\mathbf{A}_{mk}\,\delta_{k\bar{i}} = \mathbf{A}_{\bar{j}\bar{i}}.$$

Let us consider the division of the rows and columns of a matrix system into two groups, say "marked" and "unmarked." Any matrix system for which it is possible to make this division in such a way that only zero elements occur at intersections of "marked" rows and "unmarked" columns, and at intersections of "unmarked" rows and "marked" columns, is either reducible or already in reduced form. To demonstrate this, we need only point out that we can transfer the "marked" rows and columns to the top and left of the matrices and obtain the form (9.E.2) for the representation.

In what follows, we shall be concerned with matrices in representations with *nonvanishing determinants*. Then every matrix $\mathbf{D}(A)$ has an inverse. Since multiplication of any group element A with the group identity E yields A, multiplication of any representation matrix $\mathbf{D}(A)$ with the matrix $\mathbf{D}(E)$ assigned to the identity, yields $\mathbf{D}(A)$. It follows that

$$\mathbf{D}(A)\mathbf{D}(E) = \mathbf{D}(A); \qquad \mathbf{D}(E) = (\mathbf{1}). \tag{9.2}$$

The unit matrix is assigned to the identity element of the group. The product of the matrices $\mathbf{D}(A)$ and $\mathbf{D}(A^{-1})$ which correspond to inverse group elements is $\mathbf{D}(E) = \mathbf{1}$. Therefore,

$$\mathbf{D}(A)\,\mathbf{D}(A^{-1}) = \mathbf{D}(E) = \mathbf{1}; \qquad \mathbf{D}(A^{-1}) = [\mathbf{D}(A)]^{-1}, \tag{9.3}$$

and this implies

$$\mathbf{D}(A^{-1}) = \mathbf{D}(A)^{\dagger} \tag{9.3a}$$

for a representation by unitary matrices.

THEOREM 1. *Any representation by matrices with nonvanishing determinants can be transformed into a representation by unitary matrices through a similarity transformation.*

Let the matrices of the representation of the group of order h be $\mathbf{A}_1, \mathbf{A}_2, \cdots, \mathbf{A}_h$. (If the representation is not faithful, not all $\mathbf{A}_1, \mathbf{A}_2, \cdots, \mathbf{A}_h$ are distinct.) Then form the Hermitian matrix $\mathbf{H}$ by summation over all the group elements.

$$\mathbf{H} = \sum_{\varkappa} \mathbf{A}_{\varkappa}\mathbf{A}_{\varkappa}^{\dagger}. \tag{9.4}$$

The proof will be made by diagonalizing $\mathbf{H}$ and finding its inverse square root. It will be shown that successive similarity transformations of the $\mathbf{A}_{\varkappa}$, by the matrix $\mathbf{U}$ which diagonalizes $\mathbf{H}$, and by $\mathbf{d}^{1/2}$, the square root of the diagonal form of $\mathbf{H}$, produces a representation $\bar{\bar{\mathbf{A}}}_{\varkappa}$, which is unitary.

The Hermitian matrix $\mathbf{H}$ can be brought into the diagonal form $\mathbf{d}$ by the unitary matrix $\mathbf{U}$

$$\left.\begin{aligned} \mathbf{d} = \mathbf{U}^{-1}\mathbf{H}\mathbf{U} &= \sum_{\varkappa} \mathbf{U}^{-1}\mathbf{A}_{\varkappa}\mathbf{A}_{\varkappa}^{\dagger}\mathbf{U} \\ &= \sum_{\varkappa} \mathbf{U}^{-1}\mathbf{A}_{\varkappa}\mathbf{U}(\mathbf{U}^{-1}\mathbf{A}_{\varkappa}\mathbf{U})^{\dagger} = \sum_{\varkappa} \bar{\mathbf{A}}_{\varkappa}\bar{\mathbf{A}}_{\varkappa}^{\dagger}. \end{aligned}\right\} \tag{9.5}$$

All diagonal elements of $\mathbf{d}$ are real and positive, since, for example,

$$\mathbf{d}_{kk} = \sum_{\varkappa}\sum_{j} (\bar{\mathbf{A}}_{\varkappa})_{kj}(\bar{\mathbf{A}}_{\varkappa})_{kj}^{*} = \sum_{\varkappa}\sum_{j} |(\bar{\mathbf{A}}_{\varkappa})_{kj}|^2$$

can be zero only if, for this k, the representation matrix elements $(\bar{\mathbf{A}}_{\varkappa})_{kj}$ were zero for all j (and $\varkappa$). Then, however, an entire row of $\bar{\mathbf{A}}_\varkappa$ would be zero. Consequently, its determinant, and so that of $\mathbf{A}_\varkappa$, would vanish in contradiction to the hypothesis. Hence, $\mathbf{d}^{1/2}$ and $\mathbf{d}^{-1/2}$ can be formed uniquely from $\mathbf{d}$ by taking the square root or the $-1/2$ power (positive values) of the diagonal terms; $\mathbf{d}$ and $\mathbf{d}^{-1/2}$ are real diagonal matrices; $\mathbf{d}^{1/2\dagger} = \mathbf{d}^{1/2}$; $\mathbf{d}^{-1/2\dagger} = \mathbf{d}^{-1/2}$

We now demonstrate that the representation

$$\bar{\bar{\mathbf{A}}}_\lambda = \mathbf{d}^{-1/2}\bar{\mathbf{A}}_\lambda \mathbf{d}^{1/2} = \mathbf{d}^{-1/2}\mathbf{U}^{-1}\mathbf{A}_\lambda\mathbf{U}\,\mathbf{d}^{1/2}$$

is unitary. From (9.5) one obtains

$$\mathbf{1} = \mathbf{d}^{-1/2} \sum_\varkappa \bar{\mathbf{A}}_\varkappa \bar{\mathbf{A}}^\dagger \mathbf{d}^{-1/2}.$$

Using this expression for the unit matrix, we can write

$$\left.\begin{aligned}\bar{\bar{\mathbf{A}}}_\lambda\bar{\bar{\mathbf{A}}}_\lambda^\dagger &= \mathbf{d}^{-1/2}\bar{\mathbf{A}}_\lambda \mathbf{d}^{1/2}\cdot(\mathbf{d}^{-1/2}\sum_\varkappa \bar{\mathbf{A}}_\varkappa\bar{\mathbf{A}}_\varkappa^\dagger \mathbf{d}^{-1/2})\,\mathbf{d}^{1/2}\bar{\mathbf{A}}_\lambda^\dagger\,\mathbf{d}^{-1/2}\\ &= \mathbf{d}^{-1/2}\sum_\varkappa \bar{\mathbf{A}}_\lambda\bar{\mathbf{A}}_\varkappa\bar{\mathbf{A}}_\varkappa^\dagger\bar{\mathbf{A}}_\lambda^\dagger\,\mathbf{d}^{-1/2}.\end{aligned}\right\} \tag{9.6}$$

Because of the group property of the $\bar{\mathbf{A}}_\varkappa$, the $\bar{\mathbf{A}}_\lambda\bar{\mathbf{A}}_\varkappa$ for $\varkappa = 1, 2, \cdots, h$ are just the $\bar{\mathbf{A}}_\varkappa$ in a different order,[3] so that

$$\sum_\varkappa \bar{\mathbf{A}}_\lambda\bar{\mathbf{A}}_\varkappa(\bar{\mathbf{A}}_\lambda\bar{\mathbf{A}}_\varkappa)^\dagger = \sum_\varkappa \bar{\mathbf{A}}_\varkappa\bar{\mathbf{A}}_\varkappa^\dagger$$

and accordingly,

$$\bar{\bar{\mathbf{A}}}_\lambda\bar{\bar{\mathbf{A}}}^\lambda = \mathbf{d}^{-1/2}\sum_\varkappa \bar{\mathbf{A}}_\varkappa\bar{\mathbf{A}}_\varkappa^\dagger\,\mathbf{d}^{-1/2} = \mathbf{1}. \tag{9.7}$$

This proves that the representation $\bar{\bar{\mathbf{A}}}_\varkappa$ is unitary, and completes the proof of Theorem 1.

THEOREM 2. *A matrix which commutes with all the matrices of an irreducible representation is a constant matrix* (i.e., a multiple of the unit matrix).

We can assume that the representation is in unitary form, since a similarity transformation certainly leaves multiples of the unit matrix unchanged. Then let the matrix $\mathbf{M}$ commute with all $\mathbf{A}_1, \mathbf{A}_2, \cdots, \mathbf{A}_h$. That is

$$\mathbf{A}_\varkappa\mathbf{M} = \mathbf{M}\mathbf{A}_\varkappa \qquad (\varkappa = 1, 2, \cdots, h). \tag{9.8}$$

One need only consider matrices $\mathbf{M}$ which are Hermitian, as we now demonstrate. Taking the adjoint of Eq. (9.8), we obtain

$$\mathbf{M}^\dagger\mathbf{A}_\varkappa^\dagger = \mathbf{A}_\varkappa^\dagger\mathbf{M}^\dagger.$$

Upon multiplication from in front and behind by $\mathbf{A}_\varkappa$, and noting that $\mathbf{A}_\varkappa\mathbf{A}_\varkappa^\dagger = \mathbf{A}_\varkappa^\dagger\mathbf{A}_\varkappa = \mathbf{1}$,

$$\mathbf{A}_\varkappa\mathbf{M}^\dagger = \mathbf{M}^\dagger\mathbf{A}_\varkappa \qquad (\varkappa = 1, 2, \cdots, h). \tag{9.9}$$

[3] See Theorem 1, page 60.

Then not only $\mathbf{M}$, but also $\mathbf{M}^\dagger$, commutes with all $\mathbf{A}$. Hence, $\mathbf{M} + \mathbf{M}^\dagger = \mathbf{H}_1$ and $i(\mathbf{M} - \mathbf{M}^\dagger) = \mathbf{H}_2$, which are Hermitian, commute with all $\mathbf{A}$. It is therefore sufficient to show that every Hermitian matrix which commutes with all $\mathbf{A}$ is a constant matrix, since if $\mathbf{H}_1$ and $\mathbf{H}_2$ must be multiples of the identity matrix, so must $2\mathbf{M} = \mathbf{H}_1 - i\mathbf{H}_2$.

If $\mathbf{M}$ in (9.8) is Hermitian, it can be brought into the diagonal form $\mathbf{d}$ with a matrix $\mathbf{V}$ so that $\mathbf{d} = \mathbf{V}^{-1}\mathbf{M}\mathbf{V}$. We write $\overline{\mathbf{A}}_\varkappa = \mathbf{V}^{-1}\mathbf{A}_\varkappa\mathbf{V}$ (the $\overline{\mathbf{A}}_\varkappa$ retain the unitarity of the $\mathbf{A}_\varkappa$); then (9.8) implies

$$\overline{\mathbf{A}}_\varkappa \mathbf{d} = \mathbf{d}\overline{\mathbf{A}}_\varkappa \qquad (\varkappa = 1, 2, \cdots, h). \tag{9.10}$$

If the elements of the diagonal matrix $\mathbf{d}$ are not all equal, all $\overline{\mathbf{A}}_\varkappa$ must have zeros at the intersections of rows and columns whose diagonal elements are different. That is,

$$(\overline{\mathbf{A}}_\varkappa)_{kj}\, \mathbf{d}_{jj} = \mathbf{d}_{kk}(\overline{\mathbf{A}}_\varkappa)_{kj}$$

implies that for $\mathbf{d}_{jj} \neq \mathbf{d}_{kk}$, the representation matrix element $(\overline{\mathbf{A}}_\varkappa)_{kj} = 0$; then the representation would be reducible by virtue of the discussion on page 73. Since this is not the case, all $\mathbf{d}_{kk}$ are equal. That is, $\mathbf{d}$, and thus $\mathbf{V}\,\mathbf{d}\mathbf{V}^{-1} = \mathbf{M}$, is a constant matrix which commutes with every matrix. This establishes Theorem 2, which is known as Schur's Lemma.

This derivation of Theorem 2 shows not only that the representation must be reducible if a nonconstant matrix commutes with every matrix of the representation, it shows also how the representation can be reduced or brought into the form (9.E.2). This is achieved by the same similarity transformation which brings the "commuting matrix" into diagonal form.

Conversely, if the representation is reducible, there certainly exist nonconstant matrices which commute with all the matrices of the representation. In this case, the representation can be brought into the form (9.E.2) by a similarity transformation with a suitably chosen matrix $\mathbf{S}$. But all matrices $\mathbf{M}$,

$$\mathbf{M} = \begin{pmatrix} a\mathbf{1} & \mathbf{0} \\ \mathbf{0} & a'\mathbf{1} \end{pmatrix},$$

with arbitrary a and a', commute with matrices of the form (9.E.2). If $\mathbf{M}$ is transformed with $\mathbf{S}^{-1}$, it will commute with matrices of that representation which is obtained by transformation with $\mathbf{S}^{-1}$ of the representation in the form (9.E.2).

If there exists a nonconstant matrix which commutes with all matrices of the representation, then the representation is reducible; if there exists none, it is irreducible.

THEOREM 3. *Consider two irreducible representations of the same group*

$\mathbf{D}^{(1)}(A_1), \mathbf{D}^{(1)}(A_2), \cdots, \mathbf{D}^{(1)}(A_h)$ *and* $\mathbf{D}^{(2)}(A_1), \mathbf{D}^{(2)}(A_2), \cdots, \mathbf{D}^{(2)}(A_h)$, *of dimensions* l_1 *and* l_2. If there exists a matrix $\mathbf{M}$ with l_2 rows and l_1 columns such that

$$\mathbf{MD}^{(1)}(A_\varkappa) = \mathbf{D}^{(2)}(A_\varkappa)\mathbf{M} \qquad (\varkappa = 1, 2, \cdots, h), \tag{9.11}$$

then for $l_1 \neq l_2$, *the matrix* $\mathbf{M}$ *is a null matrix; for* $l_1 = l_2$, $\mathbf{M}$ *is either a null matrix or a matrix with a nonvanishing determinant.* In the latter case, $\mathbf{M}$ has an inverse, and the two irreducible representations are equivalent.

We can assume, at the outset, that the representations are already in unitary form. If this were not the case, we could make them unitary by transforming with matrices $\mathbf{S}$ and $\mathbf{R}$. Then (9.11) would become

$$\left.\begin{aligned} \mathbf{R}^{-1}\mathbf{MS}\cdot\mathbf{S}^{-1}\mathbf{D}^{(1)}(A_\varkappa)\mathbf{S} &= \mathbf{R}^{-1}\mathbf{D}^{(2)}(A_\varkappa)\mathbf{R}\cdot\mathbf{R}^{-1}\mathbf{MS} \\ \mathbf{R}^{-1}\mathbf{MS}\cdot\overline{\mathbf{D}}^{(1)}(A_\varkappa) &= \overline{\mathbf{D}}^{(2)}(A_\varkappa)\cdot\mathbf{R}^{-1}\mathbf{MS} \end{aligned}\right\} \tag{9.12}$$

and we could simply replace $\mathbf{R}^{-1}\mathbf{MS}$ by the symbol $\mathbf{M}$.

We further assume that $l_1 \leqslant l_2$. If $l_1 > l_2$, we merely take the transpose of Eq. (9.11), and what follows applies without change. Noting that because the matrices are unitary, one has $\mathbf{D}^{(1)}(A_\varkappa)^\dagger = \mathbf{D}^{(1)}(A_\varkappa)^{-1} = \mathbf{D}^{(1)}(A_\varkappa^{-1})$, and $\mathbf{D}^{(2)}(A_\varkappa)^\dagger = \mathbf{D}^{(2)}(A_\varkappa^{-1})$, we obtain by taking the adjoint of (9.11)

$$\mathbf{D}^{(1)}(A_\varkappa^{-1})\mathbf{M}^\dagger = \mathbf{M}^\dagger\mathbf{D}^{(2)}(A_\varkappa^{-1}). \tag{9.13}$$

Since (9.11) holds for all group elements, and thus for $A_\varkappa^{-1}$, multiplication of (9.13) from the left with $\mathbf{M}$ gives

$$\mathbf{MD}^{(1)}(A_\varkappa^{-1})\mathbf{M}^\dagger = \mathbf{MM}^\dagger\mathbf{D}^{(2)}(A_\varkappa^{-1}) \tag{9.14}$$

$$\mathbf{D}^{(2)}(A_\varkappa^{-1})\mathbf{MM}^\dagger = \mathbf{MM}^\dagger\mathbf{D}^{(2)}(A_\varkappa^{-1}). \tag{9.15}$$

Thus the Hermitian matrix $\mathbf{MM}^\dagger$ commutes with all the matrices $\mathbf{D}^{(2)}(A_1)$, $\mathbf{D}^{(2)}(A_2), \cdots, \mathbf{D}^{(2)}(A_h)$ of the second irreducible representation. By Theorem 2, it must, therefore, be a multiple of the unit matrix

$$\mathbf{MM}^\dagger = c\mathbf{1}. \tag{9.16}$$

If the dimension of the two representations $\mathbf{D}^{(1)}$ and $\mathbf{D}^{(2)}$ is the same, there are two possibilities. Either $c \neq 0$, in which case the determinant $|c\mathbf{1}| = c^l$ is not zero, which implies that the determinant of $\mathbf{M}$ is not zero and that $\mathbf{M}$ has a reciprocal; or $c = 0$, in which case $\mathbf{MM}^\dagger = 0$ and $\mathbf{M}$ is the null matrix. To check this, just write out

$$(\mathbf{MM}^\dagger)_{ij} = \sum_k \mathbf{M}_{ik}\mathbf{M}_{jk}^* = 0 \tag{9.17}$$

and set $i = j$ to obtain

$$\sum_k |\mathbf{M}_{ik}|^2 = 0, \tag{9.18}$$

from which it follows that $\mathbf{M}_{ik} = 0$, since no $|\mathbf{M}_{ik}|^2$ can be negative, and (9.18) prohibits any one from being positive. This establishes the theorem for the case $l_1 = l_2$.

On the other hand, if the dimension of the two representations is not the same, then **M** is not square, but rectangular. However, we can make it a square matrix merely by filling in zeros.

$$\mathbf{N} = \begin{pmatrix} \mathbf{M}_{11} & \mathbf{M}_{12} & \cdots & \mathbf{M}_{1a} & 0 & \cdots & 0 \\ \mathbf{M}_{21} & \mathbf{M}_{22} & \cdots & \mathbf{M}_{2a} & 0 & \cdots & 0 \\ \cdot & \cdot & & \cdot & \cdot & & \cdot \\ \cdot & \cdot & & \cdot & \cdot & & \cdot \\ \cdot & \cdot & & \cdot & \cdot & & \cdot \\ \mathbf{M}_{b1} & \mathbf{M}_{b2} & \cdots & \mathbf{M}_{ba} & 0 & \cdots & 0 \end{pmatrix}. \tag{9.19}$$

This process maintains $\mathbf{MM}^\dagger = \mathbf{NN}^\dagger$. The determinant of **N** as well as that of $\mathbf{NN}^\dagger = \mathbf{MM}^\dagger$ is obviously zero. Thus the c in (9.16) vanishes, so that again (9.17) and (9.18) hold true. This completely establishes Theorem 3.

Theorem 1a. If two arbitrary representations of the same group, $\mathbf{A}_1, \mathbf{A}_2, \cdots, \mathbf{A}_h$ and $\mathbf{B}_1, \mathbf{B}_2, \cdots, \mathbf{B}_h$, are unitary and equivalent, which is to say that a matrix **M** *of any kind* exists such that

$$\mathbf{MA}_\varkappa \mathbf{M}^{-1} = \mathbf{B}_\varkappa \qquad (\varkappa = 1, 2, \cdots, h), \tag{9.20}$$

then the representations can also be transformed into one another by a *unitary* transformation. That is, there exists a *unitary* matrix **U** such that

$$\mathbf{UA}_\varkappa \mathbf{U}^{-1} = \mathbf{B}_\varkappa \qquad (\varkappa = 1, 2, \cdots, h). \tag{9.21}$$

To prove this theorem, we seek a matrix **K** which commutes with all $\mathbf{B}_\varkappa$, and such that the product $\mathbf{U} = \mathbf{KM}$ is unitary. Once such a matrix is found, we shall have, from (9.20),

$$\left.\begin{aligned} \mathbf{B}_\varkappa = \mathbf{KB}_\varkappa\mathbf{K}^{-1} &= \mathbf{KMA}_\varkappa\mathbf{M}^{-1}\mathbf{K}^{-1} = (\mathbf{KM})\mathbf{A}_\varkappa(\mathbf{KM})^{-1} \\ &= \mathbf{UA}_\varkappa\mathbf{U}^{-1} \end{aligned}\right\} \tag{9.21a}$$

and the theorem will be proven.

From (9.20),

$$\mathbf{MA}_\varkappa = \mathbf{B}_\varkappa\mathbf{M} \qquad (\varkappa = 1, 2, \cdots, h), \tag{9.22}$$

and thence, just as before, it follows that $\mathbf{MM}^\dagger$ commutes with all matrices of the second representation

$$\mathbf{B}_\varkappa\mathbf{MM}^\dagger = \mathbf{MM}^\dagger\mathbf{B}_\varkappa \qquad (\varkappa = 1, 2, \cdots, h). \tag{9.22a}$$

Hence, a similarity transformation with $\mathbf{MM}^\dagger$ does not change the second representation. This suggests that the matrix $\mathbf{MM}^\dagger$, or some similar matrix, might meet our requirements for **K**. The requirement that **KM** be unitary is

$$\mathbf{M}^\dagger\mathbf{K}^\dagger\mathbf{KM} = \mathbf{1}, \quad \text{i.e.,} \quad \mathbf{K}^\dagger\mathbf{K} = (\mathbf{M}^\dagger)^{-1}(\mathbf{M})^{-1} = (\mathbf{MM}^\dagger)^{-1}. \tag{9.23}$$

Therefore, it is not $\mathbf{MM}^\dagger$ itself, which must be equal to **K**, but its $-1/2$ power.

We therefore follow the procedure used in the proof of Theorem 1 to construct $(\mathbf{MM}^\dagger)^{-1/2}$. We first transform $\mathbf{MM}^\dagger$ into diagonal form with a unitary matrix **V**.

$$\mathbf{V}^{-1}\mathbf{MM}^\dagger\mathbf{V} = \mathbf{d}; \qquad \mathbf{MM}^\dagger = \mathbf{V}\,\mathbf{d}\mathbf{V}^{-1}. \tag{9.24}$$

This can always be done, since $\mathbf{MM}^\dagger$ is Hermitian; moreover, all the diagonal elements of $\mathbf{d}$ are real and positive.[4] We can then construct the matrix $\mathbf{d}^{-1/2}$ which is also diagonal and has all positive, real elements. Finally, we transform with $\mathbf{V}^{-1}$ to obtain $\mathbf{K}$:

$$\mathbf{K} = \mathbf{V}\,\mathbf{d}^{-1/2}\mathbf{V}^{-1}. \tag{9.25}$$

We now demonstrate that $\mathbf{K}$ commutes with all $\mathbf{B}_\varkappa$, and that $\mathbf{KM}$ is unitary. Because of (9.22a) and (9.24),

$$\mathbf{B}_\varkappa \mathbf{V}\,\mathbf{d}\mathbf{V}^{-1} = \mathbf{V}\,\mathbf{d}\mathbf{V}^{-1}\mathbf{B}_\varkappa; \qquad \mathbf{V}^{-1}\mathbf{B}_\varkappa\mathbf{V}\,\mathbf{d} = \mathbf{d}\mathbf{V}^{-1}\mathbf{B}_\varkappa\mathbf{V}, \tag{9.26}$$

that is, the diagonal matrix $\mathbf{d}$ commutes with all $\mathbf{V}^{-1}\mathbf{B}_\varkappa\mathbf{V}$. Therefore, in all $\mathbf{V}^{-1}\mathbf{B}_\varkappa\mathbf{V}$, only zeros can occur at the intersections of those rows and columns whose diagonal elements in $\mathbf{d}$ are different. Then these matrices also commute with $\mathbf{d}^{-1/2}$, since in $\mathbf{d}^{-1/2}$ only those diagonal terms are different which were already different in $\mathbf{d}$. Therefore,

$$\mathbf{V}^{-1}\mathbf{B}_\varkappa\mathbf{V}\,\mathbf{d}^{-1/2} = \mathbf{d}^{-1/2}\mathbf{V}^{-1}\mathbf{B}_\varkappa\mathbf{V}; \qquad \mathbf{B}_\varkappa\mathbf{K} = \mathbf{K}\mathbf{B}_\varkappa, \tag{9.27}$$

and $\mathbf{K}$ actually does commute with all the representation matrices $\mathbf{B}_1, \mathbf{B}_2, \cdots, \mathbf{B}_h$.

Next, consider

$$\mathbf{UU}^\dagger = \mathbf{KMM}^\dagger\mathbf{K}^\dagger = \mathbf{V}\,\mathbf{d}^{-1/2}\mathbf{V}^{-1}\mathbf{MM}^\dagger\mathbf{V}^{-1\dagger}\,\mathbf{d}^{-1/2\dagger}\mathbf{V}^\dagger. \tag{9.28}$$

Because of (9.24), and since $\mathbf{V}$ is unitary and $\mathbf{d}^{-1/2}$ Hermitian (a real diagonal matrix),

$$\mathbf{UU}^\dagger = \mathbf{V}\,\mathbf{d}^{-1/2}\,\mathbf{d}\,\mathbf{d}^{-1/2}\mathbf{V}^\dagger = \mathbf{VV}^\dagger = \mathbf{1} \tag{9.29}$$

so that $\mathbf{U}$ is unitary. This proves Theorem 1a.

The importance of this theorem lies in the fact that it allows one to restrict himself to unitary similarity transformations, as long as the representations are unitary. Note that if all the representations in (9.20) are unitary and irreducible, $\mathbf{M}$ is, apart from a numerical factor, necessarily unitary. This follows from Theorem 2 when applied to (9.22a).

THEOREM 4. The fourth theorem, the most important of all in practice, is the orthogonality relation for the coefficients of an irreducible representation. *If*

$$\mathbf{D}^{(1)}(E), \mathbf{D}^{(1)}(A_2), \cdots, \mathbf{D}^{(1)}(A_h)$$

and

$$\mathbf{D}^{(2)}(E), \mathbf{D}^{(2)}(A_2), \cdots, \mathbf{D}^{(2)}(A_h)$$

are two inequivalent, irreducible, unitary representations of the same group, then

$$\sum_R \mathbf{D}^{(1)}(R)^*_{\mu\nu}\mathbf{D}^{(2)}(R)_{\alpha\beta} = 0 \tag{9.30}$$

holds for all elements $\mu\nu$ and $\alpha\beta$, where, as indicated, the summation extends over all group elements $E, A_1, A_2, \cdots, A_h$.[5] For the elements of a single unitary, irreducible representation, we have

$$\sum_R \mathbf{D}^{(1)}(R)^*_{\mu\nu}\,\mathbf{D}^{(1)}(R)_{\mu'\nu'} = \frac{h}{l_1}\,\delta_{\mu\mu'}\,\delta_{\nu\nu'}, \tag{9.31}$$

where h is the order of the group and l_1 the dimension of the representation.

[4] See the proof of Theorem 1, page 74.

[5] In what follows, R and S always denote group elements $E, A_2, \cdots, A_h$.

Theorem 4 obtains because the group property of the representation allows one easily to construct many matrices $\mathbf{M}$ satisfying Eq. (9.11) or (9.8). Equations (9.30) and (9.31) express the fact that a matrix which satisfies (9.11) must be a *null matrix*, and one which satisfies (9.8), a multiple of the *identity matrix*.

Because of the group property, all matrices of the form

$$\mathbf{M} = \sum_R \mathbf{D}^{(2)}(R)\mathbf{X}\,\mathbf{D}^{(1)}(R^{-1})$$

for arbitrary, l_2-rowed, l_1-columned $\mathbf{X}$ satisfy (9.11). The group property implies that

$$\sum_R \mathbf{D}^{(2)}(SR)\mathbf{X}\,\mathbf{D}^{(1)}(SR)^{-1} = \sum_R \mathbf{D}^{(2)}(R)\mathbf{X}\,\mathbf{D}^{(1)}(R)^{-1} = \mathbf{M},$$

since the very same matrices appear on the left and right, except in different order. Hence,

$$\mathbf{D}^{(2)}(S)\mathbf{M} = \sum_R \mathbf{D}^{(2)}(S)\mathbf{D}^{(2)}(R)\mathbf{X}\,\mathbf{D}^{(1)}(R)^{-1}$$
$$= \sum_R \mathbf{D}^{(2)}(SR)\mathbf{X}\,\mathbf{D}^{(1)}(SR)^{-1}\mathbf{D}^{(1)}(S),$$

or, more concisely,

$$\mathbf{D}^{(2)}(S)\mathbf{M} = \mathbf{M}\mathbf{D}^{(1)}(S). \tag{9.11a}$$

Then Theorem 3 states that $\mathbf{M}$ must be a *null matrix*, that is, for arbitrary $\mathbf{X}_{\varkappa\lambda}$,

$$\mathbf{M}_{\alpha\mu} = \sum_{\varkappa\lambda}\sum_R \mathbf{D}^{(2)}(R)_{\alpha\varkappa}\mathbf{X}_{\varkappa\lambda}\mathbf{D}^{(1)}(R^{-1})_{\lambda\mu} = 0.$$

By setting all the matrix elements $\mathbf{X}_{\varkappa\lambda} = 0$, except for one, $\mathbf{X}_{\beta\nu} = 1$, one obtains a generalized form of Eq. (9.30).

$$\sum_R \mathbf{D}^{(2)}(R)_{\alpha\beta}\mathbf{D}^{(1)}(R^{-1})_{\nu\mu} = 0, \tag{9.30a}$$

where $\mathbf{D}^{(2)}(R)$ and $\mathbf{D}^{(1)}(R)$ must be irreducible, but not necessarily unitary. If the matrices $\mathbf{D}^{(2)}(R)$ and $\mathbf{D}^{(1)}(R)$ are unitary,

$$\mathbf{D}^{(1)}(R^{-1}) = [\mathbf{D}^{(1)}(R)]^{-1} = \mathbf{D}^{(1)}(R)^{\dagger},$$

and (9.30a) reduces to (9.30).

To prove (9.31), we assume the form

$$\mathbf{M} = \sum_R \mathbf{D}^{(1)}(R)\mathbf{X}\,\mathbf{D}^{(1)}(R^{-1}),$$

where $\mathbf{X}$ is arbitrary. This $\mathbf{M}$ commutes with all $\mathbf{D}^{(1)}(S)$.

$$\mathbf{D}^{(1)}(S)\mathbf{M} = \sum_R \mathbf{D}^{(1)}(S)\mathbf{D}^{(1)}(R)\mathbf{X}\,\mathbf{D}^{(1)}(R^{-1})$$
$$= \sum_R \mathbf{D}^{(1)}(SR)\mathbf{X}\,\mathbf{D}^{(1)}[(SR)^{-1}]\mathbf{D}^{(1)}(S) = \mathbf{M}\,\mathbf{D}^{(1)}(S).$$

Thus, Theorem 3 requires that **M** be a multiple of the *unit* matrix; that is,

$$\sum_{\varkappa\lambda}\sum_{R}\mathbf{D}^{(1)}(R)_{\mu\varkappa}\mathbf{X}_{\varkappa\lambda}\mathbf{D}^{(1)}(R^{-1})_{\lambda\mu'} = c\,\delta_{\mu\mu'},$$

where c is independent of μ and μ' but can still depend on the $\mathbf{X}_{\varkappa\lambda}$. If we again choose one particular $\mathbf{X}_{\nu\nu'} = 1$, and let all other $\mathbf{X}_{\varkappa\lambda}$ vanish, we obtain

$$\sum_{R}\mathbf{D}^{(1)}(R)_{\mu\nu}\mathbf{D}^{(1)}(R^{-1})_{\nu'\mu'} = c_{\nu\nu'}\,\delta_{\mu\mu'},$$

where $c_{\nu\nu'}$ denotes the constant for this particular system of $\mathbf{X}_{\varkappa\lambda}$.

To determine the constant $c_{\nu\nu'}$, we set $\mu = \mu'$ and sum over μ from 1 to l_1. Then this expression becomes just the sum of the products $\mathbf{D}^{(1)}(R)\mathbf{D}^{(1)}(R^{-1}) = \mathbf{D}^{(1)}(E) = (\delta_{\nu\nu'})$.

$$\sum_{\mu}\sum_{R}\mathbf{D}^{(1)}(R^{-1})_{\nu'\mu}\mathbf{D}^{(1)}(R)_{\mu\nu} = \sum_{R}\mathbf{D}^{(1)}(E)_{\nu'\nu} = h\,\delta_{\nu\nu'} = \sum_{\mu} c_{\nu\nu'}\,\delta_{\mu\mu} = c_{\nu\nu'}l_1 .$$

Thus, $c_{\nu\nu'} = \delta_{\nu\nu'}(h/l_1)$. We therefore obtain a slightly generalized version of (9.31):

$$\sum_{R}\mathbf{D}^{(1)}(R)_{\mu\nu}\mathbf{D}^{(1)}(R^{-1})_{\nu'\mu'} = \frac{h}{l_1}\,\delta_{\mu\mu'}\,\delta_{\nu\nu'}, \qquad (9.31a)$$

which reduces to the form (9.31) for unitary representations.

The numbers

$$\mathbf{D}^{(1)}(A_1)_{\mu\nu} = \mathfrak{v}^{(\mu\nu)}_{A_1};\quad \mathbf{D}^{(1)}(A_2)_{\mu\nu} = \mathfrak{v}^{(\mu\nu)}_{A_2};\quad \cdots;\quad \mathbf{D}^{(1)}(A_h)_{\mu\nu} = \mathfrak{v}^{(\mu\nu)}_{A_h}$$

can be interpreted as the components of an h-dimensional vector $\mathfrak{v}^{(\mu\nu)}$, the components of which are labeled by the group elements. Then (9.31) states that the Hermitian length of this vector is $\sqrt{h/l_1}$, and that every pair of these l_1^2 vectors is orthogonal. Also, according to (9.30), the $\mathfrak{v}$ are orthogonal to all vectors $\mathfrak{w}$ which are obtained from some inequivalent, irreducible representation in analogous fashion:

$$\mathfrak{w}^{(\alpha\beta)}_{A_1} = \mathbf{D}^{(2)}(A_1)_{\alpha\beta},\ \cdots,\ \mathfrak{w}^{(\alpha\beta)}_{A_h} = \mathbf{D}^{(2)}(A_h)_{\alpha\beta}.$$

The representation of the symmetric group of three objects which we have already considered several times,

$$\left.\begin{aligned}
&\mathbf{D}(E) = \begin{pmatrix}1 & 0\\ 0 & 1\end{pmatrix};\quad \mathbf{D}(A) = \begin{pmatrix}1 & 0\\ 0 & -1\end{pmatrix};\quad \mathbf{D}(B) = \begin{pmatrix}-\frac{1}{2} & \frac{1}{2}\sqrt{3}\\ \frac{1}{2}\sqrt{3} & \frac{1}{2}\end{pmatrix},\\
&\mathbf{D}(C) = \begin{pmatrix}-\frac{1}{2} & -\frac{1}{2}\sqrt{3}\\ -\frac{1}{2}\sqrt{3} & \frac{1}{2}\end{pmatrix};\quad \mathbf{D}(D) = \begin{pmatrix}-\frac{1}{2} & \frac{1}{2}\sqrt{3}\\ -\frac{1}{2}\sqrt{3} & -\frac{1}{2}\end{pmatrix},\\
&\mathbf{D}(F) = \begin{pmatrix}-\frac{1}{2} & -\frac{1}{2}\sqrt{3}\\ \frac{1}{2}\sqrt{3} & -\frac{1}{2}\end{pmatrix},
\end{aligned}\right\} \qquad (7.E.1)$$

is irreducible. If it were reducible, all its matrices could be brought into diagonal form by the same similarity transformation, and thus all the matrices would have to commute, since they would be in diagonal form. This, however, is not the case, as can be seen, for example, from

$$\mathbf{D}(A)\mathbf{D}(B) = \mathbf{D}(D), \qquad \mathbf{D}(B)\mathbf{D}(A) = \mathbf{D}(F) \neq \mathbf{D}(D).$$

According to Theorem 2, only a multiple of the identity matrix can commute with all the matrices (7.E.1). In this simple example, we can see at once that only a diagonal matrix can commute with $\mathbf{D}(A)$, whereas a diagonal matrix can commute with $\mathbf{D}(B)$ only if the two diagonal elements are equal. Thus, commutation with $\mathbf{D}(A)$ and $\mathbf{D}(B)$ already limits us to multiples of the identity matrix. According to (9.31), the four vectors $\mathfrak{v}^{(11)}$, $\mathfrak{v}^{(12)}$, $\mathfrak{v}^{(21)}$, and $\mathfrak{v}^{(22)}$,

$$\begin{aligned}
&\mathfrak{v}_E^{(11)} = 1; \quad \mathfrak{v}_A^{(11)} = 1; \quad \mathfrak{v}_B^{(11)} = -\tfrac{1}{2}; \quad \mathfrak{v}_C^{(11)} = -\tfrac{1}{2};\\
&\qquad \mathfrak{v}_D^{(11)} = -\tfrac{1}{2}; \quad \mathfrak{v}_F^{(11)} = -\tfrac{1}{2}\\
&\mathfrak{v}_E^{(12)} = 0; \quad \mathfrak{v}_A^{(12)} = 0; \quad \mathfrak{v}_B^{(12)} = \tfrac{1}{2}\sqrt{3}; \quad \mathfrak{v}_C^{(12)} = -\tfrac{1}{2}\sqrt{3};\\
&\qquad \mathfrak{v}_D^{(12)} = \tfrac{1}{2}\sqrt{3}; \quad \mathfrak{v}_F^{(12)} = -\tfrac{1}{2}\sqrt{3}\\
&\mathfrak{v}_E^{(21)} = 0; \quad \mathfrak{v}_A^{(21)} = 0; \quad \mathfrak{v}_B^{(21)} = \tfrac{1}{2}\sqrt{3}; \quad \mathfrak{v}_C^{(21)} = -\tfrac{1}{2}\sqrt{3};\\
&\qquad \mathfrak{v}_D^{(21)} = -\tfrac{1}{2}\sqrt{3}; \quad \mathfrak{v}_F^{(21)} = \tfrac{1}{2}\sqrt{3}\\
&\mathfrak{v}_E^{(22)} = 1; \quad \mathfrak{v}_A^{(22)} = -1; \quad \mathfrak{v}_B^{(22)} = \tfrac{1}{2}; \quad \mathfrak{v}_C^{(22)} = \tfrac{1}{2};\\
&\qquad \mathfrak{v}_D^{(22)} = -\tfrac{1}{2}; \quad \mathfrak{v}_F^{(22)} = -\tfrac{1}{2}
\end{aligned}$$

must be mutually orthogonal. Thus, for example,

$$(\mathfrak{v}^{(11)}, \mathfrak{v}^{(12)}) = 1\cdot 0 + 1\cdot 0 + -\tfrac{1}{2}\tfrac{1}{2}\sqrt{3} + -\tfrac{1}{2}\cdot -\tfrac{1}{2}\sqrt{3} + -\tfrac{1}{2}\tfrac{1}{2}\sqrt{3} + -\tfrac{1}{2}\cdot -\tfrac{1}{2}\sqrt{3} = 0.$$

Also, the lengths of these vectors must be $\sqrt{h/l} = \sqrt{6/2} = \sqrt{3}$, as for example, in

$$(\mathfrak{v}^{(21)}, \mathfrak{v}^{(21)}) = 0^2 + 0^2 + \tfrac{3}{4} + \tfrac{3}{4} + \tfrac{3}{4} + \tfrac{3}{4} = 3.$$

To see an example of (9.30), consider the obviously irreducible representation (9.E.1) of the same group given on page 72:

$$\begin{aligned}
&\overline{\mathbf{D}}(E) = (1), \quad \overline{\mathbf{D}}(A) = (-1), \quad \overline{\mathbf{D}}(B) = (-1),\\
&\overline{\mathbf{D}}(C) = (-1), \quad \mathbf{D}(D) = (1), \quad \mathbf{D}(F) = (1),
\end{aligned} \tag{9.E.1}$$

and the trivial representation by the identity only:

$$\begin{aligned}
&\overline{\overline{\mathbf{D}}}(E) = (1), \quad \overline{\overline{\mathbf{D}}}(A) = (1), \quad \overline{\overline{\mathbf{D}}}(B) = (1)\\
&\overline{\overline{\mathbf{D}}}(C) = (1), \quad \overline{\overline{\mathbf{D}}}(D) = (1), \quad \overline{\overline{\mathbf{D}}}(F) = (1).
\end{aligned} \tag{9.E.3}$$

All four of the vectors $\mathfrak{v}$ must be orthogonal to the vector $\mathfrak{w}_R = \overline{\mathbf{D}}(R)_{11}$ and also to the vector $\mathfrak{z}_R = \overline{\overline{\mathbf{D}}}(R)_{11} = 1$. For example,

$$(\mathfrak{v}^{(22)}, \mathfrak{w}) = 1 \cdot 1 + -1 \cdot -1 + \tfrac{1}{2} \cdot -1 + \tfrac{1}{2} \cdot -1 - \tfrac{1}{2} \cdot 1 - \tfrac{1}{2} \cdot 1 = 0.$$

We now consider all the inequivalent irreducible representations of a group. The matrix $\mathbf{D}^{(1)}(R)$ has the dimension l_1; $\mathbf{D}^{(2)}(R)$ has the dimension

$l_2; \cdots ; \mathbf{D}^{(c)}(R)$ has the dimension l_c; all are assumed to be unitary. Then (9.30) and (9.31) can be summarized by

$$\left.\begin{aligned} &\sum_R \mathbf{D}^{(j)}(R)_{\mu\nu}\sqrt{\frac{l_j}{h}}\,\mathbf{D}^{(j')}(R)^*_{\mu'\nu'}\sqrt{\frac{l_{j'}}{h}} = \delta_{jj'}\,\delta_{\mu\mu'}\,\delta_{\nu\nu'} \\ &(\mu, \nu = 1, 2, \cdots, l_j;\ \mu', \nu' = 1, 2, \cdots, l_{j'};\ j, j' = 1, 2, \cdots, c). \end{aligned}\right\} \tag{9.32}$$

The $l_1^2 + l_2^2 + \cdots + l_c^2$ h-dimensional vectors in the space of the group elements

$$\mathfrak{v}_R^{(j,\mu,\nu)} = \mathbf{D}^{(j)}(R)_{\mu\nu}$$

are mutually orthogonal.

Since in a space of h dimensions, there can exist at most h orthogonal vectors, it follows that the sum of the squares of the dimensions of all inequivalent, irreducible representations $l_1^2 + l_2^2 + \cdots + l_c^2$ is at most equal to the order of the group represented. Actually, it can be shown that *the sum of the squares $l_1^2 + l_2^2 + \cdots + l_c^2 = h$ is exactly equal to the order of the group.* However, the proof of this theorem will be omitted here (cf. page 115).

We now develop Eq. (9.32) still further. We denote the diagonal sum, or trace, of the matrix $\mathbf{D}^{(j)}(R)$ by $\chi^{(j)}(R)$, so that

$$\chi^{(j)}(R) = \sum_{\mu=1} \mathbf{D}^{(j)}(R)_{\mu\mu}.$$

The set of numbers comprising the h quantities $\chi^{(j)}(E), \chi^{(j)}(A_2), \cdots, \chi^{(j)}(A_h)$ is called the *character* of the representation $\mathbf{D}^{(j)}(R)$. The specification of a representation by means of the character has the advantage that it remains *invariant under similarity transformations.* According to (9.32)

$$\sum_R \mathbf{D}^{(j)}(R)_{\mu\mu}\mathbf{D}^{(j')}(R)^*_{\mu'\mu'} = \frac{h}{l_j}\,\delta_{jj'}\,\delta_{\mu\mu'}.$$

Upon summation over μ from 1 to l_j, and over μ' from 1 to $l_{j'}$, this gives

$$\sum_R \chi^{(j)}(R)\chi^{(j')}(R)^* = \frac{h}{l_j}\,\delta_{jj'}\sum_{\mu=1}^{l_j}\sum_{\mu'}^{l_j'}\delta_{\mu\mu'} = \frac{h}{l_j}\,\delta_{jj'}\sum_{\mu=1}^{l_j} 1 = h\,\delta_{jj'}. \tag{9.33}$$

The characters $\chi^{(j)}(R)$ of the irreducible representations form an orthogonal vector system in the space of the group elements. From this it also follows that two inequivalent, irreducible representations cannot have the same character and that irreducible representations with equal characters are equivalent.

The Eq. (9.33) can be evolved somewhat further by comparing the characters $\chi^{(j)}(R)$ and $\chi^{(j)}(S)$ belonging to two elements R and S of the same class. There then exists a group element T which transforms R into S. But if $T^{-1}RT = S$, then $\mathbf{D}^{(j)}(T^{-1})\mathbf{D}^{(j)}(R)\mathbf{D}^{(j)}(T) = \mathbf{D}^{(j)}(S)$, so that $\mathbf{D}^{(j)}(R)$ can also be transformed into $\mathbf{D}^{(j)}(S)$. It follows that the trace $\chi^{(j)}(R)$ of the matrix $\mathbf{D}^{(j)}(R)$ is equal to the trace $\chi^{(j)}(S)$ of the matrix $\mathbf{D}^{(j)}(S)$. In a given representation, *elements of the same class have equal characters.*

Thus, in stating the set of characters, it suffices to give the character of one element of each class of the group. This can be considered the character of the class. If the entire group whose representation is being considered consists of k classes, say $C_1, C_2, \cdots, C_k$, and if these have $g_1, g_2, \cdots, g_k$ elements, respectively $(g_1 + g_2 + g_3 + \cdots + g_k = h)$, then the character of the representation is completely specified by the k numbers $\chi^{(j)}(C_1)$, $\chi^{(j)}(C_2), \cdots, \chi^{(j)}(C_k)$. We can introduce these numbers into (9.33) in place of the $\chi^{(j)}(R)$. When this is done, we can carry out the summation over the group elements by summing first over the g_ρ elements of the same class (the corresponding g_ρ terms are all equal), and then over all k classes.

$$\sum_{\rho=1}^{k} \chi^{(j)}(C_\rho)\chi^{(j')}(C_\rho)^* g_\rho = h\,\delta_{jj'},$$

or

$$\sum_{\rho=1}^{k} \chi^{(j)}(C_\rho)\sqrt{\frac{g_\rho}{h}} \cdot \chi^{(j')}(C_\rho)^* \sqrt{\frac{g_\rho}{h}} = \delta_{jj'}. \tag{9.34}$$

The normalized characters $\chi^{(j)}(C_\rho)\sqrt{g_\rho/h}$ form an orthonormal vector system in the k-dimensional space of the classes.

The Eqs. (9.30), (9.31), (9.33), (9.34) are the most important equations in representation theory and will be referred to again and again.

The characters of the representations (7.E.1), (9.E.1), and (9.E.3) are

$$\begin{array}{llllll}
\chi^{(E)} = 2; & \chi^{(A)} = 0; & \chi^{(B)} = 0; & \chi^{(C)} = 0; & \chi^{(D)} = -1; & \chi^{(F)} = -1 \\
\bar{\chi}^{(E)} = 1; & \bar{\chi}^{(A)} = -1; & \bar{\chi}^{(B)} = -1; & \bar{\chi}^{(C)} = -1; & \bar{\chi}^{(D)} = 1; & \bar{\chi}^{(F)} = 1 \\
\bar{\bar{\chi}}^{(E)} = 1; & \bar{\bar{\chi}}^{(A)} = 1; & \bar{\bar{\chi}}^{(B)} = 1; & \bar{\bar{\chi}}^{(C)} = 1; & \bar{\bar{\chi}}^{(D)} = 1; & \bar{\bar{\chi}}^{(F)} = 1
\end{array}$$

Since D, F and A, B, C are in the same classes, their characters are identical. The characters can, therefore, be summarized as follows:

$$\begin{array}{lll}
\chi^{(E)} = 2; & \chi^{(A,B,C)} = 0; & \chi^{(D,F)} = -1 \\
\bar{\chi}^{(E)} = 1; & \bar{\chi}^{(A,B,C)} = -1; & \bar{\chi}^{(D,F)} = 1 \\
\bar{\bar{\chi}}^{(E)} = 1; & \bar{\bar{\chi}}^{(A,B,C)} = 1; & \bar{\bar{\chi}}^{(D,F)} = 1
\end{array}$$

The normalized characters $\sqrt{g_\rho/h} \cdot \chi^{(l)}(C_\rho)$ are mutually orthogonal. As an example, for χ and $\bar{\chi}$

$$\sqrt{\tfrac{1}{6}}\,2\,\sqrt{\tfrac{1}{6}}\,1 + \sqrt{\tfrac{3}{6}}\,0 \cdot \sqrt{\tfrac{3}{6}} \cdot (-1) + \sqrt{\tfrac{2}{6}} \cdot (-1)\sqrt{\tfrac{2}{6}}\,1 = 0.$$

Since there exist at most k orthonormal k-dimensional vectors, it follows that the number c of inequivalent, irreducible representations is at most equal to the number k of classes in the group represented. In fact, one can show that the number of inequivalent, irreducible representations of a group is exactly equal to the number of classes in this group; that is, $c = k$.

We have already seen an example of this in the three representations of the symmetric group of three objects given on pages 81-82. The group consists of three classes E; A, B, C; and D, F and can have no irreducible representation other than those mentioned above. The dimensions of the representations are 2, 1, 1; and $2^2 + 1^2 + 1^2 = 6$ is indeed the order of the group.

Reduction of a representation. The preceding work dealt partly with reducible and partly with irreducible representations. Theorems 1 and 1a applied to arbitrary representations; Theorems 2, 3, and 4 (and Eqs. (9.30), (9.31), (9.33), and (9.34)) to irreducible representations.

The importance of irreducible representations rests on the fact that any representation can be decomposed into irreducible ones in a unique way. That is to say, any reducible representation can be brought into the form

$$\begin{pmatrix} \mathbf{D}^{(1)}(R) & \mathbf{0} & \cdots & \mathbf{0} \\ \mathbf{0} & \mathbf{D}^{(2)}(R) & \cdots & \mathbf{0} \\ \cdot & \cdot & & \cdot \\ \cdot & \cdot & & \cdot \\ \cdot & \cdot & & \cdot \\ \mathbf{0} & \mathbf{0} & \cdots & \mathbf{D}^{(s)}(R) \end{pmatrix} \tag{9.E.4}$$

by a similarity transformation with a suitably chosen "reducing" matrix, where the $\mathbf{D}^{(j)}(R)$ are now irreducible representations, the irreducible components of the original representation. Thus, unless a representation is already irreducible, it can be transformed into the form (9.E.2),

$$\bar{\mathbf{D}}(A_\varkappa) = \begin{pmatrix} \mathbf{D}'(A_\varkappa) & \mathbf{0} \\ \mathbf{0} & \mathbf{D}''(A_\varkappa) \end{pmatrix}, \tag{9.E.2}$$

which is to say that all its matrices can be transformed to this form. Then either both parts $\mathbf{D}'(A_\varkappa)$ and $\mathbf{D}''(A_\varkappa)$ are irreducible, or $\mathbf{D}''$, let us say, is reducible. In the latter case, one can subject $\bar{\mathbf{D}}(A_\varkappa)$ to a further transformation with

$$\begin{pmatrix} \mathbf{S} & \mathbf{0} \\ \mathbf{0} & \mathbf{T} \end{pmatrix}$$

which yields

$$\bar{\bar{\mathbf{D}}}(A_\varkappa) = \begin{pmatrix} \mathbf{S}^{-1}\mathbf{D}'(A_\varkappa)\mathbf{S} & \mathbf{0} \\ \mathbf{0} & \mathbf{T}^{-1}\mathbf{D}''(A_\varkappa)\mathbf{T} \end{pmatrix}.$$

If $\mathbf{D}''$ is reducible, $\mathbf{T}$ can be chosen so that $\mathbf{T}^{-1}\mathbf{D}''(A_\varkappa)\mathbf{T}$ has the form (9.E.2). Then $\bar{\bar{\mathbf{D}}}(A_\varkappa)$ has the form

$$\begin{pmatrix} \mathbf{D}'(A_\varkappa) & \mathbf{0} & \mathbf{0} \\ \mathbf{0} & \mathbf{D}'''(A_\varkappa) & \mathbf{0} \\ \mathbf{0} & \mathbf{0} & \mathbf{D}''''(A_\varkappa) \end{pmatrix}.$$

This can be further reduced, if at least one of the three representations $\mathbf{D}'$, $\mathbf{D}'''$, $\mathbf{D}''''$ is still reducible.

As the representation is of finite dimension, it must be possible in this way ultimately to bring it into the form (9.E.4), in which all the representations $\mathbf{D}^{(1)}, \mathbf{D}^{(2)}, \cdots, \mathbf{D}^{(s)}$ are irreducible. Since several successive similarity transformations can always be replaced by one, it is possible to bring the representation considered directly into the form (9.E.4) with a single similarity transformation. This process is called *reduction*, and (9.E.4) is referred to as the *reduced form*.

It is conceivable that upon the completion of this process of reduction, the irreducible parts $\mathbf{D}^{(1)}(R), \mathbf{D}^{(2)}(R), \cdots, \mathbf{D}^{(s)}(R)$ would not be determined uniquely (up to a similarity transformation), but rather that $\mathbf{D}(R)$ could be reduced in several ways. We can show that this is not the case. Just as an integer can be uniquely decomposed into a product of prime numbers, the irreducible components of a reducible representation are uniquely determined, except, of course, for order.

If reduction decomposes an arbitrary reducible representation into a_1 irreducible representations $\mathbf{D}^{(1)}(R)$ (with character $\chi^{(1)}(R)$), a_2 representations $\mathbf{D}^{(2)}(R)$ (with character $\chi^{(2)}(R)$), etc., then clearly

$$\chi(R) = \sum_{j=1}^{c} a_j \chi^{(j)}(R) \qquad (R = E, A_2, A_3, \cdots, A_h) \tag{9.35}$$

gives the characters of the reducible representation. But the h Eqs. (9.35) completely determine the numbers $a_1, a_2, \cdots, a_c$. If one takes the scalar product of (9.35) with $\chi^{(j')}(R)$, (i.e., multiplies it by $\chi^{(j')}(R)^*$ and sums over all group elements) one obtains (using (9.33))

$$\sum_R \chi(R)\chi^{(j')}(R)^* = \sum_R \sum_j a_j \chi^{(j)}(R)\chi^{(j')}(R)^* = h a_{j'}, \tag{9.36}$$

so that the whole number $a_{j'}$ is given uniquely by

$$a_{j'} = \frac{1}{h} \sum_R \chi(R)\chi^{(j')}(R)^*. \tag{9.37}$$

According to (9.37) *the number of times an irreducible representation appears in the reduced form of a representation is completely determined by the character of the representation. Thus, in particular, the irreducible components are independent of the procedure used in the reduction.*

Moreover, we see that two representations are equivalent if they have the same character. This implies that both will have the same form (9.E.4) after reduction, and will, therefore, be identical, except for the order of appearance of the $\mathbf{D}^{(j)}(R)$. Hence, two representations with equal characters can be transformed into equivalent reduced forms, and, therefore, are themselves equivalent.

On the other hand, the *equality of the characters* is *necessary* for the equivalence of the two representations. Thus, *it is the necessary and sufficient condition for their equivalence* (i.e., that they can be similarity-transformed into one another).

Two single matrices can be transformed into each other only if their eigenvalues are equal. The equality of the traces, that is, the equality of the *sums* of their eigenvalues is not sufficient. For two representations, however, it follows from the preceding discussion that if the sum of the eigenvalues is the same for all h pairs of corresponding matrices, the corresponding eigenvalues will be equal one by one. Even somewhat less is sufficient. Since the characters of all group elements of the same class are equal in each representation, the equality of the k numbers $\chi(C_1) = \chi'(C_1)$; $\chi(C_2) = \chi'(C_2)$; $\cdots$; $\chi(C_k) = \chi'(C_k)$ is sufficient for the equivalence of two representations with characters χ and χ'.

We will deduce one further formula dealing with the number of irreducible components contained in a representation. If we take the scalar product of (9.35) with itself, we obtain

$$\left.\begin{aligned}\sum_R |\chi(R)|^2 &= \sum_R \sum_j a_j\chi^{(j)}(R) \sum_{j'} a_{j'}\chi^{(j')}(R)^* \\ &= \sum_j \sum_{j'} h\, \delta_{jj'}a_j a_{j'} = h \sum_j a_j^2.\end{aligned}\right\} \tag{9.38}$$

The absolute square of the character of a representation is equal to the order of the group h multiplied by the sum of the squares of the number of times a_j that the individual irreducible representations are contained in this representation. For an irreducible representation, the sum

$$\sum_R |\chi(R)|^2 = h \tag{9.38a}$$

has the lowest possible value h; conversely, if (9.38a) holds, the representation with traces $\chi(R)$ is irreducible, since, by (9.38), it contains only one component after reduction.

In some cases, the general theorems given above suffice to determine the irreducible representations. Especially useful for this purpose are the theorems demonstrated partially on pages 83 and 84, giving the number of inequivalent representations (equal to the number of classes) and the sum of the squares of their dimensions (equal to the order of the group). In most cases, of course, extensive special investigation is also necessary.

As a particular case, note that each element of an Abelian group forms a class in itself, so that the group has as many classes as elements. Since the sum of the squares of the dimensions of all the representations of the group is equal to its order, each irreducible representation is of dimension one.

In addition, it should be noted that each representation of a factor group is also a representation of the whole group, as was stressed at the beginning of this chapter. For example, consider once again the symmetric group of three objects. This group has one invariant subgroup E, D, F; its factor group is of order 2. The factor group is, therefore, Abelian and has two representations of dimension one. Since the entire group has only three classes, it can have only one other irreducible representation, and this must be two-dimensional in order that $1^2 + 1^2 + 2^2 = 6 = h$.

The different irreducible representations play an especially important role in quantum mechanics, since they serve to characterize sets of states which have the same selection rules, behavior in external fields, etc. From the standpoint of pure mathematics, the theory given above, which began with S. Frobenius, H. Burnside, and I. Schur, is one of the most beautiful parts of algebra. The characters of representations also contain some interesting number-theoretic relations, which have not been discussed here.

10. Continuous Groups

1. So far, we have dealt only with finite groups, i.e., with groups with finite numbers of group elements. Our three group postulates (associative law, identity element, and inverses) can also be applied to infinite groups, that is, to an infinite manifold of elements. For example, the three-dimensional real orthogonal matrices, the rotations in space, constitute a system of objects which meet the group postulates, provided that group multiplication is made equivalent to matrix multiplication; in this system of objects, the compounding of two rotations gives rise to a single rotation, the product of the two. A similar group consists of all three-dimensional matrices with determinant 1, or with determinant ± 1, etc. All these groups are called *infinite* groups, in contrast to the *finite* groups considered previously.

If nothing more than the properties of groups already discussed were demanded, the concept of an infinite group would include too much for our purposes. For example, all two-dimensional matrices with determinant 1 which have rational numbers for all four elements do constitute such a group. Such a system would lack continuity properties which we wish to presuppose. We, therefore, narrow our discussion of infinite groups to continuous groups. A *continuous group* is a system of objects called group elements which can be characterized by parameters varying continuously in a certain region. Every set of values of the parameters within the region defines a group element; conversely, to every group element corresponds a set of values of the parameters within the specified region. These regions are called *group space;* there is a one-to-one correspondence between group elements and points in group space.

Group elements whose parameters differ only slightly from one another are said to be "adjacent." If the parameter changes continuously, we say that the group element changes continuously. The three group postulates remain valid, being supplemented by the requirement of continuity, under which it will be postulated that products and reciprocals of adjacent elements must also be adjacent.

We further assume that the parameters $p_1(RS)$, $p_2(RS)$, $\cdots$, $p_n(RS)$ of the product are at least *piecewise continuously differentiable* functions of the parameters $p_1(R)$, $p_2(R)$, $\cdots$, $p_n(R)$, and $p_1(S)$, $\cdots$, $p_n(S)$ of the two factors R and S. This is also required of the dependence of the parameters $p_1(R^{-1})$, $\cdots$, $p_n(R^{-1})$ upon the parameters of R.

Groups whose elements can be denoted by n parameters are known as n-parametric groups. The region of variability of the parameters can be simply or multiply connected, or can fall into several disjoint regions. In the latter case, we speak of a *mixed continuous group*, in contrast to a *simply continuous group* in which the region of variability of the parameters is connected.

We consider, for example, the group of rotations in three-dimensional space, the three-dimensional rotation group. An element of the group, a real three-dimensional orthogonal matrix, can be characterized, of course, by giving its nine elements. However, these cannot be considered as parameters, since they do not vary independently, but are subject to certain relationships among themselves. On the other hand, if the rotation is considered as characterized by the azimuth Φ, by the polar angle ϑ of the rotational axis, and by the angle of rotation φ, then a rotation corresponds to each triplet of values of these numbers lying in a certain region ($0 \leqslant \Phi \leqslant 2\pi$, $0 \leqslant \vartheta \leqslant \pi$, $0 \leqslant \varphi \leqslant \pi$). Conversely, to each rotation corresponds a set of values for these parameters.[1]

The one exception is the rotation with the rotation angle $\varphi = 0$, that is, the rotation which is, properly speaking, no rotation at all, but rather represents no change, or the identity of the group. It corresponds to every triplet of parameters $\Phi, \vartheta, 0$ so that the correspondence between these parameters and this group element is not unique. To obviate this difficulty, the range of variation of the other parameters, Φ and ϑ, could be considered to shrink to 0 when $\varphi = 0$. Similarly, $\Phi = 0$ must be specified if $\vartheta = 0$. Then the correspondence between rotations and triplets of parameters is unique. However, let us consider a continuous series of rotations of smaller and smaller angle about an arbitrary axis, i.e., the rotations with parameters $\Phi = \Phi_0, \vartheta = \vartheta_0, \varphi = t\varphi_0$, where t varies continuously. If for $t = 0$, the angles Φ and ϑ must also equal zero, a discontinuity occurs. Therefore, the naive requirement that $\Phi = 0$ and $\vartheta = 0$ for $\varphi = 0$ is not permissible, and we must seek another means to obviate the difficulty.

The most suitable parameters are probably the Cartesian coordinates ξ, η, ζ of the point whose polar coordinates are $\varphi/\pi, \vartheta, \Phi$; $\xi = (\varphi/\pi) \sin \vartheta \cos \Phi$, $\eta = (\varphi/\pi) \sin \vartheta \sin \Phi$, and $\zeta = \varphi/\pi \cos \vartheta$. The rest transformation, the identity of the group, which previously corresponded to the parameters Φ, ϑ, 0 now corresponds to a single point $\xi = \eta = \zeta = 0$, the origin of the coordinate system. The correspondence between points in parameter space and the rotations is illustrated in Fig. 1. Each rotation corresponds to one point in the unit sphere in $\xi\eta\zeta$-space.

In this parametrization an exception also occurs, in that the correspondence of group elements to triplets of parameters is not one-to-one. The two antipodes of the spherical surface must be identified, and the passage from one antipode of the spherical surface in $\xi\eta\zeta$-space to the other must not be considered a discontinuity in the path.

The parameter space has thus been made a *multiply-connected* one, with the result that the correspondence of group elements to points in parameter space is actually unique and one-to-one. These parameters are, therefore, especially advantageous for consideration of matters of *principle* concerning the rotation group.

Naturally, this in no way precludes the preference of other parameters for formal

[1] A point R of the parameter space does not correspond to the operation of rotation, but to its result. Hence, the rotation is completely determined by the initial and final positions of a sphere. If it is desired to describe the operation, that is, the path over which the rotation evolves, all the intermediate positions of the sphere must be given. Thus, a curve in parameter space, or a continuous sequence $R(t)$ of "rotations" which assumes the value $R(0) = E$ for $t = 0$ and goes into $R(1) = R$, is necessary to describe the rotation as an operation, i.e., the *way* in which the final position was attained.

calculations (e.g., the Euler angles, Fig. 2) in which the correspondence is not one-to-one, but in terms of which explicit formulas may be simpler.

2. That portion of the group which is adjacent to the identity is known as the *infinitesimal group*. The fundamental work of Sophus Lie[2] dealt with the

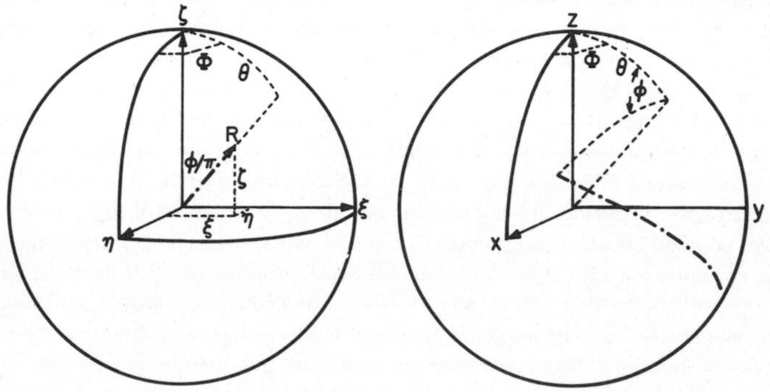

FIG. 1. The point of the arrow in the figure at the left corresponds to the rotation which transforms the solid arc in the figure at the right into the broken one.

infinitesimal groups of transformation groups. We can go into these investigations only superficially and will restrict ourselves to the basic facts, omitting all proofs of existence and convergence. In the case of the groups of

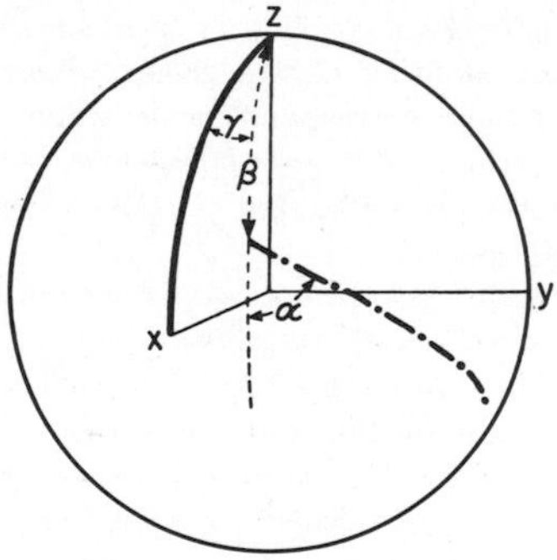

FIG. 2. The rotation in Fig. 1 which carries the solid arc into the dashed arc can also be characterized by the Euler angles α, β, and γ.

interest to us, the existence proofs can be replaced by explicit exhibition of the "infinitesimal elements."

In the following, h will be an infinitely small number. Let the parameters of the identity of the group be $\pi_1, \pi_2, \cdots, \pi_n$. Then we consider the n elements $F_1, F_2, \cdots, F_n$ with the parameters of F_k given by $\pi_1, \pi_2, \cdots, \pi_k + h, \pi_{k+1}, \cdots, \pi_n$. The elements $E, F_k, F_k^2, F_k^3, \cdots$ all lie in the same

[2] S. Lie, "Vorlesungen über kontinuierliche Gruppen mit geometrischen und anderen Anwendungen" (G. Scheffers, ed.), Teubner, Leipzig, 1893.

neighborhood if h is sufficiently small and thus form an almost continuous set of group elements. In order to arrive at a reasonable distance from the unit element of the group, one has to go to very high powers of F_k. Such a one-parametric family of (commuting!) group elements corresponds to the period of the elements of a finite group.

A simply-continuous, one-parametric group is always Abelian, since it consists of a single period.

In the parametrization of the three-dimensional rotation group which is illustrated in Fig. 1, the parameters of the identity are $\xi = \eta = \zeta = 0$; the three infinitesimal elements $\{h, 0, 0\}$, $\{0, h, 0\}$, and $\{0, 0, h\}$ are the three infinitely small angles of rotation about the three coordinate axes.

We consider now the n-parametric family $F_1^{p_1} F_2^{p_2} \cdots F_n^{p_n}$. We restrict ourselves to those values of h and $p_1, p_2, \cdots, p_n$ for which the elements of the family are all in the neighborhood of the identity; these then embrace the entire infinitesimal group, since it is n-parametric. It is advantageous, at least for the infinitesimal group, to introduce the $p_1, p_2, \cdots, p_n$ as parameters. The n parameters of the identity are all zero; the parameters of the elements of the infinitesimal group are very small.

The elements of the infinitesimal group commute. If the parameters of two factors R and S are of the order of magnitude of a small number ε, then the difference between the parameters of RS and SR is of order ε^2. Consider the elements $R(t)$ and $S(t')$ with parameters $tr_1, tr_2, \cdots, tr_n$ and $t's_1, t's_2, \cdots, t's_n$ where t and t' are continuous variables. That is, $E = R(0) = S(0)$ and t and t' are of the order ε. One can expand the parameters of $R(t)S(t')$ and $S(t')R(t)$ in a MacLaurin's series in t and t'. The series for the n parameters of $R(t)S(t')$ and of $S(t')R(t)$ will be of the form

$$u_1 + tv_1 + t'w_1 + \cdots; u_2 + tv_2 + t'w_2 + \cdots; \cdots; u_n + tv_n + t'w_n + \cdots$$

and

$$\bar{u}_1 + t\bar{v}_1 + t'\bar{w}_1 + \cdots; \bar{u}_2 + t\bar{v}_2 + t'\bar{w}_2 + \cdots; \cdots; \bar{u}_n + t\bar{v}_n + t'\bar{w}_n + \cdots.$$

To determine the u and $\bar{u}$, we set $t = t' = 0$. Then both products $R(0)S(0)$ and $S(0)R(0)$ equal E, and all the u and $\bar{u}$ are zero.

$$u_1 = u_2 = \cdots = u_n = \bar{u}_1 = \bar{u}_2 = \cdots = \bar{u}_n = 0.$$

To determine v and $\bar{v}$, we set only $t' = 0$; then $R(t)\,S(0) = R(t)E = R(t)$ and $S(0)R(t) = ER(t) = R(t)$. Therefore, $v_1 = \bar{v}_1 = r_1$; $v_2 = \bar{v}_2 = r_2$; $\cdots$; $v_n = \bar{v}_n = r_n$. Likewise, by setting $t = 0$, we obtain $w_1 = \bar{w}_1 = s_1$; $w_2 = \bar{w}_2 = s_2$; $\cdots$; $w_n = \bar{w}_n = s_n$. This shows that the parameters of the two products are the same up to the terms considered. The difference occurs only in terms in t^2, tt', or t'^2, and all these are of order ε^2.

The commutability of the infinitesimal elements to second order rests upon the fact that for arbitrary R, and $S = E$, as well as arbitrary S, and $R = E$, these commute exactly. If R differs only slightly from E, the commutation still holds approximately; likewise for $S \sim E$. But if $R \sim E$ and $S \sim E$ as well, then the commutability holds especially well.

This theorem takes a very simple form for matrix groups. The elements in the neighborhood of the identity have the form $\mathbf{1} + \varepsilon\mathbf{a}$. Then

$$(\mathbf{1} + \varepsilon\mathbf{a})(\mathbf{1} + \varepsilon\mathbf{b}) = \mathbf{1} + \varepsilon(\mathbf{a} + \mathbf{b}) + \varepsilon^2\mathbf{ab}$$

and

$$(\mathbf{1} + \varepsilon\mathbf{b})(\mathbf{1} + \varepsilon\mathbf{a}) = \mathbf{1} + \varepsilon(\mathbf{b} + \mathbf{a}) + \varepsilon^2\mathbf{ba},$$

and these differ only in terms in ε^2.

The above choice of parameters, which makes the elements $F_1^{p_1}F_2^{p_2} \cdots F_n^{p_n}$ correspond to the parameters $p_1, p_2, \cdots, p_n$ has the special property that the parameters of the product of two elements of the infinitesimal group can be obtained, up to terms of higher order, simply by *addition* of the parameters of the individual factors.

3. In a mixed continuous group, those elements which can be obtained continuously from the unit element E form a subgroup which is simply continuous. The statement that an element can be obtained continuously from the identity implies that a continuous manifold $R(t)$ of elements exists beginning at $R(0) = E$ and ending, for $t = 1$, at $R(1) = R$. If R and S are two elements of this manifold and $R(t)$ and $S(t)$ two corresponding paths, then the product $R(1)S(1) = RS$ can also be obtained from the identity in a continuous manner. The corresponding path might be $R(t)S(t)$. The same holds for the reciprocal of R, and the corresponding path is $R(t)^{-1}$. The elements attainable continuously from the identity, therefore, form a subgroup which is simply continuous since the corresponding region of parameter space is simply connected.

The elements attainable continuously from the identity even form an *invariant subgroup* of the mixed continuous group. For if R can be continuously reached from the identity, so can $X^{-1}RX$, along the path $X^{-1}R(t)X$, say. The cosets of this invariant subgroup are the other disjoint portions of parameter space. The factor group can thus be considered finite, of order equal to the number of disjoint regions of parameter space.

For what follows, we introduce the notation $\{r_1, r_2, \cdots, r_n\}$ for the *group element* with parameters $r_1, r_2, \cdots, r_n$. Then one has the notational identities $p_k(\{r_1, r_2, \cdots, r_n\}) = r_k$ and $\{p_1(R), p_2(R), \cdots, p_n(R)\} = R$.

4. The representation of a continuous group is defined exactly like that of a finite group. A correspondence exists between each element of the group and a matrix $\mathbf{D}(R)$ such that $\mathbf{D}(R)\mathbf{D}(S) = \mathbf{D}(RS)$. The continuity of the representation is the only added requirement. This requires that if R and S are neighboring group elements, then all l^2 matrix elements $\mathbf{D}(R)_{\varkappa\lambda}$ differ only infinitesimally from the corresponding matrix elements $\mathbf{D}(S)_{\varkappa\lambda}$. Here

again, we will restrict ourselves to representations with nonvanishing determinants.

We extend the theorems for the representations of finite groups to the representations of continuous groups. In this, we can begin from the fact that for the first four theorems, and in particular, for the orthogonality relationships (9.30) and (9.31), we used only one group property, namely, that a certain sum $\sum_R J_R$ can be formed for which

$$\sum_R J_R = \sum_R J_{SR}, \tag{10.1}$$

where the summations are extended over all group elements. In the above, the J_R are entirely arbitrary numbers (or matrices) which correspond to every group element R, and Eq. (10.1) holds for any element S. The same terms occur in both sums in (10.1) but in different order.

By means of one such sum $\sum_R \mathbf{D}(R)\mathbf{D}(R)^\dagger$, we have proven (Chapter 9, Theorem 1) that a representation can be made unitary. The orthogonality relationship (Chapter 9, Theorem 4) has also been established by consideration of such a sum $\sum_R \mathbf{D}^{(j)}(R)\mathbf{X}\,\mathbf{D}^{(j')}(R^{-1})$. Theorems 2 and 3 were more of a matrix theoretical nature. The extension of these requires no new group properties.

If we could define something similar to the sum $\sum_R J_R$ for continuous groups (naturally, this would be an integral taken over the entire range of the parameters), then the four theorems of representation theory for finite groups could be carried over to continuous groups.

5. In the case of finite groups, Eq. (10.1) rests on the fact that the sequence $SE, SA_2, SA_3, \cdots, SA_h$ for arbitrary S is identical except for order, with the sequence $E, A_2, A_3, \cdots, A_h$. We make the observation, a trivial one in the finite case, that if the group is parametrized in analogy to the continuous case, these two sequences have the property that the same number of group elements (one) corresponds to each volume element in parameter space (in this case, the "volume elements" are simply points corresponding to the discontinuous set of values the parameters would assume). The possibility of extending (10.1) to the continuous case depends, therefore, on the fact that we can retain this property in our generalization.

In Fig. 3 we exhibit the effect of the left multiplication with F on all elements of the group of permutations of three objects (7.E.1). Such a multiplication transforms every element into the element at the point of the arrow which starts at the element in question. The figure illustrates the fact that the set of elements FR is the same as the set of elements R if this set is a group. The same holds not only for F but for all elements S of the group. Equation (10.1) is an immediate consequence of this fact.

The same equation could at once be established for continuous groups if one could choose in them sets of elements with similar properties, and if a sequence of these sets could be chosen such that the density of group elements of the sets increases everywhere as one proceeds further and further along the sequence of sets. In other words, Eq. (10.1) could be easily established for continuous groups if a sequence of finite subgroups could be given, the elements of which form a denser and denser manifold in group space. This, unfortunately, is not possible (except in Abelian groups); continuous groups

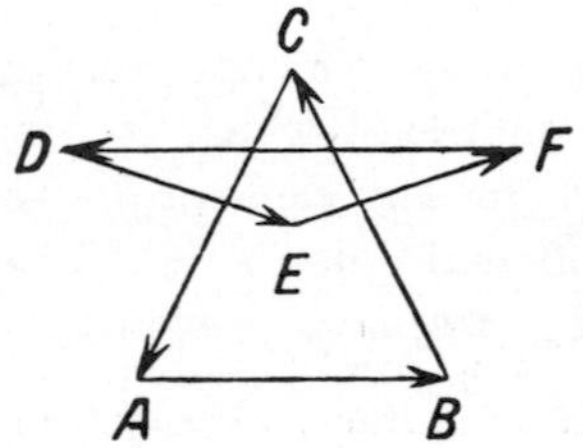

FIG. 3. Schematic representation of the effect of multiplying each element of the group of permutations of three objects (7.E.1) by the element F from the left.

cannot be considered in general as limiting cases of finite groups. Thus, for example, the largest finite subgroup of the group of rotations in three dimensions, the elements of which are spread out all over group space, is the symmetry group of the icosahedron, with only 60 elements. (The group of rotations in three dimensions has finite subgroups of order larger than 60. These are, however, symmetry groups of regular plane polygons and they do not fill the group space uniformly at all.)

Since most continuous groups cannot be regarded as limiting cases of finite groups, the analogue of the sums appearing in (10.1) must be found in another way. We shall fill group space densely with points. If these points are denoted by $R_1, R_2, \cdots$, it will be impossible to achieve in general that the set of points $SR_1, SR_2, \cdots$ be identical with the set of points $R_1, R_2, \cdots$ for all S which themselves are densely located in group space. However, it will be possible to distribute the points $R_1, R_2, \cdots$ in group space in such a way that the *density* of the points $SR_1, SR_2, \cdots$ be the same in all parts of group space as the *density* of the points $R_1, R_2, \cdots$ in the same part of group space. This will permit us to define a group integral for which the analogue of (10.1) holds. Thus, the picture of Fig. 10.3 will be replaced by another picture in which the arrowheads, representing the points $SR_1, SR_2, \cdots$ are not identical with the bases of the arrows, i.e., the points $R_1, R_2, \cdots$. However, the density of the arrowheads will be equal everywhere to the density of the points $R_1, R_2, \cdots$ with which we started. With such an "invariant distribution," for any continuous function in parameter space $J(R)$, the equality

$$\sum_i J(R_i) = \sum_i J(SR_i) \tag{10.2}$$

(where R ranges over all group space) is valid for continuous functions in group space because the number of group elements on the right side of (10.2) corresponding to a volume element in parameter space near $SR_i = Q_i$ is identical with the number of group elements R_i contained in the same volume element.

For analytical convenience, one replaces the sum on the left side of (10.2) by an integral

$$\int J(R)\, dR = \int J(R) g(R)\, dp_1, dp_2, \cdots, dp_n, \tag{10.2a}$$

where $p_1, p_2, \cdots, p_n$ are the parameters of the element R and the integration is to be extended over all values of the parameters which define group elements, i.e., over all group space. The weight function $g(R)$ is simply the density of the points R_i in the sum (10.2) in the neighborhood of R. The left side of (10.2a) is an abbreviation for the integral on the right side; it is called the *Hurwitz* or invariant integral in group space. It will follow from the invariant character of the density $g(R)$ that

$$\int J(SR)\, dR = \int J(R)\, dR \tag{10.2b}$$

holds for every continuous function J in group space (every continuous function of the group parameters) and every group element S.

What remains to be done is then to show that there is an invariant density in group space and to determine this density. We shall proceed in the opposite way: first a density will be determined assuming that it is invariant and then the invariant character of the distribution obtained will be demonstrated. Before undertaking the determination of the invariant distribution, it is well to note that this can be determined only to a constant factor; clearly, if a density $g(R)$ is invariant, every multiple of it will also be invariant. The density near one point can be chosen arbitrarily and we shall assume that the density near the unit element $g(E)$ is g_0.

Let us now consider a small volume element U in the neighborhood of the group element Q (see Fig. 4). If the size of this volume element is denoted by V, there are $g(Q)V$ summation points in it. Let us now apply the postulate of the invariance of the distribution with respect to left multiplication by Q^{-1}. The volume element U will then be transformed into a volume element U_0 (Fig. 4) containing all the points $Q^{-1}R$ where R is in U. Let us denote the volume of U_0 by V_0, then the number of summation points in U_0 must be equal to $g_0 V_0$ since U_0 is in the neighborhood of unity. The number of summation points $Q^{-1}R_i$ in the same volume element is, however, equal to $g(Q)V$ so that the requirement of invariance gives $g(Q)V = g_0 V_0$, or

$$g(Q) = (V_0/V) g_0 .$$

The weight function $g(Q)$ is proportional to the magnification which a volume element near Q undergoes when projected into the neighborhood of unity by left multiplication with Q^{-1}.

In order to calculate V_0/V, we assume that U consists of the group elements whose first parameter lies between q_1 and $q_1 + \Delta_1$, the second parameter between q_2 and $q_2 + \Delta_2, \cdots$, and whose nth parameter is between q_n

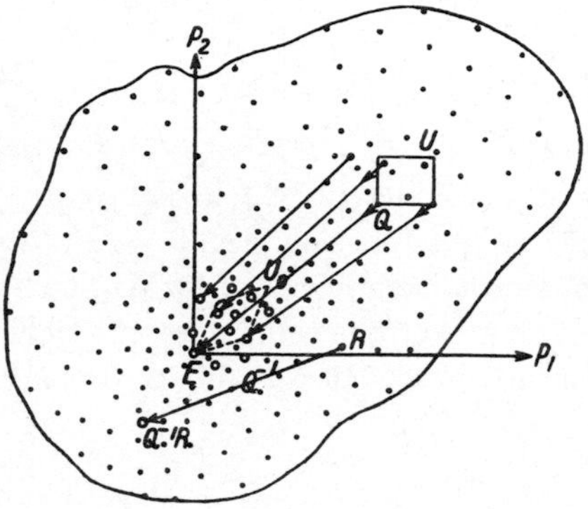

FIG. 4. The dots are the summation points R_i in (10.2); the locations into which these individual points are transformed by multiplication from the left by Q^{-1} are indicated with small circles. At the identity, the densities of dots and circles are equal.

and $q_n + \Delta_n$ where $q_1, q_2, \cdots, q_n$ are the parameters of Q. The volume of U is then

$$V = \Delta_1 \Delta_2 \cdots \Delta_n.$$

The volume of the region U_0 is, if we assume that the parameters of $E = Q^{-1}\{q_1, q_2, \cdots, q_n\}$ are zero, apart from higher order terms in the Δ's,

$$V_0 = \begin{vmatrix} p_1(Q^{-1}\{q_1 + \Delta_1, q_2, \cdots, q_n\}) \cdots p_n(Q^{-1}\{q_1 + \Delta_1, q_2, \cdots, q_n\}) \\ \cdot \qquad\qquad \cdot \\ \cdot \qquad\qquad \cdot \\ \cdot \qquad\qquad \cdot \\ p_1(Q^{-1}\{q_1, q_2, \cdots, q_n + \Delta_n\}) \cdots p_n(Q^{-1}\{q_1, q_2, \cdots, q_n + \Delta_n\}) \end{vmatrix}$$

$$= \Delta_1 \Delta_2 \cdots \Delta_n \frac{\partial[p_1(Q^{-1}\{r_1, \cdots, r_n\}), p_2(Q^{-1}\{r_1, \cdots, r_n\}), \cdots, p_n(Q^{-1}\{r_1, \cdots, r_n\})]}{\partial[r_1, r_2, \cdots, r_n]},$$

the last expression evaluated at $r_1 = p_1(Q) = q_1$; $r_2 = p_2(Q) = q_2; \cdots; r_n = p_n(Q) = q_n$. We recall that $\{q_1 \cdots q_n\}$ is the group element with the parameters $q_1, \cdots, q_n$ and $p_i(R)$ is the ith parameter of the group element R. When differentiating with respect to q_i, the group element Q must be considered to be a constant; only the r_i are variables.[3]

[3] The values $p_k(Q)$ for the r_k are introduced after carrying out the differentiation. Equation (10.3) is an expression of the type "$\frac{\partial}{\partial x} f(x, y)$ for $x = y$." If, for example, $f(x, y) = x^2 y^3$, then $\frac{\partial f(x, y)}{\partial x} = 2y^4$ for $x = y$.

This equality gives for $g(Q)$ the Jacobian,

$$g(Q) = g_0 \frac{\partial[p_1(Q^{-1}\{q_1, \cdots, q_n\}), \cdots, p_n(Q^{-1}\{q_1, \cdots, q_n\})]}{\partial[q_1, \cdots, q_n]} \tag{10.3}$$

evaluated at $q_1 = p_1(Q), \cdots, q_n = p_n(Q)$, the explicit formula for the density

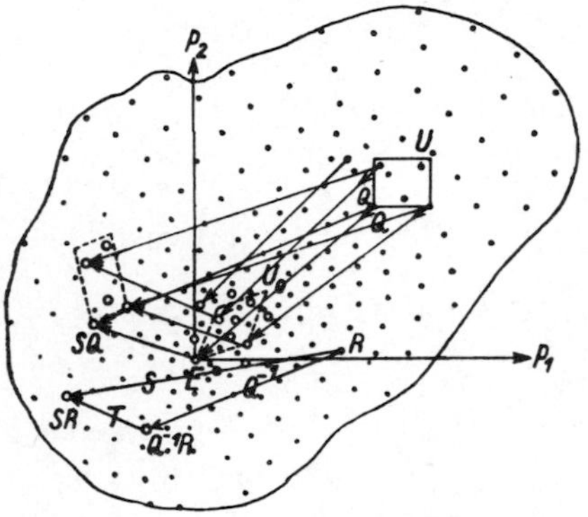

FIG. 5. This diagram illustrates in the manner of Fig. 4 the division of the substitution of SR for R into two steps: substitution of $Q^{-1}R$ for R and substitution of $SQQ^{-1}R$ for the resulting point.

which must be assumed at Q if the substitution of $Q^{-1}R_i$ for R_i is to leave the number of group elements in the neighborhood of the identity unchanged. Conversely, it can also be viewed as giving the density at Q after the substitution of QE for E, provided the density at the identity was g_0 before the substitution.

If the density of the points R_i is given by (10.3) at every point Q, the density of the points $Q^{-1}R_i$ will be g_0 at the unit element for every Q. Moreover, the density of the points QR_i will be given by (10.3) in the neighborhood of Q if that of the R_i is g_0 at E, because the transformation $R_i \rightarrow QR_i$ only returns the points whence they came. This also is valid for every Q. However, it has yet to be shown that the density of the points SR_i is given by (10.3) at every point $T = SQ$ if the density of the R_i is (10.3) at every point Q. In order to prove this, the transformation S will be decomposed into two factors $S = (SQ)Q^{-1}$. According to the first observation, the density of the points $Q^{-1}R_i$ will be g_0 at the unit element. Hence, the second observation can be applied to the distribution $Q^{-1}R_i$. This will be done with $SQ = T$ in place of Q, and shows that the density of the points $(SQ)Q^{-1}R_i$ is given by (10.3). Because of the associative law of group multiplication, the points $(SQ)Q^{-1}R_i$ are the points SR_i so that we have shown that the density of these points is given by (10.3) at the arbitrary point T if that of the R_i is given by the same equation. Figure 5 illustrates this proof, which is based, as the reader will note, on the validity of the associative law of multiplication.

It should also be noted that, if $J(R)$ is nowhere negative (i.e., for no R), then (10.2a) can vanish only when $J(R)$ is zero everywhere. This fact is important for the rederivation of the first theorem of the preceding chapter.

We now consider the explicit form of the Hurwitz invariant integral, and verify once more by direct calculation that the choice of the density function defined by (10.3) does actually reduce (10.2b) to an identity. The integral on the right of (10.2b) is

$$\int J(R)\, dR = \int \cdots \int J(\{r_1, \cdots, r_n\})g(\{r_1, \cdots, r_n\})\, dr_1 \cdots dr_n, \quad (10.4)$$

where the integration is to be taken over the entire region of variation of the parameters. We shall verify that

$$\left.\begin{aligned} \int J(R)\, dR &= \int \cdots \int J(\{r_1, r_2, \cdots, r_n\})g(\{r_1, r_2, \cdots, r_n\})\, dr_1 \cdots dr_n \\ = \int J(SR)\, dR &= \int \cdots \int J(S \cdot \{r_1, r_2, \cdots, r_n\})g(\{r_1, r_2, \cdots, r_n\})\, dr_1 \cdots dr_n \end{aligned}\right\} \quad (10.5)$$

is true for all elements S provided $g(R)$ is given by (10.3).

We first introduce new variables into the integral on the right side of (10.5); namely, the parameters $x_1, x_2, x_3, \cdots, x_n$ of the product

$$X = \{x_1, x_2, \cdots, x_n\} = SR = S \cdot \{r_1, r_2, \cdots, r_n\}.$$

That is,

$$x_k = p_k(S \cdot \{r_1, r_2, \cdots, r_n\}), \quad (10.6)$$

$$r_k = p_k(S^{-1} \cdot \{x_1, x_2, \cdots, x_n\}). \quad (10.6a)$$

The region of integration does not change since SR runs over the entire group just as did R. Then we obtain

$$\begin{aligned} \int J(SR)\, dR &= \int \cdots \int J(S \cdot \{r_1, r_2, \cdots, r_n\})g(\{r_1, r_2, \cdots, r_n\})\, dr_1 \cdots dr_n \\ &= \int \cdots \int J(\{x_1, x_2, \cdots, x_n\})g(R) \frac{\partial(r_1, r_2, \cdots, r_n)}{\partial(x_1, x_2, \cdots, x_n)}\, dx_1 \cdots dx_n, \end{aligned}$$

where R and the r_i are to be considered functions of the x_i, as given in (10.6a). If we now take $g(R)$ from (10.3), we can combine the two last factors of the integrand in accordance with the theorem on the Jacobians of implicit functions[4]

$$\left.\begin{aligned} g_0 \frac{\partial[\cdots p_k(R^{-1}\{r_1, \cdots, r_n\}) \cdots]}{\partial[\cdots r_k \cdots]} \frac{\partial(r_1, \cdots, r_n)}{\partial(x_1, \cdots, x_n)} \\ = g_0 \frac{\partial[\cdots p_k(R^{-1}\{r_1, \cdots, r_n\}) \cdots]}{\partial[\cdots x_k \cdots]} \end{aligned}\right\} \quad (10.7)$$

[4] If (10.7) holds for arbitrary values of r_k, it holds also for the value $r_k = p(R)$, which we need for (10.3).

evaluated at $r_1 = p_1(R), \cdots, r_n = p_n(R)$, where the R^{-1} is considered constant in differentiating with respect to x_i just as in (10.3), while the r_k are considered the functions (10.6a) of the x_i. Hence if $\{r_1, r_2, \cdots, r_n\} = S^{-1} \cdot \{x_1, x_2, \cdots, x_n\}$ is substituted into (10.7), it becomes (since $R^{-1}S^{-1} = X^{-1}$)

$$g_0 \frac{\partial[\cdots p_k(X^{-1}\{x_1, \cdots, x_n\}) \cdots]}{\partial[\cdots x_k \cdots]} = g(\{x_1, \cdots, x_n\}),$$

evaluated[5] at $x_1 = p_1(X), \cdots, x_n = p_n(X)$. Thus the right side of (10.5) is, in fact, identical with the left, except for the labeling of the variables of integration.

We can rewrite (10.3) by using the equation $Q^{-1} \cdot \{q_1, q_2, \cdots, q_n\} = \{e_1, e_2, \cdots, e_n\} = E$ to introduce new variables e for the q, which we look upon for the moment as varying freely (whereas Q is a constant group element). The theorem concerning the Jacobian of implicit functions gives

$$\frac{\partial[\cdots p_k(\{e_1, e_2, \cdots, e_n\}) \cdots]}{\partial[\cdots e_k \cdots]} = \frac{\partial[\cdots p_k(Q^{-1} \cdot \{q_1, \cdots, q_n\}) \cdots]}{\partial[\cdots q_k \cdots]} \frac{\partial[\cdots q_k \cdots]}{\partial[\cdots e_k \cdots]}$$

where the q_k are the functions $q_k = p_k(Q\{e_1, e_2, \cdots, e_n\})$ of the e_k. Since $p_k(\{e_1, e_2, \cdots, e_n\}) = e_k$, the left side is simply equal to 1, and we obtain by expressing the q_k in terms of the e_k

$$\left.\begin{aligned} \frac{\partial[\cdots p_k(Q^{-1}\{q_1 \cdots q_n\}) \cdots]}{\partial[\cdots q_k \cdots]} &= \left[\frac{\partial(\cdots q_k \cdots)}{\partial(\cdots e_k \cdots)}\right]^{-1} \\ &= \left[\frac{\partial[\cdots p_k(Q\{e_1 \cdots e_n\}) \cdots]}{\partial[\cdots e_k \cdots]}\right]^{-1}. \end{aligned}\right\} \tag{10.8}$$

The value of the expression on the left at $q_k = p_k(Q)$ is equal to the value of the right side at $e_k = p_k(E)$. Then we can write for (10.3)

$$g(Q) = g_0 \left[\frac{\partial[p_1(Q \cdot \{e_1, \cdots, e_n\}), \cdots, p_n(Q \cdot \{e_1, \cdots, e_n\})]}{\partial[e_1, \cdots, e_n]}\right]^{-1} \tag{10.9}$$

evaluated at $e_1 = p_1(E), \cdots, e_n = p_n(E)$. (For an example, see page 151.)

The actual calculation of the density function $g(R)$ for the Hurwitz integral is often quite laborious if done directly by (10.3) or (10.9). For many purposes, in particular for the derivation of the orthogonality relations of Chapter 9 for continuous groups, the knowledge of the *existence* of the invariant integral is all that is needed.

6. For mixed continuous groups, the Hurwitz integral can be expressed in terms of the Hurwitz integral for the part of the group which is connected

[5] The values $p_k(X)$ for the x_k are introduced here after the differentiation.

with the unit element. We denote the region connected with the identity by $\mathcal{G}_1$ and the other connected regions by $\mathcal{G}_2, \mathcal{G}_3, \cdots, \mathcal{G}_\rho$.

The elements of $\mathcal{G}_1$ form a subgroup (actually an invariant subgroup) of which the $\mathcal{G}_\nu$ are the cosets, as we have seen on page 92. If we take one arbitrary element, say A_ν, from each of the regions $\mathcal{G}_\nu$, then by multiplication with A_ν, the region $\mathcal{G}_1$ can be projected into $\mathcal{G}_\nu$. Since the weights of the regions which can be projected into one another are equal, the integral

$$\left.\begin{aligned} &\int_{\mathcal{G}_1} [J(R) + J(A_2R) + \cdots + J(A_\rho R)]\,dR \\ &= \int_{\mathcal{G}_1} [J(SR) + J(SA_2R) + \cdots + J(SA_\rho R)]\,dR \end{aligned}\right\} \tag{10.10}$$

taken over $\mathcal{G}_1$ is invariant under multiplication of the group elements by an arbitrary group element S. Thus, the Hurwitz integral for the whole group is invariant if $\int_{\mathcal{G}_1} \cdots dR$ denotes the Hurwitz integral for the simply continuous subgroup $\mathcal{G}_1$.

Since $A_\nu R$ ranges over the elements of the coset $\mathcal{G}_\nu$ as R ranges over the subgroup $\mathcal{G}_1$, one term on the left of (10.10) stands for each coset of $\mathcal{G}_1$. But the right side of (10.10) also contains one term for each coset; the coset $\mathcal{G}_\nu = A_\nu\mathcal{G}_1$ is represented by the term involving $SA_\mu R$, provided $\mathcal{G}_\mu = A_\mu\mathcal{G}_1$ is the coset which contains $S^{-1}A_\nu$. We shall show that

$$\int_{\mathcal{G}_1} J(A_\nu R)\,dR = \int_{\mathcal{G}_1} J(SA_\mu R)\,dR, \tag{10.11}$$

which implies that the terms on the two sides of (10.10) are equal one by one.

Let the coset $A_\mu\mathcal{G}_1$ contain $S^{-1}A_\nu$. Let $A_\mu T = S^{-1}A_\nu$, that is, $A_\mu = S^{-1}A_\nu T^{-1}$, where T is contained in the subgroup $\mathcal{G}_1$. Then substitution of this expression into (10.11) gives

$$\int_{\mathcal{G}_1} J(A_\nu R)\,dR = \int_{\mathcal{G}_1} J(S \cdot S^{-1}A_\nu T^{-1}R)\,dR = \int_{\mathcal{G}_1} J(A_\nu T^{-1}R)\,dR.$$

This equation is certainly true, since its right side differs from its left only in that $T^{-1}R$ occurs instead of R, and by hypothesis, the Hurwitz integral over $\mathcal{G}_1$ is invariant under this substitution (T^{-1} is an element of $\mathcal{G}_1$).

This establishes the equivalence of the expression (10.10) with the Hurwitz integral for the entire mixed continuous group, and at the same time, reduces it to an integral which is taken only over that part of the group which is simply connected with the identity. (This whole argument holds, of course, not only for $\mathcal{G}_1$ but also for every subgroup with finite index.)

7. From (10.5) it follows in exactly the same way as for finite groups that every representation can be transformed into a unitary representation (Chapter 9, Theorem 1), provided the integral

$$\int \mathbf{D}(R)_{\varkappa\lambda}\,\mathbf{D}(R)^*_{\mu\lambda}\,dR$$

converges. This is always the case if the volume of the group $\int dR$ is finite—as in the rotation group. The orthogonality relationship for the representation coefficients (Chapter 9, Theorem 4) takes the form

$$\int \mathbf{D}^{(\nu)}(R)^*_{\varkappa\lambda}\,\mathbf{D}^{(\nu')}(R)_{\varkappa'\lambda'}\,dR = \frac{\delta_{\nu\nu'}\,\delta_{\varkappa\varkappa'}\,\delta_{\lambda\lambda'}}{l_\nu}\int dR, \tag{10.12}$$

where l_ν is the dimension of the representation $\mathbf{D}^{(\nu)}(R)$. Correspondingly, the orthogonality equation, (9.33), for the characters becomes

$$\int \chi^{(\nu)}(R)^*\chi^{(\nu')}(R)\,dR = \delta_{\nu\nu'}\int dR. \tag{10.13}$$

11. Representations and Eigenfunctions

1. We consider the Schrödinger equation $\mathbf{H}\psi = E\psi$ of a system composed of two *identical particles*. For simplicity, assume that the particles have only one degree of freedom, and let the corresponding coordinates be x and y. Then

$$\mathbf{H}\psi = -\frac{\hbar^2}{2m}\left(\frac{\partial^2}{\partial x^2} + \frac{\partial^2}{\partial y^2}\right)\psi(x, y) + V(x, y)\psi(x, y) = E\psi(x, y), \tag{11.1}$$

where m is the mass of each particle. Because the particles are identical, the potential energy must be the same when the first particle is at the position a and the second at the position b, as it is when the first is at b and the second at a. That is, for all values of a and b

$$V(a, b) = V(b, a). \tag{11.2}$$

We assume that (11.1) has a discrete spectrum and that $\psi_\varkappa(x, y)$ belongs to a discrete eigenvalue $E_\varkappa$. Assume also that no other linearly independent eigenfunction belongs to this eigenvalue; that is, the most general solution of the differential equation for $\psi_\varkappa$,

$$\mathbf{H}\psi_\varkappa = E_\varkappa \psi_\varkappa, \tag{11.3}$$

which vanishes if either x or y are $+\infty$ or $-\infty$, is a constant multiple of $\psi_\varkappa$.

Consider the function $\mathbf{P}\psi_\varkappa = \bar{\psi}_\varkappa$ which is defined so that, for all values of a and b,

$$\mathbf{P}\psi_\varkappa(a, b) = \bar{\psi}_\varkappa(a, b) = \psi_\varkappa(b, a). \tag{11.4}$$

We will show that $\bar{\psi}_\varkappa(a, b)$ is also a solution of the differential equation (11.3). For the moment, we denote the derivative of a function $f(x, y)$ with respect to the first variable by $f^{(1)}(x, y)$, and with respect to the second variable by $f^{(2)}(x, y)$. That is,

$$\left.\begin{aligned} \frac{\partial f(x, y)}{\partial x} &= f^{(1)}(x, y), \qquad \frac{\partial f(x, y)}{\partial y} = f^{(2)}(x, y), \\ \frac{\partial^2 f(x, y)}{\partial x^2} &= \frac{\partial f^{(1)}(x, y)}{\partial x} = f^{(1)(1)}(x, y), \end{aligned}\right\} \tag{11.5}$$

etc. Also,

$$\frac{\partial f(y, x)}{\partial x} = f^{(2)}(y, x), \qquad \frac{\partial f(y, x)}{\partial y} = f^{(1)}(y, x).$$

Thus differentiation of (11.4) with respect to a and b yields

$$\left.\begin{aligned}\bar{\psi}_\varkappa^{(1)}(a, b) &= \psi_\varkappa^{(2)}(b, a), \qquad & \bar{\psi}_\varkappa^{(1)(1)}(a, b) &= \psi_\varkappa^{(2)(2)}(b, a),\\ \bar{\psi}_\varkappa^{(2)}(a, b) &= \psi_\varkappa^{(1)}(b, a), \qquad & \bar{\psi}_\varkappa^{(2)(2)}(a, b) &= \psi_\varkappa^{(1)(1)}(b, a).\end{aligned}\right\} \tag{11.6}$$

We now calculate

$$\left.\begin{aligned}\mathbf{H}\bar{\psi}_\varkappa(x, y) &= -\frac{\hbar^2}{2m}\left(\frac{\partial^2}{\partial x^2} + \frac{\partial^2}{\partial y^2}\right)\bar{\psi}_\varkappa(x, y) + V(x, y)\bar{\psi}_\varkappa(x, y)\\ &= -\frac{\hbar^2}{2m}[\bar{\psi}_\varkappa^{(1)(1)}(x, y) + \bar{\psi}_\varkappa^{(2)(2)}(x, y)] + V(x, y)\bar{\psi}_\varkappa(x, y).\end{aligned}\right\} \tag{11.7}$$

Using (11.6), (11.4), (11.2), and (11.3), we obtain the equation

$$\left.\begin{aligned}\mathbf{H}\bar{\psi}_\varkappa(x, y) &= -\frac{\hbar^2}{2m}[\psi_\varkappa^{(2)(2)}(y, x) + \psi_\varkappa^{(1)(1)}(y, x)] + V(y, x)\psi_\varkappa(y, x)\\ &= E_\varkappa\psi_\varkappa(y, x) = E_\varkappa\bar{\psi}_\varkappa(x, y).\end{aligned}\right\} \tag{11.8}$$

Thus $\mathbf{P}\psi_\varkappa(x, y) = \bar{\psi}_\varkappa(x, y)$ is also a solution to the differential equation (11.3), satisfying the boundary conditions at $\pm\infty$. It must be, therefore, a constant multiple of $\psi_\varkappa(x, y)$.

$$\bar{\psi}_\varkappa(x, y) = c\psi_\varkappa(x, y). \tag{11.9}$$

To determine c, we observe that because of (11.4),

$$c\psi_\varkappa(a, b) = \bar{\psi}_\varkappa(a, b) = \psi_\varkappa(b, a) \tag{11.10}$$

for all values of a and b. If we first write (11.10) for the pair of values y, x and then for the pair x, y,

$$c\psi_\varkappa(y, x) = \psi_\varkappa(x, y); \qquad c\psi_\varkappa(x, y) = \psi_\varkappa(y, x), \tag{11.11}$$

we obtain

$$c^2\psi_\varkappa(x, y) = \psi_\varkappa(x, y),$$

and since $\psi_\varkappa(x, y)$ is not identically zero, $c^2 = 1$; $c = \pm 1$. Thus we have, identically in x and y,

$$\bar{\psi}_\varkappa(x, y) = \psi_\varkappa(y, x) = \pm\psi_\varkappa(x, y). \tag{11.12}$$

The eigenfunction $\psi_\varkappa(x, y)$ at the point x, y has a value either equal to, or the negative of, its value at the point y, x. Whether the first or the second case occurs cannot be determined from general considerations; however for any given function $\psi_\varkappa(x, y)$ which meets the stated conditions (i.e., for any specific eigenvalue), only one of the two possibilities can be true. Eigenvalues or eigenfunctions for which the + sign in (11.12) applies are known as *symmetric eigenvalues* or *eigenfunctions*; those for which the — sign applies are *anti-symmetric*. We therefore obtain a qualitative classification of the eigenvalues and eigenfunctions of the Schrödinger equation into two classes. depending on whether they obey Eq. (11.12) with the + or the — sign.

An entirely analogous, but somewhat simpler, line of reasoning can be applied to the eigenvalue equation

$$\frac{-\hbar^2}{2m}\frac{\partial^2\psi(x)}{\partial x^2} + V(x)\psi(x) = E\psi(x), \tag{11.13}$$

where

$$V(x) = V(-x) \tag{11.14}$$

if one defines

$$\mathbf{P}\psi(x) = \psi(-x). \tag{11.15}$$

This yields, instead of (11.12),

$$\psi(x) = \pm\psi(-x). \tag{11.16}$$

This is simply a statement of the well-known fact that all eigenfunctions are either even or odd functions of x.

2. We shall extend these considerations to the more general case of a discrete eigenvalue with several (although only a finite number) linearly independent eigenfunctions.[1] In this process, we shall replace calculations with conceptual considerations wherever possible; it is clear that the special form of the Hamiltonian operator in (11.1) and (11.13) is unessential, and that only the equivalence of the two particles enters in the first case, and only that of the two directions, $+X$ and $-X$, in the second. We shall obtain relations analogous to (11.12) and (11.16) which, like these, present alternatives: the eigenfunctions of each eigenvalue satisfy one of several sets of equations—the eigenvalues whose eigenfunctions satisfy the same set of equations have similar properties. The distinction between the eigenvalues whose eigenfunctions satisfy different equations forms the basis for the "level zoology."

The considerations which have led us to (11.12) rest on the fact that (11.1) is invariant under the transformation

$$x' = y, \qquad y' = x. \tag{11.17}$$

This implies that the function[2] $\mathbf{P}\psi_\varkappa$ defined by the equation

$$\mathbf{P}\psi_\varkappa(a, b) = \psi_\varkappa(b, a)$$

which holds identically in a and b, is a solution of the equation $\mathbf{H}\psi = E\psi$ provided only that $\psi_\varkappa$ is a solution.

[1] The emphasis here is on "finite number" not on "discrete." The entire theory can be applied almost without change to the "discrete complex eigenvalues" with which the Gamow theory of nuclear disintegration deals, although these are not discrete in the sense used here, since the square integral of the corresponding eigenfunctions diverges.

[2] $\mathbf{P}\psi$ is the symbol for a function, just as the usual f or g is such a symbol; $\mathbf{P}\psi(x, y)$ is the value of this function at the point x, y. Thus (11.19), for example, means that $\mathbf{P_R}f$ at the point $x_1', x_2', \cdots, x_n'$ has the same value as the function f at the point $x_1, x_2, \cdots, x_n$.

To generalize the procedure, let $\mathbf{R}$ be a real orthogonal transformation

$$\left.\begin{aligned} x_1' &= \mathbf{R}_{11}x_1 + \mathbf{R}_{12}x_2 + \cdots + \mathbf{R}_{1n}x_n \\ x_2' &= \mathbf{R}_{21}x_1 + \mathbf{R}_{22}x_2 + \cdots + \mathbf{R}_{2n}x_n \\ &\cdots\cdots\cdots\cdots\cdots\cdots \\ x_n' &= \mathbf{R}_{n1}x_1 + \mathbf{R}_{n2}x_2 + \cdots + \mathbf{R}_{nn}x_n \end{aligned}\right\} \qquad (11.18a)$$

and define $\mathbf{P_R}f$ to be a function for which

$$\mathbf{P_R}f(x_1', x_2', \cdots, x_n') = f(x_1, x_2, \cdots, x_n) \qquad (11.19)$$

holds identically either in $x_1, x_2, \cdots, x_n$ (in which case the expression in (11.18a) must be considered as substituted for $x_1', x_2', \cdots, x_n'$), or identically in $x_1', x_2', \cdots, x_n'$ (in which case

$$x_i = \sum_{j=1}^{n} \mathbf{R}_{ji}x_j' \qquad (11.18b)$$

is to be inserted for the x_i). Thus, $\mathbf{P_R}$ is an operator which replaces the x_i' by the x_i. Since the latter way of speaking does not distinguish clearly between the operation $\mathbf{P_R}$ and its reciprocal, the formal definitions, embodied in Eqs. (11.19) and (11.18a) or (11.18b), will be used in all actual computations.

If now the *two points* $x_1, x_2, \cdots, x_n$ and $x_1', x_2', \cdots, x_n'$ *of configuration space,* which are transformed into one another by a given transformation $\mathbf{R}$, *are physically equivalent* (e.g., if they differ only in having the locations of the two identical particles interchanged), *then the two functions* ψ and $\mathbf{P_R}\psi$ *are also equivalent* (in $\mathbf{P_R}\psi$ the second particle merely plays the role which the first played in ψ, and conversely). If ψ is a stationary state, then so is $\mathbf{P_R}\psi$, and both have the same energy. The equation $\mathbf{H}\psi = E\psi$ implies $\mathbf{HP_R}\psi = E\mathbf{P_R}\psi$, and $\mathbf{H}$ is invariant under the operation $\mathbf{P_R}$.

The transformations $\mathbf{R}$ which transform equivalent points into one another form a group, the "group of the Schrödinger equation," since the products as well as the reciprocals of such transformations also transform equivalent positions into one another (i.e., are in the group). The identity of the group is the identity transformation, which transforms every position into itself. The group, itself, is called *the symmetry group of configuration space.*

Similar observations are valid for the operator $\mathbf{P_R}$. It is easily seen that $\mathbf{P_S} \cdot \mathbf{P_R} = \mathbf{P_{SR}}$. Transformation $\mathbf{R}$ transforms x into x', so that $\mathbf{P_R}f(x_i') = f(x_i)$ and $\mathbf{S}$ transforms x' into x'', so that $\mathbf{P_S}g(x_i'') = g(x_i')$, and thus, for $g(x) = \mathbf{P_R}f(x)$

$$\mathbf{P_S P_R}f(x_i'') = \mathbf{P_R}f(x_i') = f(x_i).$$

But $\mathbf{SR}$ transforms the x directly into the x'', so that

$$\mathbf{P_{SR}}f(x_i'') = f(x_i)$$

which is the equation defining $\mathbf{P_{SR}}f$. Since f is an arbitrary function, it follows that

$$\mathbf{P_{SR}} \equiv \mathbf{P_S} \cdot \mathbf{P_R}. \tag{11.20}$$

The group of $\mathbf{P_R}$ is isomorphic to the group of $\mathbf{R}$.

The definition (11.19) of the function $\mathbf{P_R}f$ can also be written in the form

$$\mathbf{P_R}f(x_1, \cdots, x_n) = f(\bar{x}_1, \cdots, \bar{x}_n), \tag{11.19a}$$

where

$$\bar{x}_i = \sum_j (\mathbf{R}^{-1})_{ij} x_j .$$

Hence, when calculating $\mathbf{P_S P_R}f$ one may be tempted to proceed as follows:

$$\mathbf{P_S P_R}f(x_1, \cdots, x_n) = \mathbf{P_S}f(\bar{x}_1, \cdots, \bar{x}_n) \tag{†}$$

where

$$\mathbf{P_S}f(\bar{x}_1, \cdots, \bar{x}_n) = f(\bar{\bar{x}}_1, \cdots, \bar{\bar{x}}_n),$$

$$\bar{\bar{x}}_l = \sum_i (\mathbf{S}^{-1})_{li} \bar{x}_i ,$$

and hence

$$\bar{\bar{x}}_l = \sum_{ij} (\mathbf{S}^{-1})_{li} (\mathbf{R}^{-1})_{ij} x_j = \sum_j (\mathbf{S}^{-1}\mathbf{R}^{-1})_{lj} x_j = \sum_j ((\mathbf{RS})^{-1})_{lj} x_j . \tag{*}$$

One would then conclude that

$$\mathbf{P_S P_R}f(x_1, \cdots, x_n) = f(\bar{\bar{x}}_1, \cdots, \bar{\bar{x}}_n).$$

Since, because of (11.19a), this is the definition of $\mathbf{P_{RS}}f$, one would conclude that $\mathbf{P_S P_R}f = \mathbf{P_{RS}}f$.

The question might thus arise as to which of the calculations is correct: that leading to (11.20), or the last one. The answer is, as the reader will suspect, that (11.20) is correct. The error in the last calculation is in (†). This seems to follow from (11.19a) (or (11.19)) by applying $\mathbf{P_S}$ to both sides. However, operators can be applied only to functions, and the two sides of (11.19a) represent the values of functions (numbers) for certain values of the argument. We may denote the function $\mathbf{P_R}f$ by $\bar{f}$ and infer that $\mathbf{P_S}(\mathbf{P_R}f) = \mathbf{P_S}\bar{f}$. Once this equation is obtained, one may insert any set of numbers for the variables and the resulting equation will be correct. This line of argument will lead to (11.20). On the other hand, one cannot apply $\mathbf{P_S}$ to numbers.

For example, suppose that $f(x) = g(x')$ holds for every value of x if $x' = x + 1$, and that $\mathbf{P_S}$ is the operation: replace variable by reciprocal. One might conclude that

$$\mathbf{P_S}f(x) = \mathbf{P_S}g(x'),$$

or

$$f(1/x) = g(1/x'),$$

for $x' = x + 1$. This would be clearly incorrect.

One will not be tempted to argue along the line leading from (†) to (*) if one recalls that $\mathbf{P_S P_R}f = \mathbf{P_S}(\mathbf{P_R}f)$ is a function. If it were not awkward, it would be more appropriate to write the expression, $(\mathbf{P_S P_R}f)(x_1, \cdots, x_n)$, for the value of this function at the point $x_1, \cdots, x_n$, thus showing that $\mathbf{P_S P_R}f$ is the sign for a function, just as F, g, etc. often are.

One should also note that the definition implied by (11.19), (11.18a) is the natural one. The configuration with the coordinates x_i' in the primed system, and the configuration with the coordinates x_i in the unprimed system, are physically identical. This is the meaning of (11.18a). The meaning of (11.19) is then that the wave function $\mathbf{P_R}f$ of the primed system, and the wave function f of the unprimed system, have the same values for the same configuration.

3. *The operators* **P** *are linear.* Substitution of x for x' in a sum is equivalent to performing the same operation in each of the individual summands; also, multiplication of a function, in which such a substitution has been made, by a constant gives the same result as multiplication and subsequent substitution. Formally,

$$\mathbf{P}(af + bg) = a\mathbf{P}f + b\mathbf{P}g. \tag{11.21}$$

Since the operator **P** represents simply a transformation to a new, orthogonal coordinate system in configuration space, **P** must be unitary, i.e., for two arbitrary functions f and g, the scalar product $(f, g) = (\mathbf{P}f, \mathbf{P}g)$. In summary, **P** is a unitary linear operator under the very general hypotheses we have made.

In the particular case at hand **P** has also the property

$$\mathbf{P}fg = \mathbf{P}f \cdot \mathbf{P}g, \tag{11.22}$$

which follows directly from the definition. This property of **P** is not of so general a nature as its unitary-linear character.

4. For the most part, the group of a Schrödinger equation can be determined *from general physical considerations.*

Consider a system of n electrons, in which the coordinates of the kth electron are denoted by x_k, y_k, z_k.[3] Then the Schrödinger equation is invariant under the two kinds of transformation. The first describes a permutation of electrons and is of the form

$$\left.\begin{array}{lll} x_1 = x_{\alpha_1}; & y_1 = y_{\alpha_1}; & z_1 = z_{\alpha_1} \\ x_2 = x_{\alpha_2}; & y_2 = y_{\alpha_2}; & z_2 = z_{\alpha_2} \\ \cdots & \cdots & \cdots \\ x_n = x_{\alpha_n}; & y_n = y_{\alpha_n}; & z_n = z_{\alpha_n} \end{array}\right\} \tag{11.E.1}$$

where $\alpha_1, \alpha_2, \cdots, \alpha_n$ is an arbitrary permutation of the numbers $1, 2, 3, \cdots, n$. Invariance under such transformations is implied by the physical equivalence of all the electrons. Of course the same applies to protons, α-particles, etc. The second kind of transformation describes a rotation of the coordinate system and has the form

$$\left.\begin{array}{ll} x_1' = \beta_{11}x_1 + \beta_{12}y_1 + \beta_{13}z_1; & y_1' = \beta_{21}x_1 + \beta_{22}y_1 + \beta_{23}z_1; \\ x_2' = \beta_{11}x_2 + \beta_{12}y_2 + \beta_{13}z_2; & y_2' = \beta_{21}x_2 + \beta_{22}y_2 + \beta_{23}z_2; \\ \cdots & \cdots \\ x_n' = \beta_{11}x_n + \beta_{12}y_n + \beta_{13}z_n; & y_n' = \beta_{21}x_n + \beta_{22}y_n + \beta_{23}z_n; \\ \multicolumn{2}{c}{z_1' = \beta_{31}x_1 + \beta_{32}y_1 + \beta_{33}z_1} \\ \multicolumn{2}{c}{z_2' = \beta_{31}x_2 + \beta_{32}y_2 + \beta_{33}z_2} \\ \multicolumn{2}{c}{\cdots} \\ \multicolumn{2}{c}{z_n' = \beta_{31}x_n + \beta_{32}y_n + \beta_{33}z_n} \end{array}\right\} \tag{11.E.2}$$

[3] We thus have $3n$ variables $x_1, y_1, z_1, x_2, y_2, z_2, \cdots, x_n, y_n, z_n$, from now on, instead of the n variables $x_1, x_2, \cdots, x_n$.

where $(\boldsymbol{\beta}_{ik})$ is a real orthogonal matrix; Eq. (11.E.2) denotes only a transition to a coordinate system with a different orientation. The physical equivalence of all directions in space (at least in the absence of external fields) then implies invariance under such transformations.

Clearly, the Schrödinger equation is also invariant under transformations which are compounded from (11.E.1) and (11.E.2). The transformations (11.E.1) form a group isomorphic to the group of permutations of n objects (symmetric group); those of (11.E.2), a group isomorphic to the three-dimensional rotation group.

We shall denote the elements of the group of the Schrödinger equation by letters $R, S, \cdots$. There are operators $\mathbf{P}_R, \mathbf{P}_S, \cdots$ which correspond to these group elements. Analytically, $\mathbf{P}_R$ is given by (11.19) in which $\mathbf{R}$ is the transformation which corresponds to the group element R. However, we shall use henceforth the group element as index of $\mathbf{P}$ rather than the matrix which corresponds to it. We do this, first, because it makes the notation less cumbersome and, second, because the symmetry element has a more fundamental significance than the matrix which corresponds to it. The physical significance of the $\mathbf{P}_R$ is to produce, from the wave function φ of a state, the wave function $\mathbf{P}_R\varphi$ of that state in which the role of particles is interchanged or new directions x', y', z' play the role of the directions x, y, z.

There are physical quantities, in the present case the energy, from whose point of view the states φ and $\mathbf{P}_R\varphi$ are equivalent. This means that the measurement of these quantities gives the same values with the same probabilities for φ and for the $\mathbf{P}_R\varphi$. The operators which correspond to physical quantities of this nature are called *symmetric* under the transformations $\mathbf{P}_R$. Conversely, the group is called the *symmetry group* of the physical quantity. The group of the interchanges of identical particles and of rotations of the coordinate system is the symmetry group of the energy.

5. In (11.12) or (11.16) we established the fact that the function $\mathbf{P}\psi$ must be a constant multiple of ψ, since it belongs to the eigenvalue of ψ. In the more general case where we consider an eigenvalue which has l linearly independent eigenfunctions $\psi_1, \psi_2, \cdots, \psi_l$, one can no longer draw this conclusion. One can say only that the $\mathbf{P}_R\psi_1, \mathbf{P}_R\psi_2, \cdots, \mathbf{P}_R\psi_l$ can all be written as linear combinations of the $\psi_1, \psi_2, \cdots, \psi_l$ (since every eigenfunction for this eigenvalue has this property). We denote the coefficients by $\mathbf{D}(R)_{\varkappa\nu}$, so that[4]

$$\mathbf{P}_R\psi_\nu(x_1, y_1, z_1, \cdots, x_n, y_n, z_n) = \sum_{\varkappa=1}^{l} \mathbf{D}(R)_{\varkappa\nu}\psi_\varkappa(x_1, y_1, z_1, \cdots, x_n, y_n, z_n). \tag{11.23}$$

[4] The indices $\varkappa\nu$ are written in this order so that, according to (11.25), $\mathbf{D}(R)$ itself, and not its transpose $\mathbf{D}(R)'$, might form a representation.

If S also belongs in the group of the Schrödinger equation, we have

$$\mathbf{P}_S\psi_\varkappa = \sum_{\lambda=1}^{l} \mathbf{D}(S)_{\lambda\varkappa}\psi_\lambda .$$

By subjecting the variables in (11.23) to the transformation S, that is, by applying $\mathbf{P}_S$ to both sides, we obtain ($\mathbf{P}_S$ is linear and the $\mathbf{D}(R)_{\varkappa\nu}$ are constants!)

$$\left.\begin{aligned} \mathbf{P}_S \cdot \mathbf{P}_R\psi_\nu &= \mathbf{P}_S \cdot \sum_{\varkappa=1}^{l} \mathbf{D}(R)_{\varkappa\nu}\psi_\varkappa = \sum_{\varkappa=1}^{l} \mathbf{D}(R)_{\varkappa\nu}\mathbf{P}_S\psi_\varkappa \\ &= \sum_{\varkappa=1}^{l} \mathbf{D}(R)_{\varkappa\nu} \sum_{\lambda=1}^{l} \mathbf{D}(S)_{\lambda\varkappa}\psi_\lambda = \sum_{\lambda=1}^{l} \sum_{\varkappa=1}^{l} \mathbf{D}(S)_{\lambda\varkappa}\mathbf{D}(R)_{\varkappa\nu}\psi_\lambda . \end{aligned}\right\} \quad (11.24)$$

On the other hand $\mathbf{P}_S \cdot \mathbf{P}_R\psi_\nu = \mathbf{P}_{SR}\psi_\nu$, so that

$$\mathbf{P}_S \cdot \mathbf{P}_R\psi_\nu = \mathbf{P}_{SR}\psi_\nu = \sum_{\lambda=1}^{l} \mathbf{D}(SR)_{\lambda\nu}\psi_\lambda .$$

From this, it follows, by equating the coefficients with those in (11.24), that

$$\mathbf{D}(SR)_{\lambda\nu} = \sum_{\varkappa=1}^{l} \mathbf{D}(S)_{\lambda\varkappa}\mathbf{D}(R)_{\varkappa\nu} . \quad (11.25)$$

The l-dimensional matrices $\mathbf{D}(R)$ formed from the coefficients of (11.23) convert the eigenfunctions ψ_ν of an eigenvalue into the transformed eigenfunctions $\mathbf{P}_R\psi_\nu$. Because they satisfy the equations $\mathbf{D}(SR) = \mathbf{D}(S)\mathbf{D}(R)$, they form a representation of the group under which $\mathbf{H}\psi = E\psi$ is invariant. The dimension of the representation is equal to the number l of linearly independent eigenfunctions $\psi_1, \psi_2, \cdots, \psi_l$ belonging to the eigenvalue in question.

General considerations imply as little about the question of which representation it is whose coefficients occur in (11.23) as they do about the signs in Eq. (11.12); Eq. (11.23) allows alternatives (several, in fact), just as (11.12) did. One must expect, again, that different representations may occur for different eigenvalues.

We next combine (11.23) with the equation defining $\mathbf{P}_R$,

$$\mathbf{P}_R\psi_\nu(x_1', y_1', z_1', \cdots, x_n', y_n', z_n') = \psi_\nu(x_1, y_1, z_1, \cdots, x_n, y_n, z_n). \quad (11.18\text{c})$$

If one replaces R by R^{-1}, the roles of the primed and unprimed variables are interchanged. Hence, one obtains the transformation formulas for the ψ_ν.

$$\left.\begin{aligned} \psi_\nu(x_1', y_1', z_1', \cdots, x_n', y_n', z_n') &= \mathbf{P}_{R^{-1}}\psi_\nu(x_1, y_1, z_1, \cdots, x_n, y_n, z_n) \\ &= \sum_{\varkappa=1}^{l} \mathbf{D}(R^{-1})_{\varkappa\nu}\psi_\varkappa(x_1, y_1, z_1, \cdots, x_n, y_n, z_n). \end{aligned}\right\} \quad (11.26)$$

They relate the values of the eigenfunctions at physically equivalent points in configuration space.

The group under which (11.1) is invariant consists of the identity and the interchange **R** of x and y. Since the eigenvalue was simple (by hypothesis) we must obtain a one-dimensional representation of the reflection group. Since $\mathbf{P}_E$ is the identity operator

$$\mathbf{P}_E\psi = \psi = 1 \cdot \psi.$$

That is, the identity of the group corresponds to the matrix (1). Furthermore (11.12) states that

$$\mathbf{P}_R\psi = \overline{\psi} = \pm\psi = \pm 1 \cdot \psi. \tag{11.12a}$$

For some eigenvalues, the upper sign applies; for these, the matrix (1) corresponds to the element **R** which interchanges the two particles. For other eigenvalues, the lower sign applies; for these, the matrix (-1) corresponds to the group element **R**. We thus obtain two one-dimensional representations of the symmetric group of two elements. One consists of the correspondences $\mathbf{D}(E) = (1)$, $\mathbf{D}(R) = (1)$; the other, of $\mathbf{D}(E) = (1)$, $\mathbf{D}(R) = (-1)$.

6. If we make a new choice of the linearly independent eigenfunctions choosing $\psi_1', \cdots, \psi_l'$ in place of the $\psi_1, \cdots, \psi_l$, where

$$\psi_\mu' = \sum_{\nu=1}^{l} \alpha_{\nu\mu}\psi_\nu, \tag{11.27}$$

we obtain in (11.23) another representation of the group of operators **P**. The question of how the two representations are related then arises.

Let

$$\psi_\varkappa = \Sigma\, \beta_{\lambda\varkappa}\psi_\lambda', \tag{11.28}$$

where $\boldsymbol{\beta}$ is the matrix inverse to $\boldsymbol{\alpha}$. Then, because of the linearity of the $\mathbf{P}_R$,

$$\left.\begin{aligned} \mathbf{P}_R\psi_\mu' &= \sum_\nu \alpha_{\nu\mu}\mathbf{P}_R\psi_\nu = \sum_\nu\sum_\varkappa \alpha_{\nu\mu}\mathbf{D}(R)_{\varkappa\nu}\psi_\varkappa \\ &= \sum_\nu\sum_\varkappa\sum_\lambda \alpha_{\nu\mu}\mathbf{D}(R)_{\varkappa\nu}\beta_{\lambda\varkappa}\psi_\lambda' = \sum_\lambda \Big(\sum_{\varkappa\nu} \beta_{\lambda\varkappa}\mathbf{D}(R)_{\varkappa\nu}\alpha_{\nu\mu}\Big)\psi_\lambda'. \end{aligned}\right\} \tag{11.29}$$

The matrix $\overline{\mathbf{D}}(R)$ which transforms the ψ' into the $\mathbf{P}_R\psi'$, arises from $\mathbf{D}(R)$ by similarity transformation with $\boldsymbol{\alpha}$

$$\overline{\mathbf{D}}(R) = \boldsymbol{\alpha}^{-1}\mathbf{D}(R)\boldsymbol{\alpha}. \tag{11.30}$$

A different choice of the linearly independent eigenfunctions for a given eigenvalue effects only a similarity transformation on the corresponding representation: *the representation of the group of the Schrödinger equation which belongs to a particular eigenvalue is uniquely determined up to a similarity transformation.*

If we wish to have eigenfunctions which transform not by $\mathbf{D}(R)$, but by a representation equivalent to it, then we must form new linear combinations of the eigenfunctions by means of the matrix $\boldsymbol{\alpha}$, which transforms the representation $\mathbf{D}(R)$ into the desired form $\overline{\mathbf{D}}(R)$.

The uniquely determined (to within a similarity transformation) representation is a qualitative characteristic by which the various types of eigenvalues can be distinguished. A representation belonging to a singlet S level differs from that which belongs to a triplet P level, say, or to a singlet D level, while all representations belonging to triplet P levels are equivalent. These representations will practically always be irreducible, which is one reason for the importance of irreducible representations.

7. *If the l-eigenfunctions* $\psi_1, \cdots, \psi_l$ *are mutually orthogonal* (we shall always assume this to be the case), *then the corresponding representation is unitary.* From the unitary character of the operator $\mathbf{P}_R$ it follows that the l functions $\mathbf{P}_R\psi_1, \cdots, \mathbf{P}_R\psi_l$ are also orthogonal.

$$(\mathbf{P}_R\psi_\varkappa, \mathbf{P}_R\psi_\nu) = (\psi_\varkappa, \psi_\nu) = \delta_{\varkappa\nu}, \tag{11.31}$$

or by using (11.23)

$$\left.\begin{aligned}\delta_{\varkappa\nu} &= (\mathbf{P}_R\psi_\varkappa, \mathbf{P}_R\psi_\nu) = (\sum_\lambda \mathbf{D}(R)_{\lambda\varkappa}\psi_\lambda, \sum_\mu \mathbf{D}(R)_{\mu\nu}\psi_\mu) \\ &= \sum_\lambda\sum_\mu \mathbf{D}(R)^*_{\lambda\varkappa}\,\mathbf{D}(R)_{\mu\nu}(\psi_\lambda, \psi_\mu) = \sum_\lambda \mathbf{D}(R)^*_{\lambda\varkappa}\,\mathbf{D}(R)_{\lambda\nu},\end{aligned}\right\} \tag{11.32}$$

that is,

$$\mathbf{1} = \mathbf{D}(R)^\dagger\mathbf{D}(R).$$

That is, $\mathbf{D}(R)$ is a unitary matrix.[5] Consequently, we can infer at once that the orthogonality relationships of Chapter 9 hold for the $\mathbf{D}(R)$, provided they are irreducible representations.

Equation (11.26) can also be given the form

$$\left.\begin{aligned}&\psi_\nu(x_1', y_1', z_1', \cdots, x_n', y_n', z_n') \\ &\quad= \sum_\varkappa \mathbf{D}(R^{-1})_{\varkappa\nu}\psi_\varkappa(x_1, y_1, z_1, \cdots, x_n, y_n, z_n) \\ &\quad= \sum_\varkappa \mathbf{D}(R)^*_{\nu\varkappa}\psi_\varkappa(x_1, y_1, z_1, \cdots, x_n, y_n, z_n).\end{aligned}\right\} \tag{11.26a}$$

We see also that only representations with nonvanishing determinants will be of concern to us.

[5] Since the eigenfunctions can always be chosen to be orthogonal, this is an especially simple proof of the fact that representations can always be made unitary.

12. The Algebra of Representation Theory

We shall now present some algebraic considerations which are related to the results of the preceding chapters. To begin, we derive some purely mathematical theorems.

1. Let $\mathbf{D}^{(j)}(R)$ be an irreducible unitary representation of dimension l_j of the group of unitary operators $\mathbf{P}_R$, and let $f_1^{(j)}, f_2^{(j)}, \cdots, f_{l_j}^{(j)}$ be l_j eigenfunctions for which

$$\mathbf{P}_R f_\mu^{(j)} = \sum_{\lambda=1}^{l_j} \mathbf{D}^{(j)}(R)_{\lambda\mu} f_\lambda^{(j)} \qquad (\mu = 1, 2, \cdots, l_j) \tag{12.1}$$

holds for all $\mathbf{P}_R$. A function $f_\varkappa^{(j)}$ is said to belong to the $\varkappa$th row of the irreducible representation $\mathbf{D}^{(j)}(R)$ if there exist "partner" functions $f_1^{(j)}$, $f_2^{(j)}, \cdots, f_{\varkappa-1}^{(j)}, f_{\varkappa+1}^{(j)}, \cdots, f_{l_j}^{(j)}$ such that all the $f_\lambda^{(j)}$ satisfy (12.1). This statement is well defined only when the $\mathbf{D}^{(j)}(R)$ are specified completely, not just up to a similarity transformation.

Upon multiplication of (12.1) with $\mathbf{D}^{(j')}(R)^*_{\lambda'\varkappa'}$ and summation (or integration for a continuous group) over the entire group, it follows from the orthogonality of the representation elements that

$$\left.\begin{aligned}\sum_R \mathbf{D}^{(j')}(R)^*_{\lambda'\varkappa'} \mathbf{P}_R f_\varkappa^{(j)} &= \sum_R \sum_\lambda \mathbf{D}^{(j')}(R)^*_{\lambda'\varkappa'} \mathbf{D}^{(j)}(R)_{\lambda\varkappa} f_\lambda^{(j)} \\ &= \sum_\lambda \frac{h}{l_j} \delta_{jj'}\, \delta_{\lambda\lambda'}\, \delta_{\varkappa\varkappa'} f_\lambda^{(j)} = \frac{h}{l_j} \delta_{jj'}\, \delta_{\varkappa\varkappa'} f_{\lambda'}^{(j)}.\end{aligned}\right\} \tag{12.2}$$

In particular, this implies

$$\sum_R \mathbf{D}^{(j)}(R)^*_{\varkappa\varkappa} \mathbf{P}_R f_\varkappa^{(j)} = \frac{h}{l_j} f_\varkappa^{(j)} \tag{12.3}$$

for every function $f_\varkappa^{(j)}$ which belongs to the $\varkappa$th row of the irreducible representation $\mathbf{D}^{(j)}(R)$. Conversely, for any function $f_\varkappa^{(j)}$ which satisfies (12.3), a set of partner functions $f_1^{(j)}, f_2^{(j)}, \cdots, f_{\varkappa-1}^{(j)}, f_{\varkappa+1}^{(j)}, \cdots, f_{l_j}^{(j)}$ can be found such that (12.1) holds for the whole set. *Equation* (12.3) *is the necessary and sufficient condition that* $f_\varkappa^{(j)}$ *belongs to the* $\varkappa$*th row of the irreducible representation* $\mathbf{D}^{(j)}(R)$.

It follows from (12.2) that, if $f_\varkappa^{(j)}$ has partner functions at all, these must be given by

$$f_\lambda^{(j)} = \frac{l_j}{h} \sum_S \mathbf{D}^{(j)}(S)^*_{\lambda\varkappa} \mathbf{P}_S f_\varkappa^{(j)}. \tag{12.3a}$$

We consider this the definition of $f_1^{(j)}, \cdots, f_{\varkappa-1}^{(j)}, f_{\varkappa+1}^{(j)}, \cdots, f_{l_j}^{(j)}$. Also by hypothesis, (12.3a) is true for the special case $\lambda = \varkappa$ so that it applies to all $f_\lambda^{(j)}$. We now show that (12.1) is also true for these $f_\lambda^{(j)}$. Direct substitution of the right side of (12.3a) for the $f_\mu^{(j)}, f_\lambda^{(j)}$ in (12.1) shows that (12.1) is indeed valid if only

$$\mathbf{P}_R \frac{l_j}{h} \sum_S \mathbf{D}^{(j)}(S)^*_{\mu\varkappa} \mathbf{P}_S f_\varkappa^{(j)} = \sum_\lambda \mathbf{D}^{(j)}(R)_{\lambda\mu} \frac{l_j}{h} \sum_S \mathbf{D}^{(j)}(S)^*_{\lambda\varkappa} \mathbf{P}_S f_\varkappa^{(j)}.$$

But this is true identically, as can be seen by applying $\mathbf{P}_{R^{-1}}$ to both sides and substituting $\mathbf{D}^{(j)}(R)_{\lambda\mu} = \mathbf{D}^{(j)}(R^{-1})^*_{\mu\lambda}$. Because the $\mathbf{D}^{(j)}$ form a representation, this gives

$$\sum_S \mathbf{D}^{(j)}(S)^*_{\mu\varkappa} \mathbf{P}_S f_\varkappa^{(j)} = \sum_S \sum_\lambda \mathbf{P}_{R^{-1}} \mathbf{P}_S \mathbf{D}^{(j)}(R^{-1})^*_{\mu\lambda} \mathbf{D}^{(j)}(S)^*_{\lambda\varkappa} f_\varkappa^{(j)}$$
$$= \sum_S \mathbf{P}_{R^{-1}S} \mathbf{D}^{(j)}(R^{-1}S)^*_{\mu\varkappa} f_\varkappa^{(j)},$$

and one can take the summation on the right over $R^{-1}S$ instead of over S. Therefore, for any $f_\varkappa^{(j)}$ which satisfies (12.3), Eq. (12.3a) defines the partners so that (12.1) is fulfilled for the whole set.

2. A linear combination $af_\varkappa^{(j)} + bg_\varkappa^{(j)}$ of functions $f_\varkappa^{(j)}$ and $g_\varkappa^{(j)}$, each of which belongs to the $\varkappa$th row of the representation $\mathbf{D}^{(j)}$, also belongs to the same row of the same representation. This follows directly from the linearity of (12.3), or from the definition (12.1).

3. If $\mathbf{D}^{(1)}(R), \mathbf{D}^{(2)}(R), \cdots, \mathbf{D}^{(c)}(R)$ are all the irreducible representations of the group of operators $\mathbf{P}_R$, then every function F, to which the $\mathbf{P}_R$ can be applied, can be written as a sum

$$F = \sum_{j=1}^{c} \sum_{\varkappa=1}^{l_j} f_\varkappa^{(j)}, \tag{12.4}$$

where $f_\varkappa^{(j)}$ belongs to the $\varkappa$th row of the representation $\mathbf{D}^{(j)}(R)$.

To prove this, consider the h functions $F = \mathbf{P}_E F, \mathbf{P}_{A_2} F, \mathbf{P}_{A_3} F, \cdots, \mathbf{P}_{A_h} F$ which result from application of the h operations of the group of $\mathbf{P}_R$ to F. If these functions are not linearly independent, we can omit enough of them so that no linear relationship exists among the remaining $F, F_2, \cdots, F_{h'}$. These h' functions span a representation of the group of $\mathbf{P}_R$. If we apply one of the operators $\mathbf{P}_R$ to these functions, then the resulting function can be expressed as a linear combination of the $F, F_2, \cdots, F_{h'}$. For example, let $F_k = \mathbf{P}_T F$; then $\mathbf{P}_R \mathbf{P}_T F = \mathbf{P}_{RT} F$ and either this is itself one of the F_i, or it can be expressed as a linear combination of them. Hence

$$\mathbf{P}_R F_k = \sum_{i=1}^{h'} \Delta(R)_{ik} F_i, \tag{12.5}$$

and the matrices $\Delta(R)$ form a representation of the group of $\mathbf{P}_R$. This corresponds to the representational property of eigenfunctions discussed in the preceding chapter. Explicitly,

$$\sum_n \mathbf{\Delta}(SR)_{nk} F_n = \mathbf{P}_{SR} F_k = \mathbf{P}_S \mathbf{P}_R F_k = \mathbf{P}_S \sum_i \mathbf{\Delta}(R)_{ik} F_i$$
$$= \sum_i \sum_n \mathbf{\Delta}(R)_{ik} \mathbf{\Delta}(S)_{ni} F_n ,$$

and because the F_n are linearly independent,

$$\mathbf{\Delta}(S)\mathbf{\Delta}(R) = \mathbf{\Delta}(SR).$$

This method of generating representations will play an important role in our explicit determination of irreducible representations of the symmetric group. By particular choices of the initial function F, many kinds of representations can be obtained which will be useful in determining the irreducible ones.

If the representation in (12.5) is not irreducible, it can be reduced by a similarity transformation, that is, by one which brings all the matrices $\mathbf{\Delta}(R)$ simultaneously into the form

$$\begin{pmatrix} \mathbf{D}^{(1)}(R) & \mathbf{0} & \cdots \\ \mathbf{0} & \mathbf{D}^{(2)}(R) & \cdots \\ \cdot & \cdot & \\ \cdot & \cdot & \\ \cdot & \cdot & \end{pmatrix} = \boldsymbol{\alpha}^{-1}\mathbf{\Delta}(R)\boldsymbol{\alpha}, \qquad (12.E.1)$$

where the $\mathbf{D}$ are all unitary irreducible representations. Then, according to Section 6, Chapter 11, one can construct by means of $\boldsymbol{\alpha}$ linear combinations of the F_k which transform under $\mathbf{P}_R$ according to (12.E.1) and which thus belong to the various rows of the irreducible representations $\mathbf{D}^{(1)}, \mathbf{D}^{(2)}, \cdots$. Conversely, because $\boldsymbol{\alpha}$ has an inverse, the F_k and thus also the F can be expressed in terms of these linear combinations. This proves that an arbitrary function can be expressed in the form of the sum (12.4).

To calculate the $f_\varkappa^{(j)}$ of (12.4) explicitly, we apply $\mathbf{P}_R$ to (12.4), multiply by $\mathbf{D}^{(j)}(R)^*_{\varkappa\varkappa}$, and the sum over all R. We obtain

$$\sum_R \mathbf{D}^{(j)}(R)^*_{\varkappa\varkappa} \mathbf{P}_R F = \sum_{j'} \sum_{\varkappa'} \sum_R \mathbf{D}^{(j)}(R)^*_{\varkappa\varkappa} \mathbf{P}_R f_{\varkappa'}^{(j')} = \frac{h}{l_j} f_\varkappa^{(j)}. \qquad (12.6)$$

The last part of Eq. (12.6) is implied by (12.3).

Equation (12.6) shows that $\sum_R \mathbf{D}^{(j)}(R)^*_{\varkappa\varkappa} \mathbf{P}_R \cdot F$ *belongs to the* $\varkappa$*th row of the representation* $\mathbf{D}^{(j)}(R)$ *for entirely arbitrary* F; this can be verified by substituting this expression for $f_\varkappa^{(j)}$ into (12.3), which then becomes

$$\frac{l_j}{h} \sum_S \mathbf{D}^{(j)}(S)^*_{\varkappa\varkappa} \mathbf{P}_S \left(\sum_R \mathbf{D}^{(j)}(R)^*_{\varkappa\varkappa} \mathbf{P}_R F\right) = \sum_R \mathbf{D}^{(j)}(R)^*_{\varkappa\varkappa} \mathbf{P}_R F.$$

By substituting $SR = T$ on the left and summing over T instead of S, the left side is seen to be identical with the right.

$$\sum_S \mathbf{D}^{(j)}(S)^*_{\varkappa\varkappa}\mathbf{P}_S \cdot \Big(\sum_R \mathbf{D}^{(j)}(R)^*_{\varkappa\varkappa}\mathbf{P}_R F\Big) = \sum_{T,R} \mathbf{D}^{(j)}(TR^{-1})^*_{\varkappa\varkappa}\mathbf{P}_T \mathbf{D}^{(j)}(R)^*_{\varkappa\varkappa} F,$$

$$\sum_{T,R}\sum_{\lambda} \mathbf{D}^{(j)}(T)^*_{\varkappa\lambda}\mathbf{D}^{(j)}(R^{-1})^*_{\lambda\varkappa}\mathbf{D}^{(j)}(R)^*_{\varkappa\varkappa}\mathbf{P}_T F = \frac{h}{l_j}\Big(\sum_T \mathbf{D}^{(j)}(T)^*_{\varkappa\varkappa}\mathbf{P}_T F\Big).$$

The summation over R here has been evaluated in Eq. (9.31a).

The identity

$$F = \sum_j \sum_\varkappa \sum_R \frac{l_j}{h} \mathbf{D}^{(j)}(R)^*_{\varkappa\varkappa}\mathbf{P}_R F \tag{12.6a}$$

is valid for entirely arbitrary F, that is no matter what the values of the h quantities $\mathbf{P}_R F$ are. This is possible only if

$$\sum_{j=1}^{c} \sum_{\varkappa=1}^{l_j} \frac{l_j}{h} \mathbf{D}^{(j)}(R)^*_{\varkappa\varkappa} \begin{cases} = 1 & \text{for } R = E \\ = 0 & \text{for } R \neq E. \end{cases}$$

For $R = E$, since $\mathbf{D}^{(j)}(E)_{\varkappa\varkappa} = 1$, this is just

$$\sum_{j=1}^{c} \sum_{\varkappa=1}^{l_j} \frac{l_j}{h} = \sum_{j=1}^{c} \frac{l_j^2}{h} = 1.$$

That is, the sum of the squares of the dimensions of all the irreducible representations is equal to the order of the group represented. This theorem was stated, but not proved, on page 83.

4. Two functions $f^{(j)}_\varkappa$ and $g^{(j')}_{\varkappa'}$ which belong to different irreducible representations, or to different rows of the same representation, are orthogonal. There exist partner functions $f^{(j)}_1, f^{(j)}_2, f^{(j)}_3, \cdots$ and $g^{(j')}_1, g^{(j')}_2, g^{(j')}_3, \cdots$ to $f^{(j)}_\varkappa$, and $g^{(j')}_{\varkappa'}$, such that, by definition,

$$\mathbf{P}_R f^{(j)}_\varkappa = \sum_\lambda \mathbf{D}^{(j)}(R)_{\lambda\varkappa} f^{(j)}_\lambda, \qquad \mathbf{P}_R g^{(j')}_{\varkappa'} = \sum_{\lambda'} \mathbf{D}^{(j')}(R)_{\lambda'\varkappa'} g^{(j')}_{\lambda'}.$$

Since $\mathbf{P}_R$ is unitary

$$(f^{(j)}_\varkappa, g^{(j')}_{\varkappa'}) = (\mathbf{P}_R f^{(j)}_\varkappa, \mathbf{P}_R g^{(j')}_{\varkappa'}) = \sum_\lambda \sum_{\lambda'} \mathbf{D}^{(j)}(R)^*_{\lambda\varkappa}\mathbf{D}^{(j')}(R)_{\lambda'\varkappa'}(f^{(j)}_\lambda, g^{(j')}_{\lambda'}). \tag{12.7}$$

By summing this equation over all the operators $\mathbf{P}_R$ of the group we obtain

$$h(f^{(j)}_\varkappa, g^{(j')}_{\varkappa'}) = \frac{h}{l_j}\delta_{jj'}\,\delta_{\varkappa\varkappa'} \sum_\lambda (f^{(j)}_\lambda, g^{(j')}_\lambda). \tag{12.8}$$

This implies firstly the fundamental theorem stated above that $(f^{(j)}_\varkappa, g^{(j')}_{\varkappa'})$ *vanishes for* $j \neq j'$ *or* $\varkappa \neq \varkappa'$, *and* secondly, that $(f^{(j)}_\varkappa, g^{(j)}_\varkappa)$ *is equal for all partners, i.e., is independent of* $\varkappa$.

5. In the previous chapter we have spoken of operators which are symmetric under the $\mathbf{P}_R$; for example, the Hamiltonian operator $\mathbf{H}$ was symmetric

under the operations (11.E.1) and (11.E.2). This means that $\mathbf{P}_R$ effects only such changes in functions as are irrelevant from the point of view of $\mathbf{H}$, such as interchanges in the roles of identical particles, etc.

We shall now sharpen this notion somewhat. The symmetric operators we consider are always Hermitian and correspond to physical quantities, such as the energy. The $\mathbf{P}_R$, under which an operator is symmetric, are unitary operators. However, they do not correspond to physical quantities; rather, they transform the wave function of a given state into a wave function of another state. An operator $\mathbf{S}$ is said to be symmetric if under it all $\mathbf{P}_R\varphi$ behave just as φ behaves. We shall see at once that this definition coincides with that of the previous chapter.

The statement that $\mathbf{S}$ is an operator symmetric under the $\mathbf{P}_R$, and that ψ is one of its eigenfunctions, $\mathbf{S}\psi = s\psi$, means that in the state ψ a measurement of the quantity to which $\mathbf{S}$ corresponds gives the value s with certainty. This must then also be true of $\mathbf{P}_R\psi$; that is, $\mathbf{P}_R\psi$ must also be an eigenfunction of $\mathbf{S}$ belonging to the eigenvalue s.

From $\mathbf{S}\psi = s\psi$, it follows upon application of $\mathbf{P}_R$ to both sides that $\mathbf{P}_R\mathbf{S}\psi = \mathbf{P}_R s\psi = s\mathbf{P}_R\psi$. This, together with $\mathbf{S}\mathbf{P}_R\psi = s\mathbf{P}_R\psi$ implies that $\mathbf{S}\mathbf{P}_R\psi = \mathbf{P}_R\mathbf{S}\psi$; this must be true for every eigenfunction of $\mathbf{S}$, since the eigenvalue is no longer involved. The relationship is linear and so applies equally well to every linear combination of the eigenfunctions, and thus to all functions. It therefore implies the operator identity $\mathbf{S}\mathbf{P}_R = \mathbf{P}_R\mathbf{S}$: *an operator symmetric under the $\mathbf{P}_R$ commutes with all $\mathbf{P}_R$.* It makes no difference in which order $\mathbf{S}$ and $\mathbf{P}_R$ are applied to a function. One says that $\mathbf{S}$ is invariant under the $\mathbf{P}_R$.

By applying the operator $\mathbf{S}$ to (12.1) we see that if $f_\varkappa^{(j)}$ belongs to the $\varkappa$th row of $\mathbf{D}^{(j)}$, so does $\mathbf{S}f_\varkappa^{(j)}$. Then from (12.8), it follows that

$$(f_\varkappa^{(j)}, \mathbf{S}g_{\varkappa'}^{(j')}) = \delta_{jj'}\delta_{\varkappa\varkappa'}(f_\lambda^{(j)}, \mathbf{S}g_\lambda^{(j)}) \tag{12.8a}$$

vanishes for $j \neq j'$ or $\varkappa \neq \varkappa'$; also, for $j = j'$, $\varkappa = \varkappa'$, it is independent of $\varkappa$.

Although these theorems are actually of a very general nature, they are widely known only for the simplest groups of operators. One group for which these theorems are familiar consists of the identity operator $\mathbf{P}_E$, and the operator from (11.15) of Chapter 11,

$$\mathbf{P}_R f(x) = f(-x), \qquad \mathbf{P}_R^2 = \mathbf{P}_E .$$

The group $\mathbf{P}_E$, $\mathbf{P}_R$ is the reflection group. It has two irreducible representations and both are one-dimensional:

$$\mathbf{D}^{(1)}(E) = (1), \qquad \mathbf{D}^{(1)}(R) = (1) \quad \text{and} \quad \mathbf{D}^{(2)}(E) = (1), \qquad \mathbf{D}^{(2)}(R) = (-1).$$

For functions which belong to the first representation (it has only one row), (12.1) becomes

$$\mathbf{P}_R f^{(1)}(x) = f^{(1)}(-x) = 1 \cdot f^{(1)}(x).$$

These are the even functions of x. For functions which belong to the second representation, (12.1) is

$$\mathbf{P}_R f^{(2)}(x) = f^{(2)}(-x) = -1 \cdot f^{(2)}(x).$$

These are the odd functions. The Eq. (12.3) for $f^{(1)}(x)$ is

$$\mathbf{D}^{(1)}(E)\mathbf{P}_E f^{(1)}(x) + \mathbf{D}^{(1)}(R)\mathbf{P}_R f^{(1)}(x) = 1 f^{(1)}(x) + 1 f^{(1)}(-x) = \frac{2}{1} f^{(1)}(x),$$

and for $f^{(2)}(x)$

$$\mathbf{D}^{(2)}(E)\mathbf{P}_E f^{(2)}(x) + \mathbf{D}^{(2)}(R)\mathbf{P}_R f^{(2)}(x) = 1 f^{(2)}(x) - 1 f^{(2)}(-x) = \frac{2}{1} f^{(2)}(x).$$

Conversely, it follows from these equations that $f^{(1)}(x)$ is even and $f^{(2)}(x)$, odd. Of course, it is well-known that every function can be resolved into an even and an odd part, and that every even function is orthogonal to every odd one.

6. So far we have had to assume that the representations are determined in some arbitrary way. The same arbitrariness is present in the definition of the $f_\varkappa^{(j)}$: a function which belongs to the $\varkappa$th row of an irreducible representation does not belong in general to the $\varkappa$th row of an equivalent representation. The theorems which follow are independent of the particular specification of the representation.

For every function $f_\varkappa^{(j)}$ which belongs to the $\varkappa$th row of the irreducible representation $\mathbf{D}^{(j)}(R)$, one has, according to (12.2)

$$\sum_R \mathbf{D}^{(j)}(R)^*_{\lambda\lambda} \mathbf{P}_R f_\varkappa^{(j)} = \frac{h}{l_j} \delta_{\varkappa\lambda} f_\varkappa^{(j)}. \tag{12.2a}$$

Summing over λ from 1 to l_j, this becomes

$$\sum_R \chi^{(j)}(R)^* \mathbf{P}_R f_\varkappa^{(j)} = \frac{h}{l_j} f_\varkappa^{(j)} \qquad (\text{for } \varkappa = 1, 2, \cdots, l_j). \tag{12.9}$$

Since in (12.9), $\varkappa$ is no longer essential, (12.9) is satisfied for all functions belonging to arbitrary rows of the representation $\mathbf{D}^{(j)}(R)$, and also by arbitrary linear combinations of such functions. A function which satisfies (12.9) is said to belong to the representation $\mathbf{D}^{(j)}(R)$. This fact, like the character, is independent of the special form of the representation. Conversely, every function which satisfies (12.9) is a linear combination of functions each of which belongs to one row of the representation $\mathbf{D}^{(j)}(R)$. According to (12.9)

$$\frac{h}{l_j} f^{(j)} = \sum_R \chi^{(j)}(R)^* \mathbf{P}_R f^{(j)} = \sum_\lambda \sum_R \mathbf{D}^{(j)}(R)^*_{\lambda\lambda} \mathbf{P}_R f^{(j)}. \tag{12.10}$$

But according to (12.3), every function of the form $\sum_R \mathbf{D}^{(j)}(R)^*_{\lambda\lambda} \mathbf{P}_R F$ belongs to the λth row of the representation $\mathbf{D}^{(j)}(R)$.

It also follows from (12.10) that functions which belong to inequivalent, irreducible representations are orthogonal to one another. Moreover, every function F can be resolved into a sum

$$F = \sum_{j=1}^{c} f^{(j)}, \tag{12.11}$$

where $f^{(j)}$ belongs to the representation $\mathbf{D}^{(j)}(R)$. To show this, it is necessary only to rewrite Eq. (12.4) as

$$\left.\begin{aligned} F &= \sum_{j=1}^{c} f^{(j)} \\ f^{(j)} &= \sum_{\varkappa=1}^{l_j} f_{\varkappa}^{(j)}. \end{aligned}\right\} \tag{12.4a}$$

The functions which belong to a given irreducible representation thus have properties entirely analogous to those which belong to one row of an irreducible representation. A linear combination of functions of a certain kind is again a function of that kind; an arbitrary function can be written as a sum of functions, one of each kind; two functions of different kinds are always orthogonal to one another; and an operator $\mathbf{S}$ which is invariant under $\mathbf{P}_R$ transforms a function of a given kind into another function of the same kind.

The general theorems on functions stated here can be summarized by the statement that functions of different kinds (belonging to different irreducible representations or to different rows of the same irreducible representation) belong to different eigenvalues of some Hermitian operator which, like all the $\mathbf{P}$ and functions of them, commutes with all invariant operators $\mathbf{S}$.

The operator $\mathbf{O}_{j\varkappa}$ which transforms F into

$$\mathbf{O}_{j\varkappa} F = \sum_R \mathbf{D}^{(j)}(R)_{\varkappa\varkappa}^* \mathbf{P}_R F \tag{12.12}$$

or, in the case considered in the present section, into

$$\mathbf{O}_j F = \sum_R \chi^{(j)}(R)^* \mathbf{P}_R F \tag{12.12a}$$

has two eigenvalues, 0 and h/l_j. All functions which belong to the $\varkappa$th row of the representation $\mathbf{D}^{(j)}(R)$, or simply to the representation $\mathbf{D}^{(j)}(R)$, correspond to the eigenvalue h/l_j. Those which belong to other rows of the irreducible $\mathbf{D}^{(j)}(R)$ (or to other representations) correspond to the eigenvalue 0.

The above theorems are nothing but the *orthogonality and completeness relationships* of the eigenfunctions of the operators (12.12), (12.12a). The difference between them and ordinary Hermitian operators arises solely from the fact that (12.12), (12.12a) are *infinitely degenerate operators*, since infinitely many linearly independent eigenfunctions belong to each eigenvalue. The operators $l_j \mathbf{O}_j/h$ are also called idempotents or projection operators in the mathematical literature because $(l_j \mathbf{O}_j/h)^2 = l_j \mathbf{O}_j/h$.

7. We now return to the Schrödinger equation $\mathbf{H}\psi = E\psi$. In the preceding chapter we have seen that a uniquely determined (up to a similarity transformation) representation of the group $\mathbf{P}_R$ belongs to each eigenvalue

of $\mathbf{H}$. On the other hand, we also know that this similarity transformation is at our free disposal, for it is simply the specification of the particular linear combinations of eigenfunctions which we choose to use.

There are many advantages to assuming that the representations of the individual eigenvalues, insofar as these are not irreducible, are in reduced form.

$$\mathbf{\Delta}(R) = \begin{pmatrix} \mathbf{D}^{(1)}(R) & \mathbf{0} & \cdots & \mathbf{0} \\ \mathbf{0} & \mathbf{D}^{(2)}(R) & \cdots & \mathbf{0} \\ \cdot & \cdot & & \cdot \\ \cdot & \cdot & & \cdot \\ \cdot & \cdot & & \cdot \\ \mathbf{0} & \mathbf{0} & \cdots & \mathbf{D}^{(s)}(R) \end{pmatrix}. \tag{12.13}$$

Here the $\mathbf{D}^{(1)}(R), \cdots, \mathbf{D}^{(s)}(R)$ are merely irreducible representations (not necessarily distinct), the s irreducible components of $\mathbf{\Delta}(R)$. Their dimensions might be given by $l_1, l_2, \cdots, l_s$. We will denote by

$$\psi_1^{(1)}, \psi_2^{(1)}, \cdots, \psi_{l_1}^{(1)}, \psi_1^{(2)}, \psi_2^{(2)}, \cdots, \psi_{l_2}^{(2)}, \cdots, \psi_1^{(s)}, \psi_2^{(s)}, \cdots, \psi_{l_s}^{(s)}$$

those linear combinations of eigenfunctions which correspond to this form of the representation for the eigenvalue considered. If we now write Eq. (11.23) of the previous chapter for this eigenvalue,

$$\mathbf{P}_R\psi_\varkappa^{(j)} = \sum_\nu \mathbf{D}^{(j)}(R)_{\nu\varkappa}\psi_\nu^{(j)}. \tag{12.14}$$

(On account of the zeros in (12.13), the $\mathbf{P}_R\psi_\varkappa^{(j)}$ can be expressed immediately as linear combinations of the ψ_ν with the same upper index.) But Eq. (12.14) implies that $\psi_\nu^{(j)}$ satisfy (12.3). *The eigenfunction $\psi_\varkappa^{(j)}$ belongs to the $\varkappa$th row of the representation $\mathbf{D}^{(j)}$ and its partners are $\psi_1^{(j)}, \psi_2^{(j)}, \cdots, \psi_{l_j}^{(j)}$.*

The form of the transformation formula (12.14) suggests that we consider the eigenvalues of (12.13) as s accidentally coincident eigenvalues. The eigenfunctions $\psi_1^{(1)}, \psi_2^{(1)}, \cdots, \psi_{l_1}^{(1)}$ belong to the first eigenvalue; $\psi_1^{(2)}, \psi_2^{(2)}, \cdots, \psi_{l_2}^{(2)}$ to the second; $\cdots$; and $\psi_1^{(s)}, \psi_2^{(s)}, \cdots, \psi_{l_s}^{(s)}$ to the last. To each of these eigenvalues belongs *one irreducible representation*. Consequently, if we look upon the entire eigenvalue spectrum in this way, we can state that *one irreducible representation corresponds to each eigenvalue, and one row of an irreducible representation corresponds to each eigenfunction; the partners of an eigenfunction are the other eigenfunctions belonging to the same eigenvalue.*

In general, very many eigenvalues will correspond to any given representation. We can further standardize the representation formulas, therefore, by taking the representations in the same form for all the levels to which they belong.

When several eigenfunctions which are partners belong to one eigenvalue, we speak of a "normal degeneracy." If, besides, several eigenvalues coincide, as was the case in the eigenvalue of (12.13), we refer to an *accidental degeneracy.* It will be assumed that this is a very uncommon situation, and that it occurs in the important case of the Schrödinger equation only exceptionally.

8. In order to become conversant with the concepts developed above, we wish now to utilize them in considering the Rayleigh–Schrödinger perturbation theory. We begin with an eigenvalue E of the "unperturbed" problem which shows no accidental degeneracy. The corresponding representation of the group of the Schrödinger equation is then irreducible, and the eigenfunctions $\psi_{E1}, \psi_{E2}, \cdots, \psi_{El}$ belong to the different rows of an irreducible representation. We add to the original Hamiltonian operator $\mathbf{H}$ a "symmetric perturbation" $\lambda\mathbf{V}$ which is of such a nature that it does not disturb the symmetry group of $\mathbf{H}$, that is, it is, itself, a symmetric operator in the sense of this chapter. To formulate the secular equation for the first approximation ΔE to the energy shift, we must calculate the matrix elements $(\psi_{E\varkappa}, \mathbf{V}\psi_{E\varkappa'})$. According to (12.8a), these are all zero for $\varkappa \neq \varkappa'$, and all equal for $\varkappa = \varkappa'$. Denoting their common value by v_E, the secular equation takes the form

$$\begin{vmatrix} \lambda v_E - \Delta E & 0 & \cdots & 0 \\ 0 & \lambda v_E - \Delta E & \cdots & 0 \\ \cdot & \cdot & & \cdot \\ \cdot & \cdot & & \cdot \\ \cdot & \cdot & & \cdot \\ 0 & 0 & \cdots & \lambda v_E - \Delta E \end{vmatrix} = 0$$

and has the l-fold root λv_E. Thus, in the first approximation, the eigenvalues do not split. Moreover, they cannot split even in arbitrarily high approximations, since in a splitting into, say, two eigenvalues E_1 and E_2, with l_1 and l_2 eigenfunctions ($l_1 + l_2 = l$), the l_1 eigenfunctions of E_1 must transform among themselves under the $\mathbf{P}$, and there must correspond to them a representation of dimension l_1. This representation cannot contain the original irreducible representation of the unperturbed eigenvalue because $l_1 < l$. Then these l_1 eigenfunctions of E_1 would be orthogonal to all l eigenfunctions of E, and could not be obtained from them or from their linear combinations in a continuous manner. *Under a "symmetric perturbation", an eigenvalue with an irreducible representation retains its representation and cannot split.*

9. We now consider an eigenvalue the representation of which, $\mathbf{\Delta}(R)$, contains $\mathbf{D}^{(1)}(R), \mathbf{D}^{(2)}(R), \cdots, a_1, a_2, \cdots$ times. In the sense of the development in Section 7 we can also say that a_1 eigenvalues with the representation $\mathbf{D}^{(1)}(R)$, a_2 with the representation $\mathbf{D}^{(2)}(R)$, etc., coincide accidentally. If we now allow the symmetric perturbation $\lambda\mathbf{V}$ to take effect, the greatest change that can occur is a splitting of the accidentally degenerate eigenvalues. Then after the perturbation, there will be a_1 eigenvalues with the representation

$\mathbf{D}^{(1)}(R)$, a_2 eigenvalues with the representation $\mathbf{D}^{(2)}(R)$, etc. In general, *these* $a_1 + a_2 + \cdots$ *eigenvalues* will *have different values.* The fact that exactly a_1 eigenvalues with the representation $\mathbf{D}^{(1)}(R)$ must occur after the perturbation follows from the fact that the number of eigenfunctions $a_1 l_1$ which belong to the representation $\mathbf{D}^{(1)}(R)$ cannot change. A change in this number would indicate that the eigenfunctions had changed their correspondence to irreducible representations. We have seen above that this cannot occur continuously.

In Section 8 we have considered an eigenvalue with an irreducible representation. Although l eigenfunctions belong to it, it cannot be split by a symmetric perturbation. This justifies the name "natural degeneracy" for the correspondence of these l linearly independent eigenfunctions to one eigenvalue.

An eigenvalue which, like that considered above, corresponds to a reducible representation, is said to consist of a_1 eigenvalues of the representation $\mathbf{D}^{(1)}(R)$, a_2 eigenvalues of the representation $\mathbf{D}^{(2)}(R)$, etc. The coincidence of these $a_1, a_2, \cdots$ eigenvalues is called an accidental degeneracy, because its occurrence in the absence of the perturbation is connected with the specific nature of the Hamiltonian of the problem. It does not follow from the symmetry of the underlying problem.

10. The fact that the eigenfunctions of $\mathbf{H} + \lambda\mathbf{V}$ can be assumed to belong to one row of one irreducible representation is true not only for the exact eigenfunctions, but also for each successive approximation of the perturbation procedure. First of all, it is clearly true for the exact eigenfunctions, i.e., for the entire power series in λ. But if it holds for the whole series and for arbitrary values of λ, it must also hold for every term separately.

In particular, the "correct linear combinations" for the first approximation to the eigenfunctions of a given eigenvalue E can be so chosen that they are combinations only of eigenfunctions of E which belong to the same row of the same irreducible representation. If a representation for E contains a given irreducible representation $\mathbf{D}^{(j')}(R)$ only once, then E has only one eigenfunction $\psi_\varkappa^{(j')}$ which belongs to, say, the $\varkappa$th row of $\mathbf{D}^{(j')}(R)$, and $\psi_\varkappa^{(j')}$ *is then already a "correct linear combination."* The corresponding eigenvalue is

$$(\psi_\varkappa^{(j')}, (\mathbf{H} + \lambda\mathbf{V})\, \psi_\varkappa^{(j')}).$$

If a representation for E contains the irreducible representation $\mathbf{D}^{(j)}(R)$ several times, say a_j times, then E has a_j eigenfunctions $\psi_{\varkappa 1}^{(j)}, \psi_{\varkappa 2}^{(j)}, \psi_{\varkappa 3}^{(j)}, \cdots, \psi_{\varkappa a_j}^{(j)}$ which belong to the same ($\varkappa$th) row of $\mathbf{D}^{(j)}(R)$. The correct linear combinations are then linear combinations of these a_j eigenfunctions; they cannot be completely determined without calculation.

It is still worthwhile, in all cases, to use from the very beginning the linear combinations $\psi_{\varkappa\rho}^{(j)}$ of eigenfunctions of E which belong to a row of an irreducible representation. Then by (12.8a), the expressions

$$(\psi_{\varkappa\rho}^{(j)}, \mathbf{V}\psi_{\varkappa'\rho'}^{(j')}) = \mathbf{V}_{j\varkappa\rho;j'\varkappa'\rho'} = \delta_{jj'}\,\delta_{\varkappa\varkappa'}v_{\rho\rho'}^{j}$$

must vanish for $j \neq j'$ or $\varkappa \neq \varkappa'$. The secular equation for E,

$$\left|\mathbf{V}_{j\varkappa\rho;j'\varkappa'\rho'} - \Delta E\mathbf{1}\right| = 0,$$

is, therefore, essentially simplified. It divides, as closer inspection reveals, into distinct little "irreducible secular equations" whose dimensions are the numbers a_j which specify the number of times the same irreducible representation is contained in the representation for the eigenvalue E.

Even in higher approximations, the change of the eigenvalues and the eigenfunctions of the representation $\mathbf{D}^{(j)}(R)$ can be calculated by using the eigenvalues and eigenfunctions of this representation alone. It is even sufficient to consider only eigenfunctions which belong to a given row of this representation. According to (5.22), e.g., the second approximation is

$$F_{k\nu} = E_k + \lambda(\psi_{k\nu}, \mathbf{V}\psi_{k\nu}) + \lambda^2 \sum_{E_l \neq E_k} \frac{|(\psi_l, \mathbf{V}\psi_{k\nu})|^2}{E_k - E_l}.$$

Now if ψ_l belongs to a representation different from $\mathbf{D}^{(j)}(R)$ or to a row of $\mathbf{D}^{(j)}$ other than that of $\psi_{k\nu}$, the term $(\psi_l, \mathbf{V}\psi_{k\nu})$ vanishes, and it can simply be omitted from consideration.

11. If the perturbation $\lambda\mathbf{V}$ of $\mathbf{H}$ is not invariant under the entire group of $\mathbf{P}$, but only under a subgroup, then the eigenfunctions which belong to the irreducible representations of this subgroup must be introduced. The eigenfunctions and the eigenvalues of $\mathbf{H}$ will be assumed to correspond to irreducible representations of the whole group of $\mathbf{P}$. *The matrices which correspond to the elements of the subgroup can then be interpreted as a representation of this subgroup.* For all $\mathbf{P}$, and in particular for the $\mathbf{P}_R$ of the subgroup, we have

$$\mathbf{P}_R\psi_{\varkappa}^{(j)} = \sum_{\lambda} \mathbf{D}^{(j)}(R)_{\lambda\varkappa}\psi_{\lambda}^{(j)}.$$

However, the $\mathbf{D}^{(j)}(R)$ for the R of the subgroup need not be irreducible, and to obtain functions which belong to the irreducible representations of the subgroup, these must be reduced. *The numbers and types of the irreducible components of* $\mathbf{D}^{(j)}(R)$ *as a representation of the subgroup gives us the numbers and types of eigenvalues into which the eigenvalue considered can split.*

We see that for the characterization of the eigenvalues of the Schrödinger equation a knowledge of the irreducible representations of the symmetric group of n elements and of the three-dimensional rotation group is essential. We therefore turn to the determination of these representations.

12. In this entire chapter it was necessary to assume about the operators $\mathbf{P}_R$ only that they form a group and that they are linear and unitary (for example, Eq. (11.22) has

not been used). Besides this, it was assumed only that the $\mathbf{P}_R$ transform eigenfunctions of a given eigenvalue of $\mathbf{H}$ into eigenfunctions of the same eigenvalue. Actually these assumptions already imply the transformation equation (11.23) (which we have used as a starting point in the discussion there) and the fact that *the coefficients* occurring in it *form a representation of the group of the operators* $\mathbf{P}_R$.

We note here that for operators which play the role of the $\mathbf{P}_R$ for eigenfunctions with spin (they will be called $\mathbf{O}_R$), Eq. (11.22) no longer holds. Moreover, the symmetry group of configuration space is not isomorphic to the group of these operators, but only homomorphic. The coefficients of (11.23) will then form a representation of the group of operators $\mathbf{O}_R$ and not of the symmetry group of configuration space. All the other theorems of this chapter, such as the orthogonality of eigenfunctions which belong to different irreducible representations, will remain unchanged.

Note: only if $P_R H = H P_R$, will the eigenfunction of this group have the same eigenvalue. However, if we have a larger group containing P_r, $\bar{P}_r$ for which $[\bar{P}_r, H] \neq 0$ we can still speak of ψ belonging to rows of the whole group.

13. The Symmetric Group

1. The elements of the symmetric group of the nth degree are the permutations, or the interchanges of n objects. Its order is $n!$ A permutation which replaces 1 by α_1, 2 by α_2, $\cdots$, and, finally, n by α_n is denoted by $\begin{pmatrix} 1 & 2 & \cdots & n \\ \alpha_1 & \alpha_2 & \cdots & \alpha_n \end{pmatrix}$. This is the same permutation as $\begin{pmatrix} k_1 & k_2 & \cdots & k_n \\ \alpha_{k_1} & \alpha_{k_2} & \cdots & \alpha_{k_n} \end{pmatrix}$ since both transform every k into α_k. Here $k_1, k_2, \cdots, k_n$ is an arbitrary arrangement of the numbers $1, 2, 3, \cdots, n$. By the product of two permutations $A = \begin{pmatrix} 1 & 2 & \cdots & n \\ \alpha_1 & \alpha_2 & \cdots & \alpha_n \end{pmatrix}$ and $B = \begin{pmatrix} 1 & 2 & \cdots & n \\ \beta_1 & \beta_2 & \cdots & \beta_n \end{pmatrix}$, we understand application of the two in succession. Permutation A transforms k into α_k, and B transforms this into β_{α_k}, so that AB transforms k into β_{α_k}. The transformations (11.E.1) form a group isomorphic to the symmetric group of the nth degree; these transformations transform the point $x_1, x_2, \cdots, x_n$ into the point $x_{\alpha_1}, x_{\alpha_2}, \cdots, x_{\alpha_n}$; they correspond, therefore, to the permutations A above.

There is another notation for permutations. In it the permutations are "resolved into cycles." A cycle $(r_1 r_2 \cdots r_\lambda)$ is a permutation which replaces every element r_k by the element following it, r_{k+1}, except that the last element of the cycle, r_λ, is replaced by the first element r_1. The cycle $(r_1 r_2 \cdots r_\lambda)$ is identical with the permutation $\begin{pmatrix} r_1 r_2 \cdots r_\lambda \\ r_2 r_3 \cdots r_1 \end{pmatrix}$. It is also equivalent to the cycle $(r_2 r_3 \cdots r_\lambda r_1)$ or to $(r_3 r_4 \cdots r_\lambda r_1 r_2)$.

Cycles which have no elements in common commute. For example,

$$(1\,3\,5)\,(2\,4\,6\,7) = (2\,4\,6\,7)\,(1\,3\,5) = \begin{pmatrix} 1\,3\,5\,2\,4\,6\,7 \\ 3\,5\,1\,4\,6\,7\,2 \end{pmatrix}.$$

The resolution of a permutation into cycles is its decomposition into a product of cycles which commute; the order of the individual cycles, as well as the initial element of each cycle, is still subject to arbitrary selection. The resolution into cycles can be achieved by beginning, say, with the element 1, and placing after it that element into which 1 is transformed, and next that into which this is transformed, etc. Finally, the element which is transformed into 1 appears; this is the final element in the first cycle. At this point another element which has not yet been included in the cycle is chosen arbitrarily, and the same process is repeated. This procedure is continued until the entire permutation is exhausted.

For example, the permutation $\begin{pmatrix} 1\,2\,3\,4\,5\,6 \\ 3\,4\,6\,2\,5\,1 \end{pmatrix}$ is resolved into cycles as

(1 3 6)(2 4)(5) and this equals (3 6 1)(2 4)(5) and also (2 4)(5)(1 3 6), since the order of the cycles is of no significance.

Two permutations which have the same number of cycles and whose cycles are of equal length are contained in the same class. The two permutations

$$R = (r_1 r_2 \cdots r_{\mu_1})(r_{\mu_1+1} r_{\mu_1+2} \cdots r_{\mu_2}) \cdots (r_{\mu_{\rho-1}+1} \cdots r_{\mu_\rho})$$

and

$$S = (s_1 s_2 \cdots s_{\mu_1})(s_{\mu_1+1} s_{\mu_1+2} \cdots s_{\mu_2}) \cdots (s_{\mu_{\rho-1}+1} \cdots s_{\mu_\rho})$$

can be transformed into one another by

$$T = \begin{pmatrix} s_1 & s_2 & \cdots & s_{\mu_1} & s_{\mu_1+1} & s_{\mu_1+2} & \cdots & s_{\mu_2} & \cdots & s_{\mu_{\rho-1}+1} & \cdots & s_{\mu_\rho} \\ r_1 & r_2 & \cdots & r_{\mu_1} & r_{\mu_1+1} & r_{\mu_1+2} & \cdots & r_{\mu_2} & \cdots & r_{\mu_{\rho-1}+1} & \cdots & r_{\mu_\rho} \end{pmatrix}$$

and

$$T^{-1} = \begin{pmatrix} r_1 & r_2 & \cdots & r_{\mu_1} & r_{\mu_1+1} & r_{\mu_1+2} & \cdots & r_{\mu_2} & \cdots & r_{\mu_{\rho-1}+1} & \cdots & r_{\mu_\rho} \\ s_1 & s_2 & \cdots & s_{\mu_1} & s_{\mu_1+1} & s_{\mu_1+2} & \cdots & s_{\mu_2} & \cdots & s_{\mu_{\rho-1}+1} & \cdots & s_{\mu_\rho} \end{pmatrix}.$$

That is, $S = TRT^{-1}$. Conversely, the cycle lengths of any permutation which results from R by transformation with T are again $\mu_1, \mu_2 - \mu_1, \cdots, \mu_\rho - \mu_{\rho-1}$.

If, therefore, we wish to decide whether two permutations are in the same class, we can place the longest cycle (or cycles) in both first, then the second longest, etc., until the shortest is in the last position. If the lengths of all the cycles $\lambda_1 = \mu_1, \lambda_2 = \mu_2 - \mu_1, \cdots, \lambda_\rho = \mu_\rho - \mu_{\rho-1}$ (with $\lambda_1 \geqslant \lambda_2 \geqslant \cdots \geqslant \lambda_\rho$ and $\lambda_1 + \lambda_2 + \cdots + \lambda_\rho = \mu_\rho = n$) are the same in the two permutations, they belong to the same class, otherwise they do not. The number of classes is thus equal to the number of different possible lengths of the cycles, the number of sequences $\lambda_1, \lambda_2, \cdots, \lambda_\rho$ which satisfy the conditions $\lambda_1 \geqslant \lambda_2 \geqslant \cdots \geqslant \lambda_\rho$ and $\lambda_1 + \lambda_2 + \cdots + \lambda_\rho = n$. This number, the number of possible divisions of n into positive integral summands without regard to order[1] is called the "partition number" of n. According to Chapter 9 the number of different irreducible representations is equal to the number of classes and thus to the partition number of n.

For example, the symmetric group of the fourth degree (of order 24) has five different classes. Each of the following elements typifies one class: $E = (1)(2)(3)(4)$; (1 2)(3)(4); (1 2)(3 4); (1 2 3)(4); (1 2 3 4). Thus, the group must have five irreducible representations. The symmetric group of the third degree has three classes: $E = (1)(2)(3)$; (1 2)(3); (1 2 3), corresponding to the three irreducible representations already discussed in Chapter 9.

[1] For the number of systems of numbers λ, it clearly makes no difference whether the order is disregarded or just one order is taken into consideration.

The single cycles are often omitted. For example, (1 2)(3)(4) is written simply as (1 2).

2. The simplest permutations—apart from the identity—are those which merely interchange two elements. Such a permutation is called a *transposition*; in terms of cycles it can be written (kl). Every permutation can be written as a product of a number of transpositions. For example, a permutation which consists only of one cycle can be written

$$(\alpha_1\alpha_2 \cdots \alpha_\lambda) = (\alpha_1\alpha_2)(\alpha_1\alpha_3) \cdots (\alpha_1\alpha_\lambda).$$

Clearly, the same holds for a product of several cycles, and thus for every permutation.

The concept of *even and odd permutations* plays an important role in the theory of determinants. The value of a determinant

$$\begin{vmatrix} a_{11} & a_{12} & \cdots & a_{1n} \\ a_{21} & a_{22} & \cdots & a_{2n} \\ \cdot & \cdot & & \cdot \\ \cdot & \cdot & & \cdot \\ \cdot & \cdot & & \cdot \\ a_{n1} & a_{n2} & \cdots & a_{nn} \end{vmatrix}$$

is equal to the sum of $n!$ products,

$$|a_{ik}| = \Sigma\, \varepsilon_{(\alpha_1\alpha_2\cdots\alpha_n)} a_{1\alpha_1} a_{2\alpha_2} \cdots a_{n\alpha_n},$$

where $\alpha_1\alpha_2 \cdots \alpha_n$ runs over all $n!$ permutations of the numbers $1, 2, \cdots, n$ and $\varepsilon_{(\alpha_1\cdots\alpha_n)}$ equals $+1$ or -1 according to whether $\begin{pmatrix} 1 & 2 & \cdots & n \\ \alpha_1 & \alpha_2 & \cdots & \alpha_n \end{pmatrix}$ is an even or an odd permutation; i.e., according to whether it can be written as the product of an even or an odd number of transpositions. (A permutation can be decomposed into transpositions in different ways, but the decomposition of a specified permutation gives rise either always to an even number or always to an odd number of transpositions.)

The product of two even permutations is again an even permutation, since it clearly can be written as the product of as many transpositions as the two permutations contain together. The even permutations form a subgroup, *the alternating group*. The index of the alternating group is 2, since a one-to-one correspondence can be set up between the even and the odd permutations, say, by multiplication with the transposition (1 2). The alternating group is an invariant subgroup of the symmetric group; the elements which are conjugate to an even permutation P are again even permutations $S^{-1}PS$ since they can be written as a product of twice as many transpositions as are in S plus as many transpositions as are in P.

The cycle $(\alpha_1\alpha_2 \cdots \alpha_\lambda) = (\alpha_1\alpha_2)(\alpha_1\alpha_3) \cdots (\alpha_1\alpha_\lambda)$ can be written as a product of $\lambda - 1$ transpositions. A permutation with cycle lengths

$$\lambda_1, \lambda_2, \cdots, \lambda_\rho \qquad (\text{with } \lambda_1 + \lambda_2 + \cdots + \lambda_\rho = n)$$

can thus be written as a product of $\lambda_1 - 1 + \lambda_2 - 1 + \cdots + \lambda_\rho - 1$ transposiions. For all elements of the alternating group, an even number of uneven numbers must occur among the $\lambda_\mu - 1$, and thus, among the $\lambda_1, \lambda_2, \cdots, \lambda_\rho$, an even number of even numbers. The permutations of the alternating group contain an even number of cycles of even length (cycles with two, four, etc., elements).

The factor group of the alternating group is of order 2. From its two irreducible representations, two representations of the whole symmetric group can be obtained either by assigning the matrix (1) to the elements of the alternating group as well as to the elements of its coset (the odd permutations), or by assigning the matrix (1) to the elements of the alternating group and the matrix (—1) to its coset. The former correspondence yields the *identical representation* $\mathbf{D}^{(0)}(R) = (1)$; the latter yields the representation $\mathbf{D}(E) = (1)$, $\mathbf{D}(S) = (-1)$, which is called *the antisymmetric representation* $\overline{\mathbf{D}}^{(0)}(R) = (\varepsilon_R)$. Both the identical and antisymmetric representations are one-dimensional.

3. All other representations of the symmetric group have more than one dimension. In a one-dimensional representation, the transposition (1 2) must correspond either to the matrix (1) or to the matrix (—1), since the square of this matrix must be the unit matrix (1). In the first case, however, every transposition in the representation corresponds to (1), and in the second every transposition corresponds to (—1), since all transpositions are in the same class and must, therefore, all have the same character in any representation. But the matrices which correspond to the transpositions determine the entire representation, since all group elements can be written as products of transpositions. Thus, the identical representations must be obtained in the first case, and the antisymmetric in the second.

The *Abelian* factor groups of the alternating group supply a very important relationship between pairs of irreducible representations. If we consider an irreducible representation $\mathbf{D}^{(k)}(R)$, then another representation, the associated representation $\overline{\mathbf{D}}^{(k)}(R)$, can be formed from it by leaving all matrices which correspond to the alternating group unchanged, and multiplying all others by —1. The matrices so obtained do form a representation of the group since $\overline{\mathbf{D}}^{(k)}(R)$ is the direct product of $\mathbf{D}^{(k)}(R)$ and the antisymmetric representation $\overline{\mathbf{D}}^{(0)}(R)$ (which is one-dimensional, so that its matrices are simply numbers):

$$\overline{\mathbf{D}}^{(k)}(R) = \mathbf{D}^{(k)}(R) \times \overline{\mathbf{D}}^{(0)}(R) = \varepsilon_R \mathbf{D}^{(k)}(R).$$

The associated representations play an important role in quantum mechanics as well as in the theory of irreducible representations, and we will utilize them in deriving the representations of interest to us.

The number of different irreducible representations of the symmetric group is equal to the partition number of n. This is also the number of qualitatively different eigenvalues. However, it turns out that only eigenvalues of certain representations correspond to real energy levels in the atom. Eigenvalues of other representations do not correspond to actually existing stationary states, but are forbidden by a principle independent of the eigenvalue equation. the Pauli exclusion principle. Although all the irreducible representations of the symmetric group can be determined by the method we use here, we shall carry out the determination only for those representations whose eigenvalues are not forbidden by the Pauli principle. The exact formulation of this principle will not be given here, but the method by which the representations of interest will be determined involves exactly the same considerations as will be required later in the application of the Pauli principle.

4. If we have a system of variables which can assume only one value, say 1, then the region of variability consists only of a single point, and every function is completely determined when its value at this point is given. In this space no two functions can be linearly independent; every function is constant over the "entire region of variability," and thus is a multiple of every other function. Every function in this space remains unchanged if the values of the coordinates are interchanged, since this amounts merely to replacing 1 by 1. All functions in this space belong to the identical representation.

If we consider n variables $s_1, s_2, \cdots, s_n$ each of which can assume *two values*, say $+1$ and -1, then the entire space consists of 2^n points, and we can have 2^n linearly independent functions, e.g., those which have the value 1 at one of these 2^n points and the value zero at all the others. The scalar product of two functions, φ and g, in this space is

$$\sum_{s_1=\pm 1} \sum_{s_2=\pm 1} \cdots \sum_{s_n=\pm 1} \varphi(s_1 \cdots s_n)^* g(s_1 \cdots s_n) = (\varphi, g).$$

In the space of one s_k (it consists only of two points $s = +1$ and $s = -1$) the two functions $\delta_{s_k,-1}$ and $\delta_{s_k,+1}$ form a "complete orthogonal system"; the 2^n products of these functions $\delta_{s_1\sigma_1} \delta_{s_2\sigma_2} \cdots \delta_{s_n\sigma_n}$ (with $\sigma_1 = \pm 1$, $\sigma_2 = \pm 1, \cdots, \sigma_n = \pm 1$) form a complete orthogonal system in the n dimensional space of $s_1, s_2, \cdots, s_n$. The formulas to follow can be written more conveniently if we use, instead of the functions $\delta_{s_k,+1}, \delta_{s_k,-1}$, the two functions 1 and s_k, which are also orthogonal.

$$(1, s_k) = \sum_{s_k=\pm 1} 1 \cdot s_k = 1 \cdot -1 + 1 \cdot 1 = 0.$$

Then the complete system of functions in the space of $s_1, s_2, \cdots, s_n$ consists of 2^n functions $s_1^{\gamma_1}s_2^{\gamma_2}s_3^{\gamma_3}\cdots s_n^{\gamma_n}$ (with γ_k equal to 0 or 1); these can be arranged in the following manner:

$$\left.\begin{array}{l} 1 \\ s_1, s_2, \cdots, s_n \\ s_1s_2, s_1s_3, \cdots, s_1s_n, s_2s_3, s_2s_4, \cdots, s_2s_n, \cdots, s_{n-1}s_n \\ s_1s_2s_3, \cdots, s_{n-2}s_{n-1}s_n \\ \cdots\cdots\cdots\cdots\cdots\cdots\cdots\cdots\cdots\cdots \\ s_1s_2s_3\cdots s_n. \end{array}\right\} \tag{13.1}$$

These are[2] $1 + \binom{n}{1} + \binom{n}{2} + \binom{n}{3} + \cdots + \binom{n}{n} = 2^n$ functions. If the operator $\mathbf{P}_R$, corresponding to a permutation R, is applied to one of these functions, it produces a new function of $s_1, s_2, \cdots, s_n$ which can be expressed as a linear combination of these 2^n functions (as can every function of these variables). The coefficients will give a 2^n dimensional representation of the symmetric group. This representation, $\mathbf{\Delta}(R)$, is not irreducible, but contains several irreducible components. Because the functions considered are defined in such a narrowly limited region, one expects that $\mathbf{\Delta}(R)$ does not contain all the irreducible representations of the symmetric group, and, therefore, that it can be reduced more easily than a completely arbitrary representation. Nonetheless, *its irreducible components and their associated representations are the only representations which are needed* for the physical problems connected with *electrons.*

If the operator $\mathbf{P}_R$ is applied to one of the functions (13.1), say $s_as_bs_c$, where R is an arbitrary permutation, i.e., if one carries out a "permutation of the variables," the result is again a product of three s's, say, $s_{a'}s_{b'}s_{c'}$, and thus a function which is in the same (third)[3] row of (13.1) as $s_as_bs_c$. If one wishes to express the $\binom{n}{k}$ functions which result from applying an operator $\mathbf{P}_R$ to all the functions of the kth row in terms of the functions (13.1), only the functions of the kth row need be used. These functions, therefore, provide a representation $\mathbf{\Delta}^{(k)}(R)$ of the symmetric group with dimension $\binom{n}{k}$. Since each function in the kth row is transformed by a permutation into one other function in the kth row, $\mathbf{\Delta}^{(k)}(R)$ has one element in each row equal to 1 and all other elements equal to 0. The representation $\mathbf{\Delta}(R)$ therefore decomposes into representations $\mathbf{\Delta}^{(0)}(R), \mathbf{\Delta}^{(1)}(R), \cdots, \mathbf{\Delta}^{(n)}(R)$, whose

[2] The symbol $\binom{n}{k}$ is the ordinary binomial coefficient: $\binom{n}{k} = \dfrac{n!}{k!(n-k)!}$. It gives the number of combinations of n objects taken k at a time.

[3] We begin the labeling of the rows of (13.1) with zero; the last row is the nth.

matrices have the aforementioned property. By utilizing this fact, we now calculate the trace of $\mathbf{\Delta}^{(k)}(R)$.

The trace of the matrix $\mathbf{\Delta}^{(k)}(R)$ is equal to the number of functions in the kth row of (13.1) which remain unchanged when $\mathbf{P}_R$ is applied. In the columns of $\mathbf{\Delta}^{(k)}(R)$ corresponding to these functions the 1 occurs in the main diagonal; in all other rows, it occurs elsewhere, so that a zero stands in the main diagonal. We now calculate this number.

Let R be a permutation with cycles of length $\lambda_1 = \mu_1, \lambda_2 = \mu_2 - \mu_1, \cdots, \lambda_\rho = \mu_\rho - \mu_{\rho-1}$ $(\mu_\rho = n)$, say the permutation $(1, 2 \cdots \mu_1)(\mu_1 + 1 \cdots \mu_2) \cdots (\mu_{\rho-1} + 1, \mu_{\rho-1} + 2 \cdots \mu_\rho)$. If this is to leave the function $s_1^{\alpha_1} \cdot s_2^{\alpha_2} \cdots s_n^{\alpha_n}$ unchanged, then the exponents of $s_1, s_2, \cdots, s_{\mu_1}$ must all be equal, as well as those of $s_{\mu_1+1}, s_{\mu_1+2}, \cdots, s_{\mu_2}$; etc., and, finally, the exponents of $s_{\mu_{\rho-1}+1}, s_{\mu_{\rho-1}+2}, \cdots, s_{\mu_\rho} = s_n$ must all be equal. Therefore, of all possible functions, those which can be written in the form

$$(s_1 s_2 \cdots s_{\mu_1})^{\gamma_1} (s_{\mu_1+1} s_{\mu_1+2} \cdots s_{\mu_2})^{\gamma_2} \cdots (s_{\mu_{\rho-1}+1} \cdots s_{\mu_\rho})^{\gamma_\rho} \qquad (13.2)$$

will be left unchanged by $\mathbf{P}_R$. (All γ_k are 0 or 1.) We are interested in the number of functions in the kth row of (13.1) which have the form (13.2). Since these functions are in the kth row, we must have the relationship

$$\mu_1\gamma_1 + (\mu_2 - \mu_1)\gamma_2 + \cdots + (\mu_\rho - \mu_{\rho-1})\gamma_\rho = \lambda_1\gamma_1 + \lambda_2\gamma_2 + \cdots + \lambda_\rho\gamma_\rho = k. \qquad (13.3)$$

Thus, there are as many of these functions as there are solutions of (13.3) in which only the numbers 0 and 1 are allowed for the unknowns $\gamma_1, \gamma_2, \cdots, \gamma_\rho$. This is the trace of R in $\mathbf{\Delta}^{(k)}(R)$, and also that of every other permutation which has cycle lengths $\lambda_1, \lambda_2, \cdots, \lambda_\rho$, since these are all in the same class and, therefore, all have the same trace. The total number of solutions of (13.3) for a given k is equal to the coefficient of x^k in the polynomial

$$(1 + x^{\lambda_1})(1 + x^{\lambda_2}) \cdots (1 + x^{\lambda_\rho}) \qquad (\lambda_1 + \lambda_2 + \cdots + \lambda_\rho = n) \quad (13.4)$$

since this coefficient is just the total number of ways in which the exponents of x in the individual factors can be added (with coefficient 1 or 0) to give k. Hence, *the coefficient of the kth power of x in the polynomial* (*13.4*) is *the trace of* $\mathbf{\Delta}^{(k)}(R)$.

The trace of $\mathbf{\Delta}^{(k)}(E)$ must be equal to the dimension $\binom{n}{k}$ of the representation. Since for E, all cycle lengths are equal to 1, for $\lambda_1 = \lambda_2 = \cdots = \lambda_\rho = 1$, Eq. (13.4) is equal to $(1 + x)^n$ and the coefficient of x^k is then actually $\binom{n}{k}$. The trace of the matrix which corresponds to a transposition $(1\,2) \cdot (3) \cdot (4) \cdots (n)$ is the coefficient of x^k in

$$(1 + x^2)(1 + x) \cdots (1 + x) = (1 + x^2)(1 + x)^{n-2}.$$

Upon calculation, we find that it is

$$\sum_\varkappa \mathbf{\Delta}^{(k)}(R)_{\varkappa\varkappa} = \binom{n-2}{k} + \binom{n-2}{k-2}.$$

It is clear that $\mathbf{\Delta}^{(k)}(R)$ is not an irreducible representation, since linear combinations which transform under $\mathbf{P}_R$ according to $\mathbf{\Delta}^{(k-1)}(R)$ can be formed from the $\binom{n}{k}$ functions of the kth row of (13.1), and this would not be possible in an irreducible representation.

An especially simple example of a linear combination of functions of the kth row can be used to demonstrate the reducibility of $\mathbf{\Delta}^{(k)}(R)$. This example is the sum of all the functions in the kth row. This sum clearly transforms into itself under any permutation; therefore, a linear combination of the functions of the kth row into $\binom{n}{k}$ new functions, of which this sum was the first, would effect a similarity transformation on the matrices $\mathbf{\Delta}^{(k)}(R)$ such that they all would have the form

$$\begin{pmatrix} 1 & 0 \\ 0 & \mathbf{A} \end{pmatrix}.$$

But a representation which can be brought into this form by a similarity transformation is, by definition, reducible.

The linear combinations of functions of the kth row of (13.1) which transform like the functions $s_{a_1}s_{a_2}\cdots s_{a_{k-1}}$ of the $(k-1)$th row are

$$F_{a_1a_2\cdots a_{k-1}} = s_{a_1a_2\cdots a_{k-1}}s_{a_1}s_{a_2}\cdots s_{a_{k-1}}, \tag{13.5}$$

where $s_{a_1a_2\cdots a_{k-1}}$ denotes the sum of all the $n-k+1$ variables which do *not* appear among the $s_{a_1}s_{a_2}\cdots s_{a_{k-1}}$. Under $\mathbf{P}_R$, the function s_{a_i} transforms into s_{b_i}. Thus $s_{a_1}s_{a_2}\cdots s_{a_{k-1}}$ transforms into $s_{b_1}s_{b_2}\cdots s_{b_{k-1}}$. An s_c, which is *not* one of the variables $s_{a_1}, s_{a_2}, \cdots, s_{a_{k-1}}$, transforms into an s_d which is different from all the s_b into which the s_a transform. Hence, the *sum* of all the $n-k+1$ variables, s, which do not occur among the $s_{a_1}, s_{a_2}, \cdots, s_{a_{k-1}}$, transforms into the sum of all the $n-k+1$ variables which do not occur among the variables s_b. That is, $s_{a_1a_2\cdots a_{k-1}}$ transforms into $s_{b_1b_2\cdots b_{k-1}}$. Therefore, the $F_{a_1a_2\cdots a_{k-1}}$ actually do transform exactly like the $s_{a_1}s_{a_2}\cdots s_{a_{k-1}}$ of the $(k-1)$th row.

In an appendix to this chapter we show that, for $k \leqslant \frac{1}{2}n$, the $\binom{n}{k-1}$ functions $F_{a_1a_2\ldots a_{k-1}}$ form a linearly independent set. We can therefore choose linear combinations of these functions $F_1, F_2, \cdots, F_{\binom{n}{k-1}}$ which are orthogonal as well as linearly independent. To complete the full set of $\binom{n}{k}$ functions, we can form from the $\binom{n}{k}$ functions $s_{a_1}s_{a_2}\cdots s_{a_k}$ (when $k \leqslant \frac{1}{2}n$)

$$l_k = \binom{n}{k} - \binom{n}{k-1} \tag{13.6}$$

linear combinations[4] $g_1, g_2, \cdots, g_{l_k}$ which, together with the $F_\varkappa$, form a complete orthogonal set. All the functions $s_{a_1}s_{a_2}s_{a_3}\cdots s_{a_k}$ can then be written in terms of this set, and conversely. The representation $\mathbf{\Delta}^{(k)}(R)$ will then be considered in the foım $\overline{\mathbf{\Delta}}^{(k)}(R)$, which it assumes upon introduction of this complete set $F_1, F_2, \cdots, F_{\binom{n}{k-1}}, g_1, g_2, \cdots, g_{l_k}$ in place of the set $s_{a_1}s_{a_2}s_{a_3}\cdots s_{a_k}$; this substitution effects only a similarity transformation on $\mathbf{\Delta}^{(k)}(R)$.

Since each $F_\varkappa$ is a linear combination of the $F_{a_1a_2\cdots a_{k-1}}$, the $\mathbf{P}_R F_\varkappa$ are linear combinations of the $\mathbf{P}_R F_{a_1a_2\cdots a_{k-1}}$, and, therefore, of the $F_{a_1a_2\cdots a_{k-1}}$, or of the $F_\varkappa$, that is,

$$\mathbf{P}_R F_\varkappa = \sum_{\lambda=1}^{\binom{n}{k-1}} \overline{\mathbf{\Delta}}^{(k-1)}(R)_{\lambda\varkappa} F_\lambda . \tag{13.7}$$

We have denoted the coefficients by $\overline{\mathbf{\Delta}}^{(k-1)}(R)$ since they form a representation equivalent to $\mathbf{\Delta}^{(k-1)}(R)$. The $g_\varkappa$ in (13.7) all have zero coefficients; hence $\overline{\mathbf{\Delta}}^{(k)}(R)$ has the form

$$\overline{\mathbf{\Delta}}^{(k)}(R) = \begin{pmatrix} \overline{\mathbf{\Delta}}^{(k-1)}(R) & \mathbf{A}(R) \\ \mathbf{0} & \mathbf{D}^{(k)}(R) \end{pmatrix}.$$

Furthermore, the complete set $F_1, F_2, \cdots, F_{\binom{n}{k-1}}, g_1, g_2, \cdots, g_{l_k}$ is orthogonal; therefore, $\overline{\mathbf{\Delta}}^{(k)}(R)$ is unitary.

$$\overline{\mathbf{\Delta}}^{(k)}(R) = \overline{\mathbf{\Delta}}^{(k)}(R^{-1})^\dagger .$$

That is

$$\begin{pmatrix} \overline{\mathbf{\Delta}}^{(k-1)}(R) & \mathbf{A}(R) \\ \mathbf{0} & \mathbf{D}^{(k)}(R) \end{pmatrix} = \begin{pmatrix} \overline{\mathbf{\Delta}}^{(k-1)}(R^{-1}) & \mathbf{A}(R^{-1}) \\ \mathbf{0} & \mathbf{D}^{(k)}(R^{-1}) \end{pmatrix}^\dagger$$

$$= \begin{pmatrix} \overline{\mathbf{\Delta}}^{(k-1)}(R^{-1})^\dagger & \mathbf{0} \\ \mathbf{A}(R^{-1})^\dagger & \mathbf{D}^{(k)}(R^{-1})^\dagger \end{pmatrix}.$$

Thus, $\mathbf{A}(R) = \mathbf{0}$, and

$$\overline{\mathbf{\Delta}}^{(k)}(R) = \begin{pmatrix} \overline{\mathbf{\Delta}}^{(k-1)}(R) & \mathbf{0} \\ \mathbf{0} & \mathbf{D}^{(k)}(R) \end{pmatrix}. \tag{13.8}$$

Thus, if $k \leqslant \frac{1}{2}n$, the representation $\mathbf{\Delta}^{(k)}(R)$ divides into two representations, $\overline{\mathbf{\Delta}}^{(k-1)}(R)$ and $\mathbf{D}^{(k)}(R)$, with dimensions $\binom{n}{k-1}$ and $l_k = \binom{n}{k} - \binom{n}{k-1}$, and the former is equivalent to $\mathbf{\Delta}^{k-1}(R)$. Subsequently, $\overline{\mathbf{\Delta}}^{(k-1)}(R)$ can be

[4] One example of such a function is $(s_1 - s_2)(s_3 - s_4)\cdots(s_{2k-1} - s_{2k})$.

divided into two representations, $\bar{\mathbf{\Delta}}^{(k-2)}(R)$ and $\mathbf{D}^{(k-1)}(R)$, then $\bar{\mathbf{\Delta}}^{(k-2)}$ can be divided further, etc. Finally, $\bar{\mathbf{\Delta}}^{(k)}$ divides into $\mathbf{D}^{(0)} + \mathbf{D}^{(1)} + \cdots + \mathbf{D}^{(k)}$. The function of the kth row of (13.1) which transforms by $\mathbf{D}^{(0)}$ (i.e., is invariant) was exhibited before as the sum of all functions of the kth row.

This holds for $k \leqslant \frac{1}{2}n$. For $k > \frac{1}{2}n$, the $\binom{n}{k} = \binom{n}{n-k}$ functions, in which $n - k$ variables occur in the first power, and k in the zeroth power, transform exactly like the functions above (in which the same $n - k$ variables occurred in the zeroth power and the same k, in the first power). The particular choice one makes for the orthogonal system for the s makes no difference at all. In place of 1, s, one could also use s, 1. Therefore, $\mathbf{\Delta}^{(k)}$ is equivalent to $\mathbf{\Delta}^{(n-k)}$ and can be resolved into the same components. Thus, the decomposition of $\mathbf{\Delta}(R)$ takes for even n the following form (for $n = 4$):

$$\mathbf{\Delta}(R) = \begin{cases} \mathbf{\Delta}^{(0)}(R) = \quad \mathbf{D}^{(0)} & = \mathbf{D}^{(0)} \\ \mathbf{\Delta}^{(1)}(R) = \mathbf{\Delta}^{(0)} + \mathbf{D}^{(1)} & = \mathbf{D}^{(0)} + \mathbf{D}^{(1)} \\ \mathbf{\Delta}^{(2)}(R) = \mathbf{\Delta}^{(1)} + \mathbf{D}^{(2)} & = \mathbf{D}^{(0)} + \mathbf{D}^{(1)} + \mathbf{D}^{(2)} \\ \mathbf{\Delta}^{(3)}(R) \sim \quad \mathbf{\Delta}^{(1)} & = \mathbf{D}^{(0)} + \mathbf{D}^{(1)} \\ \mathbf{\Delta}^{(4)}(R) \sim \quad \mathbf{\Delta}^{(0)} & = \mathbf{D}^{(0)} \end{cases}$$

or for odd n, ($n = 5$, for example):

$$\mathbf{\Delta}(R) = \begin{cases} \mathbf{\Delta}^{(0)}(R) = \quad \mathbf{D}^{(0)} & = \mathbf{D}^{(0)} \\ \mathbf{\Delta}^{(1)}(R) = \mathbf{\Delta}^{(0)} + \mathbf{D}^{(1)} & = \mathbf{D}^{(0)} + \mathbf{D}^{(1)} \\ \mathbf{\Delta}^{(2)}(R) = \mathbf{\Delta}^{(1)} + \mathbf{D}^{(2)} & = \mathbf{D}^{(0)} + \mathbf{D}^{(1)} + \mathbf{D}^{(2)} \\ \mathbf{\Delta}^{(3)}(R) \sim \quad \mathbf{\Delta}^{(2)} & = \mathbf{D}^{(0)} + \mathbf{D}^{(1)} + \mathbf{D}^{(2)} \\ \mathbf{\Delta}^{(4)}(R) \sim \quad \mathbf{\Delta}^{(1)} & = \mathbf{D}^{(0)} + \mathbf{D}^{(1)} \\ \mathbf{\Delta}^{(5)}(R) \sim \quad \mathbf{\Delta}^{(0)} & = \mathbf{D}^{(0)}. \end{cases}$$

We shall now show that the representations obtained above, $\mathbf{D}^{(0)}, \mathbf{D}^{(1)}, \cdots, \mathbf{D}^{(\frac{1}{2}n)}$ (or $\mathbf{D}^{(\frac{1}{2}n-\frac{1}{2})}$), are irreducible and distinct. This will be done by induction: we assume that the representations obtained in the same way for the symmetric group of the $(n - 1)$th degree, $'\mathbf{D}^{(0)}(R'), \cdots, '\mathbf{D}^{(k)}(R')$ $(k \leqslant \frac{1}{2}(n - 1))$ are irreducible and distinct, and assume that their dimensions[5] are $l'_k = \binom{n-1}{k} - \binom{n-1}{k-1}$. The main point of the proof is the demonstration that $\mathbf{D}^{(k)}$, if considered only for those R' which do not affect s_n, is a representation of the symmetric group of $(n - 1)$th degree and that its irreducible parts are $'\mathbf{D}^{(k-1)}$ and $'\mathbf{D}^{(k)}$. From this, the irreducible nature of the $\mathbf{D}^{(k)}$ and their distinctness will follow easily.

[5] The primed quantities always refer to the symmetric group of the $(n - 1)$th degree, or to functions in the $n - 1$ variables $s_1, s_2, \cdots s_{n-1}$.

5. The functions $g_1, \cdots, g_{l_k}$, being linear in the variable s_n, can be resolved into sums

$$g_\varkappa = g'_\varkappa s_n + h'_\varkappa \tag{13.9}$$

in such a way that s_n occurs in the zeroth power in both $g'_\varkappa$ and $h'_\varkappa$; $g'_\varkappa$ and $h'_\varkappa$ can then be considered functions of the variables $s_1, s_2, \cdots, s_{n-1}$ alone; $g'_\varkappa$ is of the $(k-1)$th degree and $h'_\varkappa$ is of kth degree.

It may be possible to form linear combinations of the $g_\varkappa$ which do not contain a term proportional to s_n. If there are l'' such linearly independent linear combinations, they can be orthogonalized by Schmidt's procedure and will be denoted by $\bar{g}_{0\varkappa}$.

$$\bar{g}_{0\varkappa} = \bar{h}'_{0\varkappa} \qquad (\text{for } \varkappa = 1, 2, \cdots, l''). \tag{13.9a}$$

All primed functions will be independent of s_n. Naturally, l'' could be zero but it will turn out that this is not the case in general. The remaining $g_\varkappa$ can then be orthogonalized to the $\bar{g}_{0\varkappa}$ and among themselves to give

$$\bar{g}_{1\varkappa} = \bar{g}'_{1\varkappa} s_n + \bar{h}'_{1\varkappa} \qquad (\text{for } \varkappa = 1, 2, \cdots, l_k - l''). \tag{13.9b}$$

The $\bar{g}'_{1\varkappa}$ obtained in this way are linearly independent. Otherwise, it would be possible to obtain further functions $\bar{g}$ which do not contain s_n. The representation of the symmetric group which applies to the $\bar{g}$ will be equivalent to $\mathbf{D}^{(k)}$ because the $\bar{g}$ are linear combinations of the g. It will be unitary because the $\bar{g}$ are orthogonal. We shall investigate the behavior of the functions $\bar{g}_{0\varkappa}, \bar{g}_{1\varkappa}$ under permutations $\mathbf{P}_{R'}$ which leave s_n unchanged. These permutations form a group which is isomorphic to the symmetric group of degree $n-1$. It will turn out that the $\bar{g}_{0\varkappa}$ belong to the representation $'\mathbf{D}^{(k)}$ of this group, the $\bar{g}_{1\varkappa}$ to the representation $'\mathbf{D}^{(k-1)}$. Note that the sum of the dimensions of these two representations does equal l_k

$$\begin{aligned} l'_k + l'_{k-1} &= \binom{n-1}{k} - \binom{n-1}{k-1} + \binom{n-1}{k-1} - \binom{n-1}{k-2} \\ &= \binom{n}{k} - \binom{n}{k-1} = l_k . \end{aligned} \tag{13.10}$$

Once this is established, the irreducible nature of $\mathbf{D}^{(k)}$ will follow easily.

Let us consider first the functions $\bar{g}_{1\varkappa}$. Each $\bar{g}_{1\varkappa}$ is orthogonal to all functions $F_{a_1 a_2 \cdots a_{k-1}}$ and, in particular, to the function

$$F_{a_1 a_2 \cdots a_{k-2} n} = s_{a_1} s_{a_2} \cdots s_{a_{k-2}} s_n s_{a_1 a_2 \cdots a_{k-2} n} .$$

Since $\bar{h}'_{1\varkappa}$ contains s_n in zeroth power, it, too, is orthogonal to $F_{a_1 a_2 \cdots a_{k-2} n}$; consequently $\bar{g}'_{1\varkappa} s_n$ is also. Therefore, $\bar{g}'_{1\varkappa}$ is orthogonal to every function $s_{a_1} s_{a_2} \cdots s_{a_{k-2}} s_{a_1 a_2 \cdots a_{k-2} n}$. But this orthogonality is the definition of the l'_{k-1} functions of $s_1, s_2, \cdots, s_{n-1}$ of degree $k-1$ which transform, under the permutations of these variables, according to the representation $'\mathbf{D}^{(k-1)}$ which is irreducible by hypothesis. Since there are only l'_{k-1} functions of $s_1, s_2, \cdots, s_{n-1}$ of degree $k-1$, which have this property (or which are orthogonal to the $s_{a_1}s_{a_2}\cdots s_{a_{k-2}}s_{a_1a_2\cdots a_{k-2}n}$), there can be no more than l'_{k-1} functions $\bar{g}_{1\varkappa}$. In fact, there are exactly l'_{k-1} such functions and these transform, under those permutations R' which leave s_n unchanged, according to $'\mathbf{D}^{(k-1)}$. In order to see this, one applies $\mathbf{P}_{R'}$ to (13.9b) and since this does not affect s_n, one obtains

$$\mathbf{P}_{R'}\bar{g}_{1\varkappa} = s_n\mathbf{P}_{R'}\bar{g}'_{1\varkappa} + \mathbf{P}_{R'}\bar{h}'_{1\varkappa}. \tag{13.11}$$

When these functions are expressed as linear combinations of the $\bar{g}_{0\varkappa}$ and $\bar{g}_{1\varkappa}$, comparison of the coefficient of s_n shows that the $\mathbf{P}_{R'}\bar{g}'_{1\varkappa}$ are linear combinations of the $\bar{g}'_{1\varkappa}$ themselves. Since the $\bar{g}'_{1\varkappa}$ belong to the irreducible representation $'\mathbf{D}^{(k-1)}$, this is possible only if there are l'_{k-1} linearly independent $\bar{g}'_{1\varkappa}$, or none. The latter alternative can be excluded since it would imply that all $\bar{g}$, and hence all g, are independent of s_n. Since n played no other role for the selection of the g than any other index, this is impossible. We have, therefore,

$$\mathbf{P}_{R'}\bar{g}'_{1\varkappa} = \sum_{\lambda=1}^{l'_{k-1}} {'\mathbf{D}^{(k-1)}}(R')_{\lambda\varkappa}\bar{g}'_{1\lambda} \qquad (\varkappa = 1, 2, \cdots, l'_{k-1}) \tag{13.11a}$$

and $l_k - l'' = l'_{k-1}$. If $l_k = l'_{k-1}$, there are indeed no functions of the type (13.9a), that is, in this case all the $g'_\varkappa$ in (13.9) are linearly independent. However, as will be verified later, $l_k = l'_{k-1}$ only if $k = \frac{1}{2}n$.

If $l_k > l'_k$, consider the functions (13.9a). Any permutation R' of the first $n-1$ variables in the $\bar{g}_{0\varkappa} = \bar{h}'_{0\varkappa}$ of (13.9a) still gives a function which is independent of s_n. Hence, if the $\mathbf{P}_{R'}\bar{g}_{0\varkappa}$ are expressed in terms of the $\bar{g}$, the coefficient of the $\bar{g}_{1\lambda}$ will vanish. Since the $\bar{g}'_{1\lambda}$ are linearly independent, a linear combination of the $\bar{g}_{1\lambda}$ of (13.9b) can be independent of s_n only if the coefficient of each of them vanishes. Hence, the $\mathbf{P}_{R'}\bar{g}_{0\varkappa}$ are linear combinations of the $\bar{g}_{0\varkappa}$ only; these functions belong to a representation of the symmetric group of degree $n-1$ consisting of the permutation operators $\mathbf{P}_{R'}$ which leave s_n unchanged. In order to find this representation we note that the $g_\varkappa$, and hence also the $\bar{g}_{0\varkappa}$ are orthogonal to all $F_{a_1a_2\cdots a_{k-1}}$. Let us consider, in this case, those F whose index does *not* contain n. These can be written in the form

$$F_{a_1a_2\cdots a_{k-1}} = s_{a_1}s_{a_2}\cdots s_{a_{k-1}}(s_{a_1a_2\cdots a_{k-1}n} + s_n).$$

In $\bar{g}_{0\varkappa}$, the function s_n occurs to the zeroth power. It is, therefore, orthogonal to $s_{a_1}s_{a_2}\cdots s_{a_{k-1}}s_n$ and must be orthogonal also to $s_{a_1}s_{a_2}\cdots s_{a_{k-1}}s_{a_1a_2\cdots a_{k-1}n}$. It is of the degree k. But this is just the definition of the functions of $s_1, s_2, \cdots, s_{n-1}$ which belong to the representation $'\mathbf{D}^{(k)}$ (this representation is also irreducible by hypothesis). The $\bar{g}_{0\varkappa}$ must, therefore, belong to this representation of the group of operators $\mathbf{P}_{R'}$ and one has for $\varkappa = 1, 2, \cdots, l'' = l'_k$

$$\mathbf{P}_{R'}\bar{g}_{0\varkappa} = \sum_{\lambda=1}^{l'_k} {}'\mathbf{D}^{(k)}(R')_{\lambda\varkappa}\bar{g}_{0\lambda}\,. \tag{13.11b}$$

The Eqs. (13.11b) and (13.11a) permit the determination of the representation matrices $\mathbf{D}^{(k)}(R)$ at least for those $R = R'$ which leave s_n unchanged. The expressions to be obtained become simpler if the labeling of the rows and columns of $\mathbf{D}^{(k)}$ corresponds to the labeling of the functions $\bar{g}$ of (13.9a) and (13.9b).

$$\mathbf{P}_R\bar{g}_{0\varkappa} = \sum_{\lambda=1}^{l'_k} \mathbf{D}^{(k)}(R)_{0\lambda;0\varkappa}\bar{g}_{0\lambda} + \sum_{\lambda=1}^{l'_{k-1}} \mathbf{D}^{(k)}(R)_{1\lambda;0\varkappa}\bar{g}_{1\lambda} \tag{13.12a}$$

$$\mathbf{P}_R\bar{g}_{1\varkappa} = \sum_{\lambda=1}^{l'_k} \mathbf{D}^{k}(R)_{0\lambda;1\varkappa}\bar{g}_{0\lambda} + \sum_{\lambda=1}^{l'_{k-1}} \mathbf{D}^{(k)}(R)_{1\lambda;1\varkappa}(\bar{g}'_{1\lambda}s_n + \bar{h}'_{1\lambda}). \tag{13.12b}$$

$\mathbf{D}^{(k)}$ is then a supermatrix

$$\mathbf{D}^{(k)}(R) = \begin{pmatrix} \mathbf{D}^{(k)}_{00}(R) & \mathbf{D}^{(k)}_{01}(R) \\ \mathbf{D}^{(k)}_{10}(R) & \mathbf{D}^{(k)}_{11}(R) \end{pmatrix}. \tag{13.12}$$

For an $R = R'$ which leaves s_n unchanged, comparison of (13.12a) with (13.11b) yields by virtue of the linear independence of all $\bar{g}$,

$$\mathbf{D}^{(k)}(R')_{0\lambda;0\varkappa} = {}'\mathbf{D}^{(k)}(R')_{\lambda\varkappa}; \qquad \mathbf{D}^{(k)}(R')_{1\lambda;0\varkappa} = 0. \tag{13.13a}$$

In order to compare (13.11a) with (13.12b) since $\mathbf{P}_{R'}$ does not affect s_n, the former can be substituted into the expression for $\mathbf{P}_{R'}\bar{g}_{1\varkappa}$ resulting from (13.9b).

$$\begin{aligned} \mathbf{P}_{R'}\bar{g}_{1\varkappa} &= s_n\mathbf{P}_{R'}\bar{g}'_{1\varkappa} + \mathbf{P}_{R'}\bar{h}'_{1\varkappa} \\ &= \sum_{\lambda=1}^{l'_{k-1}} {}'\mathbf{D}^{(k-1)}(R')_{\lambda\varkappa}\bar{g}'_{1\lambda}s_n + \mathbf{P}_{R'}\bar{h}'_{1\varkappa}\,. \end{aligned}$$

Since all $\bar{g}'_{1\lambda}s_n$ are linearly independent and orthogonal to all $\bar{g}_{0\lambda}$, $\bar{h}'_{1\lambda}$, and $\mathbf{P}_{R'}\bar{h}'_{1\varkappa}$ (which contain s_n in zeroth power), comparison of the last equation with (13.12b) gives

$$\mathbf{D}^{(k)}(R')_{1\lambda;1\varkappa} = {}'\mathbf{D}^{(k-1)}(R')_{\lambda\varkappa}\,. \tag{13.13b}$$

Hence, for R' which leave s_n unaffected,

$$\mathbf{D}^{(k)}(R') = \begin{pmatrix} {}'\mathbf{D}^{(k)}(R') & \mathbf{0} \\ \mathbf{B}(R') & {}'\mathbf{D}^{(k-1)}(R') \end{pmatrix},$$

where $\mathbf{B}(R')$ is, so far, unknown. However, $\mathbf{D}^{(k)}$ is unitary since the $\bar{g}$ are orthogonal so that $\mathbf{B}(R')$ must vanish. It follows that the representation $\mathbf{D}^{(k)}(R)$, considered as a representation of the symmetric group of the

$(n-1)$th degree, divides into two distinct irreducible components (unless $l_k = l'_{k-1}$). The matrices which correspond to permutations R' which leave s_n unchanged have the form

$$\mathbf{D}^{(k)}(R') = \begin{pmatrix} '\mathbf{D}^{(k)}(R') & \mathbf{0} \\ \mathbf{0} & '\mathbf{D}^{(k-1)}(R') \end{pmatrix}. \tag{13.13}$$

It is well to dispose of the case $l_k = l'_{k-1}$ at this point. This can occur only if $k = \frac{1}{2}n$. This follows most simply from the identity (13.10) according to which

$$l_k - l'_{k-1} = \binom{n-1}{k} - \binom{n-1}{k-1},$$

and this can be zero only if $k + (k-1) = n-1$. The exceptional nature of this case could have been anticipated since $'\mathbf{D}^{(k)}$ is defined only if $k \leqslant \frac{1}{2}(n-1)$ and this is not the case for $k = \frac{1}{2}n$. However, the irreducible nature of $\mathbf{D}^{(k)}$ follows in this case at once; instead of Eq. (13.13), the equality $\mathbf{D}^{(k)}(R') = {}'\mathbf{D}^{(k-1)}(R')$ applies in this case. Thus, $\mathbf{D}^{(\frac{1}{2}n)}(R)$ is irreducible by virtue of the fact that the matrices which correspond to the subgroup that leaves s_n unchanged are already irreducible.

In the general case, consider a matrix

$$\begin{pmatrix} \mathbf{M}_1 & \mathbf{M}_2 \\ \mathbf{M}_3 & \mathbf{M}_4 \end{pmatrix} \tag{13.14}$$

which commutes with all $\mathbf{D}^{(k)}(R)$. Let the division of rows and columns be the same in (13.14) as in (13.13). In particular, (13.14) must also commute with the $\mathbf{D}^{(k)}(R')$ of (13.13).

$$\begin{pmatrix} '\mathbf{D}^{(k)}(R') & \mathbf{0} \\ \mathbf{0} & '\mathbf{D}^{(k-1)}(R') \end{pmatrix}\begin{pmatrix} \mathbf{M}_1 & \mathbf{M}_2 \\ \mathbf{M}_3 & \mathbf{M}_4 \end{pmatrix} = \begin{pmatrix} \mathbf{M}_1 & \mathbf{M}_2 \\ \mathbf{M}_3 & \mathbf{M}_4 \end{pmatrix}\begin{pmatrix} '\mathbf{D}^{(k)}(R') & \mathbf{0} \\ \mathbf{0} & '\mathbf{D}^{(k-1)}(R') \end{pmatrix}.$$

Therefore, for all matrices of the irreducible representations $'\mathbf{D}^{(k-1)}(R')$ or $'\mathbf{D}^{(k)}(R')$, of the symmetric group of the $(n-1)$th degree, which is isomorphic to the permutations of $s_1, \cdots, s_{n-1}$, the following must hold:

$$\begin{aligned} '\mathbf{D}^{(k)}(R')\,\mathbf{M}_1 &= \mathbf{M}_1\,'\mathbf{D}^{(k)}(R') \\ '\mathbf{D}^{(k)}(R')\,\mathbf{M}_2 &= \mathbf{M}_2\,'\mathbf{D}^{(k-1)}(R') \\ '\mathbf{D}^{(k-1)}(R')\,\mathbf{M}_3 &= \mathbf{M}_3\,'\mathbf{D}^{(k)}(R') \\ '\mathbf{D}^{(k-1)}(R')\,\mathbf{M}_4 &= \mathbf{M}_4\,'\mathbf{D}^{(k-1)}(R'). \end{aligned}$$

But from this, it follows, according to Theorems 2 and 3 of Chapter 9, that $\mathbf{M}_2$ and $\mathbf{M}_3$ must be null matrices, and $\mathbf{M}_1$ and $\mathbf{M}_4$ multiples of the unit matrix;

then (13.14), just by virtue of its commutability with (13.13), must have the form

$$\begin{pmatrix} m_1\mathbf{1} & \mathbf{0} \\ \mathbf{0} & m_4\mathbf{1} \end{pmatrix}. \tag{13.14a}$$

Next, consider a permutation R which does not leave s_n unchanged, but transforms it into another s_i which occurs in the first power in an $\bar{h}'_{0\varkappa}$. In a linear representation of $\mathbf{P}_R\bar{h}'_{0\varkappa}$, at least one of the $\bar{g}_{1\varkappa}$ must be used. Therefore, if we write $\mathbf{D}^{(k)}(R)$ in the form

$$\mathbf{D}^{(k)}(R) = \begin{pmatrix} \mathbf{A} & \mathbf{B} \\ \mathbf{C} & \mathbf{D} \end{pmatrix}, \tag{13.14b}$$

$\mathbf{C}$ is certainly not a null matrix. Then (13.14a) can commute with (13.14b) only if $m_1 = m_4$, so that (13.14a) is a constant matrix. But this is the sufficient condition for the irreducibility of $\mathbf{D}^{(k)}(R)$ which is, therefore, established.

The fact that the representations $\mathbf{D}^{(0)}, \mathbf{D}^{(1)}, \cdots, \mathbf{D}^{(\frac{1}{2}n)}$ (or $\mathbf{D}^{(\frac{1}{2}n-\frac{1}{2})}$) are all distinct can be seen from (13.13); the matrices for just the permutations R' of $s_1, s_2, \cdots, s_{n-1}$ are inequivalent in all these representations. The representations themselves must therefore be inequivalent.

6. We still wish to calculate the character $\chi^{(k)}(R)$ of the irreducible representation $\mathbf{D}^{(k)}(R)$. Since $\mathbf{\Delta}^{(k)}(R)$ can be transformed so that

$$\mathbf{\Delta}^{(k)}(R) = \begin{pmatrix} \mathbf{\Delta}^{(k-1)}(R) & \mathbf{0} \\ \mathbf{0} & \mathbf{D}^{k}(R) \end{pmatrix}, \tag{13.8}$$

$\chi^{(k)}(R)$ is equal to the difference between the characters of $\mathbf{\Delta}^{(k)}(R)$ and $\mathbf{\Delta}^{(k-1)}(R)$. According to (13.4), the character of $\mathbf{\Delta}^{(k)}(R)$ is equal to the coefficient of x^k in the polynomial ($k \leqslant \frac{1}{2}n$).

$$(1 + x^{\lambda_1})(1 + x^{\lambda_2}) \cdots (1 + x^{\lambda_\rho}) \qquad (\lambda_1 + \lambda_2 + \cdots + \lambda_\rho = n). \tag{13.14}$$

The character of $\mathbf{\Delta}^{(k-1)}(R)$ is equal to the coefficient of x^{k-1} in this expression or to that of x^k in the product of (13.4) with x; the character $\chi^{(k)}(R)$ is given by the difference between these two coefficients, i.e., by the coefficient of x^k in the expression

$$(1 - x)(1 + x^{\lambda_1})(1 + x^{\lambda_2}) \cdots (1 + x^{\lambda_\rho}) = \Sigma\, x^k \chi^k(R), \tag{13.15}$$

where $\lambda_1, \lambda_2, \cdots, \lambda_\rho$ are the lengths of the cycles of R.

For the associated representations $\bar{\mathbf{D}}^{(k)}(R)$, this expression applies with the same or the opposite sign according to whether R is an even or an odd permutation, i.e., according to whether $\lambda_1 - 1 + \lambda_2 - 1 + \cdots + \lambda_\rho - 1 = n - \rho$ is even or odd. The character $\bar{\chi}^{(k)}(R)$ is the coefficient of x^k in

$$(-1)^{n-\rho}(1 - x)(1 + x^{\lambda_1})(1 + x^{\lambda_2}) \cdots (1 + x^{\lambda_\rho}) = \sum_k x^k \bar{\chi}^{(k)}(R). \tag{13.15a}$$

$\mathbf{D}^{(0)}(R)$ is the identical, and $\bar{\mathbf{D}}^{(0)}(R)$, the antisymmetric representation.

As was mentioned before, the preceding treatment does not give all the irreducible representations of the symmetric group but only those which play a role in atomic spectroscopy. In the mathematical theory of irreducible representations (A. Young and G. Frobenius were the pioneers of this theory), the individual representations do not correspond to individual indices k but to different divisions of the number n into positive integral summands, the total number of which is equal to the number of all the irreducible representations. The representations $\mathbf{D}^{(k)}(R)$ correspond to the partition of n into two summands, $(n - k) + k$ (because of the restriction $n - k \geqslant k$, one has $k \leqslant \frac{1}{2}n$); the representations $\overline{\mathbf{D}}^{(k)}(R)$ to the partition of n into sums of 1's and 2's, $2 + 2 \cdots + 2 + 1 + 1 + 1 = n$, where there are $(n - 2k)$ 1's and the number of 2's is k.

The fact that all the eigenfunctions occurring in nature transform according to these representations under permutations of the coordinates of the electrons is related to the fact that an electron in an external magnetic field can assume only two different directions. If three directions are possible (as, for example, is the case of the nitrogen nucleus, the spin of which is equal to one), the representations corresponding to the partition of n into three summands also occur, along with their associated representations, which correspond to the partition of n into sums of the numbers 1, 2, and 3. Conversely, when only one quantized direction is possible (for example, for the helium nucleus the spin of which is zero), then only the symmetric representations, corresponding to the partition of n into one summand, $n = n$, and the antisymmetric representation, corresponding to the partition into a sum of 1's, $n = 1 + 1 + \cdots + 1$, may occur in the physical problem.

Let us compare the results of this chapter with the irreducible representations (7.E.1), (9.E.1), (9.E.3) of the symmetric group of the third degree on pages 81 and 82, The representation merely by the matrix (1) is the identical representation $\mathbf{D}^{(0)}(R)$, $(n = 3 + 0)$; the representation associated with it is the antisymmetric representation $\overline{\mathbf{D}}^{(0)}(R)$, $(n = 1 + 1 + 1)$. The third representation is $\mathbf{D}^{(1)}(R)$, $(n = 2 + 1)$; its associated representation is $\overline{\mathbf{D}}^{(1)}(R)$, $(n = 2 + 1)$, and these two are equivalent.

For the symmetric group of the fourth degree, we have:

$$\mathbf{D}^{(0)}(R),\ (n = 4), \text{ and } \overline{\mathbf{D}}^{(0)}(R),\ (n = 1 + 1 + 1 + 1), \text{ of dimension } \binom{4}{0} - \binom{4}{-1} = 1$$

$$\mathbf{D}^{(1)}(R),\ (n = 3 + 1), \text{ and } \overline{\mathbf{D}}^{(1)}(R),\ (n = 2 + 1 + 1), \text{ of dimension } \binom{4}{1} - \binom{4}{0} = 3$$

$$\mathbf{D}^{(2)}(R),\ (n = 2 + 2), \text{ equivalent to } \overline{\mathbf{D}}^{(2)}(R),\ (n = 2 + 2), \text{ of dimension } \binom{4}{2} - \binom{4}{1} = 2.$$

In all, there are five inequivalent irreducible representations, corresponding to the five classes of the group. Also, the sum of the squares of their dimensions is equal to the order of the group: $1^2 + 1^2 + 3^2 + 3^2 + 2^2 = 24 = 4! = h$. In this group, as in the symmetric group of third degree, these representations include all the irreducible representations.

For $n = 5$, we obtain in this way six irreducible representations ($\mathbf{D}^{(2)}(R)$ is not equivalent to $\overline{\mathbf{D}}^{(2)}(R)$), but since there are seven classes, these are not all the irreducible representations. For larger n, an ever-decreasing fraction of the total number of irreducible representations occur among our $\mathbf{D}^{(k)}(R)$ and $\overline{\mathbf{D}}^{(k)}(R)$. Nevertheless, we shall come to the conclusion that, because of the Pauli principle, the others play no role in the spectral theory of the atom. They can be obtained in the same way as we have obtained these, except that one must consider functions of n variables which can assume more than just the two values we have allowed in our treatment.

Appendix to Chapter 13. A Lemma Related to the Symmetric Group

It will be shown now that for $k \leqslant \frac{1}{2}n$, the $\binom{n}{k-1}$ functions

$$F_{a_1a_2\cdots a_{k-1}} = s_{a_1}s_{a_2}\cdots s_{a_{k-1}}s_{a_1a_2\cdots a_{k-1}} \tag{13.5}$$

(where $a_1 < a_2 < \cdots < a_{k-1}$ and $s_{a_1a_2\cdots a_{k-1}}$ is the sum of all the s's whose indices do not occur among the numbers $a_1, a_2, \cdots, a_{k-1}$) are linearly independent. Only if this is true can we conclude that no more than $\binom{n}{k} - \binom{n}{k-1}$ linear combinations of the products $s_{a_1}s_{a_2}\cdots s_{a_k}$ are orthogonal to all $F_{a_1a_2\cdots a_{k-1}}$. The $F_{a_1a_2\cdots a_{k-1}}$ are linear combinations of the $s_{a_1}s_{a_2}\cdots s_{a_k}$.

$$F_{a_1a_2\cdots a_{k-1}} = \sum_b m_{a_1\cdots a_{k-1};\, b_1\cdots b_k} s_{b_1}s_{b_2}\cdots s_{b_k}, \tag{13.16}$$

where $b_1 < b_2 < \cdots < b_k$ can be assumed and

$$m_{a_1\cdots a_{k-1};b_1\cdots b_k} = \begin{cases} 1, & \text{if the } a_1, a_2, \cdots, a_{k-1} \text{ all occur} \\ & \text{among the } b_1, b_2, \cdots, b_k \\ 0, & \text{otherwise.} \end{cases} \tag{13.17}$$

In the sum in (13.16) the $b_1, b_2, \cdots, b_k$ run over all $\binom{n}{k}$ combinations of the numbers $1, 2, \cdots, n$. If there were a linear relationship among the $F_{a_1a_2\cdots a_{k-1}}$, say

$$\sum_a c_{a_1\cdots a_{k-1}} F_{a_1\cdots a_{k-1}} = \sum_{a,b} c_{a_1\cdots a_{k-1}} m_{a_1\cdots a_{k-1};\, b_1\cdots b_k} s_{b_1}\cdots s_{b_k} = 0 \tag{13.18}$$

(the summation is again to be taken over the $\binom{n}{k-1}$ combinations of the a's, and over the $\binom{n}{k}$ combinations of the b's) then it would follow that for all numbers $x_{b_1\cdots b_k}$ (defined for $b_1 < b_2 < \cdots < b_k$),

$$\sum_{a,b} c_{a_1\cdots a_{k-1}} m_{a_1\cdots a_{k-1};b_1\cdots b_k} x_{b_1\cdots b_k} = 0. \tag{13.19}$$

This can be shown by multiplying the scalar product of (13.18) and $s_{d_1}s_{d_2}s_{d_3}\cdots s_{d_k}$ by $x_{d_1\cdots d_k}$, and adding the resulting equations for all possible combinations of the d_i.

We shall now choose the $x_{b_1b_2\cdots b_k}$ so that

$$\sum_b m_{a_1\cdots a_{k-1};b_1\cdots b_k} x_{b_1\cdots b_k} = \begin{cases} 1, & \text{for } a_1 = 1, a_2 = 2, \cdots, a_{k-1} = k-1; \\ 0, & \text{otherwise.} \end{cases} \quad (13.20)$$

Then (13.19) is equivalent to

$$c_{12\cdots k-1} = 0. \quad (13.21)$$

The same equation (13.21) must also hold for all the other $c_{a_1\cdots a_{k-1}}$, since they all enter in the same way; that is, an analogous choice of $x_{b_1\cdots b_k}$ could be made to demonstrate that each c vanishes. (Replace, throughout the rest of the argument, the set $1, 2, \cdots, k-1$ by $\alpha_1, \alpha_2, \cdots, \alpha_{k-1}$.) We need therefore show only that the choice resulting in Eq. (13.20) can actually be made, and our proof that $F_{a_1a_2\cdots a_{k-1}}$ are linearly independent will be complete.

The $x_{b_1\cdots b_k}$ are at our free disposal. We choose all those $x_{b_1\cdots b_k}$ to be equal, among whose indices $b_1, b_2, \cdots, b_k$ exactly τ of the numbers $1, 2, \cdots, k-1$ occur (where $0 \leqslant \tau \leqslant k-1$); these $x_{b_1\cdots b_k}$ are denoted by x_τ. We now consider those Eqs. (13.20) in which exactly σ of the numbers $1, 2, \cdots, k-1$ occur among the $a_1, a_2, \cdots, a_{k-1}$. Since $m_{a_1a_2\cdots a_{k-1};b_1b_2\cdots b_k}$ is different from zero only if all the a_i occur among the b_i, only those terms contribute to the sum in (13.20) in which there are σ of the $1, 2, \cdots, k-1$ and $k-1-\sigma$ of the $k, k+1, \cdots, n$ among the b_i. The single index b whose value remains unspecified can either be one of the numbers $1, 2, \cdots, k-1$ or one of the numbers $k, k+1, \cdots, n$. In the former case, it can assume $k-1-\sigma$ values; in the latter, $n-k+1-(k-1-\sigma) = n - 2k+2+\sigma$ values, since it cannot be equal to any one of the $a_1, a_2, \cdots, a_{k-1}$. Thus (13.20) becomes

$$(k-1-\sigma)x_{\sigma+1} + (n-2k+2+\sigma)x_\sigma = \begin{cases} 1, & \text{for } \sigma = k \quad 1 \\ 0, & \text{for } \sigma = 0, 1, \cdots, k-2. \end{cases} \quad (13.22)$$

This yields

$$x_{k-1} = \frac{1}{(n-k+1)}$$

and

$$-\frac{x_\sigma}{x_{\sigma+1}} = \frac{k-1-\sigma}{n-2k+2+\sigma} \qquad \text{for } \sigma = 0, 1, \cdots, k-2.$$

But these equations can be satisfied for $n - 2k + 2 > 0$, or $k \leqslant \frac{1}{2}n + 1$; thus, *a fortiori*, for $k \leqslant \frac{1}{2}n$. Hence, the $x_{b_1b_2\cdots b_k}$ can be so chosen that (13.20) is satisfied; thus, (13.21) follows. Similarly, all other c in (13.18) must vanish; therefore, the linear independence of the F is established.

14. The Rotation Groups

1. The continuous group which is formed from the set of all real orthogonal n-dimensional matrices is called the *n-dimensional rotation group*. The *pure rotation group* includes only orthogonal matrices with determinant $+1$, while the *rotation-reflection group* includes also those with determinant -1; the latter thus contains *all* real orthogonal matrices. Group multiplication is again matrix multiplication, and the identity is the unit matrix.

We have seen in Chapter 3 that every real orthogonal matrix can be diagonalized by a unitary matrix. The diagonal elements then all have absolute value 1; some are $+1$, others -1, and the rest consist of conjugate pairs of complex numbers $e^{i\varphi}$ and $e^{-i\varphi}$. The eigenvectors which correspond to $+1$ or -1 eigenvalues can be written in real form, a pair which corresponds to two complex conjugate eigenvalues, as complex conjugates. Since these eigenvectors, like all eigenvectors, are orthogonal in the Hermitian sense, they are orthogonal to themselves in the complex orthogonal sense; that is, the sum of the squares of their components is zero.

An n-dimensional orthogonal matrix represents a transformation from one system of orthogonal axes to another, that is, *a rotation* of the coordinate axes. The orthogonality of the matrix implies that every pair of axes of the new coordinate system are orthogonal, and that the unit of length along the new axes is the same as it was along the old. The pure rotation group contains only transformations from one "right-handed coordinate system" to another "right-handed system"; the rotation-reflection group also includes transformations from right-handed to left-handed coordinate systems, and vice-versa. These are often called improper rotations.

In order to apply our general results on continuous groups, we must first introduce parameters. This can be done only in an asymmetric manner, because certain directions in space (the coordinate axes) must be distinguished from the others, and even the coordinate axes themselves cannot be treated on an equal footing. We first determine the number of dimensions in the parameter space to be defined. Consider an n-dimensional, real orthogonal matrix. Since the first row is an n-dimensional vector of length one (the x-axis of the new system), it involves—because the unit length implies the condition $\mathbf{a}_{11}^2 + \mathbf{a}_{12}^2 + \cdots + \mathbf{a}_{1n}^2 = 1$—exactly $n - 1$ parameters. The second row (the y-axis) must be orthogonal to the first; this implies a homogeneous linear equation $\mathbf{a}_{11}\mathbf{a}_{21} + \mathbf{a}_{12}\mathbf{a}_{22} + \cdots + \mathbf{a}_{1n}\mathbf{a}_{2n} = 0$ for the $\mathbf{a}_{21}$, $\mathbf{a}_{22}, \cdots, \mathbf{a}_{2n}$ and the unit length implies $\mathbf{a}_{21}^2 + \mathbf{a}_{22}^2 + \cdots + \mathbf{a}_{2n}^2 = 1$. Thus, there are $n - 2$ free parameters in the second row. The kth row must be orthogonal to the $k-1$ preceding rows—this implies $k-1$ homogeneous equations—and has length one. Thus it involves $n-k$ free parameters. In all, there are

$$(n-1)+(n-2)+(n-3)+\cdots+(n-(n-1))+0=\tfrac{1}{2}n(n-1)$$

free parameters.

2. In what follows we will restrict ourselves to the two- and three-dimensional rotation groups.

The general element of the two-dimensional pure rotation group is obtained by a transformation to a new coordinate system in the plane[1]

$$\begin{aligned} x' &= x\cos\varphi + y\sin\varphi \\ y' &= -x\sin\varphi + y\cos\varphi, \end{aligned} \tag{14.1}$$

where φ, *the angle of rotation*, varies from $-\pi$ to $+\pi$. The general element of the group is thus

$$\begin{pmatrix} \cos\varphi & \sin\varphi \\ -\sin\varphi & \cos\varphi \end{pmatrix}. \tag{14.2}$$

A second transformation, from x', y' to x'', y'', by means of a rotation of the coordinate system through an angle φ', yields the product

$$\begin{aligned} &\begin{pmatrix} \cos\varphi' & \sin\varphi' \\ -\sin\varphi' & \cos\varphi' \end{pmatrix} \cdot \begin{pmatrix} \cos\varphi & \sin\varphi \\ -\sin\varphi & \cos\varphi \end{pmatrix} \\ &\qquad = \begin{pmatrix} \cos(\varphi+\varphi') & \sin(\varphi+\varphi') \\ -\sin(\varphi+\varphi') & \cos(\varphi+\varphi') \end{pmatrix}. \end{aligned} \tag{14.3}$$

Equation (14.3) shows that the product is simply a single rotation through an angle $\varphi+\varphi'$.

The two-dimensional pure rotation group is Abelian since it has only one parameter. If we introduce the notation $\{\varphi\}$ of Chapter 10 for the group element with the parameter φ, then (14.3) reads

$$\{\varphi'\}\cdot\{\varphi\} = \{\varphi+\varphi'\} = \{\varphi\}\cdot\{\varphi'\}. \tag{14.4}$$

If $\varphi+\varphi'$ does not lie between $-\pi$ and $+\pi$, an integral number of 2π's must be added or subtracted to make it fall within the region over which the parameter is allowed to vary.

For the matrix (14.2), the angle φ is the complex phase of the eigenvalues $e^{\pm i\varphi}$. The columns of the unitary matrix $\mathbf{u}$ which diagonalizes (14.2) are determined from

$$|\mathbf{u}_{1\alpha}|^2 + |\mathbf{u}_{2\alpha}|^2 = 1; \qquad \mathbf{u}_{1\alpha}^2 + \mathbf{u}_{2\alpha}^2 = 0; \qquad \mathbf{u}_{1\alpha} = \pm i\mathbf{u}_{2\alpha}$$

[1] The rotation is defined to be positive when the x-axis rotates toward the y-axis, since this is consistent with the definition for three-dimensional rotations. In general a positive rotation about any axis is taken to be the rotation undergone by a right-handed screw advancing in the positive direction along that axis.

up to a factor of absolute value 1 (which can be chosen arbitrarily). These conditions give $\mathbf{u}_{11} = 1/\sqrt{2}$, $\mathbf{u}_{21} = -i/\sqrt{2}$, $\mathbf{u}_{12} = 1/\sqrt{2}$, $\mathbf{u}_{22} = +i/\sqrt{2}$, and one has

$$\begin{pmatrix} 1/\sqrt{2} & i/\sqrt{2} \\ 1/\sqrt{2} & -i/\sqrt{2} \end{pmatrix} \cdot \begin{pmatrix} \cos\varphi & \sin\varphi \\ -\sin\varphi & \cos\varphi \end{pmatrix} \cdot \begin{pmatrix} 1/\sqrt{2} & 1/\sqrt{2} \\ -i/\sqrt{2} & i/\sqrt{2} \end{pmatrix} = \begin{pmatrix} e^{-i\varphi} & 0 \\ 0 & e^{+i\varphi} \end{pmatrix}. \tag{14.5}$$

Thus, the eigenvectors are the same for all matrices (14.2). Since the two-dimensional pure rotation group is Abelian, every element forms a class of its own.

3. From every two-dimensional matrix with determinant -1 a matrix with determinant $+1$ can be obtained by multiplying the second row by -1. Conversely, the general orthogonal matrix of determinant -1 is obtained by changing the signs in the second row of (14.2).

$$\begin{pmatrix} \cos\varphi & \sin\varphi \\ \sin\varphi & -\cos\varphi \end{pmatrix} \tag{14.2a}$$

The matrices (14.2) and (14.2a), with $-\pi \leqslant \varphi \leqslant \pi$, form the two-dimensional rotation-reflection group. The matrices (14.2a) all have the eigenvalues $+1$ and -1. They differ in their eigenvectors, $\mathbf{u}_{\cdot 1} = (\cos\varphi/2, \sin\varphi/2)$, $\mathbf{u}_{\cdot 2} = (-\sin\varphi/2, \cos\varphi/2)$, whereas the matrices (14.2) all have the same eigenvectors, but different eigenvalues. We can check directly that the matrix formed from these two eigenvectors does transform the diagonal matrix into (14.2a).

$$\begin{pmatrix} \cos\varphi & \sin\varphi \\ \sin\varphi & -\cos\varphi \end{pmatrix} = \begin{pmatrix} \cos\varphi/2 & -\sin\varphi/2 \\ \sin\varphi/2 & \cos\varphi/2 \end{pmatrix} \cdot \begin{pmatrix} 1 & 0 \\ 0 & -1 \end{pmatrix} \cdot \begin{pmatrix} \cos\varphi/2 & \sin\varphi/2 \\ -\sin\varphi/2 & \cos\varphi/2 \end{pmatrix}. \tag{14.5a}$$

The product form (14.5a) of the improper rotation (14.2a) illustrates the fact that every improper rotation (14.2a) can be interpreted as a pure reflection in a straight line; (14.5a) means that (14.2a) is obtained by first *rotating* through $\varphi/2$, *then reflecting* in the x-axis, and *finally rotating back* by $-\varphi/2$. Alternatively, the reflection could have been made in the line which makes an angle $\varphi/2$ with the x-axis.

The two-dimensional rotation-reflection group is a mixed continuous group. The most natural parametrization of this group utilizes a continuous parameter φ and a discrete parameter d. The latter is equal to the determinant, i.e., ± 1. We then have

$$\{\varphi, d\} = \begin{pmatrix} \cos\varphi & \sin\varphi \\ -d\sin\varphi & d\cos\varphi \end{pmatrix} \tag{14.6}$$

$$\{\varphi, d\} \cdot \{\varphi', d'\} = \{d'\varphi + \varphi', dd'\}.$$

The group is no longer Abelian; the matrices (14.2a) do not commute, nor do they have the same eigenvectors.

The division of the group into classes also changes: (14.5a) shows that all the elements (14.2a) are *in one class*, since they can all be transformed into $\{0, -1\}$. However, the elements of (14.2) no longer form a class each; e.g.,

$$\begin{pmatrix} +1 & 0 \\ 0 & -1 \end{pmatrix} \begin{pmatrix} \cos\varphi & \sin\varphi \\ -\sin\varphi & \cos\varphi \end{pmatrix} \cdot \begin{pmatrix} +1 & 0 \\ 0 & -1 \end{pmatrix} = \begin{pmatrix} \cos\varphi & -\sin\varphi \\ \sin\varphi & \cos\varphi \end{pmatrix}, \tag{14.7}$$

thus, $\{\varphi, 1\}$ and $\{-\varphi, 1\}$ are in the same class. No other elements can be in this class, since all others have different eigenvalues and thus cannot be transformed into either of these.

4. According to the general discussion of the Hurwitz integral in Chapter 10, an invariant integral exists in the region of the two-dimensional pure rotation group, such that

$$\int_{-\pi}^{\pi} J(\{\varphi\})g(\{\varphi\})\, d\varphi = \int_{-\pi}^{\pi} J(R\{\varphi\})g(\{\varphi\})\, d\varphi \tag{14.8}$$

holds for all group elements R, provided $g(T)$ is defined by (10.9)

$$g(T) = \frac{g(E)}{\dfrac{\partial p(T \cdot \{\alpha\})}{\partial \alpha}} \qquad \text{evaluated at } \alpha = 0 \tag{14.9}$$

where $p(T)$ is the parameter of the element T.

In the case of the two-dimensional rotation group, direct inspection shows that equal regions must be given equal weight. Let t be the parameter for T; then the parameter $p(T \cdot \{\alpha\}) = t + \alpha$ according to (14.4), and this gives 1 upon differentiating with respect to α, so that

$$g(T) = g(E) \tag{14.10}$$

Thus the invariant integral is

$$\int_{-\pi}^{\pi} J(\{\varphi\})\, d\varphi = \int_{-\pi}^{\pi} J(R \cdot \{\varphi\})\, d\varphi. \tag{14.11}$$

The irreducible representations of the two-dimensional pure rotation group are all one-dimensional. Actually, this is true of all Abelian groups; continuous Abelian groups are just a special case. Let us consider a multi-dimensional, say two-dimensional, representation. We can bring some matrix of the representation into diagonal form. If the two diagonal elements were not equal, it would have the form

$$\begin{pmatrix} a & 0 \\ 0 & b \end{pmatrix}, \tag{14.E.1}$$

so that all matrices which commute with it—and thus all the matrices of the representation—would have only zeros at the intersections of different diagonal elements of (14.E.1); the representation would then be reducible. If this were not the case then the eigenvalues of the matrix (14.E.1) would all have to be equal, and this would be a constant matrix. It would then have had the diagonal form even before the transformation. But this applies to every matrix of the representation, so that they would all be multiples of the identity matrix, and the representation would be, *a fortiori*, reducible.

From (14.4) it follows that, if the element $\{\varphi\}$ corresponds to the matrix $(f(\varphi))$ in a representation, then

$$(f(\varphi)) \cdot (f(\varphi')) = (f(\varphi')) \cdot (f(\varphi)) = f(\varphi + \varphi')$$

and thus

$$f(\varphi) = e^{ik\varphi}.$$

Since the matrix for $\varphi = -\pi$ must be equal to that for $\varphi = +\pi$, we must have $e^{ik\pi} = e^{-ik\pi}$; therefore, $e^{2ik\pi} = 1$. This implies that k is a real integer. The two-dimensional pure rotation group has infinitely many irreducible representations, and all are one-dimensional. The matrix in the mth representation which corresponds to the element (14.2) with rotation angle φ, is

$$(e^{im\varphi}).$$

For every positive and negative integer, $m = \cdots - 4, -3, -2, -1, 0, +1, +2, +3, \cdots$, there exists one distinct irreducible representation of the pure two-dimensional rotation group.

The orthogonality relationships

$$\int_{-\pi}^{\pi} (e^{im'\varphi})^* (e^{im\varphi})\, d\varphi = 0 \qquad \text{for } m \neq m'$$

$$= \int_{-\pi}^{\pi} d\varphi = 2\pi \qquad \text{for } m = m'$$

are just the orthogonality relationships of the Fourier series. The completeness of the representation coefficients is likewise the completeness of the Fourier expansion.

5. We shall now determine the irreducible representations of the two-dimensional rotation-reflection group, using a method which will seem rather complicated for this purpose. However, this same method will later be applied to the three-dimensional group so that a simple demonstration is worthwhile; moreover, it offers another example of the relationships between a representation and the corresponding functions.

Consider the equation for the harmonic polynomials of two variables

$$\frac{\partial^2 f(x, y)}{\partial x^2} + \frac{\partial^2 f(x, y)}{\partial y^2} = 0. \tag{14.12}$$

This is manifestly invariant under all transformations (14.6). Also, a solution of (14.12) which is homogeneous of degree m in x and y transforms under $\mathbf{P}_R$ (where R is a transformation of the form (14.6)) into a polynomial of this same form, since the transformation $\mathbf{P}_R$ is linear in the variables x and y.

$$\mathbf{P}_{\{\varphi,d\}} f(x \cos \varphi + y \sin \varphi, -dx \sin \varphi + dy \cos \varphi) = f(x, y) \tag{14.13}$$

or, since $\{\varphi, d\}^{-1}$ is equal to $\{-d\varphi, d\}$,

$$\begin{aligned}\mathbf{P}_{\{\varphi,d\}} f(x, y) &= f(x \cos (-d\varphi) + y \sin (-d\varphi), -xd \sin (-d\varphi) + yd \cos (-d\varphi)) \\ &= f(x \cos \varphi - yd \sin \varphi, + x \sin \varphi + yd \cos \varphi).\end{aligned} \tag{14.14}$$

Thus, if $f(x, y)$ is homogeneous of mth degree, so is $\mathbf{P}_R f$.

Equation (14.12) is just the one-dimensional wave equation with an imaginary velocity i. Its general solution is

$$f(x, y) = f_-(x - iy) + f_+(x + iy). \tag{14.15}$$

If $f(x, y)$ is homogeneous of degree m in x and y, then f_+ and f_- must be given (apart from a constant factor) by

$$f_-(x - iy) = (x - iy)^m; \qquad f_+(x + iy) = (x + iy)^m. \tag{14.16}$$

The representation $\mathfrak{Z}^{(m)}(\{\varphi, d\})$ belonging to these functions is two-dimensional. Its first (—) column is determined from (11.23) and (14.14).

$$\begin{aligned}\mathbf{P}_{\{\varphi\, d\}} f_-(x, y) &= f_-(x \cos \varphi - yd \sin \varphi, x \sin \varphi + yd \cos \varphi) \\ &= [(x \cos \varphi - yd \sin \varphi) - i(x \sin \varphi + yd \cos \varphi)]^m \\ &= [x(\cos \varphi - i \sin \varphi) - iyd(\cos \varphi - i \sin \varphi)]^m \\ &= (x - iyd)^m e^{-im\varphi}.\end{aligned}$$

Written in terms of the representation coefficients, this is

$$\mathbf{P}_{\{\varphi,d\}} f_-(x, y) = \mathfrak{Z}^{(m)}(\{\varphi, d\})_{--} f_- + \mathfrak{Z}^{(m)}(\{\varphi, d\})_{+-} f_+.$$

Hence these coefficients are given by

$$\begin{aligned}\mathfrak{Z}^{(m)}(\{\varphi, 1\})_{--} &= e^{-im\varphi} \qquad & \mathfrak{Z}^{(m)}(\{\varphi, 1\})_{+-} &= 0 \\ \mathfrak{Z}^{(m)}(\{\varphi, -1\})_{--} &= 0 \qquad & \mathfrak{Z}^{(m)}(\{\varphi, -1\})_{+-} &= e^{-im\varphi}.\end{aligned} \tag{14.17}$$

The other (+) column can be determined in the same way via f_+. The matrix $\mathfrak{Z}^{(m)}(\{\varphi, 1\})$ which corresponds in this representation to a pure rotation through an angle φ, is then found to be

$$\mathfrak{Z}^{(m)}(\{\varphi, 1\}) = \begin{pmatrix} e^{-im\varphi} & 0 \\ 0 & e^{im\varphi} \end{pmatrix}, \tag{14.18}$$

where we have written the (—) row (or column) as the first, and the (+) row (or column) as the second. The matrix which corresponds to the group element appearing in (14.2a) is

$$\mathfrak{Z}^{(m)}(\{\varphi, -1\}) = \begin{pmatrix} 0 & e^{im\varphi} \\ e^{-im\varphi} & 0 \end{pmatrix}. \tag{14.18a}$$

The function f_- belongs to the (—) (or first) row of $\mathfrak{Z}^{(m)}$; the function f_+, to the (+) (or second) row.

These representations are *irreducible* and distinct for $m = 1, 2, 3, \cdots$. Only a diagonal matrix commutes with (14.18), but no diagonal matrix commutes with (14.18a), except for a constant matrix. The matrices (14.6) are of course also a "representation" of their own group. This representation is equivalent to the particular representation $m = 1$ in (14.18), (14.18a); the matrix used in (14.5) transforms (14.6) into the form (14.18), (14.18a).

It should be noted that (14.18) and (14.18a) also provide a representation for $m = 0$. However, it is not irreducible, since in this case every matrix commutes with (14.18); we can therefore diagonalize this special case of (14.18a) to divide the representation into two irreducible components

$$\mathfrak{Z}^{(0)}(\{\varphi, 1\}) = (1); \qquad \mathfrak{Z}^{(0)}(\{\varphi, -1\}) = (1) \tag{14.19}$$

and

$$\mathfrak{Z}^{(0')}(\{\varphi, 1\}) = (1); \qquad \mathfrak{Z}^{(0')}(\{\varphi, -1\}) = (-1). \tag{14.20}$$

6. We have now obtained all the representations of the two-dimensional rotation-reflection group. These are given by (14.18) and (14.18a) for $m = 1, 2, 3, \cdots$ and are two-dimensional; for $m = 0$ and $m = 0'$ they are given by (14.19) and (14.20) and are one-dimensional.

The representation coefficients $\mathfrak{Z}^{(m)}(\{\varphi, d\})_{\pm\pm}$ form a complete system of functions in the space of φ and d. That is, every function $g(\varphi, d)$ (φ varies from $-\pi$ to $+\pi$, and d is either $+1$ or -1) can be written as a linear combination of them. The functions $\frac{1}{2}(\mathfrak{Z}^{(0)} + \mathfrak{Z}^{(0')})$, $\mathfrak{Z}^{(1)}_{--}$, $\mathfrak{Z}^{(1)}_{++}$, $\mathfrak{Z}^{(2)}_{--}$, $\mathfrak{Z}^{(2)}_{++}$, $\cdots$ are given by the sequence $1, e^{-i\varphi}, e^{i\varphi}, e^{-2i\varphi}, e^{2i\varphi}, \cdots$ for $d = 1$, and vanish for $d = -1$; on the other hand, $\frac{1}{2}(\mathfrak{Z}^{(0)} - \mathfrak{Z}^{(0')})$, $\mathfrak{Z}^{(1)}_{+-}$, $\mathfrak{Z}^{(1)}_{-+}$, $\mathfrak{Z}^{(2)}_{+-}$, $\mathfrak{Z}^{(2)}_{-+}$, $\cdots$ are equal to zero for $d = 1$, and to $1, e^{-i\varphi}, e^{i\varphi}, e^{-2i\varphi}, e^{2i\varphi}, \cdots$ for $d = 1$. The function $g(\varphi, 1)$ can be expressed as a linear combination of the first set, and $g(\varphi, -1)$ of the second.

The fact that the matrix elements form a complete set in parameter space implies that beside (14.18), (14.18a), (14.19) and (14.20), no other *irreducible representations of the two-dimensional rotation group exist.*

7. We now turn to the investigation of the three-dimensional pure rotation group. The eigenvalues of $\mathbf{a}$, a real orthogonal three-dimensional matrix of determinant 1, must have the form $1, e^{-i\varphi}, e^{+i\varphi}$ since they are all of absolute value 1 and those which are complex occur in conjugate pairs. The phase φ of a complex eigenvalue is called the *rotation angle;* the eigenvector,[2] $\mathbf{v}_{\cdot 1}$ with the eigenvalue 1 is called the *axis of rotation.* It's components $\mathbf{v}_{11}, \mathbf{v}_{21}, \mathbf{v}_{31}$ may be determined most simply by beginning with $\mathbf{a}\mathbf{v}_{\cdot 1} = 1\mathbf{v}_{\cdot 1}$ and multiplying this by $\mathbf{a}^{-1} = \mathbf{a}'$ to obtain $\mathbf{v}_{\cdot 1} = \mathbf{a}'\mathbf{v}_{\cdot 1}$. This yields $(\mathbf{a} - \mathbf{a}')\mathbf{v}_{\cdot 1} = 0$ or, written out in more detail,

$$
\begin{aligned}
(\mathbf{a}_{12} - \mathbf{a}_{21})\mathbf{v}_{21} + (\mathbf{a}_{13} - \mathbf{a}_{31})\mathbf{v}_{31} &= 0 \\
(\mathbf{a}_{21} - \mathbf{a}_{12})\mathbf{v}_{11} \qquad\qquad\qquad + (\mathbf{a}_{23} - \mathbf{a}_{32})\mathbf{v}_{31} &= 0 \\
(\mathbf{a}_{31} - \mathbf{a}_{13})\mathbf{v}_{11} + (\mathbf{a}_{32} - \mathbf{a}_{23})\mathbf{v}_{21} \qquad\qquad\qquad &= 0,
\end{aligned}
\tag{14.21}
$$

and from this

$$\mathbf{v}_{11} : \mathbf{v}_{21} : \mathbf{v}_{31} = \mathbf{a}_{23} - \mathbf{a}_{32} : \mathbf{a}_{31} - \mathbf{a}_{13} : \mathbf{a}_{12} - \mathbf{a}_{21} . \tag{14.22}$$

The rotation angle φ is most easily determined by equating the sum of the eigenvalues with the trace of the matrix.

$$1 + e^{-i\varphi} + e^{i\varphi} = 1 + 2 \cos \varphi = \mathbf{a}_{11} + \mathbf{a}_{22} + \mathbf{a}_{33}, \tag{14.23}$$

where φ lies between 0 and π.

The eigenvectors $\mathbf{v}_{\cdot 2}$ and $\mathbf{v}_{\cdot 3}$ which correspond to $e^{-i\varphi}$ and $e^{+i\varphi}$ are complex conjugates $\mathbf{v}_{\cdot 2}^* = \mathbf{v}_{\cdot 3}$. On the other hand $\mathbf{v}_{\cdot 1}$ will be assumed to be real: $(\mathbf{v}_{\cdot 1}, \mathbf{v}_{\cdot 1}) = ((\mathbf{v}_{\cdot 1}, \mathbf{v}_{\cdot 1})) = 1$.

The matrix $\mathbf{v}$ whose columns are the eigenvectors $\mathbf{v}_{\cdot 1}, \mathbf{v}_{\cdot 2}, \mathbf{v}_{\cdot 3}$ of $\mathbf{a}$, diagonalizes $\mathbf{a}$. Therefore, $\mathbf{v}^\dagger \mathbf{a} \mathbf{v}$ is a diagonal matrix with the eigenvalues $1, e^{-i\varphi}, e^{+i\varphi}$ as diagonal elements. We now write $\mathbf{V} = \mathbf{v}\mathbf{v}_0$, where[3]

$$\mathbf{v}_0 = \begin{pmatrix} 1 & 0 & 0 \\ 0 & -i/\sqrt{2} & 1/\sqrt{2} \\ 0 & +i/\sqrt{2} & 1/\sqrt{2} \end{pmatrix} \tag{14.24}$$

The columns of $\mathbf{V}$ are given by $\mathbf{v}_{\cdot 1}$, $\dfrac{-i}{\sqrt{2}}(\mathbf{v}_{\cdot 2} - \mathbf{v}_{\cdot 2}^*)$, and $\dfrac{1}{\sqrt{2}}(\mathbf{v}_{\cdot 2} + \mathbf{v}_{\cdot 2}^*)$ so that $\mathbf{V}$ is real. Moreover, as the product of the unitary matrices $\mathbf{v}$ and $\mathbf{v}_0$, $\mathbf{V}$ is

[2] Although $\mathbf{v}_{\cdot 1}$ is certainly a vector, it will also play the role of a column of matrix elements in this discussion. We therefore denote it in accordance with our convention for matrix elements.

[3] $\mathbf{v}_0$ here is chosen so that $\mathbf{a}$ assumes the form of a rotation about the X-axis after transformation by $\mathbf{v}\mathbf{v}_0$. Another choice of $\mathbf{v}_0$ could clearly be made to give it, for example, the form of a rotation about Y.

also unitary, so that it is a real orthogonal matrix, and therefore an element of the rotation group. If we now transform the equation $\mathbf{v}^\dagger \mathbf{a} \mathbf{v} = \mathbf{d}$ with $\mathbf{v}_0$, we obtain

$$\mathbf{V}^\dagger \mathbf{a} \mathbf{V} = \mathbf{v}_0^\dagger \mathbf{v}^\dagger \mathbf{a} \mathbf{v} \mathbf{v}_0 = \mathbf{v}_0^\dagger \mathbf{d} \mathbf{v}_0 = \begin{pmatrix} 1 & 0 & 0 \\ 0 & \cos\varphi & \sin\varphi \\ 0 & -\sin\varphi & \cos\varphi \end{pmatrix} = \boldsymbol{\epsilon}_\varphi . \qquad (14.25)$$

In this equation we can even assume $\mathbf{V}$ to be a *pure* rotation, since we could multiply it by -1 if its determinant were -1 and (14.25) would be unaffected. We see from (14.25) that *all rotations with the same rotation angle φ are in the same class*, since they can all be transformed into $\boldsymbol{\epsilon}_\varphi$. On the other hand matrices whose rotation angle is different from φ cannot be in this same class since they have different eigenvalues and therefore cannot be transformed into $\boldsymbol{\epsilon}_\varphi$.

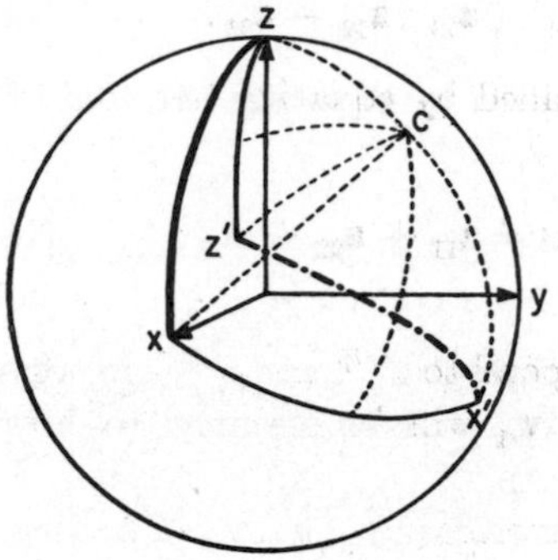

FIG. 6. The geometrical interpretation of Eq. (14.25) (see text).

The geometrical interpretation of this discussion is the well-known theorem that every orthogonal transformation in three-dimensional space can be replaced by a rotation about a suitably chosen axis $\mathbf{v}_{\cdot 1}$. (Because of $\mathbf{a}\mathbf{v}_{\cdot 1} = \mathbf{v}_{\cdot 1}$, the rotation axis remains unchanged by the rotation.) If the transformation carries the arc XZ in Fig. 6 into the arc $X'Z'$, then the axis of rotation must lie on midperpendiculars of ZZ' and XX', and thus on their point of intersection C. In fact, a rotation about C does transform Z into Z' and X into X': from the congruency of the two triangles ZCX and $Z'C'X'$ (their three sides are equal) it follows that the angles ZCX and $Z'CX'$ are equal, and therefore the angles ZCZ' and XCX' are also equal and equal to the angle of rotation φ. A rotation with the rotation angle φ can be transformed into another rotation with the same rotation angle, by bringing the axis of rotation of the first into coincidence with the axis of rotation of the second by a rotation $\mathbf{V}$, then carrying out the rotation through φ, and, finally, returning the axis to its original position by $\mathbf{V}^{-1}$.

For a unique characterization of rotations, the axis of the rotation must be given a sense of direction, which also gives meaning to the sign of the vector $\mathbf{v}_{\cdot 1}$. The rotation will take place in a clockwise direction as seen along the positive direction of the axis.

The parametrization (Fig. 1, page 90) of the three-dimensional pure rotation group discussed in Chapter 10 is based on these characteristics. The rotation through an angle φ about the axis $\mathbf{v}_{\cdot 1}$ corresponds to a point at distance φ from the origin in the direction $\mathbf{v}_{\cdot 1}$.[4] The rotation angle φ is always uniquely determined by the rotation. For the rotation with $\varphi = 0$ (which is actually no rotation at all), the direction of the axis of rotation is undetermined; the corresponding point in parameter space is nevertheless given uniquely: it is the center of the sphere.

On the surface of the sphere in parameter space $\varphi = \pi$, the sense of the axis of rotation is not unique; rotations of angle π about oppositely directed axes are identical. Therefore the same rotation corresponds to the antipodes of the spherical surface. Otherwise, the correspondence of rotations to points in parameter space is one-to-one. Elements of given classes lie on concentric spheres.

In this system of parameters we can also formulate the Hurwitz invariant integral rather easily. Since the points on a spherical surface of radius φ correspond to rotations through the same angle but with differently directed axes, and since all rotation axes in space are equivalent, $g(\{\varphi\mathbf{v}_{11}, \varphi\mathbf{v}_{21}, \varphi\mathbf{v}_{31}\})$ can depend only on the angle of rotation φ, not on the direction of $\mathbf{v}_{\cdot 1}$. It is thus sufficient to determine $g(\{\varphi, 0, 0\})$. For this purpose (see Eq. (10.9)) we first calculate the parameters of $\{\varphi, 0, 0\} \cdot \{e_1, e_2, e_3\}$ for very small e_i then allow e_i to approach zero. The rotation $\{e_1, e_2, e_3\}$ is given by

$$\{e_1, e_2, e_3\} = \begin{pmatrix} 1 & e_3 & -e_2 \\ -e_3 & 1 & e_1 \\ e_2 & -e_1 & 1 \end{pmatrix}$$

correct to the first power of e_i. (See Eq. (14.22).) We obtain for $\{\varphi, 0, 0\}\{e_1, e_2, e_3\} = \boldsymbol{\epsilon}_\varphi \cdot \{e_1, e_2, e_3\}$

$$\begin{pmatrix} 1, & e_3, & -e_2, \\ -e_3 \cos\varphi + e_2 \sin\varphi, & \cos\varphi - e_1 \sin\varphi, & e_1 \cos\varphi + \sin\varphi \\ e_3 \sin\varphi + e_2 \cos\varphi, & -\sin\varphi - e_1 \cos\varphi, & -e_1 \sin\varphi + \cos\varphi \end{pmatrix}$$

From this we calculate the angle of rotation φ' from Eq. (14.23).

$$1 + 2\cos\varphi' = 1 + 2\cos\varphi - 2e_1 \sin\varphi; \qquad \varphi' = \varphi + e_1 . \tag{14.23a}$$

From (14.22) we obtain the direction of the axis of rotation.

$$\mathbf{v}'_{11} : \mathbf{v}'_{21} : \mathbf{v}'_{31} = 2e_1 \cos\varphi + 2\sin\varphi : e_3 \sin\varphi + e_2(1 + \cos\varphi) : e_3(1 + \cos\varphi) - e_2 \sin\varphi \tag{14.22a}$$

In conjunction with the normalization condition $\mathbf{v}'^2_{11} + \mathbf{v}'^2_{21} + \mathbf{v}'^2_{13} = 1$, this yields (correct to the first order in e)

$$\mathbf{v}'_{11} = 1; \qquad \mathbf{v}'_{21} = \frac{e_2(1 + \cos\varphi)}{2\sin\varphi} + \frac{e_3}{2}; \qquad \mathbf{v}'_{31} = \frac{e_3(1 + \cos\varphi)}{2\sin\varphi} - \frac{e_2}{2}.$$

[4] For the discussion of Fig. 1 in Chapter 10, the distance from the origin was defined to be φ/π, and not φ. The left-hand portion of the figure should, in this discussion, be considered as magnified in the ratio $\pi : 1$.

Thus the parameters of $\{\varphi, 0, 0\} \cdot \{e_1, e_2, e_3\}$ are

$$\varphi + e_1, \qquad \varphi\left[\frac{e_2(1+\cos\varphi)}{2\sin\varphi} + \frac{e_3}{2}\right], \qquad \varphi\left[\frac{e_3(1+\cos\varphi)}{2\sin\varphi} - \frac{e_2}{2}\right].$$

For $e_1 = e_2 = e_3 = 0$, one obtains just the parameters of $\boldsymbol{\epsilon}_\varphi$, that is, φ, 0, 0. For $e_1 = e_2 = e_3 = 0$, the Jacobian of interest is

$$\frac{\partial(p_1(\{\varphi, 0, 0\}\{e_1, e_2, e_3\}), \cdots, p_3(\{\varphi, 0, 0\}\{e_1, e_2, e_3\}))}{\partial(e_1, e_2, e_3)}$$

$$= \begin{vmatrix} 1 & 0 & 0 \\ 0 & \varphi\dfrac{1+\cos\varphi}{2\sin\varphi} & -\dfrac{\varphi}{2} \\ 0 & +\dfrac{\varphi}{2} & \varphi\dfrac{1+\cos\varphi}{2\sin\varphi} \end{vmatrix} = \frac{\varphi^2}{4}\,\frac{(1+\cos\varphi)^2 + \sin^2\varphi}{\sin^2\varphi}$$

$$= \frac{\varphi^2}{2(1-\cos\varphi)}.$$

Thus we obtain for the weight function g (Eq. (10.9))

$$g(\{\varphi, 0, 0\}) = g(\{\mathbf{v}_{11}\varphi, \mathbf{v}_{21}\varphi, \mathbf{v}_{31}\varphi\}) = \frac{2g_0(1-\cos\varphi)}{\varphi^2}. \tag{14.26}$$

The calculation of the invariant integral of a function $J(R) = J(\varphi)$ which has the same value for all the elements of a class (as, for example, the character of a representation) is also quite simple. The integration in parameter space can then be carried out first over a spherical surface (φ = constant), i.e., over all the elements of a class, which gives $4\pi\varphi^2$, and then over φ, i.e., over all the different classes. We thus obtain

$$g_0\int_0^\pi J(\varphi) 8\pi(1-\cos\varphi)\,d\varphi \tag{14.27}$$

for the Hurwitz integral.

Another very common parametrization is that utilizing the Euler angles, as illustrated in Fig. 2, page 90. The rotation with Euler angles α, β, γ is the product of three rotations: one about Z through γ, about Y through β, and about Z through α. In subsequent chapters, $\{\alpha, \beta, \gamma\}$ will always represent the rotation with Euler angles α, β, and γ. In this representation α and γ generally vary from 0 to 2π and β from 0 to π. But if $\beta = 0$, then α and γ are not uniquely determined; the rotations $\{\alpha, 0, \gamma\}$ are all rotations through the angle $\alpha + \gamma$ about the Z-axis.

15. The Three-Dimensional Pure Rotation Group

Spherical Harmonics

1. The irreducible representations of the three-dimensional rotation group, like those of the two-dimensional group, can be derived via Laplace's differential equation

$$\frac{\partial^2 f(x, y, z)}{\partial x^2} + \frac{\partial^2 f(x, y, z)}{\partial y^2} + \frac{\partial^2 f(x, y, z)}{\partial z^2} = 0 \tag{15.1}$$

by considering the homogeneous polynomials of the lth degree which satisfy it. An orthogonal transformation R of such a polynomial produces another polynomial of the lth degree which also is a solution of (15.1), and which can therefore be expressed as a linear combination of the untransformed polynomials. The coefficients form a representation which is denoted by

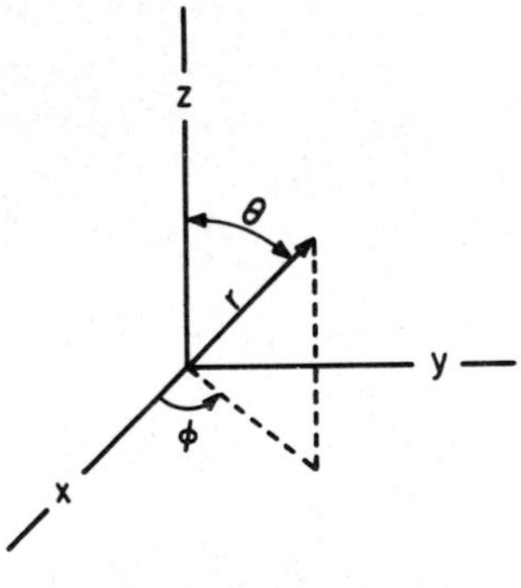

FIG. 7. The polar coordinates r, ϑ, and φ.

$\mathfrak{D}^{(l)}(R)$. Since we shall determine the irreducible representations of the three-dimensional rotation group by an alternative method, we discuss the method involving Laplace's equation only briefly.

To solve (15.1), one usually introduces polar coordinates r, ϑ, and φ in place of the x, y, and z (see Fig. 7); polynomials of the lth degree then have the form $r^l Y_{lm}(\vartheta, \varphi)$. If this form is introduced into (15.1) (written in polar coordinates), r drops out and a differential equation in the variables ϑ and φ (and involving l) results. The $(2l + 1)$ linearly independent solutions of this equation[1]

$$Y_{l,-l}(\vartheta, \varphi),\ Y_{l,-l+1}(\vartheta, \varphi),\ \cdots,\ Y_{l,l-1}(\vartheta, \varphi),\ Y_{l,l}(\vartheta, \varphi) \tag{15.2}$$

[1] See, e.g., D. Hilbert and R. Courant, "Methoden der Mathematischen Physik," pp. 420, 66, 265, Springer, Berlin, 1924 or its English translation (Interscience, New York, 1953), Vol. I, p. 510.

are known as spherical harmonics[2] of the lth degree. They have the form

$$Y_{lm}(\vartheta, \varphi) = \Phi_m(\varphi)\Theta_{lm}(\vartheta), \tag{15.3}$$

where

$$\Phi_m(\varphi) = \frac{1}{\sqrt{2\pi}} e^{im\varphi}$$

$$\Theta_{lm}(\vartheta) = (-1)^m \left[\frac{2l+1}{2} \frac{(l-m)!}{(l+m)!}\right]^{1/2} \sin^m \vartheta \frac{d^m}{d(\cos\vartheta)^m} P_l(\cos\vartheta) \qquad (m \geqslant 0)$$

$$\Theta_{l,-m}(\vartheta) = \left[\frac{2l+1}{2} \cdot \frac{(l-m)!}{(l+m)!}\right]^{1/2} \sin^m \vartheta \frac{d^m}{d(\cos\vartheta)^m} P_l(\cos\vartheta) . \tag{15.3a}$$

The $P_l(\cos\vartheta)$ are the Legendre polynomials, defined by

$$P_l(\cos\vartheta) = \frac{1}{2^l l!} \frac{d^l}{d(\cos\vartheta)^l} (\cos^2\vartheta - 1)^l . \tag{15.3b}$$

For $\vartheta = 0$, all Y_{lm} vanish, except for Y_{l0}. This must be the case since the azimuth φ is undetermined for $\vartheta = 0$; thus at this point the value of $Y_{lm}(\vartheta, \varphi) \sim e^{im\varphi} P_l^m(\cos\vartheta)$ cannot depend on φ.[3]

The most important feature of (15.3) is the φ dependence. If we apply the operator $\mathbf{P}_R$ to $r^l Y_{lm}(\vartheta, \varphi)$, where R is a rotation about the Z-axis through an angle α, the radius and the polar angle ϑ are unchanged and φ goes into $\varphi + \alpha$. Therefore, if we denote the rotation with Euler angles α, β, γ by $\{\alpha, \beta, \gamma\}$,

$$\mathbf{P}_{\{\alpha 00\}} r^l Y_{lm}(\vartheta, \varphi) = r^l \frac{e^{im(\varphi+\alpha)}}{\sqrt{2\pi}} \Theta_{lm}(\vartheta) = e^{im\alpha} r^l Y_{lm}(\vartheta, \varphi). \tag{15.4}$$

The rows and columns of the $(2l + 1)$-dimensional representation belonging to the spherical harmonics of the lth degree are labeled by the second indices of the corresponding spherical harmonics from $-l$ to $+l$. Then

$$\mathbf{P}_{\{\alpha\beta\gamma\}} r^l Y_{lm}(\vartheta, \varphi) = \sum_{m'=-l}^{l} \mathfrak{D}^{(l)}(\{\alpha, \beta, \gamma\})_{m'm} r^l Y_{lm'}(\vartheta, \varphi). \tag{15.5}$$

By equating the coefficients in the usual way we obtain

$$\mathfrak{D}^{(l)}(\{\alpha,0,0\})_{m'm} = e^{im\alpha} \delta_{mm'} .$$

Thus, in the representation $\mathfrak{D}^{(l)}$, those matrices which correspond to rotations

[2] The phases of the eigenfunctions here and throughout this translation have been chosen to conform with convention of E. U. Condon and G. H. Shortley, "The Theory of Atomic Spectra," Cambridge Univ. Press, London and New York, 1953.

[3] The function Θ_{lm} $(m \geqslant 0)$ divided by the square root in (15.3a) is the associated Legendre polynomial and is often denoted by $P_l^m(\cos\vartheta)$.

about Z are diagonal. For a rotation through an angle α one has the representation-matrix

$$\mathfrak{D}^{(l)}(\{\alpha 00\}) = \begin{pmatrix} e^{-il\alpha} & 0 & \cdots & 0 & 0 \\ 0 & e^{-i(l-1)\alpha} & \cdots & 0 & 0 \\ 0 & \cdot & \cdots & \cdot & \cdot \\ \cdot & \cdot & \cdots & \cdot & \cdot \\ \cdot & \cdot & \cdots & \cdot & \cdot \\ 0 & 0 & \cdots & e^{i(l-1)\alpha} & 0 \\ 0 & 0 & \cdots & 0 & e^{il\alpha} \end{pmatrix}. \tag{15.6}$$

We shall now show that the representations $\mathfrak{D}^{(l)}$ are irreducible by showing that a matrix which commutes with the $\mathfrak{D}^{(l)}(\{\alpha, \beta, \gamma\})$ for all values of α, β, and γ must necessarily be a constant matrix. First of all, only a diagonal matrix commutes with all the matrices (15.6). Therefore, a matrix which commutes with all the $\mathfrak{D}^{(l)}(\{\alpha, \beta, \gamma\})$ is certainly a diagonal matrix. Moreover, it will be seen below that, in general (i.e., except for certain discrete values of β), *no zeros* appear in the 0-row of $\mathfrak{D}^{(l)}(\{0, \beta, 0\})$. Then only a diagonal matrix with all diagonal elements equal (i.e., a constant matrix) commutes with these matrices. To see this, assume that the diagonal matrix with elements $\mathbf{d}_k$ commutes with $\mathfrak{D}^{(l)}(\{0, \beta, 0\})$; the elements in the 0-row of the products are

$$\mathbf{d}_0 \mathfrak{D}^{(l)}(\{0, \beta, 0\})_{0k} = \mathfrak{D}^{(l)}(\{0, \beta, 0\})_{0k} \mathbf{d}_k \,, \tag{15.E.1}$$

and this implies that $\mathbf{d}_0 = \mathbf{d}_k$.

The fact that $\mathfrak{D}^{(l)}(\{0, \beta, 0\})$ in general contains no zeros in the 0-row can be seen as follows: If R is a rotation about Y through an angle β, then $\mathbf{P}_R$ substitutes the point r, $\vartheta + \beta$, 0 for the point r, ϑ, 0. Therefore, the $r^l Y_{lm}(\vartheta + \beta, 0)$ are linear combinations of the $r^l Y_{lm'}(\vartheta, 0)$, with coefficients $\mathfrak{D}^{(l)}(\{0, \beta, 0\})_{m'm}$. If we consider the point $\vartheta = 0$, then in general $Y_{lm}(\beta, 0)$ is not zero, whereas the $Y_{lm'}(0, 0)$ are all zero, except for $Y_{l,0}(0, 0)$. Now if the coefficient of this term, $\mathfrak{D}^{(l)}(\{0, \beta, 0\})_{0m}$, were to vanish, all the terms on the right side of the equation would be zero, while the left side would be non-vanishing; therefore $\mathfrak{D}^{(l)}(\{0, \beta, 0\})_{0m}$ cannot vanish.

2. The representations $\mathfrak{D}^{(l)}(\{\alpha, \beta, \gamma\})$ are thus irreducible for all $l = 0, 1, 2, \cdots$. In order to determine their characters, we recall that the traces of matrices which belong to the same class are equal. Since in this case a class is characterized by its angle of rotation φ, the character $\chi^{(l)}(\varphi)$ is a function of the rotation angle alone, and can be determined by calculating the trace of any matrix which corresponds to an element with rotation angle φ. We have already seen such a matrix in (15.6), if $\alpha = \varphi$. We thus obtain

$$\chi^{(l)}(\varphi) = \sum_{m=-l}^{+l} e^{im\varphi} = 1 + 2\cos\varphi + 2\cos 2\varphi + \cdots + 2\cos l\varphi. \tag{15.7}$$

The orthogonality relations (using the weighting function determined in Eq. (14.27)) are

$$8\pi g(E) \int_0^\pi \chi^{(l')}(\varphi)^* \chi^{(l)}(\varphi)(1 - \cos \varphi)\, d\varphi = 8\pi^2 g(E)\, \delta_{l'l}.$$

This can easily be verified by a simple integration. One can also see that no irreducible representations exist besides the $\mathfrak{D}^{(l)}$: The characters of any such representations multiplied by $(1 - \cos \varphi)$ must be orthogonal to all $\chi^{(l)}$, and thus also to all $\chi^{(l+1)} - \chi^{(l)}$, i.e., to the functions $1, 2 \cos \varphi$, $2 \cos 2\varphi$, $2 \cos 3\varphi, \cdots$ in the domain from $\varphi = 0$ to $\varphi = \pi$; therefore, they must vanish, according to Fourier's theorem.

It follows that the $\mathfrak{D}^{(0)}, \mathfrak{D}^{(1)}, \mathfrak{D}^{(2)}, \cdots$ include all the inequivalent irreducible representations of the three-dimensional pure rotation group. There is an infinite number of them, as there must be, since the rotation group has an infinite number of classes.

The identical representation is $\mathfrak{D}^{(0)}$; the three-dimensional orthogonal matrices, as a representation of their own group, are equivalent to $\mathfrak{D}^{(1)}$, as can be seen at once either from the dimension or from the equality of the characters.

Every representation of the three-dimensional rotation group is a combination of the $\mathfrak{D}^{(0)}, \mathfrak{D}^{(1)}, \mathfrak{D}^{(2)}, \cdots$ and is specified up to a similarity transformation by the number of times each individual $\mathfrak{D}^{(0)}, \mathfrak{D}^{(1)}, \cdots$ occurs in it. But these numbers $A_0, A_1, A_2, \cdots$ can be determined just from the matrices which correspond to a subgroup which is a two-dimensional rotation group, e.g., the rotations about the Z-axis. If a representation ($\exp im\varphi$) of a two-dimensional rotation group occurs a_m times, then (for $m \geqslant 0$) $a_m = A_m + A_{m+1} + \cdots$ and $\mathfrak{D}^{(l)}$ is contained in the whole representation $A_l = a_l - a_{l+1}$ times. It is well to note that this conclusion can be reached only if one knows beforehand in some way that one is actually dealing with a representation; this criterion can not be applied to any system of matrices.

Equation (15.6) specifies the matrices $\mathfrak{D}^{(l)}(\{\alpha, 0, 0\}) = \mathfrak{D}^{(l)}(\{0, 0, \gamma\})$; we would know all the matrices $\mathfrak{D}^{(l)}(\{\alpha, \beta, \gamma\})$ if we also knew the matrices corresponding to rotations about Y. We denote $\mathfrak{D}^{(l)}(\{0, \beta, 0\})_{\kappa\lambda}$ by $\boldsymbol{d}^{(l)}(\beta)_{\kappa\lambda}$. The rotation $\{\alpha, \beta, \gamma\}$ is the product of the three rotations $\{\alpha, 0, 0\}$, $\{0, \beta, 0\}$, and $\{0, 0, \gamma\}$. The matrix corresponding to it is therefore

$$\mathfrak{D}^{(l)}(\{\alpha, \beta, \gamma\}) = \mathfrak{D}^{(l)}(\{\alpha, 0, 0\})\mathfrak{D}^{(l)}(\{0, \beta, 0\})\mathfrak{D}^{(l)}(\{0, 0, \gamma\}).$$

Therefore, the general rotation matrix can be written in terms of the matrix for a rotation about Y:

$$\mathfrak{D}^{(l)}(\{\alpha, \beta, \gamma\})_{m'm} = e^{im'\alpha} \boldsymbol{d}^{(l)}(\beta)_{m'm} e^{im\gamma}. \tag{15.8}$$

The Homomorphism of the Two-Dimensional Unitary Group onto the Rotation Group

3. We wish to deduce the irreducible representation of the three-dimensional pure rotation group by an alternative method suggested by H. Weyl. We turn to this method in spite of the fact that our discussion of the method utilizing Laplace's equation has been only a brief one, because Weyl's method permits the derivation of the so-called "double valued representations" simultaneously with the proper representations. In discussions to follow (about the theory of spin) these will play a role equal in importance to that of the proper representations.

In the symmetric group one can be content with the determination of the dimensions and the characters of the individual representations; in contrast, not only the characters, but also the elements of all representation matrices are of significance in the rotation group. As we shall see later, this results from the fact that in physically meaningful quantities all identical particles enter in the same way. But different directions in space are physically equivalent only if all directions are equivalent, not only in the mechanical problem but also in the physical quantity in which one is interested. For example, a direction is already distinguished if one is concerned with a particular component of a dipole moment.

We begin with three simple lemmas which belong properly to the elementary theory of matrices.

(*a*) A matrix which transforms every real vector into a real vector is itself real, i.e. all its elements are real. If this matrix is applied to the kth unit vector (kth component $= 1$, all others $= 0$), the result is the vector which forms the kth row of the matrix. Thus this row must be real. But this argument applies to all k, so that all the rows of the matrix must be real.

(b) We have seen in Chapter 3 (page 26) that the matrix $\mathbf{O}$ is complex orthogonal if it leaves the simple scalar product of two arbitrary vectors unchanged, i.e., if $((\mathfrak{a}, \mathfrak{b})) = ((\mathbf{O}\mathfrak{a}, \mathbf{O}\mathfrak{b}))$. An equivalent condition can be stated in terms of one arbitrary vector. A matrix $\mathbf{O}$ is complex orthogonal if the length of every single arbitrary vector $\mathfrak{v}$ is left unchanged under transformation by $\mathbf{O}$.

Consider two arbitrary vectors $\mathfrak{a}$ and $\mathfrak{b}$ and write $\mathfrak{v} = \mathfrak{a} + \mathfrak{b}$. Then our new condition for the complex orthogonality of $\mathbf{O}$ is

$$((\mathfrak{v}, \mathfrak{v})) = ((\mathbf{O}\mathfrak{v}, \mathbf{O}\mathfrak{v})).$$

Using the fact that $((\mathfrak{a}, \mathfrak{b})) = ((\mathfrak{b}, \mathfrak{a}))$, this becomes

$$((\mathfrak{a} + \mathfrak{b}, \mathfrak{a} + \mathfrak{b})) = ((\mathfrak{a}, \mathfrak{a})) + ((\mathfrak{b}, \mathfrak{b})) + 2((\mathfrak{a}, \mathfrak{b})) = ((\mathbf{O}\mathfrak{a}, \mathbf{O}\mathfrak{a})) + ((\mathbf{O}\mathfrak{b}, \mathbf{O}\mathfrak{b})) + 2((\mathbf{O}\mathfrak{a}, \mathbf{O}\mathfrak{b})).$$

However, the condition also implies that $((\mathfrak{a}, \mathfrak{a})) = ((\mathbf{O}\mathfrak{a}, \mathbf{O}\mathfrak{a}))$ and $((\mathfrak{b}, \mathfrak{b})) = ((\mathbf{O}\mathfrak{b}, \mathbf{O}\mathfrak{b}))$. It then follows that

$$((\mathfrak{a}, \mathfrak{b})) = ((\mathbf{O}\mathfrak{a}, \mathbf{O}\mathfrak{b})),$$

and from this it follows that $\mathbf{O}$ is complex orthogonal. It can be shown in a similar way that $\mathbf{U}$ is unitary if only $(\mathfrak{v}, \mathfrak{v}) = (\mathbf{U}\mathfrak{v}, \mathbf{U}\mathfrak{v})$ holds for every vector.

A matrix which leaves each real vector real, and leaves the length of every vector unchanged, is a *rotation*. The geometrical basis for this theorem is the simple fact that when all lengths are equal in the original and transformed figures, the angles also must be equal; hence the transformation is merely a rotation.

(c) We now determine the general form of a two-dimensional unitary matrix

$$\mathbf{u} = \begin{pmatrix} a & b \\ c & d \end{pmatrix}$$

of determinant $+1$ by considering the elements of the product $\mathbf{u}\mathbf{u}^\dagger = \mathbf{1}$.

$$a^*c + b^*d = 0 \quad \text{implies that} \quad c = -b^*d/a^*;$$

substitution of this into $ad - bc = 1$ yields $(aa^* + bb^*)\, d/a^* = 1$. Furthermore, since $aa^* + bb^* = 1$, it follows that $d = a^*$ and $c = -b^*$. The general two-dimensional unitary matrix with determinant $+1$ is thus

$$\mathbf{u} = \begin{pmatrix} a & b \\ -b^* & a^* \end{pmatrix}, \tag{15.9}$$

where we must still have $|a|^2 + |b|^2 = 1$.

4. We now consider the so-called "Pauli matrices"

$$\mathbf{s}_x = \begin{pmatrix} 0 & 1 \\ 1 & 0 \end{pmatrix}, \quad \mathbf{s}_y = \begin{pmatrix} 0 & i \\ -i & 0 \end{pmatrix}, \quad \mathbf{s}_z = \begin{pmatrix} -1 & 0 \\ 0 & 1 \end{pmatrix}. \tag{15.10}$$

Every two-dimensional matrix $\mathbf{h}$ with zero trace can be interpreted as a linear combination of these matrices: $\mathbf{h} = x\mathbf{s}_x + y\mathbf{s}_y + z\mathbf{s}_z = [\mathfrak{r}, \mathbf{S}]$; explicitly,

$$\mathbf{h} = [\mathfrak{r}, \mathbf{S}] = \begin{pmatrix} -z & x + iy \\ x - iy & +z \end{pmatrix} \tag{15.10a}$$

We have written $2x = \mathbf{h}_{12} + \mathbf{h}_{21}$; $2iy = \mathbf{h}_{12} - \mathbf{h}_{21}$; and $z = -\mathbf{h}_{11} = +\mathbf{h}_{22}$. In particular, if x, y, and z are real, then $\mathbf{h}$ is Hermitian.

If we transform $\mathbf{h}$ by an arbitrary unitary matrix $\mathbf{u}$ with determinant 1, we again obtain a matrix with zero trace, $\bar{\mathbf{h}} = \mathbf{u}\mathbf{h}\mathbf{u}^\dagger$; therefore $\bar{\mathbf{h}}$ can also be written as linear combination of $\mathbf{s}_x$, $\mathbf{s}_y$, $\mathbf{s}_z$.

$$\bar{\mathbf{h}} = \mathbf{u}\mathbf{h}\mathbf{u}^\dagger = \mathbf{u}[\mathfrak{r}, \mathbf{S}]\mathbf{u}^\dagger = x'\mathbf{s}_x + y'\mathbf{s}_y + z'\mathbf{s}_z = [\mathfrak{r}', \mathbf{S}] \tag{15.11}$$

$$\begin{pmatrix} a & b \\ -b^* & a^* \end{pmatrix}\begin{pmatrix} -z & x + iy \\ x - iy & z \end{pmatrix}\begin{pmatrix} a^* & -b \\ b^* & a \end{pmatrix} = \begin{pmatrix} -z' & x' + iy' \\ x' - iy' & z' \end{pmatrix}. \tag{15.11a}$$

This equation determines x', y', z' as linear functions of x, y, z. The transformation $\mathbf{R_u}$ which carries $\mathfrak{r} = (xyz)$ into $\mathbf{R_u}\mathfrak{r} = \mathfrak{r}' = (x'y'z')$ can be found from (15.11a). It is

$$\left.\begin{aligned} x' &= \tfrac{1}{2}(a^2 + a^{*2} - b^2 - b^{*2})x + \tfrac{1}{2}i(a^2 - a^{*2} + b^2 - b^{*2})y \\ &\qquad + (a^*b^* + ab)z \\ y' &= \tfrac{1}{2}i(a^{*2} - a^2 + b^2 - b^{*2})x + \tfrac{1}{2}(a^2 + a^{*2} + b^2 + b^{*2})y \\ &\qquad + i(a^*b^* - ab)z \\ z' &= -(a^*b + ab^*)x + i(a^*b - ab^*)y + (aa^* - bb^*)z. \end{aligned}\right\} \tag{15.12}$$

The particular form of the matrix $\mathbf{R_u}$ is not important in this expression[4]; it is important only that

$$x'^2 + y'^2 + z'^2 = x^2 + y^2 + z^2 \tag{15.13}$$

because of the equality of the determinants of $\bar{\mathbf{h}}$ and $\mathbf{h}$. According to (b), this fact implies that *the transformation* $\mathbf{R_u}$ *must be complex orthogonal.* This can also be seen directly from the explicit formula (15.12).

Furthermore, $\bar{\mathbf{h}}$ is Hermitian if $\mathbf{h}$ is. In other words, $\mathfrak{r}' = (x'y'z')$ *is real if* $\mathfrak{r} = (xyz)$ *is real.* This implies, according to (a), that $\mathbf{R_u}$ is *pure real*, as can also be seen directly from (15.12). Thus $\mathbf{R_u}$ *is a rotation*: every two-dimensional unitary matrix $\mathbf{u}$ of determinant 1 corresponds to a three-dimensional rotation $\mathbf{R_u}$; the correspondence is given by (15.11) or (15.12).

The determinant of $\mathbf{R_u}$ is $+1$, since as $\mathbf{u}$ is changed continuously into a unit matrix, $\mathbf{R_u}$ goes continuously into the three-dimensional unit matrix. If its determinant were -1 at the beginning of this process, it would have to make the jump to $+1$. Since this is impossible, $\mathbf{R_u}$ *is a pure rotation for all* $\mathbf{u}$.

The correspondence is such that the product $\mathbf{qu}$ *of two unitary matrices* $\mathbf{q}$ *and* $\mathbf{u}$ *corresponds to the product* $\mathbf{R_{qu}} = \mathbf{R_q} \cdot \mathbf{R_u}$ *of the corresponding rotations.* According to (15.11), applied to $\mathbf{q}$ instead of $\mathbf{u}$,

$$\mathbf{q}[\mathfrak{r}, \mathbf{S}]\mathbf{q}^\dagger = [\mathbf{R_q}\mathfrak{r}, \mathbf{S}], \tag{15.12a}$$

and upon transformation with $\mathbf{u}$ this yields

$$\mathbf{uq}[\mathfrak{r}, \mathbf{S}]\mathbf{q}^\dagger\mathbf{u}^\dagger = \mathbf{u}[\mathbf{R_q}\mathfrak{r}, \mathbf{S}]\mathbf{u}^\dagger = [\mathbf{R_u}\mathbf{R_q}\mathfrak{r}, \mathbf{S}] = [\mathbf{R_{uq}}\mathfrak{r}, \mathbf{S}],$$

using (15.11) again, with $\mathbf{R_q}\mathfrak{r}$ replacing $\mathfrak{r}$ and $\mathbf{uq}$ replacing $\mathbf{u}$. Thus, a homomorphism exists between the group of two-dimensional unitary matrices of determinant $+1$ (the "unitary group") and three-dimensional rotations; the correspondence is given by (15.11) or (15.12). However, we note that so

[4] The complex numbers a and b which characterize the rotation in (15.12) are called the Cayley-Klein parameters; $|a|^2 + |b|^2 = 1$. For sake of brevity, the group of the two-dimensional unitary matrices of determinant 1 will often be called simply the unitary group.

far we have not shown that the homomorphism exists between the two-dimensional unitary group and the whole rotation group. That would imply that $\mathbf{R}_\mathbf{u}$ ranges over all rotations as $\mathbf{u}$ covers the entire unitary group. This will be proved shortly. It must also be noted that the homomorphism is not an isomorphism, since more than one unitary matrix corresponds to the same rotation. This, too, will be seen in more detail below.

We first assume that $\mathbf{u}$ is a diagonal matrix $\mathbf{u}_1(\alpha)$ (i.e., we set $b = 0$, and, for reasons which will be apparent later, $a = e^{-\frac{1}{2}i\alpha}$). Then $|a^2| = 1$ and α is real.

$$\mathbf{u}_1(\alpha) = \begin{pmatrix} e^{-\frac{1}{2}i\alpha} & 0 \\ 0 & e^{+\frac{1}{2}i\alpha} \end{pmatrix}. \tag{15.14a}$$

From (15.12) we see that the corresponding rotation

$$\mathbf{R}_{\mathbf{u}_1} = \begin{pmatrix} \cos\alpha & \sin\alpha & 0 \\ -\sin\alpha & \cos\alpha & 0 \\ 0 & 0 & 1 \end{pmatrix} \tag{15.14a'}$$

is a rotation about Z through an angle α. We next assume $\mathbf{u}$ to be real

$$\mathbf{u}_2(\beta) = \begin{pmatrix} \cos\frac{1}{2}\beta & -\sin\frac{1}{2}\beta \\ +\sin\frac{1}{2}\beta & \cos\frac{1}{2}\beta \end{pmatrix}. \tag{15.14b}$$

From (15.12) the corresponding rotation is

$$\mathbf{R}_{\mathbf{u}_2} = \begin{pmatrix} \cos\beta & 0 & -\sin\beta \\ 0 & 1 & 0 \\ +\sin\beta & 0 & \cos\beta \end{pmatrix}, \tag{15.14b'}$$

a rotation about Y through an angle β. The product of the three unitary matrices $\mathbf{u}_1(\alpha)\mathbf{u}_2(\beta)\mathbf{u}_1(\gamma)$ corresponds to the product of a rotation about Z through an angle γ, about Y through β, and about Z through α, that is, to a rotation with Euler angles α, β, γ. It follows from this that the correspondence defined in (15.11) not only specified a three-dimensional rotation for every two-dimensional unitary matrix, but also at least one unitary matrix for every pure rotation. Specifically, the matrix

$$\left.\begin{aligned} &\begin{pmatrix} e^{-\frac{1}{2}i\alpha} & 0 \\ 0 & e^{\frac{1}{2}i\alpha} \end{pmatrix}\begin{pmatrix} \cos\frac{1}{2}\beta & -\sin\frac{1}{2}\beta \\ \sin\frac{1}{2}\beta & \cos\frac{1}{2}\beta \end{pmatrix}\begin{pmatrix} e^{-\frac{1}{2}i\gamma} & 0 \\ 0 & e^{\frac{1}{2}i\gamma} \end{pmatrix} \\ &= \begin{pmatrix} e^{-\frac{1}{2}i\alpha}\cos\frac{1}{2}\beta \cdot e^{-\frac{1}{2}i\gamma} & -e^{-\frac{1}{2}i\alpha}\sin\frac{1}{2}\beta \cdot e^{\frac{1}{2}i\gamma} \\ e^{\frac{1}{2}i\alpha}\sin\frac{1}{2}\beta \cdot e^{-\frac{1}{2}i\gamma} & e^{\frac{1}{2}i\alpha}\cos\frac{1}{2}\beta \cdot e^{\frac{1}{2}i\gamma} \end{pmatrix} \end{aligned}\right\} \tag{15.15}$$

corresponds to the rotation $\{\alpha\beta\gamma\}$. Thus the homomorphism is in fact a homomorphism of the unitary group onto the whole three-dimensional rotation group.

There is still the question of the multiplicity of the homomorphism, i.e., how many unitary matrices $\mathbf{u}$ correspond to the same rotation. It is sufficient to ascertain how many unitary matrices $\mathbf{u}_0$ correspond to the identity of the rotation group, i.e., to the transformation $x' = x, y' = y, z' = z$. For these particular $\mathbf{u}_0$'s, the identity $\mathbf{u}_0 \mathbf{h} \mathbf{u}_0^\dagger = \mathbf{h}$ must hold for all $\mathbf{h}$; this can only be the case when $\mathbf{u}_0$ is a constant matrix, ($b = 0$ and $a = a^*$, real) $\mathbf{u}_0 = (\pm \mathbf{1})$ (since $|a|^2 + |b|^2 = 1$). Thus, the two unitary matrices $(+\mathbf{1})$ and $(-\mathbf{1})$, and only these, correspond to the identity of the rotation group. These two elements form an invariant subgroup of the unitary group, and those elements (and only those) which are in the same coset of the invariant subgroup, i.e., $\mathbf{u}$ and $-\mathbf{u}$, correspond to the same rotation. That $\mathbf{u}$ and $-\mathbf{u}$ actually do correspond to the same rotation can be seen directly from (15.11) or (15.12).

Alternatively, we can simply note that only the half-Euler-angles occur in the trigonometric functions in (15.15). The Euler angles are determined by a rotation only up to a multiple of 2π; the half angles, only up to a multiple of π. Then the trigonometric functions in (15.15) are determined only up to a sign.

We have thus obtained a very important result: there exists a two-to-one homomorphism of the group of two-dimensional unitary matrices with determinant 1 onto the three-dimensional pure rotation group: there is a one-to-one correspondence between *pairs* of unitary matrices $\mathbf{u}$ and $-\mathbf{u}$ and rotations $\mathbf{R}_\mathbf{u}$ in such a way that from $\mathbf{uq} = \mathbf{t}$ it also follows that $\mathbf{R}_\mathbf{u}\mathbf{R}_\mathbf{q} = \mathbf{R}_\mathbf{t}$; conversely from $\mathbf{R}_\mathbf{u}\mathbf{R}_\mathbf{q} = \mathbf{R}_\mathbf{t}$, that $\mathbf{uq} = \pm\mathbf{t}$. If the unitary matrix $\mathbf{u}$ is known, the corresponding rotation $\mathbf{R}_\mathbf{u}$ is best obtained from (15.12); conversely, the unitary matrix for a rotation $\{\alpha\beta\gamma\}$ is best found from (15.15).

The Representations of the Unitary Group

5. The homomorphism just obtained provides a close relationship between the representations of the two groups. From every representation $\mathbf{D}(R)$ of the smaller group—this is the rotation group in this case—a representation $\mathfrak{U}(\mathbf{u})$ of the unitary group can be obtained, as we have already explained independently in Chapter 9. This is done by using the matrix $\mathfrak{U}(\mathbf{u}) = \mathbf{D}(\mathbf{R}_\mathbf{u})$ to represent all elements ($\mathbf{u}$ and $-\mathbf{u}$) of the second group which correspond in the homomorphism to the same element $\mathbf{R}_\mathbf{u}$ of the first group. Thus, in particular, the identity matrix $\mathbf{D}(E)$ corresponds to the two unitary matrices $\mathbf{1}$ and $-\mathbf{1}$. Conversely, if all the representations of the unitary group are known, then one can select those in which the same representation matrix $\mathfrak{U}(\mathbf{u}) = \mathfrak{U}(-\mathbf{u})$ corresponds to both matrices $\mathbf{u}$ and $-\mathbf{u}$. Each of these representations allows one to form a representation of the rotation group, by making the matrix $\mathbf{D}(\mathbf{R}_\mathbf{u}) = \mathfrak{U}(\mathbf{u}) = \mathfrak{U}(-\mathbf{u})$ correspond to the rotation $\mathbf{R}_\mathbf{u}$. All the representations of the rotation group can be obtained in this way.

In particular, let the representation $\mathfrak{U}(\mathbf{u})$ of the unitary group be irreducible. The element $\mathbf{u} = -\mathbf{1}$ commutes with all the elements of the group; thus $\mathfrak{U}(-\mathbf{1})$ must commute with all $\mathfrak{U}(\mathbf{u})$. Therefore, according to the general theorems on irreducible representations, it is a constant matrix. Because $(-\mathbf{1})^2 = \mathbf{1}$, the square of this group element must be represented by the unit matrix[5] $\mathfrak{U}(\mathbf{1})$. Therefore, either

$$\mathfrak{U}(-\mathbf{1}) = +\mathfrak{U}(\mathbf{1}) \quad \text{or} \quad \mathfrak{U}(-\mathbf{1}) = -\mathfrak{U}(\mathbf{1}).$$

Representations in which $\mathfrak{U}(-\mathbf{1}) = +\mathfrak{U}(\mathbf{1})$ are called even representations. In even representations $\mathfrak{U}(-\mathbf{u}) = \mathfrak{U}(-\mathbf{1}) \cdot \mathfrak{U}(\mathbf{u}) = \mathfrak{U}(\mathbf{1}) \cdot \mathfrak{U}(\mathbf{u}) = \mathfrak{U}(\mathbf{u})$, i.e., the same matrix always corresponds to two elements $\mathbf{u}$ and $-\mathbf{u}$. Even representations, therefore, give regular representations of the rotation group, all of which are known implicitly from Section 1.

Representations in which $\mathfrak{U}(-\mathbf{1}) = -\mathfrak{U}(\mathbf{1})$ are called odd representations. In odd representations, $\mathfrak{U}(-\mathbf{u}) = \mathfrak{U}(-\mathbf{1})\mathfrak{U}(\mathbf{u}) = -\mathfrak{U}(\mathbf{u})$; matrices of opposite sign correspond to elements which differ in sign. Odd representations of the unitary group do not yield regular representations of the rotation group, but only the "double-valued" or "half-integral" representations, in which not one matrix, but two matrices $\mathfrak{U}(\mathbf{u})$ and $\mathfrak{U}(-\mathbf{u}) = -\mathfrak{U}(\mathbf{u})$ correspond to each rotation $\mathbf{R}_{\mathbf{u}} = \mathbf{R}_{-\mathbf{u}}$. These two matrices differ in the signs of all their elements.

One odd representation of the unitary group is formed by the group itself: $\mathfrak{U}(\mathbf{u}) = \mathbf{u}$.

In the corresponding "double-valued" representation of the rotation group $\mathfrak{D}^{(\frac{1}{2})}$, the rotation $\{\alpha\beta\gamma\}$ corresponds to the matrix $\mathbf{u} = \mathfrak{U}(\mathbf{u})$ which corresponds to R in the homomorphism. Thus according to (15.15),

$$\mathfrak{D}^{(\frac{1}{2})}(\{\alpha\beta\gamma\}) = \pm \begin{pmatrix} e^{-\frac{1}{2}i\alpha} \cos \tfrac{1}{2}\beta \cdot e^{-\frac{1}{2}i\gamma} & -e^{-\frac{1}{2}i\alpha} \sin \tfrac{1}{2}\beta \cdot e^{\frac{1}{2}i\gamma} \\ e^{\frac{1}{2}i\alpha} \sin \tfrac{1}{2}\beta \cdot e^{-\frac{1}{2}i\gamma} & e^{\frac{1}{2}i\alpha} \cos \tfrac{1}{2}\beta \cdot e^{\frac{1}{2}i\gamma} \end{pmatrix}. \tag{15.16}$$

The first row or column is commonly called the $-\frac{1}{2}$ row or column; the second, the $+\frac{1}{2}$ row or column. In (15.16) we have the first double-valued representation of the rotation group.

For the double-valued representations, $\mathfrak{D}(R) \cdot \mathfrak{D}(S) = \mathfrak{D}(RS)$ is not necessarily true; only $\mathfrak{D}(R)\mathfrak{D}(S) = \pm\mathfrak{D}(RS)$ is guaranteed, since the representation matrices are determined only up to sign. Moreover, it is not possible to define the signs of all the matrices in such a way that the strict multiplication law of single-valued representations holds. Thus, a double-valued representation does not have the structure of a real (single-valued) representation in which the signs have simply been left undetermined. This

[5] The matrix $\mathfrak{U}(\mathbf{1})$, which corresponds to the identity of the group, is a unit matrix with the dimension of the representation. We use the symbol $\mathfrak{U}(\mathbf{1})$ in place of the simpler symbol 1 to avoid confusion with the identity $\mathbf{1}$ of the unitary group, which is always two-dimensional.

can be seen, for example, from (15.16): to a rotation about Z through an angle π corresponds the matrix $\pm i\mathbf{s}_z$; the square of this matrix, $-\mathbf{1} = -\mathbf{s}_z^2$, corresponds to a rotation through an angle 2π. But such a rotation is not properly a rotation at all, since it leaves everything unchanged; it is just the identity of the group. Therefore, the unit matrix *must* also correspond to it; it is impossible to make the representation single-valued by a choice of the signs in (15.16).

6. We shall now determine the irreducible representations of the two-dimensional unitary group.

Consider a homogeneous polynomial of the nth degree in ε and ζ. If we carry out a unitary transformation of the variables

$$\left.\begin{aligned} \varepsilon' &= a\varepsilon + b\zeta, \\ \zeta' &= -b^*\varepsilon + a^*\zeta, \end{aligned}\right\} \tag{15.17}$$

we again obtain a homogeneous polynomial of the nth degree. (Although this is true for arbitrary linear transformations, we restrict ourselves to unitary transformations.) Therefore, the $n + 1$ polynomials ε^n, $\varepsilon^{n-1}\zeta$, $\varepsilon^{n-2}\zeta^2, \cdots, \varepsilon\zeta^{n-1}$, ζ^n belong to an $(n + 1)$-dimensional representation of the unitary group. To obtain at once the notation customary for the rotation group, we write $n = 2j$; the dimension of the representation is then equal to $2j + 1$, and j can be either integral or half-integral.[6] Let the polynomial be

$$f_\mu(\varepsilon, \zeta) = \frac{\varepsilon^{j+\mu}\zeta^{j-\mu}}{\sqrt{(j+\mu)!(j-\mu)!}}, \tag{15.18}$$

where μ can assume the $2j + 1$ values $-j, -j+1, -j+2, \cdots, j-2, j-1, j$; these are integral for integral j, and half-integral for half-integral j. The constant factor $[(j+\mu)!(j-\mu)!]^{-1/2}$ is attached to $\varepsilon^{j+\mu}\zeta^{j-\mu}$ since, as we will show, it makes the representation $\mathfrak{U}^{(j)}$ for the $2j + 1$ functions (15.18) a unitary representation.

We now[7] construct $\mathbf{P}_\mathbf{u} f_\mu(\varepsilon, \zeta)$ according to Eq. (11.19).

$$\left.\begin{aligned} \mathbf{P}_\mathbf{u} f_\mu(\varepsilon, \zeta) &= f_\mu(a^*\varepsilon - b\zeta, b^*\varepsilon + a\zeta) \\ &= \frac{(a^*\varepsilon - b\zeta)^{j+\mu}(b^*\varepsilon + a\zeta)^{j-\mu}}{\sqrt{(j+\mu)!(j-\mu)!}} \end{aligned}\right\}. \tag{15.19}$$

[6] This means that it differs from a whole number by 1/2.

[7] $\mathbf{u}$ here is the unitary transformation in (15.17). In Chapter 11 $\mathbf{P}_\mathbf{R}$ was defined only for real orthogonal $\mathbf{R}$. In this case, where $\mathbf{u}$ is unitary, it follows from (11.18a) that we have

$$x_i = \sum_j \mathbf{R}_{ji}^* x_j'$$

in place of (11.18b); thus $\mathbf{R}_{ji}^*$ takes the place of $\mathbf{R}_{ji}$.

To express the right side as a linear combination of the f_μ, we expand it using the binomial theorem; it then becomes

$$\sum_{\varkappa=0}^{j+\mu}\sum_{\varkappa'=0}^{j-\mu}(-1)^{\varkappa}\frac{\sqrt{(j+\mu)!(j-\mu)!}}{\varkappa!\varkappa'!(j+\mu-\varkappa)!(j-\mu-\varkappa')!}$$
$$\times\, a^{\varkappa'}a^{*\,j+\mu-\varkappa}b^{\varkappa}b^{*\,j-\mu-\varkappa'}\varepsilon^{2j-\varkappa-\varkappa'}\zeta^{\varkappa+\varkappa'}. \qquad (15.19a)$$

The limits of summation can be omitted here and the summation taken over all whole numbers since the binomial coefficients vanish for $\varkappa, \varkappa'$ lying outside the region of summation. If we set $j-\varkappa-\varkappa'=\mu'$, then μ' must run over all integers for integral j and over all half-integers for half-integral j. Expressing all functions of ε and ζ in (15.19a) in terms of the f_μ, according to (15.18) we obtain

$$\mathbf{P_u}f_\mu(\varepsilon,\zeta)=\sum_{\mu'}\sum_{\varkappa}(-1)^{\varkappa}\frac{\sqrt{(j+\mu)!(j-\mu)!(j+\mu')!\,(j-\mu')!}}{\varkappa!(j-\mu'-\varkappa)!(j+\mu-\varkappa)!(\varkappa+\mu'-\mu)!}$$
$$\times\, a^{j-\mu'-\varkappa}a^{*\,j+\mu-\varkappa}b^{\varkappa}b^{*\,\varkappa+\mu'-\mu}f_{\mu'}(\varepsilon,\zeta). \qquad (15.20)$$

The coefficient of $f_{\mu'}$ on the right is $\mathfrak{U}^{(j)}(\mathbf{u})_{\mu'\mu}$:

$$\mathfrak{U}^{(j)}(\mathbf{u})_{\mu'\mu}=\sum_{\varkappa}(-1)^{\varkappa}\frac{\sqrt{(j+\mu)!(j-\mu)!\,(j+\mu')!(j-\mu')!}}{(j-\mu'-\varkappa)!(j+\mu-\varkappa)!\varkappa!(\varkappa+\mu'-\mu)!}$$
$$\times\, a^{j-\mu'-\varkappa}a^{*\,j+\mu-\varkappa}b^{\varkappa}b^{*\,\varkappa+\mu'-\mu}. \qquad (15.21)$$

The expression for $\mu'=j$, that is, for the last rows of the representation matrices, is somewhat simpler since the factorial eliminates all terms except that with $\varkappa=0$.

$$\mathfrak{U}^{(j)}(\mathbf{u})_{j\mu}=\sqrt{\frac{(2j)!}{(j+\mu)!(j-\mu)!}}\,a^{*\,j+\mu}b^{*\,j-\mu}. \qquad (15.21a)$$

We have now obtained the coefficients for the representations $\mathfrak{U}^{(j)}$ for all possible values of $j=0,\ \frac{1}{2},\ 1,\ \frac{3}{2},\ \cdots$; it remains only to prove that the representations in (15.21) are unitary and irreducible, and that the two-dimensional unitary group has no representations other than these.

7. First of all, we prove the unitarity of the representation (15.21). The proof rests on the fact that the polynomials f_μ in (15.18) are chosen so that

$$\sum_{\mu=-j}^{j} f_\mu f_\mu^* = \sum_{\mu}\frac{1}{(j+\mu)!(j-\mu)!}|\varepsilon^2|^{j+\mu}|\zeta^2|^{j-\mu}=\frac{(|\varepsilon^2|+|\zeta^2|)^{2j}}{(2j)!}. \qquad (15.22)$$

Similarly, because of the definition (15.19) of $\mathbf{P_u}f_\mu$

$$\sum_{\mu}|\mathbf{P_u}f_\mu(\varepsilon,\zeta)|^2=\sum_{\mu}\frac{|a^*\varepsilon-b\zeta|^{2(j+\mu)}\cdot|b^*\varepsilon+a\zeta|^{2(j-\mu)}}{(j+\mu)!(j-\mu)!} \qquad (15.22a)$$
$$=\frac{1}{(2j)!}(|a^*\varepsilon-b\zeta|^2+|b^*\varepsilon+a\zeta|^2)^{2j}=\frac{1}{(2j)!}(|\varepsilon|^2+|\zeta|^2)^{2j}.$$

The last part follows either by direct calculation or from the unitary nature of **u**. Comparison with (15.22) shows that the sum $\sum_\mu f_\mu f_\mu^*$ is invariant under the operations $\mathbf{P}_\mathbf{u}$, so that

$$\sum_\mu |\mathbf{P}_\mathbf{u} f_\mu|^2 = \sum_\mu |f_\mu|^2. \tag{15.23}$$

This will insure the unitary character of the representation $\mathfrak{U}^{(j)}$. In fact, substitution of the expression for $\mathbf{P}_\mathbf{u} f_\mu$ in terms of the f_μ by means of this representation gives

$$\sum_\mu \sum_{\mu'} \mathfrak{U}^{(j)}_{\mu'\mu} f_{\mu'} \sum_{\mu''} \mathfrak{U}^{(j)*}_{\mu''\mu} f^*_{\mu''} = \sum_\mu f_\mu f_\mu^*. \tag{15.23a}$$

If the $(2j+1)^2$ functions $f_{\mu'} f_{\mu''}$ are assumed linearly independent, (15.23) and (15.23a) give directly

$$\sum_\mu \mathfrak{U}^{(j)}(\mathbf{u})_{\mu'\mu} \mathfrak{U}^{(j)}(\mathbf{u})^*_{\mu''\mu} = \delta_{\mu'\mu''}, \tag{15.24}$$

which is the condition that $\mathfrak{U}^{(j)}$ be unitary.

Thus the unitarity of $\mathfrak{U}^{(j)}$ is established as soon as it is shown that no linear relationship exists among the $f_{\mu'} f^*_{\mu''}$, i.e., that the equation

$$\sum_{\mu'\mu''} c_{\mu'\mu''} \varepsilon^{j+\mu'} \zeta^{j-\mu'} \varepsilon^{*j+\mu''} \zeta^{*j-\mu''} = 0 \tag{15.E.2}$$

necessarily implies $c_{\mu'\mu''} = 0$. Equation (15.E.2) must hold for all values of the variables ε and ζ since (15.23) and (15.23a) hold for all complex ε and ζ. We assume in particular that ε is real; then with $\lambda = 2j + \mu' + \mu''$ the requirement that the coefficient of ε^λ vanish gives, after division by $\zeta^j \zeta^{*3j-\lambda}$,

$$\sum_{\mu'} c_{\mu',\lambda-2j-\mu'} (\zeta^*/\zeta)^{\mu'} = 0.$$

But this implies that $c_{\mu',\lambda-2j-\mu'} = 0$. The linear independence of the $f_{\mu'} f^*_{\mu''}$ also follows, since (ζ^*/ζ) is a variable which ranges freely over the complex unit circle. It can be written as exp $i\tau$, where τ can then assume all real values. But to fulfill

$$\sum_{\mu'} c_{\mu',\lambda-2j-\mu'} e^{i\mu'\tau} = 0$$

for all real values of τ, all the c's must vanish.

8. The irreducibility of the matrix system $\mathfrak{U}^{(j)}$ can be established just as the irreducibility of the representations $\mathfrak{D}^{(l)}$ of the rotation group have been established in Section 1, namely, by showing that any matrix **M** which commutes with $\mathfrak{U}^{(j)}(\mathbf{u})$ for all **u** (i.e., for all values of a and b satisfying the condition $|a|^2 + |b|^2 = 1$) must necessarily be a constant matrix. Consider first **u** of the form $\mathbf{u}_1(\alpha)$ in (15.14a); that is, set $b = 0$, $a = \exp(-\frac{1}{2}i\alpha)$. Then only the term with $\varkappa = 0$ remains in the sum (15.21), and this is nonzero only if $\mu = \mu'$; we obtain

$$\mathfrak{U}^{(j)}(\mathbf{u}_1(\alpha))_{\mu'\mu} = \delta_{\mu'\mu}\, e^{i\mu\alpha}. \tag{15.25}$$

Those matrices in $\mathfrak{U}^{(j)}$ which correspond to unitary transformations of the form $\mathbf{u}_1(\alpha)$ thus have the same form as (15.6), except that j, unlike the l in (15.6), may be half-integral as well as integral. But only a diagonal matrix commutes with these matrices, so that $\mathbf{M}$ must be diagonal. Next observe, by Eq. (15.21a), that no element in the last row of $\mathfrak{U}^{(j)}$ vanishes identically. Then by equating the elements of the j-row of $\mathfrak{U}^{(j)}\mathbf{M}$ and $\mathbf{M}\mathfrak{U}^{(j)}$, just as was done in Eq. (15.E.1), we can conclude that

$$\mathfrak{U}^{(j)}_{jk}\mathbf{M}_{kk} = \mathbf{M}_{jj}\mathfrak{U}^{(j)}_{jk}; \qquad \mathbf{M}_{kk} = \mathbf{M}_{jj}$$

and $\mathbf{M}$ is a constant matrix. Therefore, the representations $\mathfrak{U}^{(j)}$ are irreducible.

9. We can also show that there exists no representation of the unitary group besides the $\mathfrak{U}^{(j)}$, by using the same method as was used in Section 2 for the representations of the rotation group. First we determine the classes of the "unitary group." Since every unitary matrix can be diagonalized by transformation with a unitary matrix, our matrices all have the form $\mathbf{u}_1(\alpha)$ after this transformation, where α runs from 0 to 2π ($\mathbf{u}_1(-\alpha)$ is equivalent to $\mathbf{u}_1(\alpha)$). All $\mathbf{u}$ which can be transformed into the same $\mathbf{u}_1(\alpha)$ are in the same class. (The assumption that only group elements—only unitary matrices with determinant 1—occur, need not disturb us since every unitary matrix can be written as the product of a unitary matrix with determinant 1 and a constant matrix, and the transformation by the constant matrix can simply be omitted.)

To determine the character of $\mathfrak{U}^{(j)}$ it suffices to calculate the trace of one element of each class. We take $\mathbf{u}_1(\alpha)$ itself as the element of the class of $\mathbf{u}_1(\alpha)$; the corresponding matrix is given by (15.25). Its trace is

$$\xi_j(\alpha) = \sum_{\mu=-j}^{j} e^{i\mu\alpha}, \tag{15.26}$$

where the summation is to be taken in integer steps from the lower limit to the upper one.

It is now evident that the unitary group can have no irreducible representations other than the $\mathfrak{U}^{(j)}$ with $j = 0, \frac{1}{2}, 1, \frac{3}{2}, \cdots$. For the character of such a representation must, after multiplication by a weighting function, be orthogonal to all $\xi_j(\alpha)$, and therefore to $\xi_0(\alpha)$, $\xi_{1/2}(\alpha)$, $\xi_1(\alpha) - \xi_0(\alpha)$, $\xi_{3/2}(\alpha) - \xi_{1/2}(\alpha), \cdots$. But a function which is orthogonal to $1, 2\cos\frac{1}{2}\alpha$, $2\cos\alpha$, $2\cos(\frac{3}{2}\alpha), \cdots$ in the region from 0 to 2π must vanish, according to Fourier's theorem.

The Representations of the Three-Dimensional Pure Rotation Group.

10. Every representation $\mathfrak{U}^{(j)}$ of the unitary group is simultaneously a representation—either single- or double-valued—of the rotation group. The matrix $\mathfrak{U}^{(j)}(\mathbf{u})$ corresponds to the rotation $\{\alpha\beta\gamma\}$ when $\mathbf{u}$ is the unitary

transformation corresponding in the homomorphism to $\{\alpha\beta\gamma\}$. The coefficients, a and b, of $\mathbf{u}$ are given by (15.15) as

$$a = e^{-\frac{1}{2}i\alpha} \cos \tfrac{1}{2}\beta \cdot e^{-\frac{1}{2}i\gamma}, \qquad b = -e^{-\frac{1}{2}i\alpha} \sin \tfrac{1}{2}\beta \cdot e^{\frac{1}{2}i\gamma}. \qquad (15.15a)$$

To obtain the elements of the representation matrix corresponding to $\{\alpha\beta\gamma\}$, Eq. (15.15a) must be substituted into (15.21). In order to maintain notational consistency with (15.16), we transform the representation which results from this substitution with the diagonal matrix $\mathbf{M}_{\varkappa\lambda} = \delta_{\varkappa\lambda}(i)^{-2\varkappa}$; that is, we multiply the μ'-row by $i^{-2\mu'}$ and the μ-column by $i^{2\mu}$ so that the μ, μ'-coefficient is multiplied by $(i)^{2(\mu-\mu')} = (-1)^{\mu-\mu'}$.

We denote the representation which is thereby obtained from $\mathfrak{U}^{(j)}$ by $\mathfrak{D}^{(j)}(\{\alpha\beta\gamma\})$; its coefficients are

$$\mathfrak{D}^{(j)}(\{\alpha\beta\gamma\})_{\mu'\mu} = \sum_{\varkappa} (-1)^{\varkappa} \frac{\sqrt{(j+\mu)!(j-\mu)!(j+\mu')!(j-\mu')!}}{(j-\mu'-\varkappa)!\,(j+\mu-\varkappa)!\,\varkappa!\,(\varkappa+\mu'-\mu)!}$$
$$\times e^{i\mu'\alpha} \cos^{2j+\mu-\mu'-2\varkappa} \tfrac{1}{2}\beta \cdot \sin^{2\varkappa+\mu'-\mu} \tfrac{1}{2}\beta \cdot e^{i\mu\gamma}. \qquad (15.27)$$

The representation $\mathfrak{D}^{(j)}$ is $(2j+1)$-dimensional, where j can be either integral or half-integral. The rows and columns of $\mathfrak{D}^{(j)}$ are labeled by the integral or half-integral numbers $-j, -j+1, \cdots, j-1, j$. The summation over $\varkappa$ in (15.27) can be taken over all integers because the infinities in the factorials in the denominator limit it to the range between the larger of the numbers 0 and $\mu - \mu'$, and the smaller of the numbers $j - \mu'$ and $j + \mu$. The formulas for $\mu' = j$ and $\mu' = -j$ are especially simple; in the first case only the term $\varkappa = 0$ occurs, and in the second, only $\varkappa = j + \mu$:

$$\mathfrak{D}^{(j)}(\{\alpha\beta\gamma\})_{j\mu} = \sqrt{\binom{2j}{j-\mu}}\, e^{ij\alpha} \cos^{j+\mu} \tfrac{1}{2}\beta \cdot \sin^{j-\mu} \tfrac{1}{2}\beta \cdot e^{i\mu\gamma}, \qquad (15.27a)$$

$$\mathfrak{D}^{(j)}(\{\alpha\beta\gamma\})_{-j\mu} = (-1)^{j+\mu} \sqrt{\binom{2j}{j-\mu}}\, e^{-ij\alpha} \cos^{j-\mu} \tfrac{1}{2}\beta \cdot \sin^{j+\mu} \tfrac{1}{2}\beta \cdot e^{i\mu\gamma}. \qquad (15.27b)$$

All representation coefficients for rotations about the Z-axis also take an especially simple form. The rotation about Z through an angle α corresponds in the homomorphism to the unitary transformation $\mathbf{u}_1(\alpha)$; the coefficients of the corresponding representation matrix are given in (15.25). The matrix in $\mathfrak{D}^{(j)}$ which corresponds to the rotation $\{\alpha, 0, 0\}$ is therefore a diagonal matrix with diagonal elements, $\exp(-ij\alpha)$, $\exp(-i(j-1)\alpha)$, $\cdots$, $\exp(+i(j-1)\alpha)$, $\exp(+ij\alpha)$. The same result is obtained directly from (15.27) by letting $\beta = \gamma = 0$. The matrix $\mathfrak{D}^{(j)}(\{\alpha, 0, 0\})$ has already been presented explicitly in (15.6), which now applies not only for integral l but also for half-integral j. This is also true of (15.8).

The character $\chi^{(j)}(\varphi)$ of $\mathfrak{D}^{(j)}$ is the trace of a rotation with rotation angle φ.

$$\left.\begin{aligned}\chi^{(j)}(\varphi) &= \sum_{\mu=-j}^{j} e^{i\mu\varphi} \\ &= \begin{cases} 1 + 2\cos\varphi + \cdots + 2\cos j\varphi & (j \text{ integral}) \\ 2\cos\frac{1}{2}\varphi + 2\cos\frac{3}{2}\varphi + \cdots + 2\cos j\varphi & (j \text{ half-integral}) \end{cases}\end{aligned}\right\} \tag{15.28}$$

Regular representations include only those j for which $\mathfrak{U}^{(j)}(-\mathbf{1}) = \mathfrak{U}^{(j)}(\mathbf{u}_1(2\pi))$ is the positive unit matrix. From (15.25) it is seen that this is the case when μ is integral, i.e., when j is integral. Then $\mathfrak{D}^{(j)}$ is identical with the $\mathfrak{D}^{(l)}$ derived in Section 1; this is also shown by the equality of the characters.

For half-integral j, the representation $\mathfrak{D}^{(j)}$ is double-valued; the rotation $\{\alpha\beta\gamma\}$ corresponds to $\pm\mathfrak{D}^{(j)}(\{\alpha\beta\gamma\})$. This does not mean that the signs of the elements of $\mathfrak{D}^{(j)}$ can be changed individually; only the sign of the entire matrix can be changed, or the signs of all the elements simultaneously. A rotation $\mathbf{R}_\mathbf{u}$ corresponds to two unitary matrices $\mathbf{u}$ and $-\mathbf{u}$, and to each of these corresponds one matrix $\mathfrak{U}^{(j)}(\mathbf{u})$ and $\mathfrak{U}^{(j)}(-\mathbf{u})$; for half-integral j, the second of these equals $-\mathfrak{U}^{(j)}(\mathbf{u})$. These two matrices, and no others, correspond in $\mathfrak{D}^{(j)}$ to the rotation $\mathbf{R}_\mathbf{u}$. Actually, the double-valued representations are *not representations at all.* They will, however, be needed for the discussion of Pauli's spin theory.

The theory of the representations of the rotation group is due to J. Schur. The double-valued representations were first obtained by H. Weyl.

11. We now present the first few representations in explicit form. $\mathfrak{D}^{(0)}(R) = (1)$, and $\mathfrak{D}^{(\frac{1}{2})}(R)$ is given in (15.16). The next representation is $\mathfrak{D}^{(1)}(R)$:

$$\mathfrak{D}^{(1)}(\{\alpha\beta\gamma\}) = \begin{pmatrix} e^{-i\alpha}\dfrac{1+\cos\beta}{2}e^{-i\gamma} & -e^{-i\alpha}\dfrac{\sin\beta}{\sqrt{2}} & e^{-i\alpha}\dfrac{1-\cos\beta}{2}e^{i\gamma} \\ \dfrac{1}{\sqrt{2}}\sin\beta e^{-i\gamma} & \cos\beta & -\dfrac{1}{\sqrt{2}}\sin\beta e^{i\gamma} \\ e^{i\alpha}\dfrac{1-\cos\beta}{2}e^{-i\gamma} & e^{i\alpha}\dfrac{\sin\beta}{\sqrt{2}} & e^{i\alpha}\dfrac{1+\cos\beta}{2}e^{i\gamma} \end{pmatrix} \tag{15.29}$$

In this equation the trigonometric functions of the half-angles have been converted to functions of the whole angles.

The representations of rotation groups—at least the single-valued ones—are familiar to the physicist since they are the transformation formulas for vectors, tensors, etc. After a transformation to a new coordinate system, the new vector or tensor components are linear combinations of the components in the old coordinate system. If we denote the components in the old system by T_σ (σ can signify a set of several indices), then the components T'_σ in the new coordinate system are

$$T'_\rho = \sum_\sigma \mathbf{D}(R)_{\rho\sigma} T_\sigma , \tag{15.30}$$

where the dependence of the transformation coefficients on the orientation R of the new coordinate system with respect to the old one is explicitly indicated. If we transform to new coordinate axes a second time, say by a rotation S, then

$$T''_\tau = \sum_\rho \mathbf{D}(S)_{\tau\rho} T'_\rho = \sum_{\rho\sigma} \mathbf{D}(S)_{\tau\rho} \mathbf{D}(R)_{\rho\sigma} T_\sigma . \tag{15.31}$$

Now the T'' are the components of the tensor in the coordinate system rotated by SR so that we also have

$$T''_\tau = \sum_\sigma \mathbf{D}(SR)_{\tau\sigma} T_\sigma . \tag{15.32}$$

Since (15.31) and (15.32) hold for arbitrary values of the tensor components T_σ,

$$\mathbf{D}(SR)_{\tau\sigma} = \sum_\rho \mathbf{D}(S)_{\tau\rho} \mathbf{D}(R)_{\rho\sigma}; \qquad \mathbf{D}(SR) = \mathbf{D}(S)\mathbf{D}(R). \tag{15.33}$$

Thus, the transformation matrices of vector or tensor components form a representation of the rotation group.

Thus, for instance, the transformation matrices for vectors are the rotation matrices **R** themselves, and they form a representation of their own group. This representation is equivalent to $\mathfrak{D}^{(1)}$. The "transformation matrix" for scalars is $\mathfrak{D}^{(0)}$.

However, representations which belong to the tensors which occur most frequently are not irreducible, since one can form linear combinations of the tensor components which transform just among themselves. The reducible representation will be brought into reduced form by the matrix which forms these linear combinations from the original components.

Let us consider, for example, a tensor of the second rank with components T_{xx}, T_{xy}, T_{xz}, T_{yx}, T_{yy}, T_{yz}, T_{zx}, T_{zy}, T_{zz}. This tensor can be written as the sum of a symmetric and an antisymmetric tensor. The six components of the former are T_{xx}, T_{yy}, T_{zz}, $T_{xy} + T_{yx}$, $T_{zx} + T_{xz}$, $T_{yz} + T_{zy}$; the three components of the latter are $T_{xy} - T_{yx}$, $T_{yz} - T_{zy}$, $T_{zx} - T_{xz}$. The representation for the antisymmetric tensor is equivalent to $\mathfrak{D}^{(1)}$ and is irreducible, but that for the symmetric tensor is not. One linear combination $T = T_{xx} + T_{yy} + T_{zz}$ of its components exists which is invariant. The remaining five linear combinations $T_{xx} - \frac{1}{3}T$, $T_{yy} - \frac{1}{3}T$, $T_{xy} + T_{yx}$, $T_{yz} + T_{zy}$, $T_{zx} + T_{xz}$ are the mutually independent components of a symmetric tensor with zero trace. They belong to an irreducible representation equivalent to $\mathfrak{D}^{(2)}$.

The last remark also shows why it is not expedient to label the rows and columns of the irreducible representations according to the usual symbols of the tensor components to which they refer. This allows too much freedom. Thus, the component $T_{xx} - \frac{1}{3}T$ in the symmetric tensor with trace zero given above can be omitted, and $T_{zz} - \frac{1}{3}T$ could be used in its place.

The three rows in $\mathfrak{D}^{(1)}$ do not refer to the x, y, and z components of a vector, since if they did $\mathfrak{D}^{(1)}$ would be real. The representation $\mathfrak{D}^{(1)}$ rather specifies the transformation of a vector T_i, the components of which are

$$\begin{aligned} T_{-1} &= \frac{1}{\sqrt{2}} (X + iY) \\ T_0 &= Z \\ T_{+1} &= \frac{-1}{\sqrt{2}} (X - iY). \end{aligned} \tag{15.34}$$

$\mathfrak{D}^{(1)}$ can be transformed by the matrix which occurs in (15.34) into the representation which applies to the x, y, and z components of a vector, i.e., into the matrix for the rotation $\mathbf{R}$ itself. This can be seen by taking $\mathfrak{D}^{(1)}(\{\alpha 00\})$ and $\mathfrak{D}^{(1)}(\{0\beta 0\})$ from (15.29) and multiplying these by the transformation in (15.34) from the right and by its adjoint from the left. The matrix (15.14a′) is obtained in the first case and (15.14b′) in the second.

16. The Representations of the Direct Product

1. In most physical problems, not one, but several kinds of symmetry exist side by side. For example, in the case of a water molecule we have the differential equation

$$\left(-\frac{\hbar^2}{2M}\sum_{k=1}^{6}\frac{\partial^2}{\partial X_k^2}-\frac{\hbar^2}{2m}\sum_{k=1}^{30}\frac{\partial^2}{\partial x_k^2}\right)\psi + V\psi = E\psi. \tag{16.E.1}$$

Here M is the mass of each of the hydrogen nuclei; $X_1, \cdots, X_6$, their cartesian coordinates; m, the mass of the electron; $x_1, \cdots, x_{30}$, their cartesian coordinates. Because of its large mass, the oxygen atom is considered to be at rest at the center of mass; the potential energy arising from it is included in V. The problem (16.E.1) has several types of symmetry: first, the coordinates of the hydrogen nuclei can be interchanged; secondly, those of the electrons; thirdly, the entire system can be rotated. Among the rotations, not only the pure rotation group but the entire rotation-reflection group must be considered. The question thus arises how the joint effect of symmetry properties can be best considered.

2. The three types of operations mentioned above have the property that the operators of one type *commute* with the operators of the others. Clearly, it can make no difference whether the coordinates of the particles are interchanged first or the rotation is applied first and the permutation made afterwards. It is therefore assumed that the elements of every operator group commute with all elements of the other operator groups to be considered with it.

First of all, consider the case in which (16.E.1) is invariant under only two groups. Let the elements of the two groups be $E', A_2, A_3, \cdots, A_n$ and $E'', B_2, B_3, \cdots, B_m$. Then (16.E.1) *is* not only *invariant* under the operators $\mathbf{P}_{E'} = \mathbf{1}, \mathbf{P}_{A_2}, \cdots, \mathbf{P}_{A_n}$ and $\mathbf{P}_{E''} = \mathbf{1}, \mathbf{P}_{B_2}, \cdots, \mathbf{P}_{B_m}$ but *under all nm products* $\mathbf{P}_{A_\varkappa}\mathbf{P}_{B_\lambda}$ *of these operators* (because of the commutability mentioned above, $\mathbf{P}_{A_\varkappa} \cdot \mathbf{P}_{B_\lambda} = \mathbf{P}_{B_\lambda} \cdot \mathbf{P}_{A_\varkappa}$). The $\mathbf{P}_{A_\varkappa}\mathbf{P}_{B_\lambda}$ form a group according to the law of operator multiplication, since the product of two elements is again an element.

$$\mathbf{P}_{A_\varkappa}\mathbf{P}_{B_\lambda} \cdot \mathbf{P}_{A_{\varkappa'}}\mathbf{P}_{B_{\lambda'}} = \mathbf{P}_{A_\varkappa}\mathbf{P}_{A_{\varkappa'}}\mathbf{P}_{B_\lambda}\mathbf{P}_{B_{\lambda'}} = \mathbf{P}_{A_\varkappa A_{\varkappa'}}\mathbf{P}_{B_\lambda B_{\lambda'}}. \tag{16.1}$$

The identity of this group is the identity operator $\mathbf{P}_{E'} \cdot \mathbf{P}_{E''} = \mathbf{1}$. This group is known as the *direct product* of the group of $\mathbf{P}_A$ and the group of $\mathbf{P}_B$; it forms the full symmetry group of (16.E.1).

In general the direct product of two groups $E', A_2, \cdots, A_n$ and $E'', B_2, \cdots, B_m$ has as elements the *pairs* $A_\kappa B_\lambda$ from the two "factors," i.e., from the groups from which it is constructed. The law for group multiplication is

$$A_\kappa B_\lambda \cdot A_{\kappa'} B_{\lambda'} = A_\kappa A_{\kappa'} \cdot B_\lambda B_{\lambda'} = A_{\kappa''} B_{\lambda''}, \tag{16.1a}$$

where $A_{\kappa''} = A_\kappa A_{\kappa'}$, and $B_{\lambda''} = B_\lambda B_{\lambda'}$. One writes simply A_κ for $A_\kappa \cdot E''$, and B_λ for $E' \cdot B_\lambda$. The Eqs. (16.1) and (16.1a) show that the group of the $A_\kappa \cdot B_\lambda$ is isomorphic to the group of $\mathsf{P}_{A_\kappa} \cdot \mathsf{P}_{B_\lambda}$; we write $\mathsf{P}_{A_\kappa}\mathsf{P}_{B_\lambda} = \mathsf{P}_{A_\kappa B_\lambda}$. Also, we can investigate the representations of the group of $A_\kappa \cdot B_\lambda$ instead of those of the group $\mathsf{P}_{A_\kappa}\mathsf{P}_{B_\lambda}$.

3. To find a representation of the direct product of two groups, let us consider the direct product of the matrices $\mathbf{a}(A_\kappa)$ and $\mathbf{b}(B_\lambda)$ which correspond, in some representations of the individual factors, to the elements A_κ and B_λ respectively, and make it correspond to the element $A_\kappa B_\lambda$. The matrices $\mathbf{a}(A_\kappa) \times \mathbf{b}(B_\lambda) = \mathbf{d}(A_\kappa B_\lambda)$ actually do form a representation of the direct product, since by Eq. (2.7)

$$\left.\begin{aligned} \mathbf{a}(A_\kappa) \times \mathbf{b}(B_\lambda) \cdot \mathbf{a}(A_{\kappa'}) \times \mathbf{b}(B_{\lambda'}) &= \mathbf{a}(A_\kappa) \cdot \mathbf{a}(A_{\kappa'}) \times \mathbf{b}(B_\lambda) \cdot \mathbf{b}(B_{\lambda'}) \\ &= \mathbf{a}(A_\kappa A_{\kappa'}) \times \mathbf{b}(B_\lambda B_{\lambda'}). \end{aligned}\right\} \tag{16.2}$$

That is, the product of the matrices $\mathbf{a}(A_\kappa) \times \mathbf{b}(B_\lambda)$ and $\mathbf{a}(A_{\kappa'}) \times \mathbf{b}(B_{\lambda'})$ which correspond to the elements $A_\kappa B_\lambda$ and $A_{\kappa'} B_{\lambda'}$ is the matrix which corresponds to the element $A_\kappa B_\lambda A_{\kappa'} B_{\lambda'} = A_\kappa A_{\kappa'} B_\lambda B_{\lambda'}$.

The elements of the matrix $\mathbf{d}(A_\kappa B_\lambda) = \mathbf{a}(A_\kappa) \times \mathbf{b}(B_\lambda)$ are

$$\mathbf{d}(A_\kappa B_\lambda)_{\rho'\sigma';\rho\sigma} = \mathbf{a}(A_\kappa)_{\rho'\rho}\, \mathbf{b}(B_\lambda)_{\sigma'\sigma}. \tag{16.2a}$$

If $\mathbf{a}(A_\kappa)$ and $\mathbf{b}(B_\lambda)$ are irreducible, then so is the representation $\mathbf{d}(A_\kappa B_\lambda)$. If a matrix $(\mathbf{M}_{\rho'\sigma';\rho\sigma})$ commutes with all $\mathbf{d}(A_\kappa B_\lambda)$, then one can write

$$\sum_{\rho\sigma} \mathbf{M}_{\rho'\sigma';\rho\sigma} \mathbf{a}(A_\kappa)_{\rho\rho''} \mathbf{b}(B_\lambda)_{\sigma\sigma''} = \sum_{\rho\sigma} \mathbf{a}(A_\kappa)_{\rho'\rho} \mathbf{b}(B_\lambda)_{\sigma'\sigma} \mathbf{M}_{\rho\sigma;\rho''\sigma''} \tag{16.3}$$

for all κ and λ. In particular, if we first let $A = E'$ and then $B = E''$, then $\mathbf{a}(E')$ or $\mathbf{b}(E'')$ is a unit matrix, and (16.3) becomes

$$\sum_{\sigma} \mathbf{M}_{\rho'\sigma';\rho''\sigma} \mathbf{b}(B_\lambda)_{\sigma\sigma''} = \sum_{\sigma} \mathbf{b}(B_\lambda)_{\sigma'\sigma} \mathbf{M}_{\rho'\sigma;\rho''\sigma''}, \tag{16.3a}$$

or

$$\sum \mathbf{M}_{\rho'\sigma';\rho\sigma''} \mathbf{a}(A_\kappa)_{\rho\rho''} = \sum_{\rho} \mathbf{a}(A_\kappa)_{\rho'\rho} \mathbf{M}_{\rho\sigma';\rho''\sigma''}. \tag{16.3b}$$

The submatrices in

$$\begin{pmatrix} \mathbf{M}_{\rho'1;\rho''1} & \mathbf{M}_{\rho'1;\rho''2} & \cdots \\ \mathbf{M}_{\rho'2;\rho''1} & \mathbf{M}_{\rho'2;\rho''2} & \cdots \\ \cdot & \cdot & \cdots \\ \cdot & \cdot & \cdots \\ \cdot & \cdot & \cdots \end{pmatrix} \tag{16.E.2}$$

for all ρ' and ρ'' commute with all $\mathbf{b}(B_\lambda)$. Likewise, from (16.3b), the submatrices in

$$\begin{pmatrix} \mathbf{M}_{1\sigma';1\sigma''} & \mathbf{M}_{1\sigma';2\sigma''} & \cdots \\ \mathbf{M}_{2\sigma';1\sigma''} & \mathbf{M}_{2\sigma';2\sigma''} & \cdots \\ \cdot & \cdot & \cdots \\ \cdot & \cdot & \cdots \\ \cdot & \cdot & \cdots \end{pmatrix} \tag{16.E.3}$$

commute with all $\mathbf{a}(A_\varkappa)$ for all σ' and σ''. Therefore, the submatrices in both (16.E.2) and (16.E.3) are constant matrices. It follows that

$$\mathbf{M}_{\rho'\sigma';\rho''\sigma''} = \delta_{\sigma'\sigma''}\mathbf{M}_{\rho'1;\rho''1} \tag{16.4a}$$

$$\mathbf{M}_{\rho'\sigma';\rho''\sigma''} = \delta_{\rho'\rho''}\mathbf{M}_{1\sigma';1\sigma''}, \tag{16.4b}$$

from which we obtain

$$\mathbf{M}_{\rho'\sigma';\rho''\sigma''} = \delta_{\sigma'\sigma''}\mathbf{M}_{\rho'1;\rho''1} = \delta_{\sigma'\sigma''}\,\delta_{\rho'\rho''}\mathbf{M}_{11;11}\,. \tag{16.4}$$

Thus the matrix $\mathbf{M}$ must itself be a constant matrix; therefore $\mathbf{d}(A_\varkappa B_\lambda)$ is irreducible.

4. We now have a method by which we may obtain the irreducible representations of a group which is the direct product of two groups, assuming that the irreducible representations of the "factors" are known. There is still the question of whether all irreducible representations of the direct product can be obtained in this way.

Let the dimension of the irreducible representations of the group of the A be denoted by $g_1, g_2, g_3, \cdots$, and those of the representations of B by $h_1, h_2, \cdots$. If we combine every representation of the first group with every representation of the second, we obtain irreducible representations of the direct product with dimensions $g_1h_1, g_1h_2, \cdots, g_2h_1, g_2h_2, \cdots$. If we assume, by virtue of the theorem discussed in Chapter 9 (page 83), that the sum of the squares of the dimensions of all the irreducible representations of a group is equal to its order, then

$$g_1^2 + g_2^2 + \cdots = n \quad \text{and} \quad h_1^2 + h_2^2 + \cdots = m,$$

where n and m are the orders of the groups of A and B, respectively. Hence, the sum of the squares of the dimensions of representations of the direct product which were obtained above is equal to the order nm of the direct product group.

$$\begin{aligned}(g_1h_1)^2 + (g_1h_2)^2 + \cdots + (g_2h_1)^2 + (g_2h_2)^2 + \cdots + \cdots \\ = g_1^2m + g_2^2m + \cdots = nm.\end{aligned}$$

It follows that the method given does, in fact, provide all the irreducible representations.[1]

These considerations can also be presented in another way which is also applicable to continuous groups. The $g_1^2 + g_2^2 + g_3^2 + \cdots$ coefficients of the first representations, considered as functions[2] of the A, form a complete set of functions for the functions of A. Similarly, the $h_1^2 + h_2^2 + h_3^2 + \cdots$ representation coefficients, considered as functions of the B, form a complete set of functions of B. Therefore, all the products of the two sets of functions form a complete set for functions of the two variables.

5. The eigenvalues of the differential equation (16.E.1) can be divided into qualitatively different classes; a representation of the whole symmetry group of (16.E.1) (the group of operators which leaves (16.E.1) invariant) belongs to every eigenvalue. One can best characterize an irreducible representation of this group (the direct product of the three groups mentioned) by utilizing the three symbols which characterize the three irreducible representations from which this representation is built up. Thus, an eigenvalue of (16.E.1) can be said to belong to the symmetric representation for the interchange of the H nuclei, to the antisymmetric representation of the permutation of the ten electrons, and to the seven-dimensional representation of the rotation group. This statement is understood to mean that it belongs to the representation of the direct product of these three groups which is obtained from the specified representations of the "factors."

The eigenfunctions of such an eigenvalue, which correspond to the rows of the direct product of three representations, carry three indices specifying to which rows of the representations of the three component groups they belong. Two eigenfunctions which differ in one or more of these three indices are orthogonal to one another; and this remains true even if an arbitrary symmetric operator is applied to them. The orthogonality can be inferred, first, from the fact that they belong to different rows of the representation of the direct product, and secondly—if, say, their second indices differ—that they belong to different rows of the representation of the second group.

If an operator $\mathbf{P}_A = \mathbf{P}_A \mathbf{P}_{E''}$ of the first group is applied to a function which belongs to the $\rho\sigma$-row of the representation $\mathbf{a}(A) \times \mathbf{b}(B)$ of the direct product of two groups, the function obtained can be written in terms of the functions belonging to the $1\sigma, 2\sigma, 3\sigma, \cdots$ rows of the representation

[1] Two "direct products" which are essentially different are being discussed here at one time: the direct product of two groups and the direct product of two matrices. The elements of the direct product of the groups are the $A_\varkappa B_\lambda$. The representation $\mathbf{a}(A_\varkappa) \times \mathbf{b}(B_\lambda)$, which is the direct product of $\mathbf{a}(A_\varkappa)$ and $\mathbf{b}(B_\lambda)$, corresponds to the $A_\varkappa B_\lambda$.

[2] A function of A is the correspondence of a number $J(A_\varkappa)$ to each group element $A_\varkappa$.

$\mathbf{a}(A) \times \mathbf{b}(B)$. Indeed, the coefficients are the same as if the second group were not there at all.

$$\begin{aligned} \mathbf{P}_A \mathbf{P}_{E''} \psi_{\rho\sigma} &= \sum_{\rho'\sigma'} \mathbf{a}(A)_{\rho'\rho} \mathbf{b}(E'')_{\sigma'\sigma} \psi_{\rho'\sigma'} \\ &= \sum_{\rho'\sigma'} \mathbf{a}(A)_{\rho'\rho} \, \delta_{\sigma'\sigma} \psi_{\rho'\sigma'} = \sum_{\rho'} \mathbf{a}(A)_{\rho'\rho} \psi_{\rho'\sigma} . \end{aligned} \tag{16.5}$$

A function which belongs to the $\rho\sigma$-row of the representation $\mathbf{a}(A) \times \mathbf{b}(B)$ thus belongs to the ρ-row of $\mathbf{a}(A)$ and to the σ-row of $\mathbf{b}(B)$; this function has all the properties of these two classes of functions.

6. In the construction of the "correct linear combinations" for use in *perturbation theory*, linear combinations must be formed within each family of functions, a family being a set belonging to one row $\sigma\rho$ of a representation $\mathbf{a}(A) \times \mathbf{b}(B)$ of the direct product of the symmetry groups at hand. To achieve this we can proceed first to form linear combinations $f_1, f_2, \cdots$ which belong to the ρ-row of $\mathbf{a}(A)$; then every function $\psi_{\rho\sigma}$, which belongs to the $\rho\sigma$-row of $\mathbf{a}(A) \times \mathbf{b}(B)$ must be a linear combination of $f_1, f_2, \cdots$. Suppose that $\psi_{\rho\sigma}$ also contained functions $f_1', f_2', \cdots$ which do not belong to the representation $\mathbf{a}(A)$, or not to its ρ-row, so that

$$\psi_{\rho\sigma} = c_1 f_1 + c_2 f_2 + \cdots + c_1' f_1' + c_2' f_2' + \cdots . \tag{16.6}$$

Then surely $c_1' f_1' + c_2 f_2' + c_3 f_3' + \cdots = 0$. For if $c_1 f_1 + c_2 f_2 + \cdots$ in (16.6) is brought to the left side, the entire left side belongs to the ρ-row of $\mathbf{a}(A)$; the left is therefore orthogonal to all terms on the right side so that both sides must vanish.

7. We will use the theorems on the representations of the direct product for the determination of the irreducible representations of the three-dimensional rotation-reflection group. The rotation-reflection group is the group of real orthogonal three-dimensional matrices with determinant ± 1. It is the direct product of the pure rotation group and the group isomorphic to the reflection group, which consists of the identity E and the inversion I.

$$E = \begin{pmatrix} 1 & 0 & 0 \\ 0 & 1 & 0 \\ 0 & 0 & 1 \end{pmatrix}; \qquad I = \begin{pmatrix} -1 & 0 & 0 \\ 0 & -1 & 0 \\ 0 & 0 & -1 \end{pmatrix}$$

We can easily see that every real orthogonal matrix can be obtained from a pure rotation by multiplication with E or I; either its determinant is already $+1$, in which case it is already a pure rotation, or if its determinant is -1, it results from a pure rotation by multiplication with I. It is also clear that E and I commute with all the matrices of the pure rotation group (in fact, with all matrices).

The reflection group has two irreducible representations: the identical representation (also known as the positive), and the negative representation in which the matrix (1) corresponds to the identity and the matrix (—1) to the inversion I. Hence, two representations of the rotation-reflection group can be obtained from every representation $\mathfrak{D}^{(l)}(R)$ of the pure rotation group, by combining $\mathfrak{D}^{(l)}(R)$ with the positive and negative representations of the reflection group.

The three-dimensional rotation-reflection group has two (single-valued) irreducible representations of each odd dimension 1, 3, 5, $\cdots$. These can be denoted by $l = 0_+, 0_-, 1_+, 1_-, 2_+, \cdots$. Both the representations l_+ and l_- are $2l + 1$ dimensional; in both, the same matrices correspond to pure rotations as in the $2l + 1$ dimensional representation of the pure rotation group. In l_+, the same matrix $\mathfrak{D}^{(l)}(R)$, as corresponds to R, corresponds to the rotation-reflection IR; in l_-, on the other hand, the matrix $-\mathfrak{D}^{(l)}(R)$ corresponds to IR.

17. The Characteristics of Atomic Spectra

Eigenvalues and Quantum Numbers

1. We will now use our group theoretical results to explain the most important characteristics of atomic spectra.[1] The present chapter is intended only as an orientation of the reader and will contain neither details nor proofs. It is hoped that by suppressing mathematical details, one can provide a survey of the regularities of spectra as they were revealed by the experiments themselves.

Before proceeding to the actual solution of the Schrödinger equation, we first discuss the separation of the center of mass coordinates. In its original form (Eq. 4.5a), the Schrödinger equation has only a continuous spectrum, corresponding to the fact that an atom as a whole can assume, in addition to its energy of excitation, an arbitrary and continuously varying kinetic energy. If it is desired—as it practically always is—to consider only the excitation energy, then it must be assumed that the atom is at rest. Since the electron mass can be neglected in comparison with the nuclear masses, the coordinates of the nucleus are usually identified with those of the center of mass, and it is assumed that the wave functions are independent of the nuclear coordinates. Then the nucleus does not occur at all in the Schrödinger equation; it is rather considered as the fixed center of the field in which the electrons move. This is, of course, possible only in atoms, where there is only one nucleus.

The general considerations which follow later are independent of the assumption that the "motion of the nucleus" is negligible, except as they concern the question of level-splitting in external fields. The way to avoid this assumption is to consider the wave function as containing all coordinates as variables, but being independent of those of the center of mass. Thus, the wave function is assumed to be constant along lines which connect configurations of the particles which are identical except for a translation in space of the atom as a whole.[2] This is viewed as a subsidiary condition. The requirement that the scalar product of two wave functions remain finite makes it, in principle, impossible to assume wave functions which are constant even for infinite displacements of the configurations. However, since they can be assumed to be constant for an arbitrarily large displacement, this does not limit the accuracy of the results to be derived. Unquestionably, this is the more precise point of view. Nevertheless, one usually considers the wave function not to contain the coordinates of the nucleus as variables.

[1] An excellent detailed presentation of the experimentally observed features of atomic spectra is found in F. Hund's booklet, "Line Spectra and Periodic System," Springer, Berlin, 1927, and also in L. C. Pauling and S. Goudsmit, "The Structure of Line Spectra," McGraw-Hill, New York, 1930.

[2] This is the reason why we do not also introduce the translation group as a symmetry group in this problem. All wave functions will be *invariant* under translation and thus belong to the identical representation of the translation group.

The hydrogen atom has the simplest spectrum since it consists of a single electron which moves, neglecting the motion of the nucleus, in a constant potential field. The Schrödinger equation is

$$\left[-\frac{\hbar^2}{2m}\left(\frac{\partial^2}{\partial x^2}+\frac{\partial^2}{\partial y^2}+\frac{\partial^2}{\partial z^2}\right)-\frac{e^2}{\sqrt{x^2+y^2+z^2}}\right]\psi(x,y,z)=E\psi(x,y,z) \quad (17.1)$$

and can be solved exactly. In this way the spectrum of possible energy levels (the "term values" as they are called in spectroscopy) and the eigenfunctions (i.e., the stationary states) of the hydrogen atom are obtained. The spectrum has a discrete part with energy values $E = -2\pi R\hbar c/1^2, -2\pi R\hbar c/2^2, -2\pi R\hbar c/3^2, \cdots$, where R is the Rydberg constant

$$E_N = -\frac{me^4}{2\hbar^2 N^2} = -\frac{2\pi R\hbar c}{N^2} = -\frac{2.18\times 10^{-11}}{N^2}\,\text{erg} = -\frac{13.60\ \text{ev}}{N^2}. \quad (17.2)$$

The energies are negative, corresponding to the fact that the electron has a considerable negative potential in the neighborhood of the nucleus, since work must be expended to remove it to infinity, where the potential is zero. The separation between the individual levels decreases steadily with increasing principal quantum number N; the energy finally converges to zero for infinitely high quantum numbers. Physically, this corresponds to a progressive removal of the electron from the region of influence of the nucleus; if the electron becomes entirely free, it has zero energy.

A continuous spectrum joins the discrete spectrum (17.2) at zero energy and covers the entire positive energy region. In the continuum states the hydrogen atom is ionized. The positive energy is the kinetic energy of the electron after it has withdrawn to infinity. In the continuous spectrum there are no stationary states in the proper sense; the electron departs arbitrarily far from the nucleus after sufficiently long time. Also, a stationary state corresponds mathematically to a normalized wave function, but the eigenfunctions of the continuous spectrum cannot be normalized.

The occurrence of a series of the general form (17.2), converging to some finite limit where a continuous spectrum of ionized states begins, is characteristic of all atomic spectra.

The eigenvalues (17.2) are degenerate; i.e., not just one, but several linearly independent eigenfunctions belong to each eigenvalue. The eigenvalue with the running index ("principal quantum number") N is N^2-fold degenerate.

The normalized eigenfunctions will be given here for the convenience of the reader. They are most conveniently written in polar coordinates r, θ, φ (see Fig. 7, page 153), with $\eta = 2r/Nr_0$, where $r_0 = \hbar^2/me^2$ is the "radius of the first Bohr orbit." The eigenfunctions are[3]

$$\psi^N_{l\mu} = R_{Nl}(\eta) Y_{l\mu}(\vartheta, \varphi)$$

$$R_{Nl}(\eta) = \left\{\left(\frac{2}{Nr_0}\right)^3 \frac{(N-l-1)!}{2N[(N+l)!]^3}\right\}^{1/2} e^{-\frac{1}{2}\eta} \quad \eta^l L^{2l+1}_{N+l}(\eta) \tag{17.3}$$

$$Y_{l\mu}(\vartheta, \varphi) = \left[\frac{1}{\sqrt{2\pi}}\right] e^{i\mu\varphi} \cdot \left[\frac{2l+1}{2} \cdot \frac{(l-\mu)!}{(l+\mu)!}\right]^{1/2} \frac{(-\sin\vartheta)^\mu}{2^l \cdot l!} \left(\frac{d}{d\cos\vartheta}\right)^{l+\mu} (\cos^2\vartheta - 1)^l.$$

Thus,

$$Y_{l,-\mu}(\vartheta, \varphi) = (-1)^\mu Y^*_{l,\mu}.$$

We have introduced the indices l ("orbital quantum number") and μ ("magnetic quantum number") here to differentiate among the N^2 eigenfunctions belonging to the eigenvalue E_N. For a fixed N, l can assume the values $0, 1, 2, \cdots, N-1$ and μ runs from $-l$ to $+l$ (independent of N). Thus the total number of eigenfunctions belonging to E is $\sum_{l=0}^{N-1} (2l+1) = N^2$. Equation (15.3a) defines $Y_{l\mu}$, the normalized spherical harmonic.[4] The $(2l+1)$th derivative of the $(N+l)$th Laguerre polynomial L_{N+l}, where

$$L_\nu(\eta) = (-1)^\nu \left[\eta^\nu - \frac{\nu^2}{1!}\eta^{\nu-1} + \frac{\nu^2(\nu-1)^2}{2!}\eta^{\nu-2} - \cdots + (-1)^\nu \nu!\right]$$

is denoted by $L^{2l+1}_{N+l}(\eta)$.

The expression (17.3) for the wave function and its connection with the $Y_{l,\mu}$ indicate that the orbital or azimuthal quantum number l is connected with the $(2l+1)$-dimensional representation of the rotational group.

The spectra of the helium ion, of the doubly ionized lithium atom, and of all other systems in which there are only one electron and one nucleus, are closely related to the spectrum of hydrogen. One need only replace the potential energy in the Schrödinger equation by $-Ze^2/r$ (Z is the nuclear charge) and the energy levels by

$$E^{(Z)}_N = -\frac{mZ^2e^4}{2\hbar^2} \cdot \frac{1}{N^2} \tag{17.2a}$$

and η in (17.3) by

$$\eta^{(Z)} = \frac{2me^2Z}{\hbar^2 N} r = \frac{2Zr}{Nr_0}. \tag{17.3a}$$

Also ψ must be multiplied by $Z^{3/2}$ to retain the correct normalization.

[3] The radial eigenfunction $R_{Nl}(\eta)$ is normalized so that $\int |R_{Nl}|^2 r^2\, dr = 1$. The spherical harmonics $Y_{l\mu}$ are the same as those given on page 154. Note that Condon and Shortley (see footnote 4) write R_{Nl} to represent the radial eigenfunction *multiplied* by $\eta = \dfrac{2r}{Nr_0}$.

[4] As has been noted previously, the phases of the spherical harmonics have been chosen to conform with the definition of E .U. Condon and G. H. Shortley "The Theory of Atomic Spectra," Cambridge Univ. Press, London and New York, 1953. The conventions adopted in this translation are in conformity with those of M. E. Rose, "Multipole Fields," Wiley, New York, 1955. These conventions are defined and discussed in Appendix A.

2. The spectrum of an atom with several, say n, electrons cannot be calculated exactly. This results from the relatively complicated form of the potential energy

$$V = \sum_i^n \frac{-e^2 Z}{\sqrt{x_i^2 + y_i^2 + z_i^2}} + \tfrac{1}{2} \sum_{i,j\neq} \frac{e^2}{\sqrt{(x_i - x_j)^2 + (y_i - y_j)^2 + (z_i - z_j)^2}}. \tag{17.4}$$

If the second term in (17.4), involving the mutual repulsions of the electrons, did not appear, the electrons would move just under the influence of the constant field of the nucleus. The Schrödinger equation

$$(\mathbf{H}_1 + \mathbf{H}_2 + \cdots + \mathbf{H}_n)\psi(x_1, y_1, z_1, x_2, y_2, z_2, \cdots, x_n y_n z_n) = E\psi, \tag{17.5}$$

where

$$\mathbf{H}_k = -\frac{\hbar^2}{2m}\left(\frac{\partial^2}{\partial x_k^2} + \frac{\partial^2}{\partial y_k^2} + \frac{\partial^2}{\partial z_k^2}\right) - \frac{Ze^2}{\sqrt{x_k^2 + y_k^2 + z_k^2}}, \tag{17.5a}$$

could then be solved. The eigenvalues would be the sums, and the eigenfunctions the products, of the eigenvalues or eigenfunctions of (17.5a), and could be expressed by means of (17.2a), (17.3), (17.3a):

$$\psi(x_1, y_1, z_1, \cdots, x_n, y_n, z_n) = \psi^{N_1}_{l_1\mu_1}(x_1, y_1, z_1) \cdots \psi^{N_n}_{l_n\mu_n}(x_n, y_n, z_n) \tag{17.6}$$

$$E = E_{N_1} + E_{N_2} + \cdots + E_{N_n}. \tag{17.6a}$$

To see this, just substitute into (17.5) and form $\mathbf{H}_k\psi(x_1, \cdots, z_n)$; this gives $E_{N_k}\psi(x_1, \cdots, z_n)$, since

$$\mathbf{H}_k \cdot \psi^{N_k}_{l_k\mu_k}(x_k, y_k, z_k) = E_{N_k}\psi^{N_k}_{l_k\mu_k}(x_k, y_k, z_k),$$

and the other factors of $\psi(x_1, \cdots, z_n)$ behave like constants upon the application of $\mathbf{H}_k$.

Naturally, (17.5) represents a very poor approximation to the actual Schrödinger equation. In spite of this, we are accustomed, at least conceptually, to begin from this or a similar approximation and to consider the effects of the electrons on one another as a "perturbation."

In general, very many eigenfunctions belong to each of the eigenvalues (17.6a) since the quantum numbers l_k, μ_k in (17.6) can take several values and do not affect the value of the energy. Moreover, for a given set of principal quantum numbers N_k the individual electrons can be permuted arbitrarily without changing the energy eigenvalue. However, if the effect of the electrons on one another is introduced as a perturbation, the degeneracy would be partially removed, and the levels would split. Of the resulting levels, most of which are still degenerate, nothing is known on a purely theoretical basis (apart from a rough estimate of their positions) except their symmetry properties. These are manifested in the transformation properties of the corresponding eigenfunctions under permutations of the electrons, pure rotations, and inversion[5] (reflection). Accordingly, each level corresponds to three representations—one of the symmetric group, one of the pure rotation group, and one of the reflection group. (The latter two are usually combined into a representation of the rotation-reflection group.) The corresponding quantum numbers (characteristic of the representations) are[6]

Multiplet System S

Orbital Angular Momentum Quantum Number L

Parity w.

3. The orbital quantum number can assume the values $L = 0, 1, 2, 3, \cdots$ for the different levels. The corresponding eigenvalues belong to the representations $\mathfrak{D}^{(0)}(R)$, $\mathfrak{D}^{(1)}(R)$, $\cdots$ of the rotation group.[7] These are known as the S, P, D, F, $\cdots$ levels, respectively. Only one eigenfunction belongs to an S level, three to a P level, five to a D level, etc. The $2L + 1$ eigenfunctions which belong to a term with orbital quantum number L are distinguished by their magnetic quantum number m, which also assumes integral values and runs from $-L$ to $+L$ (see Fig. 8). The corresponding

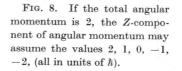

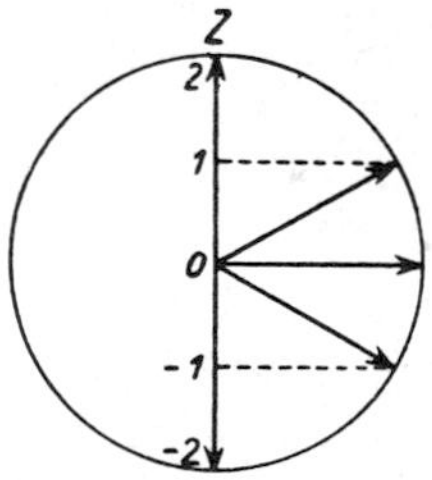

FIG. 8. If the total angular momentum is 2, the Z-component of angular momentum may assume the values 2, 1, 0, -1, -2, (all in units of $\hbar$).

eigenfunctions belong to the mth row of the irreducible representation $\mathfrak{D}^{(L)}$.

Physically, the orbital quantum number is the total angular momentum.[8] The magnetic quantum number, on the other hand, corresponds to the component of angular momentum along the Z-axis. Specification of m distinguishes one particular direction in space; it therefore requires that we fix

[5] The changing of the signs of all coordinates $x_1, \cdots, z_n$, is called inversion.

[6] It is customary to use capital letters for the quantum numbers of the whole atom and small letters for those of the individual electrons. The orbital angular momentum (or simply "orbital") quantum number is often called the azimuthal quantum number.

[7] Eq. (19.9b) page 214, will show that this is also true for the $\psi^N_{l\mu}$; with $l = 0, 1, 2, \cdots$.

[8] The existence of spin is disregarded at this point.

the representation entirely (not only up to a similarity transformation) so as to define the functions which belong to one row of a representation. This is done by assuming that rotations about the Z-axis correspond to diagonal matrices (Eq. (15.6)). On the other hand, the statement that all eigenfunctions of the D-levels belong to the representation $\mathfrak{D}^{(2)}(R)$ does not require that any direction in space be distinguished.

Levels which belong to the identical (positive) representation of the reflection group are said to have *even parity* (or more simply, to be *even*); the others, to have *odd parity*, or to be *odd* levels. The concept of parity, which is very important for the understanding of spectra, has no analogy in classical theory comparable to the analogy between the orbital quantum number and the angular momentum. The reflection character or parity of the level is affixed as an index to the symbol for the level $S_+, S_-, P_+, P_-, \cdots$. The corresponding representations of the three-dimensional rotation-reflection group are $0_+, 0_-, 1_+, 1_-, \cdots$. The most common levels are the $S_+, P_-, D_+, F_-, \cdots$, etc.

The concept of a multiplet system S is also alien to classical theory. To every level of an n-electron system there corresponds a representation of the symmetric group of the nth degree. All the representations do not occur; rather only the representations *associated* with the representations denoted in Chapter 13 by $\mathbf{D}^{(0)}, \mathbf{D}^{(1)}, \cdots, \mathbf{D}^{(\frac{1}{2}n)}$ (for an even number of electrons) or $\mathbf{D}^{(\frac{1}{2}(n-1))}$ (for an odd number of electrons), appear in nature—for reasons which cannot be explained without a discussion of electron spin and the Pauli principle. For an even number of electrons a level with $S = 0$ belongs to the representation $\overline{\mathbf{D}}^{(\frac{1}{2}n)}$; with $S = 1$, to the representation $\overline{\mathbf{D}}^{(\frac{1}{2}n-1)}$; the representation belonging to $S = \frac{1}{2}n$ is $\overline{\mathbf{D}}^{(0)}$. In order to be able to read the S-value directly from the representation and also to avoid confusion with the representations of the rotation group, we write from now on

$$\overline{\mathbf{D}}^{(k)} = \overline{\mathbf{A}}^{(S)}, \qquad \text{where } S = \tfrac{1}{2}n - k. \tag{17.7}$$

The quantity S can assume the values $0, 1, 2, \cdots, \frac{1}{2}n$ for atoms with an even number n of electrons; for an odd number of electrons, we still retain (17.7), and the possible S values are then $\frac{1}{2}, \frac{3}{2}, \frac{5}{2}, \cdots, \frac{1}{2}n$. In the hydrogen atom there is only one value possible, $S = \frac{1}{2}$, and the symmetric group of the first degree actually does have only one representation. The S-value of the level determines its "multiplicity," $2S + 1$. For an even number of electrons we have singlet, triplet, quintet, etc., levels, since $2S + 1$ can assume the values $1, 3, 5, \cdots$; for an odd number of electrons, doublet, quartet, sextet, etc., levels occur. The levels of the one-electron problem are all doublet terms. The degree of multiplicity, that is, the value of $2S + 1$, is prefixed as a superscript to the symbol for the levels. ${}^1S_+$ denotes an even singlet-S level; ${}^2P_-$, an odd doublet-P level, etc. The levels belonging to the antisymmetric representation $\overline{\mathbf{D}}^{(0)} = \overline{\mathbf{A}}^{(\frac{1}{2}n)}$ have the highest multiplicity $n + 1$, while in a singlet level $S = 0$, and the representation is $\overline{\mathbf{D}}^{(\frac{1}{2}n)} = \overline{\mathbf{A}}^{(0)}$.

Energy levels have three qualitative characterizations S, L, w, since they belong to the different representations $\mathbf{A}^{(S)} \times \mathfrak{D}^{(L,w)}$ of the direct product of the symmetric group and the rotation-reflection group. But since several levels of the same spectrum belong to the same representation, a running number N must be introduced to distinguish among them. A level E^N_{SLw} then carries four indices N, S, L, and w. To this level belong $(2L + 1)g_s$ eigenfunctions, where g_s is the dimension of the representation $\mathbf{A}^{(S)}$. To distinguish among them, one must state to which row $\varkappa$ of the representation $\mathbf{A}^{(S)}$ they belong, and what value m the magnetic quantum assumes. An eigenfunction $\psi^{NSLw}_{\varkappa m}$ will thus carry six indices in all, of which at most one can be suppressed (namely the $\varkappa$, which has no physical significance). The experimental properties of levels with different S, L, and w are well known: the most important is the fact that optical transitions of considerable intensity occur only between levels whose *orbital quantum numbers are either equal or differ by 1.* Moreover, the levels must have *different reflection characters* (different parity) and the *same multiplet system.* Quantum mechanics must imply these intercombination rules; their derivation on quantum mechanical grounds will be the problem of the next chapter.

4. The introduction of the spin and magnetic moment of the electron (Chapter 20) will force a radical modification of the Schrödinger equation.

The effect of spin is most apparent in the *fine structure of spectral lines.* At the energy where the simple Schrödinger theory requires a single level with orbital quantum number L and multiplet system S one actually observes a "multiplet," i.e., several adjacent levels. There are $2L + 1$ or $2S + 1$ levels in the multiplet, whichever is the smaller number; $S(L = 0)$ levels are always simple; P levels $(L = 1)$ are simple only in the singlet system $(S = 0)$, and double in doublet systems; in triplet and all higher systems P levels are triple; etc. For sufficiently high orbital quantum numbers, $L \geqslant S$, the multiplicity is $2S + 1$.

To distinguish among the fine structure components of a multiplet, one ascribes to them different *total quantum numbers* J, where

$$J = |L - S|, |L - S| + 1, \cdots, L + S - 1, L + S.$$

There are $2L + 1$ or $2S + 1$ values of J, according to whether L is smaller or larger than S. The total quantum number plays the role of the total angular momentum, including angular momentum due to the electron spin.

The selection rules for L, S, and w will hold for all $2L + 1$ or $2S + 1$ levels of the multiplet.[9] In addition one has the selection rule for J which is the same as the rule for L; in an optical transition J changes by ± 1 or 0; transitions between two levels with $J = 0$ are forbidden.

5. We now return to the development which we interrupted at the end of Section 2. In Section 2 we set up a simple Schrödinger equation, (17.5), whose solutions (17.6), (17.6a) could be written down directly. In general, the eigenvalues were very highly degenerate, but it has been noted that inclusion of the mutual repulsions of the electrons as given in the correct potential (17.4), by use, say, of the Rayleigh–Schrödinger procedure, would split the eigenvalues (17.6a) and give rise to levels characterized by the symbols discussed above. The determination of the number and kinds of levels which arise from a given level (Eq. (17.6a)) will be called the *building-up principle.*[10]

In the derivation of the building-up principle one must not overlook the fact that the Schrödinger equation also gives levels for states which are excluded by the Pauli principle, and so do not actually exist. However, we shall determine only the number of levels which actually exist.

These are, if one disregards the spin, just the levels with the representations $\bar{\mathbf{D}}^{(k)} = \bar{\mathbf{A}}^{(\frac{1}{2}n-k)}$; if one introduces the spin, all actual eigenvalues have antisymmetric eigenfunctions (see Chapter 22). The building-up principle will be derived by the method due to Slater.

The Vector Addition Model

6. Let us treat here a simple, greatly schematized case of the building-up principle, in which the equivalence of the electrons receives no consideration and the rotation group alone is considered to comprise the entire symmetry group of the Schrödinger equation.[11]

We consider two systems each of which consists in the simplest case of a single electron; both electrons are thought to be circling about the same nucleus. The energy of the first system is E, and it is in a state with orbital quantum number l. Let the $2l + 1$ eigenfunctions for this eigenvalue be $\psi_{-l}, \psi_{-l+1}, \cdots, \psi_l$. Then

$$\mathbf{P}_R\psi_\mu = \sum_{\mu'} \mathfrak{D}^{(l)}(R)_{\mu'\mu}\psi_{\mu'}, \tag{17.8}$$

where $\mathbf{P}_R$ is a rotation of the coordinates of the first system. Let the energy

[9] Actually, the rules for L and S hold only so long as the forces due to the spin are small.

[10] This expression was proposed by G. Herzberg, "Atomic Spectra and Atomic Structure," Prentice–Hall, 1937, for the German "Aufbauprinzip." Although not in common usage, it will be adopted in the present translation.

[11] See E. Fues, *Z. Physik* **51**, 817 (1928).

of the second system be $\bar{E}$, the orbital quantum number be $\bar{l}$, and the eigenfunctions $\bar{\psi}_{-\bar{l}}, \bar{\psi}_{-\bar{l}+1}, \cdots, \bar{\psi}_{\bar{l}}$. Then

$$\overline{\mathbf{P}}_R\bar{\psi}_\nu = \sum_{\nu'} \mathfrak{D}^{(\bar{l})}(R)_{\nu'\nu}\bar{\psi}_{\nu'} . \tag{17.8a}$$

The two operators $\overline{\mathbf{P}}_R$ and $\mathbf{P}_R$ are different, since $\mathbf{P}_R$ rotates the variables of ψ_μ, while $\overline{\mathbf{P}}_R$ rotates those of $\bar{\psi}_\nu$, and the two sets of variables are distinct. Hence, *all* $\mathbf{P}_R$ *commute with all* $\overline{\mathbf{P}}_R$, and $\mathbf{P}_R\bar{\psi}_\nu = \bar{\psi}_\nu$ and $\overline{\mathbf{P}}_R\psi_\mu = \psi_\mu$, since $\mathbf{P}_R$ does not affect the variables of $\bar{\psi}_\nu$ at all, nor does $\overline{\mathbf{P}}_R$ affect those of ψ_μ.

If we now consider the two systems as a single one, then according to (17.6) and (17.6a), the eigenvalues are the sums and the eigenfunctions the products of the corresponding quantities for the individual systems. The $(2l + 1) \cdot (2\bar{l} + 1)$ eigenfunctions

$$\left.\begin{array}{cccccc} \psi_{-l}\bar{\psi}_{-\bar{l}}, & \psi_{-l}\bar{\psi}_{-\bar{l}+1}, & \cdots, & \psi_{-l}\bar{\psi}_{\bar{l}-1}, & \psi_{-l}\bar{\psi}_{\bar{l}}, \\ \cdot\ , & \cdot\ , & \cdots, & \cdot\ , & \cdot\ , \\ \psi_{l}\bar{\psi}_{-\bar{l}}, & \psi_{l}\bar{\psi}_{-\bar{l}+1}, & \cdots, & \psi_{l}\bar{\psi}_{\bar{l}-1}, & \psi_{l}\bar{\psi}_{\bar{l}}, \end{array}\right\} \tag{17.9}$$

belong to the eigenvalue $E + \bar{E}$. We have to inquire now which operators comprise the group of the composite system when the interaction of the two systems is taken into account. Clearly, not the entire direct product of the two operator groups $\mathbf{P}_R$ and $\overline{\mathbf{P}}_R$ whose elements $\mathbf{P}_R\overline{\mathbf{P}}_{\bar{R}}$ would correspond to simultaneous, but different, rotations of the coordinate systems of the variables of ψ and $\bar{\psi}$. The group which we must consider is rather that in which the two systems of axes undergo the same rotations; it does not consist of all the operators $\mathbf{P}_R\overline{\mathbf{P}}_{\bar{R}}$, but only of the $\mathbf{P}_R\overline{\mathbf{P}}_R$. The group of the $\mathbf{P}_R\overline{\mathbf{P}}_R$ is isomorphic to the simple rotation group. From $RQ = T$, it follows that

$$\mathbf{P}_R\overline{\mathbf{P}}_R \cdot \mathbf{P}_Q\overline{\mathbf{P}}_Q = \mathbf{P}_R\mathbf{P}_Q \cdot \overline{\mathbf{P}}_R\overline{\mathbf{P}}_Q = \mathbf{P}_T\overline{\mathbf{P}}_T .$$

If we apply the operators $\mathbf{P}_R\overline{\mathbf{P}}_R$ to the functions (17.9), the resulting functions can be written as linear combinations of the original ones.

According to (17.8) and (17.8a)

$$\begin{aligned} \mathbf{P}_R\overline{\mathbf{P}}_R\psi_\mu\bar{\psi}_\nu &= \mathbf{P}_R\psi_\mu \cdot \overline{\mathbf{P}}_R\bar{\psi}_\nu \\ &= \sum_{\mu'} \mathfrak{D}^{(l)}(R)_{\mu'\mu}\psi_{\mu'} \sum_{\nu'} \mathfrak{D}^{(\bar{l})}(R)_{\nu'\nu}\bar{\psi}_{\nu'} = \sum_{\mu'\nu'} \Delta(R)_{\mu'\nu';\mu\nu}\psi_{\mu'}\bar{\psi}_{\nu'} . \end{aligned} \tag{17.10}$$

The representation $\Delta(R)$ *belonging to the* $(2l + 1)(2\bar{l} + 1)$ *functions* (17.9) *of the composite system is the direct product*[12] *of the two representations* $\mathfrak{D}^{(l)}$ *and* $\mathfrak{D}^{(\bar{l})}$ *of the individual systems.*

$$\Delta(R)_{\mu'\nu';\mu\nu} = \mathfrak{D}^{(l)}(R)_{\mu'\mu}\mathfrak{D}^{(\bar{l})}(R)_{\nu'\nu}; \qquad \Delta(R) = \mathfrak{D}^{(l)}(R) \times \mathfrak{D}^{(\bar{l})}(R). \tag{17.11}$$

[12] We deal here with a kind of direct product other than in the preceding chapter There we combined two symmetries (rotation R and reflection I), and the group was thus enlarged. Here we combine two systems which have equal symmetry; the composite system then has the same symmetry.

We shall now determine the irreducible components of $\mathbf{\Delta}(R)$. This is done most simply by resolving its character into characters of irreducible representations. The character of $\mathbf{\Delta}(R)$, where R corresponds to a rotation through an angle φ, is equal to

$$\begin{aligned}\sum_{\mu\nu} \mathbf{\Delta}(R)_{\mu\nu;\mu\nu} &= \sum_{\mu} \mathfrak{D}^{(l)}(R)_{\mu\mu} \sum_{\nu} \mathfrak{D}^{(\bar{l})}(R)_{\nu\nu} \\ &= \chi^{(l)}(\varphi)\chi^{(\bar{l})}(\varphi) = \sum_{\mu=-l}^{+l} \exp(i\mu\varphi) \sum_{\nu=-\bar{l}}^{+\bar{l}} \exp(i\nu\varphi).\end{aligned} \tag{17.12}$$

To resolve this expression into irreducible characters, one can tabulate (17.12) symbolically: form a column for each exponential function $\exp(i\varkappa\varphi)$ (where $\varkappa = -l - \bar{l}, \cdots, -2, -1, 0, 1, 2, \cdots, +l + \bar{l}$) and place in this column a plus sign for each time $\exp(i\varkappa\varphi)$ occurs in (17.12). The smallest $\varkappa$ occurring is $-\bar{l} - l$; the largest is $l + \bar{l}$; thus $2l + 2\bar{l} + 1$ columns are needed in all. The rows of the table are denoted by the value of ν in $\varkappa = \nu + \mu$; thus, we write into the row ν the plus signs which arise from $2l + 1$ terms, $\exp[i(\nu - l)\varphi]$, $\exp[i(\nu - l + 1)\varphi], \cdots, \exp[i(\nu + l)\varphi]$. If we assume that $l > \bar{l}$, we obtain Table I.

TABLE I

ν		Occurrence of $\exp(i\varkappa\varphi)$ in the character										
	$\varkappa=$	$-l-\bar{l}$	·	·	·	$-l+\bar{l}$	·	$l-\bar{l}$	·	·	·	$l+\bar{l}$
$-\bar{l}$		+	+	+	+	+	+	+				
·			+	+	+	+	+	+	+			
0	→			+	+	+	+	+	+	+		
·					+	+	+	+	+	+	+	
$\bar{l}$						+	+	+	+	+	+	+

We now arrange that each row represents an irreducible character by shifting the plus signs within the columns. (This certainly does not change the number of times $\exp(i\varkappa\varphi)$ occurs in the sum.) For example, if the part of the table which lies to the left of the dotted line is rotated about the row indicated by → (the row with $\nu = 0$), then the result is Table II, shown on page 187.

The first sign in the ν-row is now in the $-\nu - l$ column; the exponentials which correspond to the ν-row in Table II are

$$\exp[-i(\nu + l)\varphi] + \exp[-i(\nu + l - 1)\varphi] + \cdots + \exp[+i(\nu + l - 1)\varphi] + \exp[i(\nu + l)\varphi] = \chi^{(l+\nu)}(\varphi). \tag{17.13}$$

Together they give just the character of an irreducible representation with $L = l + \nu$. Then the whole table represents the irreducible representations with

$$L = l - \bar{l},\, l - \bar{l} + 1, \cdots, l + \bar{l} - 1,\, l + \bar{l}. \tag{17.E.1}$$

Thus, for $\bar{l} \leqslant l$, the level $E + \bar{E}$ splits under the interaction into $2\bar{l} + 1$ levels with orbital quantum numbers (17.E.1). The irreducible components

TABLE II

ν	Irreducible characters which occur in the matrix $\Delta(R)$										
	$\varkappa = -l-\bar{l}$	·	·	·	$-l+\bar{l}$	·	$l-\bar{l}$	·	·	·	$l+\bar{l}$
$-\bar{l}$					+	+	+				
·				+	+	+	+	+			
0	→		+	+	+	+	+	+	+		
·		+	+	+	+	+	+	+	+	+	
$\bar{l}$	+	+	+	+	+	+	+	+	+	+	+

of $\mathfrak{D}^{(l)}(R) \times \mathfrak{D}^{(\bar{l})}(R)$ in this case are the $\mathfrak{D}^{(L)}$ with the L of (17.E.1), and each of the L values occurs exactly once. If $l \leqslant \bar{l}$, then the roles of l and $\bar{l}$ are interchanged; thus, in general, the L values are

$$L = |l - \bar{l}|,\, |l - \bar{l}| + 1, \cdots, l + \bar{l} - 1,\, l + \bar{l}. \tag{17.14}$$

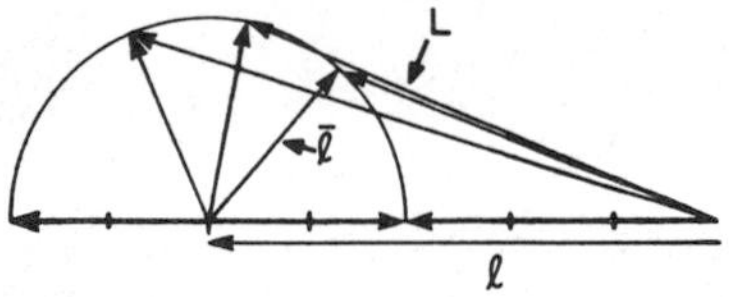

FIG. 9. The composition of the two angular moments, $l = 5$ and $\bar{l} = 2$, yields 3, 4, 5, 6, and 7 as possible values of L.

This "vector addition model" (Fig. 9) is of very general validity and basic significance for all of spectroscopy. The two systems which it combines need not consist simply of single electrons,[13] but could themselves be composite systems. The vector addition model even applies, as we shall see, to the composition of the spin quantum number and the orbital quantum number (the resulting L will be referred to as the "total quantum number"), or to the composition of the total quantum number and the nuclear spin, etc.

[13] Indeed, in the simple form given here, the model can not provide all the details for the case of two electrons, since it does not allow for the fact that the particles are identical.

7. We now know that the representation $\mathfrak{D}^{(l)} \times \mathfrak{D}^{(\bar{l})}$ is equivalent to the representation

$$\begin{pmatrix} \mathfrak{D}^{(|l-\bar{l}|)} & \mathbf{0} & \cdots & \mathbf{0} & \mathbf{0} \\ \mathbf{0} & \mathfrak{D}^{(|l-\bar{l}|+1)} & \cdots & \mathbf{0} & \mathbf{0} \\ \cdot & \cdot & \cdots & \cdot & \cdot \\ \cdot & \cdot & \cdots & \cdot & \cdot \\ \cdot & \cdot & \cdots & \cdot & \cdot \\ \mathbf{0} & \mathbf{0} & \cdots & \mathfrak{D}^{(l+\bar{l}-1)} & \mathbf{0} \\ \mathbf{0} & \mathbf{0} & \cdots & \mathbf{0} & \mathfrak{D}^{(l+\bar{l})} \end{pmatrix} = \mathbf{M}(R) \qquad (17.15)$$

which we denote by $\mathbf{M}(R)$ for short. There must therefore exist a matrix $\mathbf{S}$ which transforms these into one another

$$\mathfrak{D}^{(l)}(R) \times \mathfrak{D}^{(\bar{l})}(R) = \mathbf{S}^{-1}\mathbf{M}(R)\mathbf{S}. \qquad (17.16)$$

Since $\mathbf{M}(R)$ and also $\mathfrak{D}^{(l)} \times \mathfrak{D}^{(\bar{l})}$ are unitary, it can be assumed (Theorem 1a, Chapter 9, page 78) that $\mathbf{S}$ is unitary, i.e., $\mathbf{S}^{-1} = \mathbf{S}^{\dagger}$.

The matrix $\mathbf{S}$ is a square matrix in the broader sense, as discussed in Chapter 2. The rows and columns of $\mathfrak{D}^{(l)} \times \mathfrak{D}^{(\bar{l})}$ are labeled by two indices μ and ν, and so must be the columns of $\mathbf{S}$. The rows and columns of $\mathbf{M}(R)$ also carry two indices but these are of a different kind: the first index L states which representation, $\mathfrak{D}^{(L)}$, occurs in the row, and the second m, states which row of this representation is concerned. The elements of $\mathbf{M}(R)$ are

$$\mathbf{M}(R)_{L'm';Lm} = \delta_{LL'}\mathfrak{D}^{(L)}(R)_{m'm}\,. \qquad (17.17)$$

The rows of $\mathbf{S}$ must therefore be labeled by the indices L, m, where L runs from $|l - \bar{l}|$ to $l + \bar{l}$ and m from $-L$ to L. Written out in detail, (17.16) is

$$\mathfrak{D}^{(l)}(R)_{\mu'\mu}\mathfrak{D}^{(\bar{l})}(R)_{\nu'\nu} = \sum_{m'm}\sum_{L} \mathbf{S}^{*}_{Lm';\mu'\nu'}\mathfrak{D}^{(L)}(R)_{m'm}\mathbf{S}_{Lm;\mu\nu} \qquad (17.16a)$$

The significance of the matrix $\mathbf{S}$ is that it defines the linear combinations of the products $\psi_\mu\bar{\psi}_\nu$,

$$\Psi^{L}_{m} = \sum_{\mu\nu} \mathbf{S}^{*}_{Lm;\mu\nu}\psi_\mu\bar{\psi}_\nu\,, \qquad (17.18)$$

which transform according to irreducible representations under the operations $\mathbf{P}_R\overline{\mathbf{P}}_R$, which leave the system (including the interaction between the angular momenta l and $\bar{l}$) invariant. The Ψ^{L}_{m} transform as follows:

$$\left.\begin{aligned} \mathbf{P}_R\overline{\mathbf{P}}_R\Psi^{L}_{m} &= \sum \mathbf{S}^{*}_{Lm;\mu\nu}\mathbf{P}_R\psi_\mu \cdot \overline{\mathbf{P}}_R\bar{\psi}_\nu \\ &= \sum_{\mu\nu}\sum_{\mu'\nu'} \mathbf{S}^{*}_{Lm;\mu\nu}\mathfrak{D}^{(l)}(R)_{\mu'\mu}\mathfrak{D}^{(\bar{l})}(R)_{\nu'\nu}\psi_{\mu'}\bar{\psi}_{\nu'} \\ &= \sum_{\mu\mu'}\sum_{\nu\nu'}\sum_{L'm'} \mathbf{S}^{*}_{Lm;\mu\nu}\mathfrak{D}^{(l)}(R)_{\mu'\mu}\mathfrak{D}^{(\bar{l})}(R)_{\nu'\nu}\mathbf{S}_{L'm';\mu'\nu'}\Psi^{L'}_{m'} \\ &= \sum_{L'm'} [\mathbf{S} \cdot \mathfrak{D}^{(l)}(R) \times \mathfrak{D}^{(\bar{l})}(R) \cdot \mathbf{S}^{-1}]_{L'm';Lm}\Psi^{L'}_{m'} \\ &= \sum_{L'm'} \mathbf{M}(R)_{L'm';Lm}\Psi^{L'}_{m'} = \sum_{m'} \mathfrak{D}^{(L)}(R)_{m'm}\Psi^{L}_{m'}\,. \end{aligned}\right\} \qquad (17.19)$$

They therefore form the eigenfunctions for the first approximation (the "correct linear combinations" of Chapter 5) to the perturbed composite system.

To determine the coefficients $\mathbf{S}^*_{Lm;\mu\nu}$ we first apply an operator $\mathbf{P}_R\overline{\mathbf{P}}_R$ to (17.18), where R is a rotation about Z through an angle α. The left side is thereby multiplied by exp $(+im\alpha)$ and this must also hold for the right side.

$$\sum_{\mu\nu} \mathbf{S}^*_{Lm;\mu\nu} e^{im\alpha}\psi_\mu\bar{\psi}_\nu = \sum_{\mu\nu} \mathbf{S}^*_{Lm;\mu\nu}\mathbf{P}_R\psi_\mu\overline{\mathbf{P}}_R\bar{\psi}_\nu$$
$$= \sum_{\mu\nu} \mathbf{S}^*_{Lm;\mu\nu} e^{i\mu\alpha}e^{i\nu\alpha}\psi_\mu\bar{\psi}_\nu. \tag{17.20}$$

Therefore, because of the linear independence of the $\psi_\mu\bar{\psi}_\nu$,

$$\mathbf{S}_{Lm;\mu\nu} = 0 \quad \text{for} \quad m \neq \mu + \nu. \tag{17.20a}$$

The same result is obtained from (17.16a) if the dependence of the representation coefficients on α and γ is made explicit according to Eq. (15.8), and the terms with the same dependence upon α and γ are equated. If we write[14]

$$\mathbf{S}_{L,\mu+\nu;\mu\nu} = s_{L\mu\nu}, \tag{17.20b}$$

then (17.16a) becomes

$$\mathfrak{D}^{(l)}(R)_{\mu'\mu}\mathfrak{D}^{(\bar{l})}(R)_{\nu'\nu} = \sum_{L=|l-\bar{l}|}^{l+\bar{l}} s^*_{L\mu'\nu'}\mathfrak{D}^{(L)}(R)_{\mu'+\nu';\mu+\nu}s_{L\mu\nu}. \tag{17.16b}$$

The matrix $\mathbf{S}$ is not uniquely determined by (17.16). Since $\mathbf{M}(R)$ commutes with a diagonal matrix

$$\mathbf{u} = \begin{pmatrix} \boldsymbol{\omega}_{|l-\bar{l}|}\mathbf{1} & \mathbf{0} & \cdot & \cdot & \cdot & \mathbf{0} & \mathbf{0} \\ \mathbf{0} & \boldsymbol{\omega}_{|l-\bar{l}|+1}\mathbf{1} & \cdot & \cdot & \cdot & \mathbf{0} & \mathbf{0} \\ \cdot & \cdot & \cdot & \cdot & \cdot & \cdot & \cdot \\ \cdot & \cdot & \cdot & \cdot & \cdot & \cdot & \cdot \\ \cdot & \cdot & \cdot & \cdot & \cdot & \cdot & \cdot \\ \mathbf{0} & \mathbf{0} & \cdot & \cdot & \cdot & \boldsymbol{\omega}_{l+\bar{l}-1}\mathbf{1} & \mathbf{0} \\ \mathbf{0} & \mathbf{0} & \cdot & \cdot & \cdot & \mathbf{0} & \boldsymbol{\omega}_{l+\bar{l}}\mathbf{1} \end{pmatrix}$$

$$\mathbf{u}_{L'm';Lm} = \boldsymbol{\omega}_L\,\delta_{L'L}\,\delta_{m'm}$$

the right side of (17.16) does not change if $\mathbf{S}$ is replaced by $\mathbf{uS}$. For $\mathbf{uS}$ to

[14] The elements of the matrix $\mathbf{S}$, namely $\mathbf{S}_{L,\mu+\nu;\mu\nu} = s^{(l\bar{l})}_{L\mu\nu}$, which provide those linear combinations of the products $\psi^{(l)}\psi^{(\bar{l})}$, which transform according to $\mathfrak{D}^{(L)}$, are known as vector coupling coefficients. The notation of Condon and Shortley for these quantities is $s^{(l\bar{l})}_{L\mu\nu} = (l\,\bar{l}\,\mu\,\nu|l\,\bar{l}\,L\,m)$. (E. U. Condon and G. H. Shortley, "The Theory of Atomic Spectra," Cambridge Univ. Press, London and New York, 1953.)

remain unitary, $\mathbf{u}$ must be unitary, which is the case when the absolute values of the $\boldsymbol{\omega}$ are all 1. The elements of $\mathbf{uS}$, which will replace $\mathbf{S}$, are

$$(\mathbf{uS})_{Lm;\mu\nu} = \boldsymbol{\omega}_L \mathbf{S}_{Lm;\mu\nu}.$$

By suitable choice of the $\boldsymbol{\omega}$, one can always arrange that

$$\mathbf{S}_{L,l-\bar{l};l,-\bar{l}} = s_{L,l,-\bar{l}} = |s_{L,l,-\bar{l}}| \tag{17.21}$$

will be real and positive. This choice is assumed to have been made in what follows.[15] We now multiply (17.16b) by $\mathfrak{D}^{(L')}(R)^*_{\mu'+\nu';\mu+\nu}$ and integrate over the entire group. Because of the orthogonality relationships of the representation coefficients, only one term remains on the right side; if we set $L' = L$ (and write $h = \int dR$), we obtain

$$\int \mathfrak{D}^{(l)}(R)_{\mu'\mu} \mathfrak{D}^{(\bar{l})}(R)_{\nu'\nu} \mathfrak{D}^{(L)}(R)^*_{\mu'+\nu';\mu+\nu}\, dR = h\, \frac{s^*_{L\mu'\nu'} s_{L\mu\nu}}{2L+1}. \tag{17.22}$$

To determine the $s_{L\mu\nu}$, it is not necessary to evaluate the integral in (17.22) for all possible values of L, μ', ν', μ, and ν; it is sufficient if it is known for a single pair of values μ', ν' and all L, μ, ν (and l, $\bar{l}$). To make the formulas as simple as possible we set $\mu' = l$ and $\nu' = -\bar{l}$ and obtain according to Eqs. (15.27a) and (15.27b)

$$\sqrt{\binom{2l}{l-\mu}\binom{2\bar{l}}{\bar{l}-\nu}} \sum_{\varkappa} (-1)^{\varkappa+\bar{l}+\nu}$$

$$\times \frac{\sqrt{(L+\mu+\nu)!(L-\mu-\nu)!(L+l-\bar{l})!(L-l+\bar{l})!}}{(L-l+\bar{l}-\varkappa)!(L+\mu+\nu-\varkappa)!\varkappa!(\varkappa+l-\bar{l}-\mu-\nu)!}$$

$$\times \int \cos^{2L+2\bar{l}+2\mu-2\varkappa}\tfrac{1}{2}\beta \cdot \sin^{2l-2\mu+2\varkappa}\tfrac{1}{2}\beta\, dR = h\, \frac{s^*_{L,l,-\bar{l}}\, s_{L\mu\nu}}{2L+1}. \tag{17.23}$$

As was to be expected, α and γ drop out.

What we now need are integrals of the form

$$\int \cos^{2a} \tfrac{1}{2}\beta \sin^{2b} \tfrac{1}{2}\beta\, dR.$$

The orthogonality relations for the representation coefficients also provide us with these; these relations are

$$\frac{h}{2j+1} = \int |\mathfrak{D}^{(j)}(R)_{j\mu}|^2\, dR = \binom{2j}{j-\mu} \int \cos^{2j+2\mu} \tfrac{1}{2}\beta \sin^{2j-2\mu} \tfrac{1}{2}\beta\, dR.$$

[15] This choice leads to the same vector coupling coefficients as those of E. U. Condon and G. H. Shortley and M. E. Rose (see discussion in Appendix A), as well as those used by G. Racah, *Phys. Rev.* **62**, 438 (1942) and *Phys. Rev.* **63**, 367 (1943). As will be seen below, the resulting coefficients are all real, so that no distinction need be made between $\mathbf{S}$ and $\mathbf{S}^*$.

Then if we write $j + \mu = a, j - \mu = b$,

$$\int \cos^{2a} \tfrac{1}{2}\beta \sin^{2b} \tfrac{1}{2}\beta \, dR = g \frac{b!a!}{(a+b+1)!}. \tag{17.24}$$

When this is substituted into (17.23), it yields

$$\sum_{\varkappa} (-1)^{\varkappa+\bar{l}+\nu} \frac{\sqrt{(2l)!(2\bar{l})!(L+\mu+\nu)!(L-\mu-\nu)!(L+l-\bar{l})!(L-l+\bar{l})!}}{(L+l+\bar{l}+1)!\sqrt{(l-\mu)!(l+\mu)!(\bar{l}-\nu)!(\bar{l}+\nu)!}}$$

$$\times \frac{(L+\bar{l}+\mu-\varkappa)!(l-\mu+\varkappa)!(2L+1)}{(L-l+\bar{l}-\varkappa)!(L+\mu+\nu-\varkappa)!\varkappa!(\varkappa+l-\bar{l}-\mu-\nu)!} = s^*_{L,l,-l} s_{L\mu\nu}. \tag{17.25}$$

In order to determine $s_{L,l,-l}$, we set $\mu = l$, $\nu = -\bar{l}$; then

$$\frac{2L+1}{(L+l+\bar{l}+1)!} \sum_{\varkappa} \frac{(-1)^{\varkappa}(L+l-\bar{l})!(L-l+\bar{l})!(L+\bar{l}+l-\varkappa)!}{(L-l+\bar{l}-\varkappa)!(L+l-\bar{l}-\varkappa)!\varkappa!}$$

$$= |s_{L,l,-l}|^2 = (s_{L,l,-l})^2, \tag{17.25a}$$

where (17.21) has been used to obtain the latter part of Eq. (17.25a). Furthermore, it will be shown in an appendix to this chapter that

$$\sum_{\varkappa} (-1)^{\varkappa} \binom{L-l+\bar{l}}{\varkappa} \frac{(L+\bar{l}+l-\varkappa)!}{(L+l-\bar{l}-\varkappa)!} = (2\bar{l})! \binom{2l}{L+l-\bar{l}}. \tag{17.26}$$

Using this in (17.25a), we finally obtain

$$s_{L,l,-l} = \sqrt{\frac{(2L+1)(2l)!(2\bar{l})!}{(L+l+\bar{l}+1)!(l+\bar{l}-L)!}}, \tag{17.27a}$$

and, with the help of (17.25),

$$s^{(l\bar{l})}_{L\mu\nu} = \frac{\sqrt{(L+l-\bar{l})!(L-l+\bar{l})!(l+\bar{l}-L)!(L+\mu+\nu)!(L-\mu-\nu)!}}{\sqrt{(L+l+\bar{l}+1)!(l-\mu)!(l+\mu)!(\bar{l}-\nu)!(\bar{l}+\nu)!}}$$

$$\times \sum_{\varkappa} \frac{(-1)^{\varkappa+\bar{l}+\nu}\sqrt{(2L+1)}(L+\bar{l}+\mu-\varkappa)!(l-\mu+\varkappa)!}{(L-l+\bar{l}-\varkappa)!(L+\mu+\nu-\varkappa)!\varkappa!(\varkappa+l-\bar{l}-\mu-\nu)!} \tag{17.27}$$

This equation shows that the convention adopted in (17.21) does indeed make *all* the $s_{L\mu\nu}$ real: $s^*_{L\mu\nu} = s_{L\mu\nu}$.

The summation over $\varkappa$ in this equation is to be taken over all integers, just as in Eq. (15.27); the infinities of the factorials in the denominator suffice to limit $\varkappa$ between the larger of the two numbers 0, $\bar{l} - l + \mu + \nu$, and the smaller of $L + \mu + \nu$ and $L - l + \bar{l}$, just as they did in Chapter 15. The quantities s still depend on the two numbers l and $\bar{l}$ besides their indices L, μ, ν; l and $\bar{l}$ serve to denote which direct product $\mathfrak{D}^{(l)} \times \mathfrak{D}^{(\bar{l})}$ can be reduced by them. Moreover, s will remain essentially unchanged[16] if l and $\bar{l}$ and simultaneously μ and ν are interchanged; this cannot be seen at once from (17.27), since the summation over $\varkappa$ cannot be obtained in closed form. In case $\mu + \nu = L$, however, only one term ($\varkappa = L - l + \bar{l}$) of the whole sum does not vanish, and we obtain

$$s^{(l\bar{l})}_{L,\mu,L-\mu} =$$

$$(-1)^{l-\mu}\sqrt{\frac{(2L+1)!(l+\bar{l}-L)!(l+\mu)!(L+\bar{l}-\mu)!}{(L+l+\bar{l}+1)!(L+l-\bar{l})!(L-l+\bar{l})!(l-\mu)!(\bar{l}-L+\mu)!}}. \tag{17.27b}$$

We also present explicitly the equations for the s which follow from the unitarity of $\mathbf{S}$ (Eq. (17.27) shows that $\mathbf{S}$ is real):

$$\sum_{\mu} s^{(l\bar{l})}_{L,\mu,m-\mu} s^{(l\bar{l})}_{L',\mu,m-\mu} = \delta_{LL'}; \qquad \sum_{L} s^{(l\bar{l})}_{L,\mu,m-\mu} s^{(l\bar{l})}_{L,\mu',m-\mu'} = \delta_{\mu\mu'}. \tag{17.28}$$

8. We have now determined all the coefficients appearing in (17.16b) and in (17.18).

$$\Psi'^{L}_{m} = \sum_{\mu} s^{(l\bar{l})}_{L,\mu,m-\mu} \psi_{\mu} \bar{\psi}_{m-\mu}. \tag{17.18a}$$

It should be noted that in (17.18a) we have a case—and, indeed, one of the most important ones—in which the "correct linear combinations" for the first approximation of the perturbation procedure can be determined from general considerations alone; Eq. (17.18a) holds with complete generality for all perturbations which do not distinguish a spatial direction. This results from the fact that we know from the start that the correct linear combinations all "belong to one row of an irreducible representation" and that only one linear combination can be constructed from the functions (17.9) which belong to the mth row of $\mathfrak{D}^{(L)}$—if any can be constructed (that is, if L lies between $|l - \bar{l}|$ and $l + \bar{l}$). On the other hand, if other eigenfunctions besides (17.9) belong to the same eigenvalue in the unperturbed problem, then it is possible that several linear combinations with the desired property exist, and the "correct" one might be a linear combination of these, but of no others.

The formula (17.16b) has many applications. First of all, it holds not only for the real representations (for integral l), but also for the double-valued representations of Chapter 15. It contains, among others, the intensity formulas for the multiplet lines and the Zeeman components (Chapter 23).

[16] l and $\bar{l}$ do not enter in precisely the same way in (17.21), hence $s^{(l\bar{l})}_{L\mu\nu} = (-1)^{l+\bar{l}-L} s^{(\bar{l}l)}_{L\nu\mu}$.

It is clear that $\mathfrak{D}^{(l)}(R)_{\mu'\mu}\mathfrak{D}^{(\bar{l})}(R)_{\nu'\nu}$ can be expressed in terms of representation coefficients, since these form a complete set of functions. It is also clear that only the coefficients which occur in some representation in the $(\mu' + \nu')$th row and the $(\mu + \nu)$th column can occur in (17.16b), since only these have the correct α and γ dependence. Furthermore, (17.16b) also

TABLE III

The vector coupling coefficients $s^{(l\frac{1}{2})}_{L\mu\nu}$

L	$\nu = -\frac{1}{2}$	$\nu = +\frac{1}{2}$
$l - \frac{1}{2}$	$\dfrac{\sqrt{l+\mu}}{\sqrt{2l+1}}$	$-\dfrac{\sqrt{l-\mu}}{\sqrt{2l+1}}$
$l + \frac{1}{2}$	$\dfrac{\sqrt{l-\mu+1}}{\sqrt{2l+1}}$	$\dfrac{\sqrt{l+\mu+1}}{\sqrt{2l+1}}$

TABLE IV

The vector coupling coefficients $s^{(l1)}_{L\mu\nu}$

L	$\nu = -1$	0	$+1$
$l - 1$	$\sqrt{\dfrac{(l+\mu)(l+\mu-1)}{2l(2l+1)}}$	$-\sqrt{\dfrac{(l-\mu)(l+\mu)}{l(2l+1)}}$	$\sqrt{\dfrac{(l-\mu-1)(l-\mu)}{2l(2l+1)}}$
l	$\sqrt{\dfrac{(l-\mu+1)(l+\mu)}{2l(l+1)}}$	$\dfrac{\mu}{\sqrt{l(l+1)}}$	$-\sqrt{\dfrac{(l+\mu+1)(l-\mu)}{2l(l+1)}}$
$l + 1$	$\sqrt{\dfrac{(l-\mu+1)(l-\mu+2)}{(2l+1)(2l+2)}}$	$\sqrt{\dfrac{(l-\mu+1)(l+\mu+1)}{(2l+1)(l+1)}}$	$\sqrt{\dfrac{(l+\mu+1)(l+\mu+2)}{(2l+1)(2l+2)}}$

shows that L must vary between $|l - \bar{l}|$ and $l + \bar{l}$. If l and $\bar{l}$ are both integral or half-integral, then the L in (17.16b) are all integral; if on the other hand, one is integral and the other half-integral, then the L are all half-integral. The summation is always taken in integral steps from the lower to the upper limit.

For $\bar{l} = 0$, Eq. (17.16b) is trivial; for $\bar{l} = \frac{1}{2}$ and 1 we summarize the $s^{(l\bar{l})}_{L\mu\nu}$ in tables.[17]

[17] The $s^{(l\bar{l})}_{L\mu\nu}$ can easily be remembered by keeping in mind that they vanish if $|\mu| > l$ or $|\mu + \nu| > L$, that is, whenever one of the representation coefficients in (17.22) is meaningless.

Appendix to Chapter 17. A Relationship Among Binomial Coefficients

In order to prove (17.26) we start from the identity

$$\sum_{\varkappa} \binom{a}{\varkappa}\binom{b}{c-\varkappa} = \binom{a+b}{c}. \tag{17.29}$$

The left side contains the coefficient of $x^{\varkappa}$ in $(1+x)^a$ multiplied by the coefficient of $x^{c-\varkappa}$ in $(1+x)^b$ and summed over all $\varkappa$, that is, the coefficient of x^c in $(1+x)^a(1+x)^b = (1+x)^{a+b}$; and this is the expression on the right side. Let a be a positive integer; b can be negative or positive. Also, for $u < 0$, note that

$$\begin{aligned}
\binom{u}{v} &= \frac{u(u-1)\cdots(u-v+2)(u-v+1)}{1\cdot 2\cdots(v-1)\cdot v} \\
&= (-1)^v \frac{(v-u-1)(v-u-2)\cdots(1-u)(-u)}{1\cdot 2\cdots(v-1)\cdot v} \\
&= (-1)^v \binom{v-u-1}{v}.
\end{aligned} \tag{17.30}$$

Identifying $(L+l-\bar{l}-\varkappa)$ in (17.26) with v, and using (17.30), we obtain

$$\begin{aligned}
&\sum_{\varkappa} (-1)^{\varkappa} \binom{L-l+\bar{l}}{\varkappa}\binom{L+\bar{l}+l-\varkappa}{L+l-\bar{l}-\varkappa}(2\bar{l})! \\
&= \sum_{\varkappa} (-1)^{L+l-\bar{l}}(2\bar{l})! \binom{L-l+\bar{l}}{\varkappa}\binom{-2\bar{l}-1}{L+l-\bar{l}-\varkappa} \\
&= (-1)^{L+l-\bar{l}}(2\bar{l})! \binom{L-l-\bar{l}-1}{L+l-\bar{l}} = (2\bar{l})! \binom{2l}{L+l-\bar{l}},
\end{aligned}$$

which proves (17.26). Equation (17.29) was used to obtain the first part of the last line, and Eq. (17.30) to reduce it to the final form.

18. Selection Rules and the Splitting of Spectral Lines

1. In Chapter 6 we calculated, via the time-dependent Schrödinger equation, the increase in the excitation probability $|a_F(t)|^2 = |b(t)|^2$ of a stationary state ψ_F resulting from impinging light, polarized in the X-direction and of intensity J (energy density per unit circular frequency interval, $d\omega = 2\pi\, d\nu$). We obtained the result that if the atom were initially entirely in the stationary state ψ_E, this excitation probability would be (Eqs. (6.17) and (6.6))

$$|a_F(t)|^2 = B_{EF}Jt = \frac{e^2}{\hbar^2}|\mathbf{X}_{FE}|^2 Jt, \tag{18.1}$$

where $\mathbf{X}_{FE}$, the *matrix element*,

$$\mathbf{X}_{FE} = (\psi_F, (x_1 + x_2 + \cdots + x_n)\psi_E), \tag{18.2a}$$

is the "X-component of the dipole moment" for the transition $E \to F$. If the light were polarized in the Y- or Z-directions,

$$\mathbf{Y}_{FE} = (\psi_F, (y_1 + y_2 + \cdots + y_n)\psi_E) \tag{18.2b}$$

$$\mathbf{Z}_{FE} = (\psi_F, (z_1 + z_2 + \cdots + z_n)\psi_E) \tag{18.2c}$$

would appear in (18.1) instead of $\mathbf{X}_{FE}$; if it were polarized in a direction with direction cosines α_1, α_2, α_3, then the corresponding expression would be

$$\alpha_1\mathbf{X}_{FE} + \alpha_2\mathbf{Y}_{FE} + \alpha_3\mathbf{Z}_{FE}\,. \tag{18.2}$$

According to the well known considerations of Einstein,[1] the probability $A_{FE}\,dt$ that an atom which is in the excited state ψ_F makes a transition during a small time interval dt to the state ψ_E by spontaneous emission of radiation can be calculated from these matrix elements. This quantity is actually called the "transition probability" and is given by

$$A_{FE} = \frac{4e^2\omega^3}{3\hbar c^3}(|\mathbf{X}_{FE}|^2 + |\mathbf{Y}_{FE}|^2 + |\mathbf{Z}_{FE}|^2). \tag{18.1a}$$

If a spectral line with frequency $(F - E)/\hbar$ does not occur in a spectrum, although the existence of the atom in the state ψ_F is established by the occurrence of other lines, it can be concluded that the expressions (18.2a) (18.2b), (18.2c) vanish. In the vast majority of cases these "selection rules"

[1] A. Einstein, *Verhandl. deut. physik. Ges.* p. 318 (1916); *Physik. Z.* **18** p. 121 (1917).

follow from the transformation properties of the eigenfunctions concerned. The three kinds of selection rules correspond to the transformation properties of the eigenfunctions under the symmetric group, the three-dimensional rotation group, and the reflection group.

It is to be noted, however, that the complete absence of the line $F \rightarrow E$ need not follow from the vanishing of (18.2). In the derivation of (18.1) the important and not strictly correct assumption was made that the dimension of the atom is negligible compared to the wavelength of the light; thus the calculations were done as though the perturbation potential due to the light were *constant in the direction of the light rays* since it changes significantly only over a distance of the order of magnitude of a wavelength. If one considers the fact that the potential actually varies sinusoidally in the direction of the rays, a somewhat different expression for the transition probability (and therefore for the lifetime) results, and a correction term B' is added to B_{EF} in (18.1).

The transition probability calculated in (18.1) or (18.1a) results from the dipole radiation; the correction B' is limited to quadrupole and higher moments. It is thus about 10^7 times ((atomic dimension/wavelength)^2) smaller than the B_{EF} due to dipole radiation, and it is negligible compared with B_{EF} as long as (18.2) does not vanish. Nevertheless, transitions for which (18.2) is zero are not absolutely forbidden, but only very much weaker than dipole transitions. The crucial quantity for determining the intensity of quadrupole radiation itself is the quadrupole matrix element

$$\frac{\omega}{c}\,(\psi_F, (x_1y_1 + x_2y_2 + \cdots + x_ny_n)\psi_E). \tag{18.3}$$

This must be substituted for $\mathbf{X}_{FE}$ in (18.1) to obtain the quadrupole transition probability.[2]

A. Dipole transitions do not occur between levels with different multiplicities. Levels of different multiplicity $2S + 1$ belong to different representations of the symmetric group. Since multiplication by $(x_1 + x_2 + \cdots + x_n)$ is an operation symmetric under the permutation of the electrons, the scalar product (18.2) must vanish according to Chapter 12. The radiation of quadrupole and higher moments also vanishes for the same reason.

It is known empirically that this so-called *intercombination prohibition* is well fulfilled only for elements with *low atomic numbers.* In heavier elements, relatively strong lines occur for transitions between levels of different multiplicity. These transitions result from the auxiliary terms in the Schrödinger equation due to the magnetic moment of the electron and rapidly become more probable as the number of electrons increases.

B. Multiplication by $(x_1 + x_2 + \cdots + x_n)$ is not an operation symmetric under rotations so that the selection rule for the azimuthal quantum number L will be different from that for S. If the orbital quantum number of ψ_E is L, then the second factor in the product $(x_1 + x_2 + \cdots + x_n)\psi_E$ belongs to $\mathfrak{D}^{(L)}$; the first factor is a vector component and belongs to $\mathfrak{D}^{(1)}$.

[2] Quadrupole radiation was first exhaustively investigated in quantum mechanics by A. Rubinowicz. See, for example, *Z. Physik.* **61,** 338 (1930); **65,** 662 (1930).

The $(2\bar{L}+1)(2L+1)$ products of every pair of functions, the first of which $f_{\bar{\varkappa}}^{(\bar{L})}$ belongs to the $\bar{\varkappa}$th row of $\mathfrak{D}^{(\bar{L})}$, and the second of which $\psi_{\varkappa}^{(L)}$ belongs to the $\varkappa$th row of $\mathfrak{D}^{(L)}$, transform according to $\mathfrak{D}^{(\bar{L})} \times \mathfrak{D}^{(L)}$. (See the analogous development of Chapter 17.)

$$\mathbf{P}_R f_{\bar{\varkappa}}^{(\bar{L})} \psi_{\varkappa}^{(L)} = \mathbf{P}_R f_{\bar{\varkappa}}^{(\bar{L})} \cdot \mathbf{P}_R \psi_{\varkappa}^{(L)} = \sum_{\bar{\lambda}\lambda} \mathfrak{D}^{(\bar{L})}(R)_{\bar{\lambda}\bar{\varkappa}} \, \mathfrak{D}^{(L)}(R)_{\lambda\varkappa} f_{\bar{\lambda}}^{(\bar{L})} \psi_{\lambda}^{(L)}.$$

By means of the matrix $\mathbf{S}$ which reduces $\mathfrak{D}^{(\bar{L})} \times \mathfrak{D}^{(L)}$, linear combinations $F_{\mu}^{(k)}$ of the $f_{\bar{\varkappa}}^{(\bar{L})} \psi_{\varkappa}^{(L)}$ can be formed which belong to the irreducible components $\mathfrak{D}^{(k)}$ of $\mathfrak{D}^{(\bar{L})} \times \mathfrak{D}^{(L)}$. Conversely, the functions $f_{\bar{\varkappa}}^{(\bar{L})} \psi_{\varkappa}^{(L)}$ can be expressed in terms of the $F_{\mu}^{(k)}$ by means of the reciprocal matrix $\mathbf{S}^{-1}$.

In our case $\bar{L} = 1$, and the irreducible components of $\mathfrak{D}^{(1)} \times \mathfrak{D}^{(L)}$ for $L \neq 0$ are

$$\mathfrak{D}^{(L-1)}, \mathfrak{D}^{(L)}, \mathfrak{D}^{(L+1)}. \tag{18.E.1}$$

The product $(x_1 + x_2 + \cdots + x_n)\psi_E$ can therefore be written as the sum of three functions, one of which belongs to each of the representations (18.E.1). If the azimuthal quantum number L' of ψ_F is not equal to $L-1$, L, or $L+1$, then all three parts of the scalar product (18.2) vanish. *The orbital quantum number L can change only by* ± 1 or 0 in a spontaneous dipole transition.

If $L = 0$, then $(x_1 + x_2 + \cdots + x_n)\psi_E$ belongs to the representation $\mathfrak{D}^{(1)}$, since in this case $\mathfrak{D}^{(1)} \times \mathfrak{D}^{(0)}$ is identical with $\mathfrak{D}^{(1)}$. If $L' \neq 1$, Eq. (18.2) vanishes; S levels combine only with P levels ($L' = 1$); *the transition $S \rightarrow S$ is also forbidden.*

These rules, too, are exact only for the light elements. Their failure for higher numbers of electrons is also due to perturbations involving the magnetic moment of the electron. Lines which appear in violation of these rules are not so conspicuous as those which disobey the intercombination prohibition since other selection rules exist which are valid in spite of these perturbations, and which of themselves eliminate many of the transitions forbidden by the selection rules for L.

Quadrupole and higher moments need not vanish under the same conditions. Indeed, to show that the dipole transition was forbidden, we made explicit use of the fact that $(x_1 + x_2 + \cdots + x_n)$ belongs to the representation $\mathfrak{D}^{(1)}$. The corresponding expression for quadrupole radiation $(x_1 y_1 + \cdots + x_n y_n)$ belongs not to $\mathfrak{D}^{(1)}$ but to $\mathfrak{D}^{(2)}$; consequently, the orbital quantum number can change by ± 2, ± 1, or 0 in a quadrupole transition. Moreover, in quadrupole transitions, $S \rightarrow P$ is forbidden, as well as $S \rightarrow S$.

C. *In dipole radiation the reflection symmetry always changes*; even levels combine only with odd, and odd levels only with even. For if ψ_E remains unchanged upon substitution of $-x, -y, -z$ for x, y, z then $(x_1 + x_2 + \cdots + x_n)\psi_E$ changes its sign; conversely, the expression $(x_1 + x_2 + \cdots + x_n)\psi_E$ remains unchanged under the inversion if ψ_E changes sign; this expression thus has a parity opposite to ψ_E. If the scalar products (18.2) are not to vanish, ψ_F must also have the parity opposite to ψ_E.

The rule that the parity changes in allowed transitions was first found by Laporte and by Russell from the analysis of complex spectra. By its very derivation it applies only to dipole radiation;[3] on the other hand *it remains valid when the magnetic moment of the electron is considered* and applies to heavy elements as well as light ones. Optical transitions contradicting it are scarcely known—in spite of very plentiful data. The best known case occurs in the "Nebulium spectrum," where the initial state is metastable. This allows the possibility of an extremely long decay time, and thus a small transition probability, especially under the circumstances which exist in the rarefied stellar atmosphere.

The three selection rules actually forbid most transitions: the multiplet system cannot change, L can change only by ± 1 or 0 (0 to 0 is also forbidden), and the reflection character (parity) must change. Thus, for example, a ${}^3S_+$ level can combine only with a ${}^3P_-$ level,[4] a ${}^4D_-$ level only with ${}^4P_+$, ${}^4D_+$, and ${}^4F_+$ levels,[5] etc.

We re-emphasize that so far the magnetic moment of the electron has not been considered at all, and the fine structure of the spectral lines has not been accounted for. The rules above will hold for all the fine structure components of a line. The first two rules will hold only when the influence of the magnetic moment is small (for small multiplet splitting, that is, in the light elements), while the last one will hold exactly, for reasons which will become clear later.

2. The situation in the presence of an external field, when the strict rotational symmetry of space is destroyed, remains yet to be considered, As we know, external fields cause a splitting of the lines into several components. For a magnetic field this is known as the Zeeman effect and has been studied experimentally with great precision; the analogous phenomenon in an electric field, the Stark effect, is in most cases not so easily accessible to observation. In our present preliminary survey, the details will not be thoroughly discussed; we shall obtain the Zeeman and Stark effects only as they would appear if the electron had no magnetic moment.

A magnetic field along the Z-axis diminishes the symmetry group of configuration space. Of all possible rotations only those about the Z axis

[3] For quadrupole transitions, the opposite rule holds: the reflection character does *not* change in these transitions.

[4] For quadrupole radiation only with ${}^3D_+$ levels.

[5] For quadrupole radiation with ${}^4S_-$, ${}^4P_-$, ${}^4D_-$, ${}^4F_-$, ${}^4G_-$, levels.

remain symmetry operations. In addition, the two directions Z and $-Z$ will still be equivalent because of the axial nature of the magnetic field vector, which insures that the XY-plane remains a plane of symmetry. However, for the same reason, the YZ-plane, for example, is *not* a plane of symmetry since a sense of rotation is preferred. This is seen most clearly by considering the classical path of an electron in a magnetic field and in the field of a nucleus. By reflection of the path in the plane perpendicular to the field through the nucleus, a classically possible path is obtained; on the other hand reflection in the YZ-plane parallel to the direction of the field does not yield a possible path (see Fig. 10a).

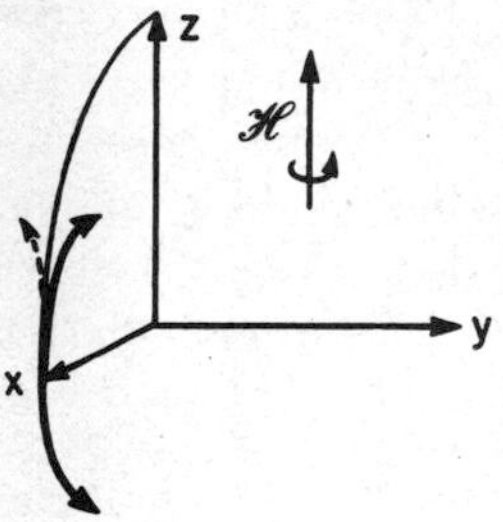

FIG. 10a. Magnetic field in the Z-direction. The reflection of the path of a particle in the XY-plane again yields a possible path, but reflection in the XZ-plane does not.

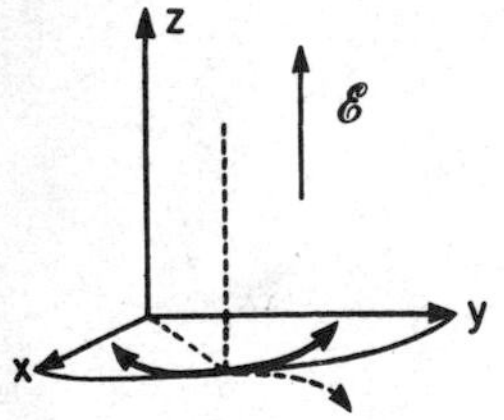

FIG. 10b. Electric field in the Z-direction. Reflection of the path of a particle in a plane through the Z-axis gives a possible path, but reflection in the XY-plane does not. (See section 4.)

It follows from this that the inversion symmetry of the problem is not disturbed by a magnetic field: the inversion ($x_k' = -x_k$, $y_k' = -y_k$, $z_k' = -z_k$) is the product of a rotation about Z through an angle π ($x_k' = -x_k$, $y_k' = -y_k$, $z_k' = +z_k$) and a reflection in the XY plane ($x_k' = +x_k$, $y_k' = +y_k$, $z_k' = -z_k$), and is therefore an element of the symmetry group of the system. The overall symmetry is the direct product of the group of pure rotations about Z, the reflection group (which contains only the inversion and the identity) and the symmetric group. The first two groups, and thus also their direct product, are Abelian.

Even if the full rotational symmetry of the problem is broken down by the external field, the eigenvalues and eigenfunctions still have approximately the same values and properties as they had in the absence of a magnetic field, so long as the magnetic field is weak—and experimentally achievable fields are always weak in this sense. In particular, the orbital quantum number L remains well defined and the ordinary selection rules will still hold for L. Moreover, each level naturally belongs to an irreducible representation of the three symmetry groups, even if the external field is arbitrarily strong, so that each has a multiplet system S and a reflection character just like the levels of the zero-field system. The selection rules A and C which follow from the relationship of the eigenfunctions to the representations of the symmetric and the reflection groups are therefore rigidly maintained. A new quantum number appears: the magnetic quantum number μ; it gives the representation $(\exp(+i\mu\varphi))$ of the two-dimensional pure rotation group to which the level belongs. A new selection rule is obtained for μ which takes different forms for light polarized in different directions, so that many transitions can only be induced by light polarized in the field direction (π-components), and many only by light polarized perpendicular to the field direction (σ-components). Since the different directions in space are no longer equivalent, this is not surprising.

For transitions with light polarized in the Z-direction

$$\mathbf{Z}_{FE} = (\psi_F, (z_1 + z_2 + \cdots + z_n)\psi_E) \tag{18.2c}$$

is the determining expression. Since multiplication by $(z_1 + z_2 + \cdots + z_n)$ is an operation symmetric under rotations about Z, the states ψ_F and ψ_E must belong to the same representation $(\exp(+i\mu\varphi))$ and have the same magnetic quantum number if (18.2c) is not to vanish. *If the light is polarized parallel to the field direction, the magnetic quantum number does not change.*

For a transition in which the light is polarized perpendicular to the field direction (σ-components), $\mathbf{X}_{FE}$ and $\mathbf{Y}_{FE}$ are the determining quantities. Now $(x_1 + x_2 + \cdots + x_n) - i(y_1 + y_2 + \cdots + y_n)$ belongs to the representation $(\exp(-i\varphi))$ so that $[(x_1 + x_2 + \cdots + x_n) - i(y_1 + y_2 + \cdots + y_n)] \cdot \psi_E$ belongs to the representation $(\exp[+i(\mu - 1)\varphi])$. Thus if

$$\mathbf{X}_{FE} - i\mathbf{Y}_{FE} = (\psi_F, [(x_1 + \cdots + x_n) - i(y_1 + \cdots + y_n)]\psi_E)$$

is to be nonvanishing, ψ_F must also belong to the representation $(\exp[+i(\mu-1)\varphi])$. Likewise, ψ_F must belong to $(\exp[+i(\mu+1)\varphi])$, if

$$\mathbf{X}_{FE} + i\mathbf{Y}_{FE} = (\psi_F, [(x_1 + \cdots + x_n) + i(y_1 + \cdots + y_n)]\psi_E)$$

is to be different from zero. It follows that $\mathbf{X}_{FE}$ and $\mathbf{Y}_{FE}$ can be finite only if the magnetic quantum numbers of ψ_F and ψ_E differ by 1. *Only transitions with $\Delta\mu = \pm 1$ are induced by light polarized perpendicular to the field direction.*

Note that a scalar, for instance, must be multiplied with the *conjugate complex* of the 1-component of a vector (as given in (15.34)), to convert it into a wave function with $\mu = 1$. This point will be more systematically treated in chapter 21.

For the emission process, this implies that light emitted in a direction perpendicular to the field direction is polarized parallel to the field direction in transitions with $\Delta\mu = 0$, and perpendicular to it in transitions with

$\Delta\mu = \pm 1$ (Transverse effect). This fixes the direction of polarization uniquely since it must also be perpendicular to the direction of radiation.

On the other hand, light emitted in the direction of the magnetic field (longitudinal effect) must be polarized perpendicular to the field direction; it can thus contain no π-components, but only σ-components. However, the state of polarization of the σ-components is not determined by the specification "perpendicular to the field direction." We know experimentally that it consists in part of right- and in part of left-circularly polarized light. Conversely, this implies that some of the transitions cannot be excited by left-circularly polarized light and that others cannot be excited by right-circularly polarized light.[6] A calculation which is completely analogous to that in Chapter 6 shows that the matrix elements $(1/\sqrt{2})(\mathbf{X}_{FE} + i\mathbf{Y}_{FE})$ or $(1/\sqrt{2})(\mathbf{X}_{FE} - i\mathbf{Y}_{FE})$—depending on whether the sense of rotation of the electric vector is from the X-axis towards the Y-axis, or vice versa—appear in (18.1) in place of $\mathbf{X}_{FE}$ for transitions which are excited by light circularly polarized in the XY-plane. Thus, if the light is right-circularly polarized when viewed along the field (i.e., from below, if we take the Z-axis positive upward), then it induces a transition with an increase of μ by 1; if left-circularly polarized, a transition with a decrease of μ by 1. Conversely, if in spontaneous emission, μ decreases by 1, then the emitted light (viewed in the same direction) is right-circularly polarized; if it increases, left-circularly polarized.

3. We now consider a level in a zero-field system, and investigate how it behaves upon the application of a magnetic field. The level E_{SLw}, of the zero-field system splits in the magnetic field, and several new levels arise from the original one. However, the multiplet system S and the reflection character w will not be affected; the levels which arise from the same zero field level retain the original S and w. This follows from the fact that each eigenfunction changes continuously as the field strength grows. Since at every stage each eigenfunction belongs to a representation of the symmetric group and to one of the reflection groups, and since these, if they changed, could only change discontinuously, they cannot change at all.

There is still the question of what μ-values the levels arising from E_{SLw} will have. Let R be a rotation about Z through an angle φ. Then according

[6] To determine the state of polarization of radiation emitted in a transition, it is necessary to know only those states for which light will not be absorbed in the converse process. For example, a transition which emits light polarized parallel to the Z-axis will also be excited (although more weakly) by light polarized in a direction which is inclined with respect to the Z-axis. It is fundamental that such a transition cannot be excited by light polarized *perpendicular* to Z. Similarly, a transition which emits right-circularly polarized light cannot be excited by left-circularly polarized light, and vice versa.

The need to determine the polarization of emitted light via the detour of the inverse process of absorption, results from the form of the Schrödinger equation used, which is not able to explain emission at all.

to Eq. (15.6) the representation matrix $\mathfrak{D}^{(L)}(R)$ has the form

$$\begin{pmatrix} e^{-iL\varphi} & 0 & \cdots & 0 & 0 \\ 0 & e^{-i(L-1)\varphi} & \cdots & 0 & 0 \\ \cdot & \cdot & & \cdot & \cdot \\ \cdot & \cdot & & \cdot & \cdot \\ \cdot & \cdot & & \cdot & \cdot \\ 0 & 0 & \cdots & e^{i(L-1)\varphi} & 0 \\ 0 & 0 & \cdots & 0 & e^{iL\varphi} \end{pmatrix} \tag{18.E.2}$$

and if $\psi_{\varkappa\mu}$ is an eigenfunction of E_{SLw} which belongs to the $\varkappa$th row of $\bar{\mathbf{A}}^{(S)}$ and the μth row of $\mathfrak{D}^{(L)}$,

$$\mathbf{P}_R \psi_{\varkappa\mu} = \sum_{\mu'} \mathfrak{D}^{(L)}(\{\varphi, 0, 0\})_{\mu'\mu} \psi_{\varkappa\mu'} = e^{i\mu\varphi} \psi_{\varkappa\mu}, \tag{18.4}$$

that is, $\psi_{\varkappa\mu}$ belongs to the representation $(\exp(+i\mu\varphi))$ of the group of rotations about Z. Furthermore, this fact remains true while the field increases, and since μ runs from $-L$ to $+L$ in the representation $\mathfrak{D}^{(L)}$, a level with orbital quantum number L will split into $2L + 1$ levels $E_{SLw,\mu}$ *with magnetic quantum numbers* $\mu = -L, -L+1, \cdots, L-1, L$. In the first approximation, the eigenfunctions belonging to $E_{SLw,\mu}$ are the $\psi_{\varkappa\mu}$ themselves, since they must belong to one row of $\bar{\mathbf{A}}^{(S)}$ and to a representation $(\exp(+i\mu\varphi))$, and no other linear combination of the $\psi_{\varkappa\mu}$ has this property. Again the "correct linear combinations" of the first approximation are determined by group theoretical considerations.

The ease with which the "correct linear combinations" were determined in this case results from the fact that in $\mathfrak{D}^{(L)}$ the matrices which correspond to rotations about Z, as a representation of the group of rotations about Z, are already in the reduced form (18.E.2). If we had applied the magnetic field in, say, the Y-direction, we would have had to reduce the matrices $\boldsymbol{d}^{(L)}(\varphi)$, which correspond to rotations about Y, that is, to bring them into the form (18.E.2). The matrix $(\mathbf{T}_{\mu'\mu})$ which effects this reduction would then also provide for this case the correct linear combinations

$$\psi'_{\varkappa\mu'} = \sum_{\mu} \mathbf{T}_{\mu'\mu} \psi_{\varkappa\mu}.$$

The first approximation for the eigenvalues $E_{SLw,\mu}$ can be calculated from the eigenfunctions of the first approximation if we know the change in the *Hamiltonian* operator for the system due to the magnetic field $\mathscr{H}_z$. In classical theory the term $\frac{e}{c}(\mathfrak{A}, \mathfrak{v}) = \frac{e}{mc}(\mathfrak{A}_x p_x + \mathfrak{A}_y p_y + \mathfrak{A}_z p_z)$ is added to the zero-field Hamiltonian function when a magnetic field is considered (neglecting higher powers of the field strength). $\mathfrak{A}$ here is the vector potential, the curl of which gives the field strength. In quantum mechanics we substitute $-i\hbar\partial/\partial x_i$ for p_{x_i}, thus obtaining in the same approximation the added potential due to the magnetic field

$$\mathbf{V} = \frac{-ie\hbar}{mc}(\mathfrak{A}_x\partial/\partial x + \mathfrak{A}_y\partial/\partial y + \mathfrak{A}_z\partial/\partial z), \tag{18.5}$$

or the sum of several such terms for several electrons.[7] For a constant magnetic field of intensity $\mathscr{H}_z$ along the Z-axis,

$$\mathfrak{A}_x = -\tfrac{1}{2}\mathscr{H}_z y; \qquad \mathfrak{A}_y = \tfrac{1}{2}\mathscr{H}_z x; \qquad \mathfrak{A}_z = 0.$$

The first approximation for the added magnetic energy can then be calculated by Eq. (5.22).

$$E_{SLw,\mu} - E_{SLw} = (\psi_{\varkappa\mu}, \mathbf{V}\psi_{\varkappa\mu}) = \frac{e\mathscr{H}_z}{2mc}(\psi_{\varkappa\mu}, \mathbf{L}_z\psi_{\varkappa\mu}), \tag{18.6}$$

where

$$\mathbf{L}_z = -i\hbar(x_1\partial/\partial y_1 + \cdots + x_n\partial/\partial y_n - y_1\partial/\partial x_1 - \cdots - y_n\partial/\partial x_n). \tag{18.6a}$$

The scalar product appearing in (18.6) can be evaluated exactly. It will be shown that for every function f,

$$\mathbf{L}_z f = -i\hbar\frac{\partial}{\partial\varphi}(\mathbf{P}_{\{\varphi 00\}}f)\Big|_{\varphi=0}, \tag{18.7}$$

and this is equal to the difference between the values of f in a "rotated state" and in the original state divided by the rotation angle. Since

$$\{\varphi, 0, 0\} = \begin{pmatrix} \cos\varphi & \sin\varphi & 0 \\ -\sin\varphi & \cos\varphi & 0 \\ 0 & 0 & 1 \end{pmatrix}$$

we have

$$\mathbf{P}_{\{\varphi 00\}}f(\cdots x_k y_k z_k \cdots) = f(\cdots, x_k\cos\varphi - y_k\sin\varphi, x_k\sin\varphi + y_k\cos\varphi, z_k, \cdots)$$

and differentiating this with respect to φ gives, for $\varphi = 0$,

$$-i\hbar\frac{\partial}{\partial\varphi}(\mathbf{P}_{\{\varphi 00\}}f)\Big|_{\varphi=0} = \sum_k -i\hbar\left(x_k\frac{\partial f}{\partial y_k} - y_k\frac{\partial f}{\partial x_k}\right), \tag{18.7a}$$

which is equivalent to (18.7). By using (18.4) we can evaluate this in terms of μ.

$$-i\hbar\frac{\partial}{\partial\varphi}(\mathbf{P}_{\{\varphi 00\}}\psi_{\varkappa\mu}) = -i\hbar\frac{\partial}{\partial\varphi}(e^{i\mu\varphi}\psi_{\varkappa\mu}) = \mu\hbar(e^{i\mu\varphi}\psi_{\varkappa\mu}). \tag{18.7b}$$

[7] For a better approximation the additional term $(\mathfrak{A}_x^2 + \mathfrak{A}_y^2 + \mathfrak{A}_z^2)\dfrac{e^2}{2mc^2}$ should be added to (18.5); this term accounts, in particular, for diamagnetism.

Because of normalization $(\psi_{\varkappa\mu}, \psi_{\varkappa\mu}) = 1$; therefore, (18.6) becomes

$$E_{SLw,\mu} - E_{SLw} = \frac{e\hbar\mathscr{H}_z\mu}{2mc} \qquad (\mu = -L, -L+1, \cdots, L-1, L). \tag{18.8}$$

According to (18.8), a level with orbital quantum number L in this first approximation (i.e., if we limit ourselves to terms proportional to the first power of $\mathscr{H}_z$) splits into $2L + 1$ equally spaced levels. Of these, the middle level ($\mu = 0$) has the same energy as the original level; also, the separation between levels for a given field strength is the same for any level split in this way, since only universal constants occur in (18.8).

If we now consider the Zeeman components of the line $F \to E$, we see—since the level F splits to just the same extent as E—that all the lines with the same μ-changes coincide. But since μ can change only by ± 1 or 0 in optical transitions, a total of only three lines is expected, and the two displaced components are separated from the one in the center by the same distance for all lines. This splitting pattern is referred to as the *normal Zeeman effect.*

This pattern agrees with experiment only in the case of *singlet levels.* In the corresponding states the magnetic moments (spins) of the electrons, which usually produce deviations from the "normal" pattern, combine in such a way that their effect vanishes. This is also the reason why singlet terms have no fine structure. In all other terms the splitting is sometimes greater and sometimes smaller than calculated above and varies, usually, from level to level. Therefore, the lines which involve the same change in μ do not coincide and the splitting pattern of the *anomalous Zeeman effect* results; it is considerably more complicated. The calculation of the relative intensities of the individual Zeeman components will be postponed until later.[8]

It should be noted that the levels will be split by a magnetic field to as great an extent as can be achieved by any external field. The remaining degeneracies are all due to the symmetric group, and the equivalence of the electrons cannot be destroyed by any external field.

4. In a constant electric field along the Z-axis the symmetry is not the same as in a magnetic field, since the electric field has the character of a polar vector. In this case there is no longer a center of inversion, but the planes *parallel* to the field through the nucleus are planes of symmetry. The circumstances are thus opposite to those in the magnetic field (see Fig. 10b, page 199). The symmetry group is the two-dimensional rotation-reflection group (and is not Abelian!), while in the magnetic field it is the direct product of the two-dimensional pure rotation group and the three-dimensional

[8] This will be done in Chapter 23. The intensities of the three lines considered are the same as predicted by the classical theory of the Zeeman effect, which, in fact, predicts the normal Zeeman effect exactly.

reflection group. Besides its multiplet system S, each level has an electric quantum number $m = 0, 0', 1, 2, \cdots$ which specifies to which representation $\mathfrak{Z}^{(m)}$ of the two-dimensional rotation-reflection group the level belongs.

The irreducible representations of the two-dimensional rotation-reflection group have been determined in Chapter 14. In $\mathfrak{Z}^{(0)}$, $\mathfrak{Z}^{(0')}$, $\mathfrak{Z}^{(1)}$, $\mathfrak{Z}^{(2)}$, $\cdots$ the matrices

$$(1), (1), \begin{pmatrix} e^{-i\varphi} & 0 \\ 0 & e^{i\varphi} \end{pmatrix}, \begin{pmatrix} e^{-2i\varphi} & 0 \\ 0 & e^{2i\varphi} \end{pmatrix}, \cdots,$$

correspond to a rotation through an angle φ, while the matrices

$$(1), (-1), \begin{pmatrix} 0 & 1 \\ 1 & 0 \end{pmatrix}, \begin{pmatrix} 0 & 1 \\ 1 & 0 \end{pmatrix}, \cdots$$

correspond to a reflection in the X-axis.

To determine the m values of the levels into which a level with orbital quantum number L splits, we must first determine which $\mathfrak{Z}^{(m)}$ occur in $\mathfrak{D}^{(L)}(R)$, where R corresponds to a rotation-reflection about Z, and how many times each occurs. From the form (18.E.2) of $\mathfrak{D}^{(L)}(R)$, we see directly that if R is a pure rotation about Z, then $\mathfrak{Z}^{(1)}, \mathfrak{Z}^{(2)}, \cdots, \mathfrak{Z}^{(L)}$ are each contained once in $\mathfrak{D}^{(L)}$; the eigenfunctions belonging to the first or second rows of $\mathfrak{Z}^{(m)}$ belong to the $-m$th or $+m$th row of $\mathfrak{D}^{(L)}$. On the other hand, the eigenfunctions which belong to the zeroth row of $\mathfrak{D}^{(L)}$ could belong either to $\mathfrak{Z}^{(0)}$ or to $\mathfrak{Z}^{(0')}$. To decide which is actually the case, some rotation-reflection, say $y' = -y$, must also be considered. (The representations $\mathfrak{Z}^{(0)}$ and $\mathfrak{Z}^{(0')}$ are identical for pure rotations.)

In order to determine the trace of the matrix in $\mathfrak{D}^{(L)}$ corresponding to this transformation, we note that it is a product of an inversion and a rotation about Y through π; its trace is therefore

$$\begin{aligned} &w(1 + 2\cos\pi + 2\cos 2\pi + \cdots + 2\cos L\pi) \\ &\qquad = w(1 - 2 + 2 - \cdots + 2(-1)^L) = w(-1)^L, \end{aligned} \tag{18.9}$$

where w is $+1$ for even levels and -1 for odd levels. Since the components $\mathfrak{Z}^{(1)}, \mathfrak{Z}^{(2)}, \cdots, \mathfrak{Z}^{(L)}$ do not contribute to the traces of reflections, the level left over is a 0-level if $w(-1)^L = +1$ and a $0'$-level if $w(-1)^L = -1$.

We see that the splitting of a level in an electric field is not as complete as that in a magnetic field; only $L + 1$ levels arise from a level with orbital quantum number L.

The selection rules which hold for strong electric fields are similar to those which hold for magnetic fields. The electric quantum number m does not change in a transition involving light polarized along the Z-axis since multiplication by $z_1 + z_2 + \cdots + z_n$ is an operation symmetric under the two-dimensional rotation-reflection group of rotations about Z. Therefore, any transition between a 0-level and a 0′-level is forbidden. On the other hand, m changes by ± 1 in a transition in which the emitted light is polarized perpendicular to the field direction.

The selection rule for the orbital quantum number will be broken in strong electric fields because the full rotation symmetry no longer exists, so that the eigenfunctions no longer belong to representation of the three-dimensional rotation group. Laporte's rule also loses its validity (while it was not affected by magnetic fields); only the prohibition of transitions from a 0-level to a 0′-level remains.

The perturbation of the eigenvalues by an electric field can also be calculated formally by the Rayleigh–Schrödinger procedure. The results are valid only in a limited sense, since the procedure must diverge because of the form of the perturbation term[9]

$$\mathbf{V} = e\mathscr{E}_z(z_1 + z_2 + \cdots + z_n). \tag{18.10}$$

If the potential is plotted graphically as a function of the distance from the nucleus, say in the H-atom, it is seen that in the neighborhood of the nucleus there is a deep potential minimum, but that the electron always has sufficient energy to escape to infinity in the direction of the field.

This suggests that, strictly speaking, there exists no discrete spectrum at all in an electric field and that there are no genuine stationary states. In spite of this, the first or second approximations which are calculated by the Schrödinger procedure are not entirely meaningless. They give states which, even if not actually stationary, behave like stationary states for very long times because an electron near the nucleus will tunnel out of the potential well and escape from the nucleus only after it has made many many trips around the nucleus.

In the first approximation, the energy perturbation due to an electric field does not split the eigenvalues at all. The coefficients

$$\mathbf{V}_{\varkappa'\mu';\varkappa\mu} = e\mathscr{E}_z(\psi_{\varkappa'\mu'}, (z_1 + z_2 + \cdots + z_n)\,\psi_{\varkappa\mu}) = 0 \tag{18.11}$$

of the secular equation (5.18) are all zero, since $\psi_{\varkappa'\mu'}$ and $(z_1 + z_2 + \cdots + z_n)\psi_{\varkappa\mu}$ have *different* parity. If *no accidental degeneracy exists*, then all the eigenfunctions which belong to the same eigenvalue E have the same parity; thus $\psi_{\varkappa'\mu'}$ and $(z_1 + z_2 + \cdots + z_n)\psi_{\varkappa\mu}$ will have different parities. We have already seen this behavior in connection with the transition operator on pages 197–198 and (18.11) is identical with (18.2c) except for a constant factor. The eigenvalues of $(\mathbf{V}_{\varkappa'\mu';\varkappa\mu}) = \mathbf{0}$ are all 0. In the first approximation all levels coincide with the unperturbed level; in terms of the expansion of the energy perturbation in powers of the field strength, the coefficient of

[9] See J. R. Oppenheimer, *Phys. Rev.* **31**, 66, 1928.

the first power is zero; thus the separation of the levels goes to zero as the square for small field strengths. Only in the hydrogen atom, in which levels of different parity coincide by an accidental degeneracy, does level splitting occur in first order.

The complications resulting from the magnetic moment are the chief obstruction to the experimental verification of the laws derived above for the Stark effect, just as they were in the case of the Zeeman effect. The only result of general validity is the absence of a level separation proportional to the first power of the field strength, since this follows from consideration of the reflection character alone.

5. For free atoms constant magnetic or electric fields are probably the most important kinds of external perturbations. For atoms in crystals other types are more important. For these the symmetry of the "external" field,[10] which in this case originates with the surrounding atoms, is given by the crystal symmetry and can result in interesting splitting forms. This was investigated thoroughly for most symmetry classes by H. A. Bethe. From his examples, we take only the relatively simple case of rhombic (hemimorphic) symmetry, the symmetry of a rhombic pyramid.[11]

The rhombic pyramid has three symmetry elements: the rotation about Z through an angle π, and reflections in the ZX- and in the ZY-planes. Its symmetry group V_d consists of the identity and these three elements. It is isomorphic to the four-group (see page 63) since all its elements are of order 2. Since it is Abelian, it has four irreducible one-dimensional representations, the matrices of which are given in Table V.

TABLE V
Representations of the Group of the Rhombic Pyramid

Representation	E	Rotation by π about Z	Reflection in the ZX-plane	Reflection in ZY-plane
I	(1)	(1)	(1)	(1)
II	(1)	(−1)	(−1)	(1)
III	(1)	(−1)	(1)	(−1)
IV	(1)	(1)	(−1)	(−1)

The first is the identical representation, the second and third are similar

[10] This statement implies the assumption that the surrounding atoms are excluded from the system discussed, the "external" field is being supposed to reproduce their chief influence on the atom. Clearly, this is not fully accurate, so that the treatment based on this assumption is not a complete one. In particular, the "exchange forces" are omitted by such a treatment.

[11] A rhombic pyramid is one whose base is an equilateral parallelogram.

since they differ only by an interchange of the roles of the X- and Y-axes, while the fourth plays a special role.

If we bring an atom to its position in a crystal, then it is influenced by forces which remove the full spatial symmetry, so that only the rhombic-hemimorphic symmetry remains. Since the irreducible representations of this group are all one-dimensional, a level with orbital quantum number L splits into $2L+1$ levels.

The question we wish to answer concerns the number of levels with representation properties I, II, III, and IV which arise in a crystal from one level with azimuthal quantum number L and reflection character w. This question can be answered by the general theory, i.e., by determining the number of times the representations I, II, III, and IV are contained in a representation $\mathfrak{D}^{(L,w)}$ of the rotation-reflection group, if this is viewed as a representation of its rhombic-hemimorphic subgroup. These numbers $\alpha_{\rm I}$, $\alpha_{\rm II}$, $\alpha_{\rm III}$, and $\alpha_{\rm IV}$ are found most simply by determining the characters of $\mathfrak{D}^{(L,w)}$ for the operations of V_d. For the unit element

$$2L+1 = \alpha_{\rm I} + \alpha_{\rm II} + \alpha_{\rm III} + \alpha_{\rm IV}\,. \tag{18.12a}$$

On the other hand, for a rotation about Z through π, and for reflections in the ZX- or ZY-planes, according to (18.9),

$$(-1)^L = \alpha_{\rm I} - \alpha_{\rm II} - \alpha_{\rm III} + \alpha_{\rm IV} \tag{18.12b}$$

$$w(-1)^L = \alpha_{\rm I} - \alpha_{\rm II} + \alpha_{\rm III} - \alpha_{\rm IV} = \alpha_{\rm I} + \alpha_{\rm II} - \alpha_{\rm III} - \alpha_{\rm IV}\,. \tag{18.12c}$$

From (18.12c) it follows that $\alpha_{\rm II} = \alpha_{\rm III}$ and $w(-1)^L = \alpha_{\rm I} - \alpha_{\rm IV}$. From (18.12a) and (18.12b) it follows that $(2L+1) + (-1)^L = 2\alpha_{\rm I} + 2\alpha_{\rm IV}$. Thus, we obtain the values for the numbers, α which are shown in Table VI.

TABLE VI
Multiplicity of Representations of the Group of the Rhombic Pyramid in Various Representations of the Rotation Group

Levels	$\alpha_{\rm I}$	$\alpha_{\rm II}, \alpha_{\rm III}$	$\alpha_{\rm IV}$
S_+	1	0	0
S_-	0	0	1
P_+	0	1	1
P_-	1	1	0
D_+	2	1	1
etc.			

In the work mentioned above, H. A. Bethe has determined the splitting for almost all the thirty-two types of symmetry which occur in crystals, and he has drawn further conclusions from them. Thus, for example, the selection rules for levels of types *I*, *II*, *III*, and *IV* are obtained very simply by noting, for example, for radiation polarized along the *Z*-axis, that multiplication by $(z_1 + z_2 + \cdots + z_n)$ is an operation symmetric under the rhombic hemimorphic group, so that only transitions between levels of the same representation are allowed.

19. Partial Determination of Eigenfunctions from Their Transformation Properties

1. The transformation properties of eigenfunctions discussed in the preceding chapter result from relationships among the values of the eigenfunctions for arguments which can be transformed into one another by the transformations of the group. For example, if the group consists of the identity and the transformation $x' = -x$, then for functions which belong to the identical representation (even functions),

$$g(-x) = g(x), \tag{19.1}$$

while for functions which belong to the negative representation (odd functions),

$$f(-x) = -f(x). \tag{19.1a}$$

In general, it follows from

$$\mathbf{P}_R \psi_\varkappa(x_1, x_2, \cdots, x_n) = \sum_\lambda \mathbf{D}(R)_{\lambda\varkappa} \psi_\lambda(x_1, x_2, \cdots, x_n), \tag{19.2}$$

by Eq. (11.26a), that

$$\psi_\varkappa(x_1', x_2', \cdots, x_n') = \sum_\lambda \mathbf{D}(R)^*_{\varkappa\lambda} \psi_\lambda(x_1, x_2, \cdots, x_n), \tag{19.3}$$

where the $x_1', \cdots, x_n'$ result from the $x_1, x_2, \cdots, x_n$ by the transformation R. If the entire domain of the arguments of the wave function (i.e., the entire configuration space) is divided into parts, each of which results from one part—the *fundamental region*—by a transformation of the group, then the $\psi_\varkappa$ can be calculated everywhere by (19.3) if only they are known in the fundamental region. Equation (19.3) represents a reduction in the region of variability of the arguments $x_1, \cdots, x_n$, the extent of the reduction depending on the magnitude of the group under which the eigenvalue problem is invariant; it also presents the transformation properties of the $\psi_\varkappa$ in explicit form. Therefore, all results which follow from the invariance properties of the $\psi_\varkappa$ must be derivable from (19.3).

For example, consider the scalar product of an odd and an even function

$$\int_{-\infty}^{\infty} g(x)^* f(x)\, dx. \tag{19.4}$$

By dividing the region of integration into two parts, from $-\infty$ to 0, and from 0 to $+\infty$ (these are transformed into one another by the transformation $x = -x$), one obtains

$$\int_{-\infty}^{\infty} g(x)^* f(x)\, dx = \int_{-\infty}^{0} g(x)^* f(x)\, dx + \int_{0}^{\infty} g(x)^* f(x)\, dx.$$

If we now let the variable y replace $-x$ in the first integral, and express $g(-y)$ and $f(-y)$ by (19.1) and (19.1a), then this becomes

$$-\int_{0}^{\infty} g(y)^* f(y)\, dy + \int_{0}^{\infty} g(x)^* f(x)\, dx = 0 \tag{19.5}$$

and the two parts of the integral (19.4) cancel.

The argument that f and g belong to different irreducible representations, and that their scalar product must therefore vanish is simpler than the calculation just performed. On the other hand, starting from (19.3) has the advantage, besides its greater visualizability, that a partial calculation of the eigenfunctions is achieved which is rather effective in the case of simple problems which are invariant under the rotation group.

2. Equation (19.3) gives the wave function $\psi_\varkappa$ at all those positions which arise from the position $P = (x_1, y_1, z_1, x_2, y_2, z_2, \cdots, x_n, y_n, z_n)$ by transformations of the group, in terms of the values of $\psi_\varkappa$'s partner functions ψ_λ at the point P. For the rotation group, these are all the points of configuration space for which the relative positions of the particles, that is the *geometrical form of the atom,* is the same. The points in configuration space can be represented by an n-pod standing in the center of the three-dimensional space. The tip of each leg in three-dimensional space shows where the corresponding electron is located in the configuration concerned. To know the wave function for all points in configuration space is to know it for all conceivable n-pods.

According to the discussion of the "separation of the center of mass" on page 177, the wave function will also contain the coordinates of the nucleus as variables. Thus it will be defined not just for those positions in which the n-pod stands in the center of three-dimensional space; rather, the midpoint of the n-pod denotes the position of the nucleus and can occupy every position in space. However, since the value of the wave function will be the same for all positions of the n-pod which result from one another by parallel displacement, it is sufficient to give it for all n-pods standing in the center. The wave function will not change if all x-coordinates (including the coordinates of the nucleus), or all y-coordinates, or all z-coordinates are increased or diminished by the same amount.

Positions which arise from one another by a *rotation* correspond to the *same form but different orientations* of the n-pod. We choose the fundamental region to be those positions for which the first leg (corresponding to the first electron) lies on the Z-axis, and the second in the ZX-plane. This region corresponds to the points of configuration space for which $x_1 = y_1 = y_2 = 0$. If the values of the $2L + 1$ wave functions $\psi_{-L}, \psi_{-L+1}, \cdots, \psi_L$ belonging to the representation $\mathfrak{D}^{(L)}(\{\alpha\beta\gamma\})$ in the fundamental region are $G_{-L}, G_{-L+1}, \cdots, G_{L-1}, G_L$ (i.e., $G_\lambda = \psi_\lambda(0, 0, z_1, x_2, 0, z_2, \cdots, x_n y_n z_n)$, the G_λ depend only on the geometrical form of the configuration of the particles), then the value of the wave function at each position $x_1', y_1', z_1', \cdots, x_n', y_n', z_n'$, which arise from $0, 0, z_1, x_2, 0, z_2, \cdots, x_n, y_n, z_n$ by the rotation $\{\pi - \alpha, \beta, -\pi - \gamma\}$ is,[1] according to (19.3)

$$\psi_\mu(x_1', y_1', z_1', \cdots, x_n', y_n', z_n') = \sum_{\lambda=-L}^{+L} \mathfrak{D}^{(L)}(\{\pi - \alpha, \beta, -\pi - \gamma\})^*_{\mu\lambda} G_\lambda(g)$$
$$= \sum_{\lambda=-L}^{L} (-1)^{\mu-\lambda} \mathfrak{D}^{(L)}(\{\alpha, \beta, \gamma\})_{\mu\lambda} G_\lambda(g). \tag{19.6}$$

In this expression[2] α and β are, by definition, the azimuthal and polar angles of the first electron, and γ is the angle included between the plane through the Z-axis and the first electron, and the plane through the origin and the first two electrons. The G_λ depend only on the geometrical form, g, of the n-pod.

For $L = 0$, (S-levels) (19.6) is

$$\psi(x_1', y_1', z_1', \cdots, x_n', y_n', z_n') = G_0(g). \tag{19.7}$$

In this case the wave function depends *only* on the form of the n-pod and not at all on its orientation in space; S-states are spherically symmetric.[3] This is completely reasonable since only one eigenfunction belongs to an S-state, and it cannot specify a direction. For higher azimuthal quantum numbers, all directions are equivalent for the total set of the eigenfunctions, but no single eigenfunction can be selected without distinguishing a direction, so that the individual eigenfunctions are no longer spherically symmetric.

It is possible to derive the selection rules from (19.6). However, we shall be principally concerned here with the extent to which the *eigenfunctions* can be explicitly determined from this equation.

3. For a rigid body, the geometrical form g is fixed, so that the G_λ are simply constants. In this case, the eigenfunctions depend only on α, β, and

[1] The relation

$$\mathfrak{D}^{(l)}(\{\pi - \alpha, +\beta, -\pi - \gamma\})^*_{\mu\lambda} = (-1)^{\mu-\lambda}\, \mathfrak{D}^{(l)}(\{\alpha, \beta, \gamma\})_{\mu\lambda}$$

comes directly from Eq. (15.8),

$$\mathfrak{D}^{(l)}(\{\alpha, \beta, \gamma\})_{\mu\lambda} = e^{i\mu\alpha}\, \boldsymbol{d}^{(l)}(\beta)_{\mu\lambda}\, e^{i\lambda\gamma},$$

and the fact that $\boldsymbol{d}^{(l)}(\beta)_{\mu\lambda}$ is real.

[2] The rotation is chosen so that the polar and azimuthal angles of the first electron, and not their negatives, may be defined by α and β. See the discussion in Appendix A, Section 2, at the end of this book.

[3] A. Unsöld, *Ann. Physik* [4] **82,** 355 (1927).

γ, and they are completely determined by (19.6). The simplest rigid body is a thin rod free to rotate about its mid-point (the rigid rotator).

The Schrödinger equation for the rigid rotator is

$$-\frac{\hbar^2}{2\mathscr{I}}\left[\frac{1}{\sin\vartheta}\frac{\partial}{\partial\vartheta}\sin\vartheta\,\frac{\partial\psi_\mu^{NL}(\vartheta,\varphi)}{\partial\vartheta}+\frac{1}{\sin^2\vartheta}\frac{\partial^2\psi_\mu^{NL}(\vartheta,\varphi)}{\partial\varphi^2}\right]=E_L^N\psi_\mu^{NL}(\vartheta,\varphi), \tag{19.8}$$

where $\mathscr{I}$ is the moment of inertia and ϑ and φ the polar angle and azimuth of the rotator. The fundamental region here is a single point, $\vartheta = 0$, the "normal position" of the rotator. We denote the values of the eigenfunctions at this point by G_λ^{NL}; then, according to Eqs. (15.8) and (19.6), we have[4]

$$\psi_\mu^{NL}(\vartheta,\varphi)=\sum_\lambda(-1)^{\mu-\lambda}\mathfrak{D}^{(L)}(\{\alpha,\beta,\gamma\})_{\mu\lambda}G_\lambda^{NL}. \tag{19.8a}$$

But ψ_μ^{NL} must be independent of γ since the rotator has the same position for all values of this variable. Thus, $G_\lambda^{NL} = 0$ for $\lambda \neq 0$, and (19.8a) becomes[4]

$$\psi_\mu^{NL}(\vartheta,\varphi)=(-1)^\mu e^{i\mu\varphi}\,\boldsymbol{d}^{(L)}(\vartheta)_{\mu 0}G_0^{NL}=(-1)^\mu\mathfrak{D}^{(L)}(\{\varphi,\vartheta,0\})_{\mu 0}G_0^{NL}. \tag{19.8b}$$

This equation expresses the eigenfunctions completely in terms of the representation coefficients. Equation (19.8b) also shows that the eigenfunctions ψ_μ^{NL} for the same L and μ and different N differ at most by a constant factor. Since this is not possible for eigenfunctions of different eigenvalues, only a single eigenvalue belongs to each L. The index N can therefore be omitted in (19.8), (19.8a), and (19.8b).

The solutions of (19.8) are known as the spherical harmonics of the Lth degree; (19.8b) shows that the $\mathfrak{D}^{(l)}(\{\varphi,\vartheta,\gamma\})_{m0}$ is identical with the spherical harmonics $Y_{lm}(\vartheta,\varphi)$ except for normalization and the factor $(-1)^m$.

It should not be too surprising that (19.8) can be solved completely without calculation. Indeed, one method for the determination of the representations was (Chapter 15, Section 1) based on solving Laplace's equation which is essentially equivalent to (19.8). We may say that we now have substituted this solution into (19.8) again.

To demonstrate the fact that Eq. (19.8) is relevant for *all* spherically symmetric problems, we mention the case of the H-atom, which is described by the equation

$$-\frac{\hbar^2}{2m}\left(\frac{\partial^2}{\partial x^2}+\frac{\partial^2}{\partial y^2}+\frac{\partial^2}{\partial z^2}\right)\psi_\mu^{Nl}-\frac{e^2}{r}\psi_\mu^{Nl}=E_{Nl}\psi_\mu^{Nl}. \tag{19.9}$$

Equation (19.6) states that its solutions are of the form

$$\psi_\mu^{Nl}=\sum_\lambda(-1)^{\mu-\lambda}\mathfrak{D}^{(l)}(\{\alpha,\beta,\gamma\})_{\mu\lambda}G_\lambda^{Nl}(r). \tag{19.9a}$$

[4] See footnote (2), this Chapter, and Appendix A.

G_λ^{Nl} is a function only of r here since the n-pod degenerates into a unipod whose geometrical form is completely specified by the length r of the leg (the distance of the electron from the nucleus). In this case α and β are the azimuth and polar angle of the electron, while γ has no significance; for this reason Eq. (19.9a) must be independent of γ. From this it follows, just as in (19.8b), that G_λ^{Nl} must vanish for $\lambda \neq 0$.

$$\psi_\mu^{Nl}(r, \vartheta, \varphi) = (-1)^\mu \mathfrak{D}^{(l)}(\{\varphi, \vartheta, 0\})_{\mu 0} G_0^{Nl}(r) \propto Y_{l\mu}(\vartheta, \varphi) G_0^{Nl}(r). \tag{19.9b}$$

According to Eq. (17.3), the eigenfunctions for the H-atom actually do have this form. We see also that ψ_μ^{Nl} does in fact belong to the μth row of $\mathfrak{D}^{(l)}$, as must be the case for an eigenfunction with the magnetic quantum number μ and the orbital quantum number l.

The simplest problem in which the full scope of this method can be exhibited is that of the quantum mechanical rigid body (top). We first consider the asymmetric top. The position of the top can be characterized by the three Euler angles α, β, γ of the rotation which brings the top from its normal position (in which the largest moment of inertia coincides with the Z-axis, the next largest with the Y-axis, and the smallest with the X-axis) into the position in question. The wave function will depend only on these three angles; in fact, according to (19.6), it is

$$\begin{aligned} \psi_\mu^{Nl}(\alpha, \beta, \gamma) &= \sum_\lambda (-1)^{\mu-\lambda} \mathfrak{D}^{(l)}(\{\alpha, \beta, \gamma\})_{\mu\lambda} G_\lambda^{Nl} \\ &= \sum_\lambda (-1)^{\mu-\lambda} e^{i\mu\alpha} \boldsymbol{d}^{(l)}(\beta)_{\mu\lambda} e^{i\lambda\gamma} G_\lambda^{Nl}. \end{aligned} \tag{19.10}$$

The G_λ^{Nl} are again constants because the geometrical form is fixed in a rigid body. These, as well as the eigenvalues E_{Nl}, can be determined by substituting (19.10) into the Schrödinger equation. One obtains $2l + 1$ linear homogeneous equations for the $G_{-l}^{Nl}, \cdots, G_{+l}^{Nl}$. The requirement that the determinant of this system of equations vanish gives an algebraic equation of the $(2l + 1)$th degree for the energy E^{Nl}, so that $2l + 1$ eigenvalues have the orbital quantum number l.

We now consider a top whose two smaller moments of inertia are equal. Then the "normal position" of the top is not uniquely determined, since a rotation about the Z-axis remains arbitrary. This has the consequence that an eigenfunction remains an eigenfunction if γ is replaced by $\gamma + \gamma_0$. Moreover, a linear combination

$$\begin{aligned} &\int_0^{2\pi} \psi_\mu^{Nl}(\alpha, \beta, \gamma + \gamma_0) e^{-i\nu\gamma_0}\, d\gamma_0 \\ &\qquad = \sum_\lambda (-1)^{\mu-\lambda} G_\lambda^{Nl} e^{+i\mu\alpha} \boldsymbol{d}^{(l)}(\beta)_{\mu\lambda} e^{+i\lambda\gamma} \int e^{i\gamma_0(\lambda-\nu)}\, d\gamma_0 \\ &\qquad = (\text{constant}) \cdot (-1)^{\mu-\nu} G_\nu^{Nl} \mathfrak{D}^{(l)}(\{\alpha,\beta,\gamma\})_{\mu\nu} \end{aligned} \tag{19.11}$$

of such functions is also an eigenfunction. But if G_ν^{Nl} is not zero, (19.11) shows that, except for a constant of proportionality, the eigenfunctions can be written[5]

$$\psi_\mu^{\nu l}(\alpha, \beta, \gamma) = (-1)^{\mu-\nu}\mathfrak{D}^{(l)}(\{\alpha, \beta, \gamma\})_{\mu\nu} \qquad (\nu = -l, -l+1, \cdots, l-1, l). \tag{19.11a}$$

Later when we consider reflectional symmetry, it will turn out that pairs of eigenvalues are equal: $E_{\nu l} = E_{-\nu l}$, so that in all $l + 1$ distinct eigenvalues have the same orbital quantum number.

If all three moments of inertia are equal, then the normal position is completely undetermined, and the eigenfunctions (19.11a) remain eigenfunctions if $\{\alpha, \beta, \gamma\} \cdot R$ is substituted for $\{\alpha, \beta, \gamma\}$, where R is an arbitrary rotation. Thus

$$(-1)^{\mu-\nu}\mathfrak{D}^{(l)}(\{\alpha, \beta, \gamma\}R)_{\mu\nu} = \sum_\varkappa (-1)^{\mu-\nu}\mathfrak{D}^{(l)}(\{\alpha, \beta, \gamma\})_{\mu\varkappa}\mathfrak{D}^{(l)}(R)_{\varkappa\nu}$$

belongs to the same eigenvalue as $(-1)^{\mu-\nu}\mathfrak{D}^{(l)}(\{\alpha, \beta, \gamma\})_{\mu\nu}$. So does

$$\int \sum_\varkappa (-1)^{\mu-\nu}\mathfrak{D}^{(l)}(\{\alpha, \beta, \gamma\})_{\mu\varkappa}\mathfrak{D}^{(l)}(R)_{\varkappa\nu}\mathfrak{D}^{(l)}(R)^*_{\lambda\nu}\, dR$$
$$= (\text{constant}) \cdot (-1)^{\mu-\lambda}\mathfrak{D}^{l}(\{\alpha,\beta,\gamma\})_{\mu\lambda}. \tag{19.12}$$

Therefore, in this case, all the eigenvalues $E_{-l,l}, E_{-l+1,l}, \cdots, E_{l,l}$ coincide, and only one eigenvalue belongs to each orbital quantum number; this eigenvalue is $(2l + 1)^2$ degenerate.

Thus, if at least two moments of inertia of the top are equal, the eigenfunctions are given explicitly by (19.11a). The corresponding eigenvalues can be calculated by substituting the eigenfunctions for each eigenvalue (e.g., $\mathfrak{D}^{(l)}(\{\alpha\beta\gamma\})_{\nu\nu}$) into the Schrödinger equation, specifying values for α, β, and γ for which $\psi_\mu^{\nu l}(\alpha\beta\gamma)$ does not vanish (e.g., $\alpha = \beta = \gamma = 0$), and dividing by $\psi_\mu^{\nu l}(\alpha\beta\gamma)$.

The Schrödinger equation for the symmetric top[6] can also be solved

[5] The state is specified by the quantum numbers l, μ and the running quantum number N which distinguishes between different states which have the same values of l and μ. In the case at hand, this running quantum number N is given simply by ν.

[6] The quantum mechanics of the symmetric top has been dealt with by
H. Rademacher and F. Reiche, *Z. Physik* **39,** 444 (1926); **41,** 453 (1927).
R. de L. Kronig and I. I. Rabi, *PR* **29,** 262 (1927).
C. Maneback, *Zeitschr. f. Phys.* **28,** 76 (1927).
J. H. van Vleck, *PR* **33,** 476 (1929).
That of the asymmetric top is treated by
E. E. Witmer, *Proc. Nat. Acad.* **13,** 60 (1927).
S. C. Wang, *PR* **34,** 243 (1929).
H. A. Kramers and G. P. Ittmann, *Zeitschr. f. Phys.* **53,** 553 (1929); **58,** 217 (1929); **60,** 663 (1930).
O. Klein, *Zeitschr. f. Phys.* **58,** 730 (1929).
H. Casimir, *Zeitschr. f. Phys.* **59,** 623 (1930).

directly in terms of hypergeometric functions.[7] The relation between the representation coefficients and the hypergeometric function (for $\mu \geqslant \nu$) is:

$$\boldsymbol{d}^{(l)}(\beta)_{\mu\nu} = \sqrt{\frac{(l-\nu)!(l+\mu)!}{(l+\nu)!(l-\mu)!}}\, \frac{\cos^{2l+\nu-\mu} \frac{1}{2}\beta \sin^{\mu-\nu} \frac{1}{2}\beta}{(\mu-\nu)!}$$

$$\times F(\mu - l, -\nu - l, \mu - \nu + 1, -\tan^2 \tfrac{1}{2}\beta). \qquad (19.13)$$

4. Before going on to the discussion of the parity, we derive one more relation:

$$\boldsymbol{d}^{(l)}(\pi - \beta)_{\mu\nu} = (-1)^{l-\mu} \boldsymbol{d}^{(l)}(\beta)_{\mu,-\nu} \,. \qquad (19.14)$$

In Chapter 15 the representation coefficients have been completely determined; we take $\boldsymbol{d}^{(l)}(\beta)_{\mu\nu}$ from Eq. (15.27),

$$\boldsymbol{d}^{(l)}(\beta)_{\mu\nu} = \sum_{\varkappa} (-1)^{\varkappa} \frac{\sqrt{(l+\mu)!(l-\mu)!(l+\nu)!(l-\nu)!}}{(l-\mu-\varkappa)!(l+\nu-\varkappa)!\varkappa!(\varkappa+\mu-\nu)!}$$

$$\times \cos^{2l-\mu+\nu-2\varkappa} \tfrac{1}{2}\beta \sin^{2\varkappa+\mu-\nu} \tfrac{1}{2}\beta. \qquad (19.15)$$

If we substitute $\pi - \beta$ for β in this expression the cos in (19.15) goes into the sin, and the sin into cos (since $\cos(\frac{1}{2}\pi - x) = \sin x$). If at the same time we introduce $\varkappa' = l - \mu - \varkappa$ as the summation index in place of $\varkappa$, then (19.15) becomes

$$\boldsymbol{d}^{(l)}(\pi - \beta)_{\mu\nu} = \sum_{\varkappa'} (-1)^{l-\mu-\varkappa'} \frac{\sqrt{(l+\mu)!(l-\mu)!(l+\nu)!(l-\nu)!}}{\varkappa'!(\mu+\nu+\varkappa')!(l-\mu-\varkappa')!(l-\nu-\varkappa')!}$$

$$\times \sin^{2\varkappa'+\mu+\nu} \tfrac{1}{2}\beta \cos^{2l-\mu-\nu-2\varkappa'} \tfrac{1}{2}\beta. \qquad (19.16)$$

Since $\varkappa'$ is integral, $(-1)^{\varkappa'} = (-1)^{-\varkappa'}$ so that the right side of (19.16) is just $(-1)^{l-\mu} \boldsymbol{d}(\beta)_{\mu,-\nu}$, and (19.14) is established.

In a one-body problem the reflection character of the wave function is determined by its angular dependence. For a unipod the inversion $\mathbf{P}_I$ consists simply of the substitution of $\varphi \pm \pi$ for φ and $\pi - \vartheta$ for ϑ; the length r of the leg remains unchanged. Under this substitution, (19.9b) transforms into

$$\mathbf{P}_I \psi_\mu^{Nl}(r, \vartheta, \varphi) = (-1)^\mu e^{+i\mu(\varphi \pm \pi)} \boldsymbol{d}^{(l)}(\pi - \vartheta)_{\mu 0} G^{Nl}(r)$$

$$= e^{+i\mu\varphi}(-1)^{l-\mu} \boldsymbol{d}^{(l)}(\vartheta)_{\mu 0} G^{Nl}(r) = (-1)^l \psi_\mu^{Nl}(r, \vartheta, \varphi). \qquad (19.17)$$

Levels with even l have even parity; those with odd l, odd parity.[8]

For two independent particles, as in the helium atom, we have, according to (19.6),

$$\psi_\mu^L = \sum_\lambda (-1)^{\mu-\lambda} \mathfrak{D}^{(L)}(\{\alpha, \beta, \gamma\})_{\mu\lambda} G_\lambda(r_1, r_2, \varepsilon) \qquad (19.18)$$

[7] See, for example, P. M. Morse and H. Feshbach, "Methods of Theoretical Physics," Part I, pp. 388 and 542, McGraw-Hill, New York, 1953.

[8] Thus an optical transition with $\Delta l = 0$ is forbidden in a one-electron system, since it would have to proceed without changing the parity.

since the configuration is specified by the geometry of a dipod which can be characterized by lengths r_1, r_2 of the two legs and the included angle ε. Only the position of a dipod changes under reflection, not its geometrical form.

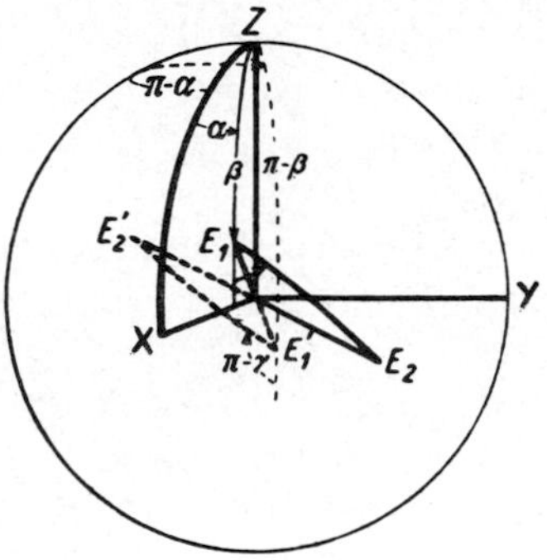

FIG. 11. Behavior of a dipod under reflection.

If we carry out an inversion, α, β, and γ become $\alpha \pm \pi$, $\pi - \beta$, and $\pi - \gamma$ (see Fig. 11).[9]

Therefore

$$\mathbf{P}_I \psi_\mu^L = \sum_\lambda (-1)^{\mu-\lambda} \mathfrak{D}^{(L)}(\{\alpha \pm \pi, \pi - \beta, \pi - \gamma\})_{\mu\lambda} G_\lambda$$

$$= \sum_\lambda (-1)^{\mu-\lambda} \mathfrak{D}^{(L)}(\{\alpha, \beta, \gamma\})_{\mu,-\lambda} (-1)^{L+\lambda} G_\lambda \tag{19.18a}$$

because by (19.14)

$$\mathfrak{D}^{(L)}(\{\alpha \pm \pi, \pi - \beta, \pi - \gamma\})_{\mu\lambda} = e^{i\mu(\alpha\pm\pi)}(-1)^{L-\mu} \boldsymbol{d}^{(L)}(\beta)_{\mu,-\lambda} e^{i\lambda(\pi-\gamma)}$$

$$= (-1)^{L+\lambda} \mathfrak{D}^{(L)}(\{\alpha\beta\gamma\})_{\mu,-\lambda}\,. \tag{19.14a}$$

Thus, for even levels $\mathbf{P}_I \psi_\mu = \psi_\mu$ implies

$$G_{-\lambda}(r_1, r_2, \varepsilon) = (-1)^{L+\lambda} G_\lambda(r_1, r_2, \varepsilon), \tag{19.19}$$

while for odd levels,[10] for which $\mathbf{P}_I \psi_\mu = -\psi_\mu$,

$$G_{-\lambda}(r_1, r_2, \varepsilon) = -(-1)^{L+\lambda} G_\lambda(r_1, r_2, \varepsilon). \tag{19.19a}$$

[9] In Fig. 11 we have assumed $r_1 = r_2 = 1$ for simplicity. The points E_1 and E_2 are the positions of the two electrons before the inversion, and E_1' and E_2' the positions afterwards.

[10] It is also true in the case of the asymmetric top that $G_{-\lambda} = G_\lambda$ for $l + 1$ of the eigenvalues with the orbital quantum number l and that $G_{-\lambda} = -G_\lambda$ for the other l eigenvalues. Thus, the secular equation of the $(2l + 1)$th degree divides into two equations of degree $(l + 1)$ and l. Since, by (19.14a), $\psi_\mu^{-\nu l}$ and $\psi_\mu^{\nu l}$ for the symmetric top (Eq. (19.11a)) transform into one another under inversion, it follows that they belong to the same eigenvalue.

The function G_0 is different from zero only if $w = (-1)^L$ (S_+, P_-, D_+, etc.). It follows that He has no S_- level: wave functions for S-levels have the same value for all positions of the dipod so that S-levels necessarily have positive parity.

Substituting (19.6) into the Schrödinger equation and equating the coefficients of similar functions of α, β, and γ, yields in general $2L + 1$ equations for the $2L + 1$ functions $G_{-L}, G_{-L+1}, \cdots, G_{L-1}, G_L$ of the variables which describe the form of the n-pod. For He, the number of independent functions can be substantially reduced by (19.19), (19.19a) leaving only one unknown function for S_+ and P_+ levels, two for P_- and D_- levels, three for D_+ and F_+ levels, etc.[11]

For several electrons, it is not possible to substitute a pure rotation for the inversion of the n-pod. Inversion transforms an n-pod into its "optical isomer," or mirror image. This has a different geometrical form from the original n-pod if only $n \geqslant 3$. For $n = 2$, this phenomenon does not occur; the geometrical form of a dipod is always identical with that of its isomeric form, or mirror image.

If we denote the coordinates which describe the form of n-pods isomeric to g by $\bar{g}$, then, according to (19.6), Fig. 11, and (19.14a)

$$\mathbf{P}_I \psi_\mu^L = \sum_\lambda (-1)^{\mu-\lambda} \mathfrak{D}^{(L)}(\{\alpha \pm \pi, \pi - \beta, \pi - \gamma\})_{\mu\lambda} G_\lambda(\bar{g})$$

$$= \sum_\lambda (-1)^{\mu-\lambda} \mathfrak{D}^{(L)}(\{\alpha, \beta, \gamma\})_{\mu,-\lambda} (-1)^{L+\lambda} G_\lambda(\bar{g}).$$

On the other hand,

$$\mathbf{P}_I \psi_\mu^L = w\psi_\mu = \sum_\lambda w(-1)^{\mu-\lambda} \mathfrak{D}^{(L)}(\{\alpha, \beta, \gamma\})_{\mu\lambda} G_\lambda(g).$$

Where for even levels $w = +1$, for odd levels $w = -1$. It follows that

$$(-1)^{L+\lambda} G_\lambda(\bar{g}) = wG_{-\lambda}(g). \tag{19.20}$$

Equation (19.20) cannot be used for explicit calculation of the eigenfunctions, but it does show how information going beyond Eq. (19.6) can be obtained about the form of the eigenfunctions by means of the symmetry of the eigenfunctions under the reflection group. However, not too much additional information could be expected by the consideration of this group. Inversions permit the comparison of the wave function at only two points in configuration space, while the rotation group allows the possibility of relating its values to one another at a continuous three-parametric family of points. Accordingly, three variables could be eliminated by the rotation group, even if an increase in the number of unknown functions ($G_{-L}, \cdots, G_L$)

[11] See G. Breit, *Phys. Rev.* **35**, 369 (1930).

had to be accepted in the bargain. Perhaps this number, $2L + 1$, could again be reduced slightly by the reflection group, but the simplification would be relatively unessential.

It is natural to attempt to use the symmetry under permutations of electrons to reduce the number of unknown functions still further. This is possible to a certain extent. The considerations involved in such a procedure are not as simple, however, as those of the preceding discussion, in which the first and the second electrons play a role different from the other (α and β are the azimuth and polar angle of the first electron). This makes the formulas which follow from the consideration of the interchange of electrons rather complicated. These will not be given here.

20. Electron Spin

The Physical Basis for the Pauli Theory

1. In the preceding chapter the most important properties of atomic spectra which could be treated without the introduction of electron spin have been discussed. However, many of the less obvious characteristics—among which the fine structure is perhaps the most prominent—could not be described since they are closely related to another property of the electron, its magnetic moment.

The hypothesis that the electron has a magnetic moment and an angular momentum, in short a "spin," was suggested by *Goudsmit* and *Uhlenbeck*. They noted, even before the discovery of quantum mechanics, that complete description of spectra was not possible unless a magnetic moment and a mechanical moment were ascribed to the electron—the concept of an electron as a point charge was insufficient. As is well known, in classical electrodynamics a magnet is equivalent to a point charge rotating about the axis of the magnetic moment. The vector of the magnetic moment $\mathfrak{M}$ is then calculated from the angular momentum vector $\mathfrak{L}$ by

$$\mathfrak{M} = \frac{e\mathfrak{L}}{2mc} = \eta\,\mathfrak{L} \tag{20.E.1}$$

where e is the charge of the rotating particle and m its mass. However, according to Goudsmit and Uhlenbeck, Eq. (20.E.1) does not apply to the magnetic moment resulting from spin if one uses the normal electronic charge and mass. Rather, one must assume that the angular momentum is of amount

$$|\mathfrak{S}| = \tfrac{1}{2}\cdot\hbar, \tag{20.1}$$

whereas the magnetic moment is a whole Bohr magneton

$$|\mathfrak{M}| = e\hbar/2\,mc = (e/mc)|\mathfrak{S}| = 2\eta|\mathfrak{S}|. \tag{20.1a}$$

The quantum mechanics of electron spin shows that these statements cannot be taken literally. Even the Pauli theory requires that no experiment can be performed which allows the determination of the direction (and thus, say, of the direction cosines) of the mechanical or magnetic moment. It is possible only to differentiate between one direction and its opposite. The question of the probability for the different spatial directions of spin consequently has no meaning, i.e., will be unanswerable by experiment, and only the component of the spin in a single direction can be measured. These measurements, which are exemplified by the Stern–Gerlach experiment, can give only two answers: either that the spin is in the direction in question, or that it is in the opposite direction. The possible experimental results for the component of the angular momentum in the direction in question are $+\frac{\hbar}{2}$ or $-\frac{\hbar}{2}$. If the former result has been obtained when measuring the component of the spin in the Z-direction, then a second measurement of the Z-component carried out immediately afterwards will yield $+Z$ *with certainty*, and with certainty does *not* yield $-Z$. A measurement of the Y-component, on the other hand, yields the two possible results $+Y$ and $-Y$ with equal probabilities. It is important, therefore, to ascribe independent probabilities to all directions of the spin; even if the spin is certainly in the Z-direction (i.e., if the Z-component of the angular momentum is $+\hbar/2$ with certainty) the probability for the $+Y$ direction is 1/2, and for all directions except $-Z$ the probability is different from zero.

Spin obtains an even more symbolic character in Dirac's relativistic theory of the electron, as was emphasized particularly by N. Bohr. According to this theory (which we shall not discuss here) the existence of the magnetic moment is entirely a relativistic effect which appears automatically when space and time are treated equivalently.

2. In the Pauli theory the magnetic moment is described by an extra coordinate s in the wave function, which then has the form, $\Phi(x, y, z, s)$. While the domain of x, y, z extends from $-\infty$ to $+\infty$, the coordinate s can only assume two values -1 and $+1$. The wave function for an electron therefore actually consists of two functions of x, y, z: $\Phi(x, y, z, -1)$ and $\Phi(x, y, z, 1)$. The fact that the variable s, in contrast to x, y, z, can assume only two values reflects the fact that the component of spin in, say, the Z direction can have only two values ($+\hbar/2$ and $-\hbar/2$) while the position coordinates can assume all values from $-\infty$ to $+\infty$.

The scalar product of two functions of x, y, z and s, is defined by a direct generalization of the scalar products we have already seen. The scalar product of two functions $\varphi(x, y, z)$ and $g(x, y, z)$ was obtained by taking the limit of the sum

$$\sum_{x,y,z} \varphi(x, y, z)^* g(x, y, z),$$

where the summation must be extended over the whole domain, from $-\infty$ to $+\infty$. Similarly, the scalar product of $\Phi(x, y, z, s)$ and $G(x, y, z, s)$ is

$$\sum_{s=\pm 1} \sum_{x,y,z} \Phi(x, y, z, s)^* G(x, y, z, s), \tag{20.2}$$

where the summation is again taken over the entire range of all the variables.

By going to the limit one obtains

$$(\Phi, G) = \sum_{s=\pm 1} \iiint_{-\infty}^{\infty} \Phi(x, y, z, s)^* G(x, y, z, s)\, dx\, dy\, dz$$

$$= \iiint_{-\infty}^{\infty} [\Phi(x, y, z, -1)^* G(x, y, z, -1) \tag{20.3}$$

$$+ \Phi(x, y, z, 1)^* G(x, y, z, 1)]\, dx\, dy\, dz.$$

3. The quantities which involve only the Cartesian coordinates remain an important special class among physical quantities. These quantities—like the X-coordinate, or the velocity—also have a meaning in a theory which does not consider spin at all. Experiments which measure these quantities will be called "spin-free" experiments. The quantities themselves correspond in the Pauli theory to operators *which affect only the Cartesian coordinates* x, y, z, so that the spin coordinate s can be treated as a parameter.

Let us sharpen the concept of operators which affect only some of the coordinates. Every operator $\mathbf{X}$ which can be applied to a function $f(\xi)$ of only one variable ξ (such as differentiation with respect to ξ) can also be applied to a function of two variables, since any function $F(\xi, \sigma)$ of two variables can be interpreted as a family of functions of the variable ξ alone; for each particular value of σ, a function $F(\xi, \sigma)$ is a function of ξ alone.[1] If the operator $\mathbf{X}$ is applied to all these functions of ξ, one obtains another family of functions of ξ, one for each σ value. *This family then forms the function* $\mathbf{X}F(\xi, \sigma)$. The statement that $\mathbf{X}$ affects only ξ thus means that the value of $\mathbf{X}F$ at ξ, σ depends only on the values of $F(\xi', \sigma')$ at $\sigma' = \sigma$.

Now let $\Psi_k(x, y, z, s)$ be an eigenfunction of an operator $\mathbf{H}$ which affects only x, y, and z. If λ_k is the corresponding eigenvalue, then the function of x, y, z, s

$$\mathbf{H}\Psi_k(x, y, z, s) - \lambda_k \Psi_k(x, y, z, s) = 0 \tag{20.4}$$

must vanish; i.e., both functions of this family ($s = +1$ and $s = -1$) must vanish

$$\mathbf{H}\Psi_k(x, y, z, -1) - \lambda_k \Psi_k(x, y, z, -1) = 0,$$

$$\mathbf{H}\Psi_k(x, y, z, +1) - \lambda_k \Psi_k(x, y, z, +1) = 0.$$

If, for a given λ_k, the equation

$$\mathbf{H}\psi_k(x, y, z) = \lambda_k \psi_k(x, y, z)$$

[1] We think of ξ here as representing the coordinate triplet x, y, z, and σ as representing the spin coordinate s.

has only one solution, then both $\Psi_k(x, y, z, +1)$ and $\Psi_k(x, y, z, -1)$ must be constant multiples of $\psi_k(x, y, z)$.[2]

$$\Psi_k(x, y, z, -1) = u_{-1}\psi_k(x, y, z); \quad \Psi_k(x, y, z, 1) = u_1\psi_k(x, y, z); \qquad \Psi_k(x, y, z, s) = u_s\psi_k(x, y, z). \tag{20.5}$$

No matter how u_{-1} and u_1 are chosen, $u_s\psi_k(x, y, z)$ remains an eigenfunction of $\mathbf{H}$ belonging to the eigenvalue λ_k. This shows that the introduction of the spin coordinate s has made the eigenvalue λ_k into a double eigenvalue, to which belong the two linearly independent, mutually orthogonal eigenfunctions

$$\Psi_{k-} = \delta_{s,-1}\psi_k(x, y, z) \tag{20.5a}$$

$$\Psi_{k+} = \delta_{s,1}\psi_k(x, y, z). \tag{20.5b}$$

The scalar product of Ψ_{k-} and Ψ_{k+} actually does vanish, since one factor in each term of the integrand of (20.3) is zero.

The eigenfunctions

$$\delta_{s,-1}\psi_1; \quad \delta_{s,1}\psi_1; \quad \delta_{s,-1}\psi_2; \quad \delta_{s,1}\psi_2; \quad \delta_{s,-1}\psi_3; \quad \cdots$$

correspond to the possible results of two measurements carried out simultaneously: (a) the measurement of the quantity which corresponds to the operator $\mathbf{H}$ and (b) the measurement of the Z-component of the spin. For Ψ_{k-} the value of the first quantity is certainly λ_k, and the spin is certainly in the $-Z$ direction, while for Ψ_{k+} the first quantity is still certainly λ_k but the spin is in the $+Z$ direction, i.e., the probability for its appearing in the $-Z$ direction is zero. In general, if the wave function is

$$\Phi = a_1\Psi_{1-} + a_2\Psi_{2-} + a_3\Psi_{3-} + \cdots + b_1\Psi_{1+} + b_2\Psi_{2+} + b_3\Psi_{3+} + \cdots, \tag{20.6}$$

the probability that $\mathbf{H}$ has the value λ_k and that the spin simultaneously is in the $-Z$ direction is equal to $|a_k|^2$; the probability of a value λ_k for $\mathbf{H}$ and a spin $+Z$ is $|b_k|^2$.

Invariance of the Description under Spatial Rotation

4. In the description of the electron by a wave function which depends upon s, the Z-axis is preferred over all directions, even over the directions of the two other coordinate axes. It is thus very appropriate here to investigate how the isotropy of space is retained in this description, i.e., which wave function $\mathbf{O}_R\Phi$ a second observer ascribes to the state Φ if he describes

[2] It may seem somewhat disturbing at first that s appears as a variable on the left side of the equation and as an index on right, but it just re-emphasizes that every function of x, y, z, and s can be interpreted as a correspondence between a function of x, y, and z and each value of s.

physical systems and all quantities *exactly as the first observer does* except that he uses a *coordinate system rotated* with respect to the coordinate system of the first observer. The positions of the two coordinate systems are such that the coordinates of a point x, y, z in the second system of axes are

$$\begin{aligned}\mathbf{R}_{xx}x + \mathbf{R}_{xy}y + \mathbf{R}_{xz}z &= x',\\ \mathbf{R}_{yx}x + \mathbf{R}_{yy}y + \mathbf{R}_{yz}z &= y',\\ \mathbf{R}_{zx}x + \mathbf{R}_{zy}y + \mathbf{R}_{zz}z &= z'.\end{aligned}$$

($\mathbf{R}$ is a real, orthogonal, three-dimensional matrix with determinant 1.) $\mathbf{O}_R\Phi$ can be defined either as the wave function of the state Φ observed by the second observer, or as the wave function of the original state, rotated by R, and observed by the original observer.

When the wave functions depended only upon the Cartesian coordinates of the particles, the operation $\mathbf{O}_R$ was merely a point transformation (see Chapter 11):

$$\mathbf{P}_R\varphi(x', y', z') = \varphi(x, y, z). \tag{20.7}$$

Equation (20.7) is simply the statement that the wave function $\mathbf{P}_R\varphi$ of the second observer at the point x', y', z' assumes the same value as that of the wave function of the first observer at the point x, y, z. This must be true because the point x, y, z is called x', y', z' by the second observer.

When we include spin coordinates as well as Cartesian coordinates the transformation $\mathbf{O}_R$ cannot be a simple point transformation, since s cannot be subjected to a point transformation. For this reason $\mathbf{O}_R$ will be a more general operator than $\mathbf{P}_R$ was. We assume the existence of the system of operators $\mathbf{O}_R$ (to each rotation R there belongs an operator $\mathbf{O}_R$) and then attempt to determine it from the basic assumptions of the Pauli theory plus the requirement that observers working in different coordinate axes are equivalent. We shall find that *there exists essentially only one system of operators which satisfies these conditions*. Its determination will allow important conclusions to be drawn on the properties of the spinning electron.

5. The description of the second observer who ascribes to the state Φ the wave function $\mathbf{O}_R\Phi$, must be completely equivalent to the original description. In particular it must give the same *transition probabilities* between two arbitrary states Ψ and Φ as the first gives

$$|(\Psi, \Phi)|^2 = |(\mathbf{O}_R\Psi, \mathbf{O}_R\Phi)|^2. \tag{20.8}$$

It is important to note here that although the *state* Φ, which appears as the state $\mathbf{O}_R\Phi$ for the observer with the rotated coordinate system, is completely given by stating its wave function, the second observer's wave function for this state is not uniquely determined. It can be multiplied by an arbitrary constant c of absolute value 1, because the wave functions $\mathbf{O}_R\Phi$ and $c\mathbf{O}_R\Phi$ describe the same physical state. This means that the operator $\mathbf{O}_R$ is many-valued—for every function Φ there is still a free factor in $\mathbf{O}_R$. It will be shown (see the appendix at the end of the chapter) that this freedom in $\mathbf{O}_R$ can be so disposed of that for all Ψ and all Φ one has

$$\left.\begin{aligned} (\Psi, \Phi) &= (\mathbf{O}_R\Psi, \mathbf{O}_R\Phi) \\ \text{and} \qquad \mathbf{O}_R(a\Psi + b\Phi) &= a\mathbf{O}_R\Psi + b\mathbf{O}_R\Phi \end{aligned}\right\} \tag{20.8a}$$

(a and b are constants); i.e., *so that* $\mathbf{O}_R$ *becomes a linear unitary operator.* Then the two methods of description—the one for the observer in the original system and the other for the observer in the rotated system of axes—*differ only by a canonical transformation,* which insures that they are completely equivalent physically. The second observer sees the state with the wave function Φ as $\mathbf{O}_R\Phi$; the quantity which corresponds to the operator $\mathbf{H}$ for the first observer corresponds for him to $\mathbf{O}_R\mathbf{H}\mathbf{O}_R^{-1}$.

Conversely, the requirement (20.8a) that $\mathbf{O}_R$ be a linear unitary operator determines the constants c_Φ uniquely for all wave functions except one. If $c\mathbf{O}_R\Phi$ is substituted for a wave function $\mathbf{O}_R\Phi$, then to maintain (20.8a) all wave functions must at the same time be replaced by c times themselves. To see this, suppose that we substitute $c\mathbf{O}_R\Phi$ for $\mathbf{O}_R\Phi$ in (20.8a) while we leave, say, $\mathbf{O}_R\Psi$ unchanged; then if (20.8a) is to apply to this new system it follows that

$$(\Psi, \Phi) = (\mathbf{O}_R\Psi, c\mathbf{O}_R\Phi) = c(\mathbf{O}_R\Psi, \mathbf{O}_R\Phi)$$

which, together with (20.8a) implies that $c = 1$. In what follows we will always take the $\mathbf{O}_R\Phi$ so that (20.8a) is true; then among all $\mathbf{O}_R\Phi$ (where R is a given rotation), only *one constant* is free. This constant may, however, depend on R.

6. We now consider the two states $\Psi_- = \psi(x, y, z)\delta_{s,-1}$ and $\Psi_+ = \psi(x, y, z)\delta_{s,+1}$. For spin-free experiments these two states both behave as if their wave functions were $\psi(x, y, z)$. For the observer in the rotated system of coordinates they therefore appear, as far as spin-free experiments are concerned, like a state with the wave function $\mathbf{P}_R\psi(x, y, z)$. Therefore, according to (20.5), the wave functions $\mathbf{O}_R\Psi_-$ and $\mathbf{O}_R\Psi_+$ must have the form

$$\left.\begin{aligned} \mathbf{O}_R\delta_{s,-1}\psi(x, y, z) &= \mathbf{u}_{s,-1}\mathbf{P}_R\psi(x, y, z) \\ \mathbf{O}_R\delta_{s,1}\psi(x, y, z) &= \mathbf{u}_{s,1}\mathbf{P}_R\psi(x, y, z), \end{aligned}\right\} \tag{20.9}$$

where $\mathbf{u}_{s,-1}$ and $\mathbf{u}_{s,1}$ are independent of x, y, z and, so far, can be different for different ψ. However, if φ is a state different from ψ for which

$$\mathbf{O}_R \delta_{s,-1}\varphi(x, y, z) = \bar{\mathbf{u}}_{s,-1}\mathbf{P}_R\varphi(x, y, z)$$

holds, it follows from the linearity of $\mathbf{O}_R$ that

$$\begin{aligned}\mathbf{O}_R\delta_{s,-1}(\varphi + \psi) &= \bar{\bar{\mathbf{u}}}_{s,-1}\mathbf{P}_R(\varphi + \psi) = \bar{\bar{\mathbf{u}}}_{s,-1}\mathbf{P}_R\varphi + \bar{\bar{\mathbf{u}}}_{s,-1}\mathbf{P}_R\psi \\ &= \mathbf{O}_R\delta_{s,-1}\varphi + \mathbf{O}_R\delta_{s,-1}\psi = \bar{\mathbf{u}}_{s,-1}\mathbf{P}_R\varphi + \mathbf{u}_{s,-1}\mathbf{P}_R\psi.\end{aligned}$$

Because of the linear independence of $\mathbf{P}_R\varphi$ and $\mathbf{P}_R\psi$, this implies that

$$\bar{\mathbf{u}}_{s,-1} = \bar{\bar{\mathbf{u}}}_{s,-1} = \mathbf{u}_{s,-1}.$$

Likewise,

$$\bar{\mathbf{u}}_{s,1} = \mathbf{u}_{s,1}.$$

Thus, the $\mathbf{u}_{st}$ are the same for all wave functions, and the matrix $\mathbf{u} = \mathbf{u}(R)$ can depend only on the rotation R. If $\Phi(x, y, z, s)$ is an arbitrary wave function,

$$\Phi(x, y, z, s) = \delta_{s,-1}\Phi(x, y, z, -1) + \delta_{s,1}\Phi(x, y, z, 1), \tag{20.10}$$

it follows, again from the linearity of $\mathbf{O}_R$ and (20.9) that

$$\begin{aligned}\mathbf{O}_R\Phi(x, y, z, s) &= \mathbf{O}_R\delta_{s,-1}\Phi(x, y, z, -1) + \mathbf{O}_R\delta_{s,1}\Phi(x, y, z, 1) \\ &= \mathbf{u}_{s,-1}\mathbf{P}_R\Phi(x, y, z, -1) + \mathbf{u}_{s,1}\mathbf{P}_R\Phi(x, y, z, 1) \qquad (20.11)\\ \mathbf{O}_R\Phi(x, y, z, s) &= \sum_{t=\pm 1} \mathbf{u}_{st}\mathbf{P}_R\Phi(x, y, z, t).\end{aligned}$$

The operator $\mathbf{O}_R$ thus can be split into two factors

$$\mathbf{O}_R = \mathbf{Q}_R\mathbf{P}_R. \tag{20.12}$$

The operator $\mathbf{P}_R$ is the familiar transformation operator defined in (20.7) and affects only the position coordinates of the wave function; $\mathbf{Q}_R$ is defined by

$$\mathbf{Q}_R\Phi(x, y, z, s) = \sum_{t=\pm 1} \mathbf{u}(R)_{st}\Phi(x, y, z, t) \tag{20.12a}$$

and affects only the spin coordinate s. Since the region of variability of s consists only of the two points $+1$ and -1, (20.12a) shows that $\mathbf{Q}_R$ is equivalent to a two-dimensional matrix:

$$\mathbf{u}(R) = \begin{pmatrix} \mathbf{u}(R)_{-1,-1} & \mathbf{u}(R)_{-1,1} \\ \mathbf{u}(R)_{1,-1} & \mathbf{u}(R)_{1,1} \end{pmatrix}. \tag{20.13}$$

The operators $\mathbf{P}$ and $\mathbf{Q}$ commute; therefore, one has for two arbitrary rotations R and S

$$\left.\begin{aligned}\mathbf{P}_S\mathbf{Q}_R &= \mathbf{Q}_R\mathbf{P}_S \\ \text{and in particular,}\qquad & \\ \mathbf{P}_R\mathbf{Q}_R &= \mathbf{Q}_R\mathbf{P}_R.\end{aligned}\right\} \tag{20.14}$$

The possibility of resolving $\mathbf{O}_R$ into two factors $\mathbf{P}_R$ and $\mathbf{Q}_R$ is based essentially on the assumption that there exist "spin-free experiments" which can be described by a wave function dependent only upon x, y, and z. This assumption is abandoned in Dirac's relativistic theory, and, in his theory, $\mathbf{O}_R$ cannot be decomposed into two factors satisfying (20.14) if R is a transition to a moving coordinate system.

Connection with Representation Theory

7. From the unitary nature of $\mathbf{O}_R$, and of $\mathbf{P}_R$ (and thus of $\mathbf{P}_R^{-1}$ as well), it follows that $\mathbf{Q}_R = \mathbf{O}_R\mathbf{P}_R^{-1}$ must be unitary. Therefore, for all functions Φ and Ψ

$$(\mathbf{Q}_R\Phi, \mathbf{Q}_R\Psi) = (\Phi, \Psi). \tag{20.15}$$

It follows that the matrix $\mathbf{u}(R)$ must also be unitary. If we set $\Phi = \delta_{s\sigma}\psi$ and $\Psi = \delta_{s\tau}\psi$, then according to (20.3) (if ψ is normalized), $(\Phi, \Psi) = \delta_{\sigma\tau}$. Therefore, according to (20.15) and (20.12a), we have

$$\delta_{\sigma\tau} = (\mathbf{Q}_R\delta_{s\sigma}\psi, \mathbf{Q}_R\delta_{s\tau}\psi) = (\mathbf{u}_{s\sigma}\psi, \mathbf{u}_{s\tau}\psi)$$
$$= \sum_{s=\pm1} \iiint_{-\infty}^{+\infty} \mathbf{u}_{s\sigma}^*\psi^*\mathbf{u}_{s\tau}\psi \, dx\, dy\, dz = \sum_{s=\pm1} \mathbf{u}_{s\sigma}^*\mathbf{u}_{s\tau}.$$

But this is just the condition that $\mathbf{u}$ be unitary.

Furthermore, because of the fact that $\mathbf{O}_R$ is determined by the physical facts and (20.8a) only up to a constant of absolute value 1 which depends on R, we can substitute $c_R\mathbf{O}_R$ for $\mathbf{O}_R$ without changing the physical content of the theory or modifying (20.8a) (where $|c_R| = 1$). We can attach the factor c_R to $\mathbf{Q}_R$, that is, to $\mathbf{u}(R)$, and arrange thereby *that the determinant of* $\mathbf{u}(R)$ *be equal to* $+1$.

Finally, to determine the matrix $\mathbf{u}(R)$ entirely, we consider the fact that $\mathbf{O}_R\Phi$ is the wave function for the state Φ rotated by R, and $\mathbf{O}_S \cdot \mathbf{O}_R \cdot \Phi$ is the wave function of the state rotated first by R and then by S, or in all by SR. The operator $\mathbf{O}_S\mathbf{O}_R$ is thus completely equivalent physically to the operator $\mathbf{O}_{SR}$. Since it also satisfies (20.8a)—the product of two linear unitary operators is itself also linear and unitary—it can differ from $\mathbf{O}_{SR}$ only by a constant factor,

$$\mathbf{O}_{SR} = c_{S,R}\mathbf{O}_S\mathbf{O}_R. \tag{20.16}$$

Now because of $\mathbf{P}_{SR} = \mathbf{P}_S \cdot \mathbf{P}_R$ and (20.14), Eq. (20.12) implies that

$$\mathbf{Q}_{SR}\mathbf{P}_{SR} = c_{S,R}\mathbf{Q}_S\mathbf{P}_S\mathbf{Q}_R\mathbf{P}_R; \quad \mathbf{Q}_{SR} = c_{S,R}\mathbf{Q}_S\mathbf{Q}_R,$$

or with the help of (20.12a), that

$$\sum_{=\pm1} \mathbf{u}(SR)_{st}\Phi(x, y, z, t) = c_{S,R} \sum_{r=\pm1} \sum_{t=\pm1} \mathbf{u}(S)_{sr}\mathbf{u}(R)_{rt}\Phi(x, y, z, t),$$
$$\mathbf{u}(SR) = c_{S,R}\mathbf{1} \cdot \mathbf{u}(S) \cdot \mathbf{u}(R). \tag{20.17}$$

Since we have normalized the determinants of all **u** to 1, it follows from (20.17) that also the determinant $|c_{S,R}\mathbf{1}| = 1$, and $c_{S,R} = \pm 1$. Thus, except for sign, the matrices $\mathbf{u}(R)$ form a representation of the three-dimensional rotation group

$$\mathbf{u}(SR) = \pm \mathbf{u}(S)\mathbf{u}(R). \tag{20.17a}$$

This suggests that the $\mathbf{u}(R)$ are either identical with the matrices discussed in Chapter 15,

$$\mathbf{u}(\{\alpha\beta\gamma\}) = \mathfrak{D}^{(1/2)}(\{\alpha\beta\gamma\}) = \begin{pmatrix} e^{-\frac{1}{2}i\alpha} \cos \frac{1}{2}\beta e^{-\frac{1}{2}i\gamma} & -e^{-\frac{1}{2}i\alpha} \sin \frac{1}{2}\beta e^{\frac{1}{2}i\gamma} \\ e^{\frac{1}{2}i\alpha} \sin \frac{1}{2}\beta e^{-\frac{1}{2}i\gamma} & e^{\frac{1}{2}i\alpha} \cos \frac{1}{2}\beta e^{\frac{1}{2}i\gamma} \end{pmatrix}, \tag{20.18}$$

or, at least, result from them by a similarity transformation. This is in fact correct, and we show in the next chapter that every system of two-dimensional matrices which satisfies (20.17a) consists either of unit matrices, or can be obtained from $\mathfrak{D}^{(1/2)}$ by a similarity transformation. The first possibility is ruled out here since it would mean, for example, that a state for which the spin was certainly in the Z-direction would still have this property after an arbitrary rotation.

The matrix **u** can be a diagonal matrix only for rotations with $\beta = 0$ (which leave the Z-axis unchanged); for these it must be diagonal. For if the spin in the first coordinate system is in the $-Z$ direction so that $\Phi(x, y, z, 1) = 0$, then this must also be the case in the second coordinate system. But if this is true, Eq. (20.11) implies that $\mathbf{u}_{1,-1} = 0$; similarly $\mathbf{u}_{-1,1} = 0$; and $\mathbf{u}(\{\alpha, 0, 0\})$ is a diagonal matrix. Since it is equivalent to $\mathfrak{D}^{1/2}(\{\alpha\, 00\})$ it can be either

$$\mathbf{u}(\{\alpha\, 00\}) = \begin{pmatrix} e^{-\frac{1}{2}i\alpha} & 0 \\ 0 & e^{\frac{1}{2}i\alpha} \end{pmatrix} \quad \text{or} \quad \begin{pmatrix} e^{\frac{1}{2}i\alpha} & 0 \\ 0 & e^{-\frac{1}{2}i\alpha} \end{pmatrix}. \tag{20.E.2}$$

But the second case would imply that the angular momentum of the electron in the state $\psi\delta_{s,-1}$ was in the $+Z$ direction, and in the state $\psi\delta_{s,1}$ in the $-Z$ direction. We exclude this choice since it would ascribe the wave function, $\Phi(x, y, z, -s)$ to the physical state which we want to describe with the wave function $\Phi(x, y, z, s)$.

Thus, $\mathbf{u}(\{\alpha\, 00\}) = \mathfrak{D}^{(1/2)}(\{\alpha\, 00\})$, and the unitary matrix **S**, which transforms $\mathfrak{D}^{(1/2)}$ into **u**, must commute with $\mathfrak{D}^{(1/2)}(\{\alpha\, 00\})$; it must therefore be a diagonal matrix. Let its two diagonal elements be a and a' ($|a| = |a'| = 1$). Then we can change our notation and ascribe the wave function $\mathbf{S}\Phi(x, y, z, s)$ to the state whose wave function was previously $\Phi(x, y, z, s)$, where

$$\mathbf{S}\Phi(x, y, z, -1) = a\Phi(x, y, z, -1)$$
$$\mathbf{S}\Phi(x, y, z, 1) = a'\Phi(x, y, z, 1).$$

This is permissible because so far we have attributed no significance to the complex phase of the ratio $\Phi(x, y, z, -1)/\Phi(x, y, z, 1)$. In the description which arises from the original one in this way, and which is completely equivalent to it, we have in every case

$$\mathbf{u}(\{\alpha, \beta, \gamma\}) = \mathfrak{D}^{(1/2)}(\{\alpha, \beta, \gamma\}), \tag{20.18a}$$

and we obtain the result *that every description of the spin which is based upon the ideas discussed in Section 1, 2, and 3 is completely equivalent physically to the description in which the wave function for a state Φ rotated by R is given*[3] *by* $\mathbf{O}_R\Phi$. Here $\mathbf{O}_R = \mathbf{P}_R\mathbf{Q}_R$ is the operator defined by

$$\begin{aligned}\mathbf{O}_R\Phi(x, y, z, s) &= \sum_{t=\pm 1} \mathfrak{D}^{(1/2)}(R)_{\frac{1}{2}s,\frac{1}{2}t}\mathbf{P}_R\Phi(x, y, z, t)\\ &= \sum_{t=\pm 1} \mathfrak{D}^{(1/2)}(R)_{\frac{1}{2}s,\frac{1}{2}t}\Phi(x'', y'', z'', t),\end{aligned} \tag{20.19}$$

where x'', y'', z'' result from x, y, z, by the rotation R^{-1}. In $\mathfrak{D}^{(1/2)}$ the indices $\frac{1}{2}s$, $\frac{1}{2}t$ appear because the rows and columns of $\mathfrak{D}^{(1/2)}$ are denoted by $-\frac{1}{2}$ and $+\frac{1}{2}$, instead of -1 and $+1$ as in $\mathbf{u}$.

For example, let

$$\Phi(x, y, z, s) = (x + iy) \exp(-r/2r_0) \quad \text{for} \quad s = \pm 1. \tag{20.E.3}$$

The function $(x + iy) \exp(-r/2r_0)$ is, except for normalization, the eigenfunction of the H atom with $N = 2$, $l = 1$, and $\mu = +1$. See Eq. (17.3). Consider the state (20.E.3) in a coordinate system whose Y-axis is the old Y-axis and whose Z-axis is the old X-axis. The rotation R is then $\{0, \pi/2, 0\}$,

$$x' = -z, \quad y' = y, \quad z' = x$$

and the inverse rotation is

$$x'' = z, \quad y'' = y, \quad z'' = -x.$$

The matrix $\mathfrak{D}^{(1/2)}(\{0, \frac{1}{2}\pi, 0\})$ is

$$\begin{pmatrix} 1/\sqrt{2} & -1/\sqrt{2} \\ 1/\sqrt{2} & 1/\sqrt{2} \end{pmatrix}.$$

The wave function of the state (20.E.3) for the new coordinate system is, by (20.19),

$$\begin{aligned}\mathbf{O}_R\Phi(x, y, z, s) &= \begin{cases} \dfrac{1}{\sqrt{2}}(z + iy)e^{-r/2r_0} - \dfrac{1}{\sqrt{2}}(z + iy)e^{-r/2r_0} & \text{for} \quad s = -1 \\ \dfrac{1}{\sqrt{2}}(z + iy)e^{-r/2r_0} + \dfrac{1}{\sqrt{2}}(z + iy)e^{-r/2r_0} & \text{for} \quad s = +1 \end{cases}\\ &= \delta_{s1}\sqrt{2}(z + iy)e^{-r/2r_0}.\end{aligned}$$

In the new coordinate system the spin is thus certainly in the $+Z$-direction, consequently it was certainly in the $+X$-direction in the old one.

8. We will now derive certain physical implications from the transformation formulas (20.19). A very important question which can be answered by (20.19) is the following: What are the probabilities for a measurement of the Z'-component of the spin to give the results of $+\hbar/2$ and $-\hbar/2$, if it is known that the Z-component has the value $+\hbar/2$? In other words: what is

[3] R here is always a pure rotation.

the probability relationship between the spin components for two different directions Z' and Z which include an angle β? If the spin is in the Z-direction, the wave function has the form $\Phi(x, y, z, s) = \delta_{s1}\varphi(x, y, z)$; if we consider this state from a coordinate system rotated by $\{0, \beta, 0\}$, then because $\mathbf{P}_{\{0\beta0\}}\Phi(x, y, z, s) = \delta_{s1}\mathbf{P}_{\{0,\beta,0\}}\varphi(x, y, z)$, we have (since $\Phi(x, y, z, -1) = 0$, and (using $\mathfrak{D}^{(1/2)}\{0, \beta, 0\}_{st}$ from Eq. (15.16))

$$\begin{aligned} \mathbf{O}_{\{0\beta0\}}\Phi(x, y, z, -1) &= \cos \tfrac{1}{2}\beta \mathbf{P}_{\{0\beta0\}}\Phi(x, y, z, -1) - \sin \tfrac{1}{2}\beta \mathbf{P}_{\{0\beta0\}}\Phi(x, y, z, 1) \\ &= -\sin \tfrac{1}{2}\beta \cdot \mathbf{P}_{\{0\beta0\}}\varphi(x, y, z), \qquad (20.20) \\ \mathbf{O}_{\{0\beta0\}}\Phi(x, y, z, 1) &= \sin \tfrac{1}{2}\beta \mathbf{P}_{\{0\beta0\}}\Phi(x, y, z, -1) + \cos \tfrac{1}{2}\beta \mathbf{P}_{\{0\beta0\}}\Phi(x, y, z, 1) \\ &= \cos \tfrac{1}{2}\beta \cdot \mathbf{P}_{\{0\beta0\}}\varphi(x, y, z). \end{aligned}$$

Now the second observer can calculate the probability of a given result for the spin along the Z'-axis, which is a direction including an angle β with the original Z-direction, directly from the wave function $\mathbf{O}_{\{0\beta0\}}\Phi$. Equation (20.20) yields $|\cos \frac{1}{2}\beta|^2$ for the probability of a result in the $+Z'$ direction, and $|\sin \frac{1}{2}\beta|^2$ for the probability of the $-Z'$ direction. *If the probability for a certain direction of the spin is 1, then for a direction lying at an angle β to this the probability equals* $|\cos \frac{1}{2}\beta|^2$. For $\beta = 0$ this is 1, as it must when the two directions coincide; for $\beta = \frac{1}{2}\pi$, when the two directions are perpendicular to one another, it equals $\frac{1}{2}$; for $\beta = \pi$, when the directions are opposite, the probability is zero.

Let us now ask under what conditions there exists a direction along which the spin certainly does *not* lie. Let this direction be, say, the Z'-direction, so that the wave function $\mathbf{O}_{\{\alpha,\beta,\gamma\}}\Phi$ in a coordinate system whose Z-axis is Z' has the form

$$\mathbf{O}_{\{\alpha,\beta,\gamma\}}\Phi(x, y, z, s) = \delta_{s,-1}\varphi(x, y, z).$$

The wave function Φ, itself, (we write $R = \{\alpha, \beta, \gamma\}$ for short) is

$$\begin{aligned} \Phi(x, y, z, s) &= \mathbf{O}_{R^{-1}}\mathbf{O}_{R}\Phi = \mathbf{O}_{R^{-1}}\delta_{s,-1}\varphi(x, y, z) \\ &= \mathfrak{D}^{(1/2)}(R^{-1})_{\frac{1}{2}s,-\frac{1}{2}}\mathbf{P}_{R^{-1}}\varphi(x, y, z). \end{aligned}$$

Hence, such a direction will exist only if $\Phi(x, y, z, -1)$ and $\Phi(x, y, z, 1)$ differ only by a constant factor independent of x, y, z:

$$\Phi(x, y, z, -1)/\Phi(x, y, z, 1) = \mathfrak{D}^{(1/2)}(R)_{-\frac{1}{2}-\frac{1}{2}}/\mathfrak{D}^{(1/2)}(R)_{\frac{1}{2}-\frac{1}{2}} = e^{-i\alpha} \cot \tfrac{1}{2}\beta. \qquad (20.E.4)$$

The absolute value and complex phase of this factor can be entirely arbitrary, as (20.E.4) shows. The fact that $\Phi(x, y, z, -1)$ and $\Phi(x, y, z, 1)$ differ only by a factor indicates that in the simultaneous measurement of the Z-component of spin and an arbitrary spin-free quantity the probability for the latter is, according to Section 3, *statistically independent* of the spin direction. In this case there always exists a direction—its azimuth α and the polar angle β are given in (20.E.4)—along which the spin certainly does not lie; otherwise there exists no such direction.

9. It is worth calling attention to the fact that far-reaching concrete statements about the behavior of the spinning electron could be obtained solely on the basis of invariance requirements and the general principles of quantum mechanics, together with certain rather qualitative postulates. The two results just derived, especially that which deals with the relations between the probabilities of different spin directions, are susceptible, at least in principle, to experimental verification.

The determination of the operator $\mathbf{O}_R$ has been made under the hypothesis that the different coordinate systems are physically equivalent. External fields, which destroy the isotropy of space can also involve a modification of the operators $\mathbf{O}_R$. Naturally, as long as the external field is weak, the operators which effect the transition to rotated axes will still be determined approximately by (20.19). However, the validity of (20.19) will be assumed also in strong fields in what follows.

Finally, let us call attention to a point of rather decisive significance in the derivation of (20.19), which has perhaps been submerged in the mathematical formalism. It is the fact that the equivalence of two coordinate systems also implies the equivalence of the operators $\mathbf{O}_R$ which effect the transformation to similarly rotated coordinate systems.

The operators $\mathbf{O}_R$ are linear and unitary, but they are not point transformations as were the $\mathbf{P}_R$. For this reason Eq. (11.22) does apply to them. That is,

$$\mathbf{O}_R \Phi \Psi \neq \mathbf{O}_R \Phi \cdot \mathbf{O}_R \Psi.$$

Moreover, it should be noted that a rotation R corresponds not to one, but to two operators, $\mathbf{O}_R$ and $-\mathbf{O}_R$, since the $\mathfrak{D}^{(1/2)}(\{\alpha, \beta, \gamma\})$ which occurs in (20.19) is determined by the rotation only up to sign. Also $\mathbf{O}_{SR} = \mathbf{O}_S \mathbf{O}_R$ does not hold, but only

$$\mathbf{O}_{SR} = \pm \mathbf{O}_S \mathbf{O}_R. \qquad (20.16a)$$

Nor is it possible arbitrarily to omit one of the operators, $+\mathbf{O}_R$ or $-\mathbf{O}_R$, in such a manner that (20.16a) be valid for the remaining ones with just the upper sign.

10. The Z-component of spin is a "physical quantity" just like the position or the angular momentum. Thus, according to the statistical interpretation of quantum mechanics, it must correspond to a linear Hermitian operator; this operator will be denoted by $\mathbf{S}_z = \frac{\hbar}{2} \mathbf{s}_z$. The eigenvalues of $\mathbf{s}_z$ are -1 and $+1$, corresponding to the possible values $-\frac{\hbar}{2}$ and $+\frac{\hbar}{2}$ for the Z-component of the spin. The eigenfunctions for the first eigenvalue are all the functions, $\Psi_-(x, y, z, s) = \delta_{s,-1}\, \psi(x, y, z)$; these are different

from zero only for $s = -1$. Those for the second eigenvalue are all the functions $\Psi_+(x, y, z, s) = \delta_{s,1}\psi'(x, y, z)$, which differ from zero only for $s = +1$. Thus,

$$\mathbf{s}_z\, \delta_{s,-1}\psi(x, y, z) = -\delta_{s,-1}\psi(x, y, z)$$
$$\mathbf{s}_z\, \delta_{s,1}\psi'(x, y, z) = +\delta_{s,1}\psi'(x, y, z),$$

and for arbitrary

$$\Phi(x, y, z, s) = \delta_{s,-1}\Phi(x, y, z, -1) + \delta_{s,1}\Phi(x, y, z, 1),$$

we have

$$\begin{aligned}\mathbf{s}_z\Phi(x, y, z, s) &= \mathbf{s}_z(\delta_{s,-1}\Phi(x, y, z, -1) + \delta_{s,1}\Phi(x, y, z, 1))\\ &= -\delta_{s,-1}\Phi(x, y, z, -1) + \delta_{s,1}\Phi(x, y, z, 1) \qquad (20.21)\\ \mathbf{s}_z\Phi(x, y, z, s) &= \sum_{t=\pm 1} t\delta_{st}\Phi(x, y, z, t) = s\Phi(x, y, z, s)\end{aligned}$$

because of the linearity of $\mathbf{s}_z$.

Since $\mathbf{s}_z$ affects only the spin coordinates, it, like $\mathbf{Q}_R$, has a matrix form,

$$\mathbf{s}_z = \begin{pmatrix} -1 & 0 \\ 0 & 1 \end{pmatrix}. \qquad (20.21\text{a})$$

We now determine the operator $\mathbf{h}$ which corresponds to the Z'-component of the spin. For an observer in the system of axes whose Z-axis is Z', this operator is simply $\mathbf{s}_z$, since for this observer, by definition, all operators are written exactly as they are for the first observer, except that they refer to his own system of axes. On the other hand, this operator results from $\mathbf{h}$ by transformation with $\mathbf{O}_R$ so that

$$\mathbf{s}_z = \mathbf{O}_R\mathbf{h}\mathbf{O}_R^{-1}; \quad \mathbf{h} = \mathbf{O}_{R^{-1}}\mathbf{s}_z\mathbf{O}_R$$

Then by (20.12) (and because $\mathbf{P}_R$ commutes with $\mathbf{s}_z$), it follows that

$$\mathbf{h} = \mathbf{Q}_{R^{-1}}\mathbf{P}_{R^{-1}}\mathbf{s}_z\mathbf{P}_R\mathbf{Q}_R = \mathbf{Q}_{R^{-1}}\mathbf{s}_z\mathbf{Q}_R. \qquad (20.22)$$

If the matrix form is used for all operators occurring in (20.22) (they operate only on the s), we obtain

$$\mathbf{h} = \mathbf{u}(R)^\dagger\mathbf{s}_z\mathbf{u}(R).$$

It now follows from eq. (15.11) that our $\mathbf{h}$ is identical with the matrix used there if we set $\bar{\mathbf{h}} = \mathbf{s}_z$ (i.e., $x' = y' = 0$; $z' = 1$). The $\mathfrak{r} = (x, y, z)$ in Eq. (15.11) is the vector whose components result from $\mathfrak{r}'$ (with $x' = y' = 0$; $z' = 1$) by the transformation R^{-1}, and is thus the unit vector in the Z'-direction. Therefore, Eq. (15.10a) defining $\mathbf{h}$ is

$$\mathbf{h} = \alpha_1\mathbf{s}_x + \alpha_2\mathbf{s}_y + \alpha_3\mathbf{s}_z \qquad (20.22\text{a})$$

where $\alpha_1, \alpha_2, \alpha_3$, are the direction cosines of Z'. From (20.22a) we see that the operator for the Z'-component of the spin is composed of the operators for the X, Y, Z components given in Eq. (15.10),

$$\mathbf{s}_x = \begin{pmatrix} 0 & 1 \\ 1 & 0 \end{pmatrix}, \quad \mathbf{s}_y = \begin{pmatrix} 0 & i \\ -i & 0 \end{pmatrix}, \quad \mathbf{s}_z = \begin{pmatrix} -1 & 0 \\ 0 & 1 \end{pmatrix},$$

in the same way as the operator for the Z'-component of the coordinate (multiplication by $\alpha_1 x + \alpha_2 y + \alpha_2 z$) is formed from the operators for the X, Y, Z coordinates. Operators of this type are called "vector operators."

Equation (15.11) states that the operator $[\mathbf{R}\mathfrak{r}, \mathbf{s}] = [\mathfrak{r}', \mathbf{s}]$ for the $\mathbf{R}\mathfrak{r}$-component of the spin is obtained from the operator $[\mathfrak{r}, \mathbf{s}]$ for the $\mathfrak{r}$-component of the spin by transformation with $\mathbf{u}(R)^{-1}$ (i.e., with $\mathbf{Q}_R^{-1}$).

In the theory of spin it is often customary to begin directly from (20.22a) and to base the whole theory on this equation.

Appendix to Chapter 20. Linearity and Unitarity of Rotation Operators

Let $\overline{\Phi}$ be the wave function ascribed by the second observer to the state which the first observer describes by Φ, and use a similar notation for all other states. Then, according to (20.8), we have, for all functions Ψ and Φ,

$$|(\Psi, \Phi)| = |(\overline{\Psi}, \overline{\Phi})|. \tag{20.8}$$

Actually (20.8) holds only if Ψ and Φ correspond to physical states, and thus are normalized. Otherwise we cannot discuss the "second description" of the state Φ at all, since only normalized Φ represent states. However, it is suitable to define $\overline{\Phi}'$ even for unnormalized Φ'. Specifically, we make $\overline{\Phi}' = a\overline{\Phi}$ if $\Phi' = a\Phi$, and Φ is normalized. Then (20.8) holds for all functions.

Furthermore, (20.8) does not change if Ψ and Φ are multiplied by constants of absolute value 1. It will now be shown that these constants c_Ψ, c_Φ, can be chosen so that we have not only

$$|(\mathbf{O}_R\Psi, \mathbf{O}_R\Phi)| = |(\Psi, \Phi)| \tag{20.8}$$

but also

$$\begin{aligned} (\mathbf{O}_R\Psi, \mathbf{O}_R\Phi) &= (\Psi, \Phi), \\ \mathbf{O}_R(a\Psi + b\Phi) &= a\mathbf{O}_R\Psi + b\mathbf{O}_R\Phi \end{aligned} \tag{20.8a}$$

for all $c_\Psi\overline{\Psi} = \mathbf{O}_R\Psi$ and $c_\Phi\overline{\Phi} = \mathbf{O}_R\Phi$, where a and b are arbitrary constants. The difficulty in the step from (20.8) to (20.8a) lies in the fact that (20.8) requires only the equality of the absolute values of $(\mathbf{O}_R\Psi, \mathbf{O}_R\Phi)$ and (Ψ, Φ) while (20.8a) requires that the complex phases also be equal, and for all functions simultaneously.

If the functions $\Psi_1, \Psi_2, \cdots$ form a complete orthogonal system, then the $\overline{\Psi}_1, \overline{\Psi}_2, \cdots$ do also. From $(\Psi_i, \Psi_k) = \delta_{ik}$ and (20.8) it follows that $(\overline{\Psi}_i, \overline{\Psi}_k) = \delta_{ik}$ and if no function exists which is orthogonal to all Ψ_i, then neither can a function exist which is orthogonal to all $\overline{\Psi}_i$.

We now consider the functions $\overline{F}_\varkappa$ which correspond to the functions $F_\varkappa = \Psi_1 + \Psi_\varkappa$, for $\varkappa = 1, 2, 3, 4, \cdots$. If we expand $\overline{F}_\varkappa$ in the complete orthogonal system $\overline{\Psi}_1, \overline{\Psi}_2, \cdots$, then all the expansion coefficients $(\overline{\Psi}_\varkappa, \overline{F}_\varkappa)$ are zero except for those of $\overline{\Psi}_1$ and $\overline{\Psi}_\varkappa$, and these are of absolute value 1, since $(\Psi_\lambda, F_\varkappa)$ is non-vanishing only for $\lambda = 1$ and $\lambda = \varkappa$, and for these values of λ it has the value 1. Thus we have

$$\bar{F}_\varkappa = y_\varkappa(\overline{\Psi}_1 + x_\varkappa\overline{\Psi}_\varkappa); \; |y_\varkappa| = |x_\varkappa| = 1 \qquad (\text{for } \varkappa = 2, 3, \cdots). \tag{20.23}$$

We now choose one of the constants, $c_{\Psi_1} = 1$, and write $c_{\Psi_\varkappa} = x_\varkappa$ and $c_{F_\varkappa} = 1/y_\varkappa$. Then

$$\left.\begin{aligned} \mathbf{O}_R\Psi_1 = \overline{\Psi}_1; \; \mathbf{O}_R\Psi_\varkappa = c_{\Psi_\varkappa}\overline{\Psi}_\varkappa = x_\varkappa\overline{\Psi}_\varkappa, \\ \mathbf{O}_R(\Psi_1 + \Psi_\varkappa) = \mathbf{O}_R F_\varkappa = c_{F_\varkappa}\bar{F}_\varkappa = \bar{F}_\varkappa/y_\varkappa = \mathbf{O}_R\Psi_1 + \mathbf{O}_R\Psi_\varkappa. \end{aligned}\right\} \tag{20.24}$$

Now let Φ be an arbitrary function which has been expanded in terms of the $\Psi_\varkappa$

$$\Phi = a_1\Psi_1 + a_2\Psi_2 + a_3\Psi_3 + \cdots. \tag{20.25}$$

We expand $\overline{\Phi}$ in the complete orthogonal system of the $\mathbf{O}_R\Psi_1$, $\mathbf{O}_R\Psi_2$, etc.

$$\overline{\Phi} = \bar{a}_1\mathbf{O}_R\Psi_1 + \bar{a}_2\mathbf{O}_R\Psi_2 + \bar{a}_3\mathbf{O}_R\Psi_3 + \cdots.$$

Thus

$$|\bar{a}_\varkappa| = |(\mathbf{O}_R\Psi_\varkappa, \overline{\Phi})| = |(x_\varkappa\overline{\Psi}_\varkappa, \overline{\Phi})| = |(\Psi_\varkappa, \Phi)| = |a_\varkappa| \tag{20.26}$$

and in particular $|\bar{a}_1| = |a_1|$. We therefore choose $c_\Phi = a_1/\bar{a}_1$, so that

$$\mathbf{O}_R\Phi = c_\Phi\overline{\Phi} = a_1\mathbf{O}_R\Psi_1 + a_2'\mathbf{O}_R\Psi_2 + a_3'\mathbf{O}_R\Psi_3 + \cdots \tag{20.27}$$

In addition, $|a_\varkappa'| = |a_\varkappa|$. It will in fact turn out that $a_\varkappa' = a_\varkappa$. To prove this, let us apply (20.8) to the pair of functions $F_\varkappa = \Psi_1 + \Psi_\varkappa$ and Φ. We have first,

$$|(F_\varkappa, \Phi)| = |(\Psi_1 + \Psi_\varkappa, \Phi)| = |a_1 + a_\varkappa|.$$

Similarly, since $\bar{F}_\varkappa$ and $\overline{\Phi}$ differ from $\mathbf{O}_R F_\varkappa$ and $\mathbf{O}_R\Phi$ only in a constant factor of modulus 1,

$$\begin{aligned} |(\bar{F}_\varkappa, \overline{\Phi})| &= |(\mathbf{O}_R F_\varkappa, \mathbf{O}_R\Phi)| \\ &= |(\mathbf{O}_R\Psi_1 + \mathbf{O}_R\Psi_\varkappa, a_1\mathbf{O}_R\Psi_1 + a_2'\mathbf{O}_R\Psi_2 + \cdots)| = |a_1 + a_\varkappa'|. \end{aligned}$$

Hence $\quad |a_1 + a_\varkappa|^2 = |a_1 + a_\varkappa'|^2$, or

$$|a_1|^2 + a_1^*a_\varkappa' + a_1a_\varkappa'^* + |a_\varkappa'|^2 = |a_1|^2 + a_1^*a_\varkappa + a_1a_\varkappa^* + |a_\varkappa|^2.$$

The $a_\varkappa'^*$ can be eliminated from this equation by using $a_\varkappa'a_\varkappa'^* = a_\varkappa a_\varkappa^*$ to obtain a quadratic equation for $a_\varkappa'$:

$$a_1^*a_\varkappa'^2 - (a_1^*a_\varkappa + a_1a_\varkappa^*)a_\varkappa' + a_1|a_\varkappa|^2 = 0. \tag{20.28}$$

From (20.28) it follows that either

$$a_\varkappa' = a_\varkappa \quad \text{or} \quad a_\varkappa' = a_\varkappa^*a_1/a_1^*. \tag{20.29}$$

In the first case, for every $\Phi = \sum_\varkappa a_\varkappa \Psi_\varkappa$ and $\Psi = \sum_\varkappa b_\varkappa \Psi_\varkappa$,

$$\mathbf{O}_R\Phi = \sum_\varkappa a_\varkappa \mathbf{O}_R\Psi_\varkappa; \quad \mathbf{O}_R\Psi = \sum_\varkappa b_\varkappa \mathbf{O}_R\Psi_\varkappa, \tag{20.30}$$

and also

$$\mathbf{O}_R(a\Phi + b\Psi) = \mathbf{O}_R \sum_\varkappa (aa_\varkappa + bb_\varkappa)\Psi_\varkappa = \sum_\varkappa (aa_\varkappa + bb_\varkappa)\mathbf{O}_R\Psi_\varkappa$$
$$= a\mathbf{O}_R\Phi + b\mathbf{O}_R\Psi,$$

so that $\mathbf{O}_R$ is in fact *linear*. Furthermore,

$$(\mathbf{O}_R\Psi, \mathbf{O}_R\Phi) = (\sum_\varkappa b_\varkappa \mathbf{O}_R\Psi_\varkappa, \sum_\lambda a_\lambda \mathbf{O}_R\Psi_\lambda)$$
$$= \sum_{\varkappa\lambda} b_\varkappa^* a_\lambda \delta_{\varkappa\lambda} = \sum_\varkappa b_\varkappa^* a_\varkappa,$$

and also

$$(\Psi, \Phi) = (\sum_\varkappa b_\varkappa \Psi_\varkappa, \sum_\lambda a_\lambda \Psi_\lambda) = \sum_{\varkappa\lambda} b_\varkappa^* a_\lambda \delta_{\varkappa\lambda} = \sum_\varkappa b_\varkappa^* a_\varkappa.$$

The operator $\mathbf{O}_R$ is also *unitary*, which proves (20.8a).

We have still to show only that the second alternative in (20.29) cannot occur. For this purpose we substitute

$$\mathbf{O}_R\Phi = \mathbf{O}_R \sum_\varkappa a_\varkappa \Psi_\varkappa = \sum_\varkappa a_\varkappa^* \mathbf{O}_R\Psi_\varkappa \tag{20.31}$$

for

$$\mathbf{O}_R\Phi = \mathbf{O}_R \sum_\varkappa a_\varkappa \Psi_\varkappa = \frac{a_1}{a_1^*} \sum_\varkappa a_\varkappa^* \mathbf{O}_R\Psi_\varkappa,$$

i.e., multiply $\mathbf{O}_R\Phi$ by a_1^*/a_1. This certainly cannot change the content of the description.

We now consider two eigenfunctions of the Hamiltonian operator; that is, two stationary states $\chi = \sum_\varkappa u_\varkappa \Psi_\varkappa$ and $\chi' = \sum_\varkappa u'_\varkappa \Psi_\varkappa$ with *different* energies E and E'. Then

$$\chi e^{-i(E/\hbar)t} + \chi' e^{-i(E'/\hbar)t} = \sum_\varkappa (u_\varkappa e^{-i(E/\hbar)t} + u'_\varkappa e^{-i(E'/\hbar)t})\Psi_\varkappa \tag{20.32}$$

is a solution of the time-dependent Schrödinger equation. In the second description, by (20.31),

$$\mathbf{O}_R\chi = \sum_\varkappa u_\varkappa^* \mathbf{O}_R\Psi_\varkappa$$

would correspond to the state χ, and

$$\mathbf{O}_R\chi' = \sum_\varkappa u'^*_\varkappa \mathbf{O}_R\Psi_\varkappa$$

to the state χ'. Also, the energies are still E and E' in the second description.

Therefore,

$$e^{-i(E/\hbar)t}\mathbf{O}_R\chi + e^{-i(E'/\hbar)t}\mathbf{O}_R\chi' = \sum_\varkappa (u_\varkappa^* e^{-i(E/\hbar)t} + u_\varkappa'^* e^{-i(E'/\hbar)t})\mathbf{O}_R\Psi_\varkappa \quad (20.33)$$

must also be a solution to the Schrödinger equation which represents the same state for $t = 0$ as (20.32), and will consequently represent the same state for all later times. But this is not possible, since according to (20.31)

$$\sum_\varkappa (u_\varkappa e^{-i(E/\hbar)t} + u_\varkappa' e^{-i(E'/\hbar)t})^* \mathbf{O}_R\Psi_\varkappa$$

corresponds to the state (20.32), which is identical with (20.33) for $t \neq 0$, *only if* $E = E'$. The second alternative of (20.29) thus leads to a contradiction so that the selection of c which was used in (20.24) and (20.27) leads to the first alternative in (20.29). The *linear unity* character of the $\mathbf{O}_R$ then follows.

With this we obtain the important result that two physically equivalent descriptions—after suitable changes in the free constants of the wave functions—can be transformed into one another by a *canonical transformation*. It should be noted, however, that in order to exclude the second alternative, the "antiunitary" (20.31), it was necessary to consider also the time dependence of the wave functions. More precisely, it was postulated that if the state Φ becomes the state Φ' in the course of the time interval t, then the state $\overline{\Phi}$ becomes $\overline{\Phi}'$ during the same time interval. This is a justified, and, in fact, a necessary assumption in the context of the present discussion but will not be valid when the operation of "time inversion" will be considered, in Chapter 26.

21. The Total Angular Momentum Quantum Number

1. In the transformation formula of the preceding chapter, Eq. (20.19),

$$\mathbf{O}_R\Phi(x, y, z, s) = \sum_{t=\pm1} \mathfrak{D}^{(1/2)}(R)_{\frac{1}{2}s,\frac{1}{2}t}\mathbf{P}_R\Phi(x, y, z, t)$$

$$= \sum_{t=\pm1} \mathfrak{D}^{(1/2)}(R)_{\frac{1}{2}s,\frac{1}{2}t}\Phi(x'', y'', z'', t), \tag{21.1}$$

R is a pure rotation. If we wish to write the wave function in a coordinate system which is obtained from the original one by an improper rotation, we can first carry out an inversion of the coordinate system

$$x' = -x, \quad y' = -y, \quad z' = -z \tag{21.2}$$

and then follow this by a rotation. The real question is therefore only how the wave function $\mathbf{O}_I\Phi$ for the state Φ appears to an observer whose coordinate axes are *oppositely* directed to those of the original system.

We consider first of all the state $u_s\psi(x, y, z)$. In spin-free experiments it behaves for the first observer as if its wave function were ψ, and therefore for the observer in the inverted coordinate system as if its wave function were $\mathbf{P}_I\psi$, where

$$\mathbf{P}_I\psi(x, y, z) = \psi(-x, -y, -z). \tag{21.2}$$

Therefore $\mathbf{O}_I u_s\psi(x, y, z) = u_s' \cdot \mathbf{P}_I\psi(x, y, z)$. The magnetic moment has a given direction for $u_s\psi(x, y, z)$. Under inversion of the coordinates, this direction transforms into the opposite direction, because the magnetic moment is an *axial* vector. But the opposite direction in the new coordinate system is labeled exactly as was the original direction in the old system. For the second observer the spin direction is the same as for the first, and the factor u_s' before $\mathbf{P}_I\psi$ in $\mathbf{O}_I u_s\psi(x, y, z)$ is equal to u_s.

We know that a magnetic dipole can always be replaced by a circular current. If this circular current lies, say, in the XY plane and runs from X toward Y, it also lies in the $X'Y'$ plane and runs from X' to Y'.

Consequently, for all u_s and all $\psi(x, y, z)$ we have

$$\mathbf{O}_I u_s\psi(x, y, z) = u_s\mathbf{P}_I\psi(x, y, z) = \mathbf{P}_I u_s\psi(x, y, z), \tag{21.3}$$

except for a constant which can still depend on u and ψ. But it can be shown exactly as was done after (20.8a) that this constant must be of the same magnitude for all u and for all ψ, if we require the linearity of $\mathbf{O}_I$. Since a factor in $\mathbf{O}_I$ is already entirely arbitrary, we can omit this constant entirely. Furthermore since every function $\Phi(x, y, z, s)$ can be written as a linear combination of functions of the form $u_s\psi(x, y, z)$, it follows from (21.3) and the linearity of $\mathbf{O}_I$ and $\mathbf{P}_I$ that $\mathbf{O}_I \equiv \mathbf{P}_I$

$$\mathbf{O}_I\Phi(x, y, z, s) = \mathbf{P}_I\Phi(x, y, z, s) = \Phi(-x, -y, -z, s). \tag{21.4}$$

The operator $\mathbf{O}_I$ which effects an inversion (21.2) of the coordinate system does not operate on the spin coordinates at all; it is given by (21.4). We have $\mathbf{O}_I^2 = \mathbf{1}$ or $\mathbf{O}_I\mathbf{O}_I\Phi = \Phi$; thus the identity operator and the operator $\mathbf{O}_I$ form a group isomorphic to the reflection group.

In (21.1) and (21.4) we have the transformation formulas for the wave function for an arbitrary change of axes. Moreover, the formulas (21.1) and (21.4) hold not only for electrons, but also for protons. However, the magnetic moment of protons is very much smaller than that of an electron (the mass of the proton is some 1840 times as large) and is therefore not so easily accessible to observation as that due to the electron spin. In what follows, we shall not consider the "nuclear spin."

Equations (21.1) and (21.4) are also valid in Dirac's relativistic theory of the electron without essential changes.[1] According to Dirac a wave function consists not of two functions of position $\Phi(x, y, z, -1)$ and $\Phi(x, y, z, 1)$, but of four. One can introduce, besides s, a fifth coordinate s', which can also assume only two values. Then for pure rotations, Eq. (21.1) remains unchanged: s' does not take part in the transformation at all; on the other hand, under inversion, the two s' values are interchanged.

2. The formulas (21.1) and (21.4) refer to a system which contains only one electron. In cases of several electrons, the wave function $\Phi(x_1, y_1, z_1, s_1, \cdots, x_n, y_n, z_n, s_n)$ contains the spin coordinates of all the particles as well as their Cartesian coordinates. The scalar product of two functions Φ and G is

$$(\Phi, G) = \sum_{s_1=\pm 1} \sum_{s_2=\pm 1} \cdots \sum_{s_n=\pm 1} \int\int_{-\infty}^{\infty} \cdots \int \Phi(x_1, \cdots, s_n)^* G(x_1, \cdots, s_n)\, dx_1 \cdots dz_n. \tag{21.5}$$

In the simple spinless theory the operator $\mathbf{P}_R$ affected all the coordinate triplets, and all in the same way. Similarly, the operator $\mathbf{O}_R$, which in the Pauli theory transforms to another system of axes, now operates on all the.

[1] J. A. Gaunt, *Proc. Roy. Soc.* A **124**, 163 (1929).

coordinates x_k, y_k, z_k, and s_k, in the same way as it operates on x, y, z, and s in Eq. (21.1) or (21.4). Thus one has

$$\mathbf{O}_R\Phi(x_1, y_1, z_1, s_1, \cdots, x_n, y_n, z_n, s_n)$$
$$= \sum_{t_1 \ldots t_n} \mathfrak{D}^{(1/2)}(R)_{\frac{1}{2}s_1,\frac{1}{2}t_1} \cdots \mathfrak{D}^{(1/2)}(R)_{\frac{1}{2}s_n,\frac{1}{2}t_n} \mathbf{P}_R\Phi(x_1, y_1, z_1, t_1, \cdots, x_n, y_n, z_n, t_n) \tag{21.6}$$

and

$$\mathbf{O}_I\Phi(x_1, y_1, z_1, s_1, \cdots, x_n, y_n, z_n, s_n)$$
$$= \mathbf{P}_I\Phi(x_1, y_1, z_1, s_1, \cdots, x_n, y_n, z_n, s_n)$$
$$= \Phi(-x_1, -y_1, -z_1, s_1, \cdots, -x_n, -y_n, -z_n, s_n). \tag{21.7}$$

The operator $\mathbf{O}_R$ is the product of two operators $\mathbf{P}_R$ and $\mathbf{Q}_R$, the first of which affects only the cartesian coordinates.

$$\mathbf{P}_R\Phi(x_1', y_1', z_1', s_1, \cdots, x_n', y_n', z_n', s_n') = \Phi(x_1, y_1, z_1, s_1, \cdots, x_n, y_n, z_n, s_n). \tag{21.6a}$$

Here x_k', y_k', z_k' result from the x_k, y_k, z_k by the rotation R. The second operator operates only on the spin coordinates.

$$\mathbf{Q}_R\Phi(x_1, y_1, z_1, s_1, \cdots, x_n, y_n, z_n, s_n)$$
$$= \sum_{t_1=\pm1} \cdots \sum_{t_n=\pm1} \mathfrak{D}^{(1/2)}(R)_{\frac{1}{2}s_1,\frac{1}{2}t_1} \cdots \mathfrak{D}^{(1/2)}(R)_{\frac{1}{2}s_n,\frac{1}{2}t_n} \Phi(x_1, y_1, z_1, t_1, \cdots, x_n, y_n, z_n, t_n). \tag{21.6b}$$

Since the system of spin coordinates can assume 2^n different sets of values, $\mathbf{Q}_R$ is equivalent to a 2^n-dimensional matrix; its rows and columns are numbered by n indices and each index can have the values ±1, corresponding to the possible values for the spin coordinates. The matrix form of $\mathbf{Q}_R$ is

$$\begin{aligned} \mathbf{Q}_R &= \mathfrak{D}^{(1/2)}(R) \times \mathfrak{D}^{(1/2)}(R) \times \cdots \times \mathfrak{D}^{(1/2)}(R) \\ (\mathbf{Q}_R)_{s_1s_2\cdots s_n;\, t_1t_2\cdots t_n} &= \mathfrak{D}^{(1/2)}(R)_{\frac{1}{2}s_1,\frac{1}{2}t_1} \cdots \mathfrak{D}^{(1/2)}(R)_{\frac{1}{2}s_n,\frac{1}{2}t_n}. \end{aligned} \tag{21.6c}$$

The operators $\mathbf{P}$ all commute with the operators $\mathbf{Q}_R$.

and in particular,

$$\left.\begin{aligned} \mathbf{P}_S\mathbf{Q}_R &= \mathbf{Q}_R\mathbf{P}_S \\ \mathbf{O}_R = \mathbf{P}_R\mathbf{Q}_R &= \mathbf{Q}_R\mathbf{P}_R. \end{aligned}\right\} \tag{21.8}$$

Also, the operator $\mathbf{O}_I = \mathbf{P}_I$ commutes with all $\mathbf{P}_R$, and therefore by (21.8) with all $\mathbf{O}_R$, where R is any pure rotation.

The $\mathbf{Q}_R$ are determined by the rotation only up to sign, since the sign is free in $\mathfrak{D}^{(1/2)}(R)$. For an even number of electrons this ambiguity can be removed by the convention that all $\mathfrak{D}^{(1/2)}(R)$ in (21.6) and (21.6c) are to be taken *with the same sign*. For an odd number of electrons it is not possible to make the $\mathbf{Q}_R$ single-valued.

3. If we transform first to a coordinate system rotated by R and then to one rotated with respect to this one by S, the wave function Φ transforms first into $\mathbf{O}_R\Phi$ and then into $\mathbf{O}_S\mathbf{O}_R\Phi$. But the same coordinate system is obtained by a single rotation by SR. In this case $\mathbf{O}_{SR}\Phi$ is obtained for the wave function, and this can differ from $\mathbf{O}_S\mathbf{O}_R\Phi$ only by a constant. Furthermore, since $\mathbf{O}_S\mathbf{O}_R$ and $\mathbf{O}_{SR}$ are linear-unitary, this constant is the same for all wave functions and can depend only on the rotations S and R,

$$\mathbf{O}_{SR} = c_{S,R}\mathbf{O}_S\mathbf{O}_R. \tag{21.9}$$

Since the transformation to another coordinate system always can be effected by a linear unitary operator, Eq. (21.9) still contains none of the special assumptions of the Pauli theory, and is a necessary consequence of the invariance of the system of equations under spatial rotations. We will investigate this equation further at the conclusion of the chapter and derive some consequences which must hold in every quantum mechanical theory.

Equation (21.9) can, of course, be verified by calculation. To begin with, by (21.8),

$$\mathbf{O}_S\mathbf{O}_R = \mathbf{P}_S\mathbf{Q}_S\mathbf{P}_R\mathbf{Q}_R = \mathbf{P}_S\mathbf{P}_R\mathbf{Q}_S\mathbf{Q}_R = \mathbf{P}_{SR}\mathbf{Q}_S\mathbf{Q}_R.$$

For an even number of electrons the matrices (21.6c), which are the matrix forms of the $\mathbf{Q}$, form a *single-valued representation* of the rotation group, so that $\mathbf{Q}_S\mathbf{Q}_R = \mathbf{Q}_{SR}$ and we have

$$\mathbf{O}_S\mathbf{O}_R = \mathbf{P}_{SR}\mathbf{Q}_S\mathbf{Q}_R = \mathbf{P}_{SR}\mathbf{Q}_{SR} = \mathbf{O}_{SR}. \tag{21.10a}$$

In this case the constant $c_{S,R} = 1$ in (21.9), and the operators $\mathbf{O}_R$ form a group isomorphic to the pure rotation group. Therefore, in this case functions can be defined which, with respect to the operators $\mathbf{O}_R$, belong to one row of an irreducible representation, or simply to an irreducible representation of the rotation group.

For an odd number of electrons the matrices (21.6c) form only a double-valued representation of the pure rotation group; since $\mathbf{Q}_S\mathbf{Q}_R = \pm\mathbf{Q}_{SR}$,

$$\mathbf{O}_S\mathbf{O}_R = \mathbf{P}_{SR}\mathbf{Q}_S\mathbf{Q}_R = \pm\mathbf{P}_{SR}\mathbf{Q}_{SR} = \pm\mathbf{O}_{SR}. \tag{21.10b}$$

The constant $c_{S,R} = \pm 1$ in (21.9), and the operators $\mathbf{O}_R$ are no longer isomorphic to the rotation group. Because of the double-valuedness of the $\mathbf{Q}_R$, two operators $+\mathbf{O}_R$ and $-\mathbf{O}_R$ correspond to each rotation.

Since in the homomorphism of the unitary group[2] onto the rotation group,

[2] More exactly, the group of two-dimensional unitary matrices with determinant 1.

two unitary matrices $\mathbf{u} = \mathfrak{D}^{(1/2)}(R)$ and $\mathbf{u} = -\mathfrak{D}^{(1/2)}(R)$ correspond to each rotation, one can attempt to establish a one-to-one correspondence between the $\mathbf{O}$ and the $\mathbf{u}$. This can be accomplished by letting $\mathbf{O}_{\mathbf{u}} = \mathbf{Q}_{\mathbf{u}} \cdot \mathbf{P}_{R_{\mathbf{u}}}$ correspond to $\mathbf{u}$, and assuming that $\mathbf{u} \times \mathbf{u} \times \cdots \times \mathbf{u}$ is the matrix form of $\mathbf{Q}_{\mathbf{u}}$, in accordance with (21.6c), while $R_{\mathbf{u}}$ is the rotation corresponding to $\mathbf{u}$ by the homomorphism. Then each $\mathbf{Q}_{\mathbf{u}}$ corresponds uniquely to one $\mathbf{u}$. Since the $R_{\mathbf{u}}$ also correspond uniquely to the $\mathbf{u}$, so do the operators $\mathbf{P}_R$. Moreover, from

$$(\mathbf{u} \times \mathbf{u} \times \cdots \times \mathbf{u}) \cdot (\mathbf{v} \times \mathbf{v} \times \cdots \times \mathbf{v}) = \mathbf{uv} \times \mathbf{uv} \times \cdots \times \mathbf{uv}$$

and from $R_{\mathbf{u}} R_{\mathbf{v}} = R_{\mathbf{uv}}$, it follows that $\mathbf{P}_{R_{\mathbf{u}}} \mathbf{P}_{R_{\mathbf{v}}} = \mathbf{P}_{R_{\mathbf{uv}}}$, and therefore

$$\mathbf{O}_{\mathbf{u}} \mathbf{O}_{\mathbf{v}} = \mathbf{O}_{\mathbf{uv}}.$$

Thus for an odd number of electrons the functions $f_{-j}, f_{-j+1}, \cdots, f_{j-1}, f_j$ for which

$$\mathbf{O}_{\mathbf{u}} f_{\mu}^{(j)} = \sum_{\mu'=-j}^{j} \mathfrak{U}^{(j)}(\mathbf{u})_{\mu'\mu} f_{\mu'}^{(j)} \tag{21.11}$$

holds, belong to different rows of the representation $\mathfrak{U}^{(j)}$ of the unitary group. Therefore, they fulfill the relations which were derived in Chapter 12 for functions which belong to irreducible representations of *any* group.

On the subsequent pages, the equation

$$\mathbf{O}_R f_{\mu}^{(j)} = \pm \sum_{\mu'=-j}^{j} \mathfrak{D}^{(j)}(R)_{\mu'\mu} f_{\mu'}^{(j)} \tag{21.11a}$$

will always appear in place of (21.11); Eq. (21.11a) seems to imply (21.11), except for the $\pm$ sign.

$$\mathbf{O}_{\mathbf{u}} f_{\mu}^{(j)} = \pm \sum_{\mu'} \mathfrak{U}^{(j)}(\mathbf{u})_{\mu'\mu} f_{\mu'}^{(j)}. \tag{21.11b}$$

Actually, it is always (21.11) that is derived. Moreover, (21.11a) really implies (21.11) itself, rather than just (21.11b). To see that the lower sign in (21.11b) must be ruled out, assume that it is correct. Then we could change $\mathbf{u}$ continuously into the unit matrix. In this process both sides of (21.11b) change continuously, so that the lower sign would have to be retained throughout. But for $\mathbf{u} = \mathbf{1}$, Eq. (21.11b) with the lower sign is

$$\mathbf{O}_{\mathbf{1}} f_{\mu}^{(j)} = -\sum_{\mu'} \delta_{\mu'\mu} f_{\mu'}^{(j)} = -f_{\mu}^{(j)},$$

which is certainly not correct, since $\mathbf{O}_{\mathbf{1}}$ is the identity operator and must leave every function unchanged. Therefore in (21.11b) only the upper sign can hold. Hence (21.11a) is actually identical with (21.11); we prefer the form (21.11a) only because it emphasizes the significance of the operation $\mathbf{O}$ as a spatial rotation.

Let us next set $\mathbf{u} = -\mathbf{1}$ in (21.11). Then O_{-1} is the negative of the identity operator, since $\mathsf{P} = \mathsf{P}_E$ is the positive, and $-\mathbf{1} \times -\mathbf{1} \times \cdots \times -\mathbf{1}$ in (21.6c) is the negative identity operator. (We are dealing with an odd number of electrons.) It then follows from (21.11) that $\mathfrak{U}^{(j)}(-\mathbf{1}) = -\mathbf{1}$ and from this, according to Chapter 15, that j must be half-integral. *For an odd number of electrons* a wave function can belong only to an *odd representation* of the unitary group or of the group of the $\mathsf{O}_{\mathbf{u}}$ and thus to a *double-valued representation* of the rotation group. Naturally, for an even number of electrons only regular representations of the rotation group occur (or even representations of the unitary group).

The complication with the double-valued representations arises from the fact that the $c_{S,R}$ in (21.9) can equal -1 as well as 1; *the operators* O *which express the invariance of the description under spatial rotations do not form a group isomorphic to the rotation group, but a group isomorphic to the unitary group.*

4. When spin is taken into consideration, the Hamiltonian operator H of the Schrödinger equation $\mathsf{H}\Psi = E\Psi$ for the energy E is no longer a simple operator affecting only the Cartesian coordinates, like that which formed the basis for the earlier considerations. The forces which arise from the magnetic moment of the electrons make additional terms necessary, and we shall discuss the significance of these later. Although the exact form of these terms is still in some doubt, it must be true that no direction in space can be preferred as long as no external magnetic or electric fields exist; if Ψ_μ is a stationary state, then the rotated state $\mathsf{O}_R\Psi_\mu$ or $\mathsf{O}_{\mathbf{u}}\Psi_\mu$ is also stationary, and both have the same energy. From this it follows that $\mathsf{O}_R\Psi_\mu$ or $\mathsf{O}_{\mathbf{u}}\Psi_\mu$ can be expressed as a linear combination of the other eigenfunctions for the same eigenvalue.

$$\mathsf{O}_R\Psi_\mu = \sum_\nu \mathbf{D}(R)_{\nu\mu}\Psi_\nu \quad \text{or} \quad \mathsf{O}_{\mathbf{u}}\Psi_\mu = \sum_\nu \mathbf{D}(\mathbf{u})_{\nu\mu}\Psi_\nu. \tag{21.12}$$

From $\mathsf{O}_S\mathsf{O}_R = \mathsf{O}_{SR}$ or, for an odd number of electrons, $\mathsf{O}_S\mathsf{O}_R = \pm\mathsf{O}_{SR}$ (or $\mathsf{O}_{\mathbf{u}}\mathsf{O}_{\mathbf{v}} = \mathsf{O}_{\mathbf{uv}}$), we can conclude in the familiar way that

$$\mathbf{D}(S)\mathbf{D}(R) = \mathbf{D}(SR) \tag{21.13a}$$

or, for an odd number of electrons,

$$\mathbf{D}(S)\mathbf{D}(R) = \pm\mathbf{D}(SR) \quad \text{or} \quad \mathbf{D}(\mathbf{u})\mathbf{D}(\mathbf{v}) = \mathbf{D}(\mathbf{uv}). \tag{21.13b}$$

The matrices $\mathbf{D}(R)$ form a single-valued representation of the rotation group for an even number of electrons and a double-valued representation of the rotation group (or a single-valued representation of the unitary group) for an odd number of electrons.

It can also be concluded, just as in Chapter 12, that these representations can be assumed irreducible.[3] For an even number of electrons, $\mathbf{D}(R)$ can be $\mathfrak{D}^{(0)}, \mathfrak{D}^{(1)}, \mathfrak{D}^{(2)}, \cdots$; for an odd number of electrons, it is one of the representations $\mathfrak{D}^{(1/2)}, \mathfrak{D}^{(3/2)}, \mathfrak{D}^{(5/2)}, \cdots$ (and $\mathbf{D}(\mathbf{u})$ equals $\mathfrak{U}^{(1/2)}, \mathfrak{U}^{(3/2)}, \mathfrak{U}^{(5/2)}, \cdots$).

$$\mathbf{O}_R \Psi_\mu^{(j)} = \sum_{\mu'} \mathfrak{D}^{(j)}(R)_{\mu'\mu} \Psi_{\mu'}^{(j)} \tag{21.12a}$$

The upper index of these representations is called the total angular momentum quantum number and is denoted by the letter j or J; it is integral for an even number of electrons, and half-integral for an odd number ("alternation of multiplicities"). The row μ to which the eigenfunction belongs is called the magnetic quantum number here also; μ, too, is integral for an even number of electrons, and half-integral for an odd number.

5. Let $\mathbf{S}$ be an operator symmetric under the $\mathbf{O}_R$, that is, a *scalar*, which is unaffected by a change of axes. We then know that the matrix element

$$\mathbf{S}_{Nj\mu;N'j'\mu'} = (\Psi_\mu^{Nj}, \mathbf{S}\Psi_{\mu'}^{N'j'}) = \delta_{jj'}\delta_{\mu\mu'}S_{Nj;N'j} \tag{21.14}$$

for two eigenfunctions which belong to different representations $\mathfrak{D}^{(j)}$ and $\mathfrak{D}^{(j')}$ or to different rows of the same representation must *vanish*. On the other hand, if $j = j'$ and $\mu = \mu'$ in (21.14) then (21.14) is the same for all μ, i.e., it is independent of the magnetic quantum number.

It is natural to look for similar formulas for vector and tensor operators. The scalar operator has been defined by the requirement that it is independent of the system of axes; the energy, for example, is such a quantity, while the X-component of the dipole moment is not. The former quantity corresponds to the same operator for all observers. On the other hand, since the physical quantity to which the second observer ascribes the operator $\mathbf{S}$ is ascribed the operator $\mathbf{O}_R^{-1}\mathbf{S}\mathbf{O}_R$ by the first observer, it must be true that

$$\mathbf{O}_R^{-1}\mathbf{S}\mathbf{O}_R = \mathbf{S}; \; \mathbf{S}\mathbf{O}_R = \mathbf{O}_R\mathbf{S}. \tag{21.15}$$

Thus a symmetric operator commutes with all transformations.

In contrast, if $\mathbf{V}_x, \mathbf{V}_y, \mathbf{V}_z$ are the X', Y', Z' components of a *vector* operator, then the X, Y, Z components of this operator are[4]

$$\begin{aligned} \mathbf{O}_R^{-1}\mathbf{V}_x\mathbf{O}_R &= \mathbf{R}_{xx}\mathbf{V}_x + \mathbf{R}_{xy}\mathbf{V}_y + \mathbf{R}_{xz}\mathbf{V}_z, \\ \mathbf{O}_R^{-1}\mathbf{V}_y\mathbf{O}_R &= \mathbf{R}_{yx}\mathbf{V}_x + \mathbf{R}_{yy}\mathbf{V}_y + \mathbf{R}_{yz}\mathbf{V}_z, \\ \mathbf{O}_R^{-1}\mathbf{V}_z\mathbf{O}_R &= \mathbf{R}_{zx}\mathbf{V}_x + \mathbf{R}_{zy}\mathbf{V}_y + \mathbf{R}_{zz}\mathbf{V}_z. \end{aligned} \tag{21.16}$$

[3] By viewing an eigenvalue as several accidentally coinciding eigenvalues.

[4] In spite of their apparent similarity (11.18a) and (21.16) express quite different relations. The former gives the components x' of a vector in the second coordinate system, in terms of the components x in the first system. The three equations (21.16) express vectors directed along the X', Y', Z' axes in terms of vectors in the directions X, Y, Z. The coefficients in the two equations are identical because they form a real orthogonal matrix. Otherwise, one would be the transpose of the reciprocal of the other.

Thus the $\mathbf{V}_x$, $\mathbf{V}_y$, $\mathbf{V}_z$ do not transform according to $\mathfrak{D}^{(0)}$ as $\mathbf{S}$ does; i.e., under the transformation to a new system of axes they do not remain unchanged but are transformed by the rotation matrix $\mathbf{R}$. Now $\mathfrak{D}^{(1)}$ as a representation of the rotation group is equivalent to a representation by the matrices $\mathbf{R}$; for later calculations it is well to use the components

$$\begin{aligned}
\mathbf{V}^{(-1)} &= \frac{1}{\sqrt{2}}\mathbf{V}_x + \frac{i}{\sqrt{2}}\mathbf{V}_y, \\
\mathbf{V}^{(0)} &= \mathbf{V}_z, \qquad\qquad\qquad\qquad (21.17)\\
\mathbf{V}^{(1)} &= \frac{-1}{\sqrt{2}}\mathbf{V}_x + \frac{i}{\sqrt{2}}\mathbf{V}_y
\end{aligned}$$

instead of the X, Y, Z components. For these we have, because of (15.34),

$$\mathbf{O}_R^{-1}\mathbf{V}^{(\rho)}\mathbf{O}_R = \sum_{\sigma=-1}^{1} \mathfrak{D}^{(1)}(R)_{\rho\sigma}\mathbf{V}^{(\sigma)} \qquad (21.16a)$$

instead of (21.16).

More generally we can consider an irreducible tensor operator of the ωth degree, which is defined by the condition that its $2\omega + 1$ components $\mathbf{T}^{(\rho)}$ transform under rotation of the axes as follows:

$$\mathbf{O}_R^{-1}\mathbf{T}^{(\rho)}\mathbf{O}_R = \sum_{\sigma=-\omega}^{\omega} \mathfrak{D}^{(\omega)}(R)_{\rho\sigma}\mathbf{T}^{(\sigma)}. \qquad (21.16b)$$

If we replace R by R^{-1} in (21.16), we obtain, because $\mathbf{O}_{R^{-1}} = \mathbf{O}_R^{-1}$ and $\mathfrak{D}^{(\omega)}(R^{-1})_{\rho\sigma} = \mathfrak{D}^{(\omega)}(R)^*_{\sigma\rho}$,

$$\mathbf{O}_R\mathbf{T}^{(\rho)}\mathbf{O}_R^{-1} = \sum_{\sigma=-\omega}^{\omega} \mathfrak{D}^{(\omega)}(R)^*_{\sigma\rho}\mathbf{T}^{(\sigma)}. \qquad (21.16c)$$

From these equations we shall now derive the equations analogous to (21.14) for vector and tensor operators. In order to introduce (21.16c), we apply the unitary operator $\mathbf{O}_R$ to both parts of the scalar product

$$\mathbf{T}^{(\rho)}_{Nj\mu;N'j'\mu'} = (\Psi^{Nj}_{\mu}, \mathbf{T}^{(\rho)}\Psi^{N'j'}_{\mu'}) \qquad (21.18)$$

and obtain

$$\begin{aligned}
\mathbf{T}^{(\rho)}_{Nj\mu;N'j'\mu'} &= (\mathbf{O}_R\Psi^{Nj}_{\mu}, \mathbf{O}_R\mathbf{T}^{(\rho)}\mathbf{O}_R^{-1}\mathbf{O}_R\Psi^{N'j'}_{\mu'}) \qquad (21.18a)\\
&= \sum_{\nu}\sum_{\sigma}\sum_{\nu'} \mathfrak{D}^{(j)}(R)^*_{\nu\mu}\mathfrak{D}^{(\omega)}(R)^*_{\sigma\rho}\mathfrak{D}^{(j')}(R)_{\nu'\mu'}\mathbf{T}^{(\sigma)}_{Nj\nu;N'j'\nu'}.
\end{aligned}$$

Had one integrated the analogous formula for scalar operators over all rotations, the orthogonality relationships would have given (21.14) directly. To evaluate the integral over the product of three rotation coefficients, which is needed for (21.18a), one first writes the product of the first two by means of Eq. (17.16b).

$$\mathfrak{D}^{(j)}(R)^*_{\nu\mu}\mathfrak{D}^{(\omega)}(R)^*_{\sigma\rho} = \sum_{L=|j-\omega|}^{j+\omega} s^{(j\omega)}_{L\nu\sigma}\mathfrak{D}^{(L)}(R)^*_{\nu+\sigma,\mu+\rho}s^{(j\omega)}_{L\mu\rho}.$$

Substituting this into (21.18a) and using the orthogonality relationships (10.12) for the integration over all rotations, one obtains

$$\mathbf{T}^{(\rho)}_{Nj\mu,N'j'\mu'} = \sum_{L=|j-\omega|}^{j+\omega} s^{(j\omega)}_{L\mu\rho} \sum_{\nu\sigma\nu'} s^{(j\omega)}_{L\nu\sigma} \frac{\delta_{Lj'}\delta_{\nu+\sigma,\nu'}\delta_{\mu+\rho,\mu'}}{2j'+1} \cdot \mathbf{T}^{(\sigma)}_{Nj\nu;N'j'\nu'}$$

where both sides have been divided by $\int dR$. This expression vanishes if j' does not lie between the limits $|j-\omega|$ and $j+\omega$; for $|j-\omega| \leq j' \leq j+\omega$, the expression equals

$$\mathbf{T}^{(\rho)}_{Nj\mu;N'j'\mu'} = s^{(j\omega)}_{j'\mu\rho}\,\delta_{\mu+\rho,\mu'} T_{Nj;N'j'}, \tag{21.19}$$

where $T_{Nj;N'j'}$ no longer depends on μ, μ', and ρ[5].

This formula is a very general one.[6] It gives, numerically, the ratio $\mathbf{T}^{(\rho)}_{Nj\mu;N'j'\mu'}/\mathbf{T}^{(\sigma)}_{Nj\mu;N'j'\mu'}$ of "matrix elements," that is, of the scalar products (21.18), whose first factors Ψ^{Nj}_{μ} are different eigenfunctions of the same eigenvalue, whose operators are different components of the same irreducible tensor, and whose second factors $\Psi^{N'j'}_{\mu'}$ are also eigenfunctions of one and the same eigenvalue (which may be different from the eigenvalue of the Ψ^{Nj}_{μ}).

We revert to the case of *vector* operators by setting $\omega = 1$ in (21.19). With the help of the table of vector-coupling coefficients on page 193 we obtain the formulas analogous to (21.14) for vector operators:

$$\begin{aligned}
\mathbf{V}^{(-1)}_{Nj\mu;N'j-1\mu-1} &= \sqrt{j+\mu}\,\sqrt{j+\mu-1}\; V'_{Nj,N'j-1},\\
\mathbf{V}^{(0)}_{Nj\mu;N'j-1\mu} &= -\sqrt{j+\mu}\,\sqrt{j-\mu}\,\sqrt{2}\; V'_{Nj;N'j-1},\\
\mathbf{V}^{(1)}_{Nj\mu;N'j-1\mu+1} &= \sqrt{j-\mu-1}\,\sqrt{j-\mu}\; V'_{Nj;N'j-1}.
\end{aligned} \tag{21.19a}$$

$$\begin{aligned}
\mathbf{V}^{(-1)}_{Nj\mu;N'j\mu-1} &= \sqrt{j-\mu+1}\,\sqrt{j+\mu}\; V'_{Nj;N'j},\\
\mathbf{V}^{(0)}_{Nj\mu;N'j\mu} &= \mu\sqrt{2}\; V'_{Nj;N'j},\\
\mathbf{V}^{(1)}_{Nj\mu;N'j\mu+1} &= -\sqrt{j+\mu+1}\,\sqrt{j-\mu}\; V'_{Nj;N'j}.
\end{aligned} \tag{21.19b}$$

$$\begin{aligned}
\mathbf{V}^{(-1)}_{Nj\mu;N'j+1\mu-1} &= \sqrt{j-\mu+1}\,\sqrt{j-\mu+2}\; V'_{Nj;N'j+1},\\
\mathbf{V}^{(0)}_{Nj\mu;N'j+1\mu} &= \sqrt{j-\mu+1}\,\sqrt{j+\mu+1}\,\sqrt{2}\; V'_{Nj;N'j+1},\\
\mathbf{V}^{(1)}_{Nj\mu;N'j+1\mu+1} &= \sqrt{j+\mu+1}\,\sqrt{j+\mu+2}\; V'_{Nj;N'j+1}.
\end{aligned} \tag{21.19c}$$

All matrix elements of vector operators not enumerated here vanish;

[5] The $T_{Nj;N'j'}$ are sometimes referred to as reduced or "double bar" matrix elements and written $(Nj\|T\|N'j')$.

[6] In this generality the formula originates with C. Eckart, *Revs. Modern Phys.* **2**, 305 (1930).

elements with $j = j' = 0$ are also zero. Of course the $V'_{Nj;N'j'}$ cannot be determined from general considerations. While the matrix elements of a scalar operator are zero if either the total quantum numbers or the magnetic quantum numbers of the rows and columns differ at all (j and j' and/or μ and μ'), these quantum numbers can differ by 1 in the case of vector operators.

In the derivation of (21.19) no assumption was made concerning the particular form of the operators $\mathbf{O}_R$; Eq. (21.19) must therefore apply also in a theory which does not consider the spin, if only the $\mathbf{P}_R$ are substituted for the $\mathbf{O}_R$ and the azimuthal quantum number l for the total quantum number j. Actually, we have already made statements rather frequently about the vanishing of matrix elements of a vector operator. For example, multiplication by

$$x_1 + x_2 + \cdots + x_n, \quad y_1 + y_2 + \cdots + y_n, \quad z_1 + z_2 + \cdots + z_n$$

are the three components of a vector operator, and we have found that the transition probability for a radiative transition from the state ψ_F into the state ψ_E, which is determined by

$$(\psi_F, (x_1 + x_2 + \cdots + x_n)\psi_E), \qquad \text{etc.,}$$

vanishes if the difference of the azimuthal quantum numbers of ψ_F and ψ_E is not 0 or ± 1. Later, we saw that the magnetic quantum number is unchanged if the light is polarized in the Z-direction ($\rho = 0$), and changes by ± 1 if the light is polarized in the X or Y directions.

The additional terms in the Schrödinger equation due to a magnetic field $\mathscr{H}_z$ in the Z direction,

$$\mathbf{V}_z = \mathbf{V}^{(0)} = \frac{-ie\hbar\mathscr{H}_z}{2mc}\Big[x_1\partial/\partial y_1 + x_2\partial/\partial y_2 + \cdots + x_n\partial/\partial y_n$$
$$- y_1\partial/\partial x_1 - y_2\partial/\partial x_2 - \cdots - y_n\partial/\partial x_n\Big],$$

form the Z-component of a vector operator. In this case we have actually calculated the matrix elements $\mathbf{V}_{Nl\mu;Nl\mu}$. From the middle equation of (21.19b) we see that they must be proportional to the magnetic quantum number μ. We have also found that the proportionality constant is independent of N and l and equal to $e\hbar\mathscr{H}_z/2mc$.

In a certain sense, Eq. (21.19) is the counterpart of Eq. (19.6) in which the dependence of the eigenfunctions on the orientation of the configuration-n-pod is explicitly determined. The latter combined into a single equation, at least for the spinless theory, all the information which the rotational symmetry of the system yields for the *wave function*. For both the elementary theory and the theory with spin, Eq. (21.19) combines all the information which the rotational symmetry yields for the *matrix elements* without the use of any approximations.

6. It is interesting to note[7] that the existence of a total quantum number

[7] The rest of this chapter is not essential for the following chapters.

and also (21.19) already follow from the very general Eq. (21.9), except that (21.9) does not permit the determination of the integral or half-integral nature of j. This feature would be too much to expect since the number of electrons does not occur in (21.9).

If Eq. (21.9) is used for the derivation of the multiplication property (21.13) of the $\mathbf{D}$, one obtains instead of (21.13) only the result that the matrices $\mathbf{D}(R)$ defined in (21.12),

$$\mathbf{D}(SR) = c_{S,R}\mathbf{D}(S)\mathbf{D}(R), \tag{21.20a}$$

form a representation of the rotation group *up to a factor*. However, the identity E is still represented by the unit matrix. It will now be shown that by multiplying each matrix $\mathbf{D}(R)$ which satisfies (21.20a) by a suitably chosen number c_R, a system of matrices $\bar{\bar{\mathbf{D}}}(R) = c_R\mathbf{D}(R)$ can be obtained which forms a representation of the unitary group, that is, for which

$$\bar{\bar{\mathbf{D}}}(S)\bar{\bar{\mathbf{D}}}(R) = \pm\bar{\bar{\mathbf{D}}}(SR). \tag{21.20}$$

Therefore, according to Chapter 15, this system of matrices can be resolved into the representations $\mathfrak{D}^{(0)}$, $\mathfrak{D}^{(1/2)}$, $\mathfrak{D}^{(1)}$, $\cdots$ by a similarity transformation. This means that the set of matrices to which (21.9) first leads are essentially the single-valued and double-valued representations of Chapter 15.

In particular, a set of two-dimensional matrices which satisfies (20.17) contains either just constant matrices (if it contains $\mathfrak{D}^{(0)}$ twice) or is equivalent to $\mathfrak{D}^{(1/2)}$, as we have concluded in the preceding chapter.

We shall first form $\bar{\mathbf{D}}(R) = c_R\mathbf{D}(R)$ from the $\mathbf{D}(R)$ and choose c_R equal to the $(-1/\lambda)$th power of the determinant of $\mathbf{D}(R)$. Here λ is the dimension of $\mathbf{D}(R)$. This makes the determinant $|\bar{\mathbf{D}}(R)| = 1$:

$$|\bar{\mathbf{D}}(R)| = |c_R\mathbf{1}\cdot\mathbf{D}(R)| = |c_R\cdot\mathbf{1}|\cdot|\mathbf{D}(R)| = c_R^{\lambda}\cdot|\mathbf{D}(R)| = 1. \tag{21.21}$$

The values of c_R and the elements of $\bar{\mathbf{D}}(R)$ are still not determined uniquely, but only up to the λ-valued λth root of unity, ω. Thus, λ matrices correspond to each group element R, namely, all the multiples of $\mathbf{D}(R)$ whose determinant is 1.

If $\bar{\mathbf{D}}(S)$ is multiplied by $\bar{\mathbf{D}}(R)$, a $\bar{\mathbf{D}}(SR)$ is obtained. Because of (21.20a) this product is just a multiple of every $\bar{\mathbf{D}}(SR)$; its determinant is the product of the determinants of $\bar{\mathbf{D}}(S)$ and $\bar{\mathbf{D}}(R)$, which is 1.

From the representation up to a factor $\mathbf{D}(R)$, *we have obtained a many-valued, indeed a λ-valued, representation*; the product of every $\bar{\mathbf{D}}(S)$ with every $\bar{\mathbf{D}}(R)$ yields a $\bar{\mathbf{D}}(SR)$.

We can attempt to reduce this multiplicity of the representation simply by selecting and retaining one of the λ matrices $\bar{\mathbf{D}}(R)$ and omitting the others. Naturally, this cannot be done arbitrarily, but only in such a way that any one of the retained matrices $\overline{\mathbf{D}}(S)$ multiplied by any other of the retained matrices $\overline{\mathbf{D}}(R)$ again gives a matrix $\overline{\mathbf{D}}(SR)$, which has been retained. Following a method of H. Weyl,[8] we base this selection on the continuity properties of representations.

If S and S' are two adjacent group elements $S \sim S'$, then we must have had, for the original form of the $\mathbf{D}(R)$

$$\mathbf{D}(S) \sim \mathbf{D}(S') \quad \text{and} \quad |\mathbf{D}(S)| \sim |\mathbf{D}(S')|.$$

From the latter equation it follows that the λ values of c_S are adjacent to the λ values of $c_{S'}$ in pairs. Also the λ matrices $\overline{\mathbf{D}}(S)$ are adjacent to the λ matrices $\overline{\mathbf{D}}(S')$ in pairs, and in such a way that a $\overline{\mathbf{D}}(S)$ is neighbor to one and only one $\overline{\mathbf{D}}(S')$, while the other $\lambda - 1$ are essentially different, since they arise from them by multiplication by a number which differs essentially from 1 (a λth root of 1).

If we connect the identity $E = S(0)$ with the element $S = S(1)$ by a continuous line $S(t)$ in parameter space, then we can require that the matrices $\mathbf{D}(S(t))$ run over a continuous sequence. Then, starting with $\overline{\mathbf{D}}(S(0)) = \overline{\mathbf{D}}(E) = \mathbf{1}$ and proceeding along a given path $S(t)$, only one of the λ matrices $\overline{\mathbf{D}}(S)$ will be obtained. We denote this by $\overline{\mathbf{D}}(S)_{S(t)}$. If the path $S(t)$ is deformed continuously while the end points are held fixed, then $\overline{\mathbf{D}}(S)_{S(t)}$ does not change at all, since it can only change continuously in a continuous deformation of the path, whereas the transition to another $\overline{\mathbf{D}}(S)$ would necessarily imply a jump.

The product $\overline{\mathbf{D}}(S)_{S(t)} \cdot \overline{\mathbf{D}}(R)_{R(t)}$ is one of the matrices $\overline{\mathbf{D}}(SR)$, which also arise continuously from $\overline{\mathbf{D}}(E) = \mathbf{1}$. The corresponding path travels first of all from E along $S(t)$ to S—during which $\mathbf{D}(E) = \mathbf{1}$ changes continuously into $\overline{\mathbf{D}}(S)_{S(t)}$, then the path travels to SR over the points $S \cdot R(t)$—while $\overline{\mathbf{D}}(S)_{S(t)} = \overline{\mathbf{D}}(S)_{S(t)} \cdot \mathbf{1}$ transforms continuously to $\overline{\mathbf{D}}(S)_{S(t)}\overline{\mathbf{D}}(R)_{R(t)}$ via the matrices $\overline{\mathbf{D}}(S)_{S(t)} \cdot \overline{\mathbf{D}}(R(t))$:

$$\overline{\mathbf{D}}(S)_{S(t)}\overline{\mathbf{D}}(R)_{R(t)} = \overline{\mathbf{D}}(SR)_{S(t), S \cdot R(t)}. \tag{21.22}$$

If all paths from E to S can be deformed into one another continuously, the parameter space is simply connected and there exists only *one single* $\overline{\overline{\mathbf{D}}}(S) = \overline{\mathbf{D}}(S)_{S(t)}$ which can be obtained continuously from $\overline{\mathbf{D}}(E) = 1 = \overline{\overline{\mathbf{D}}}(E)$. These $\overline{\overline{\mathbf{D}}}(S)$ therefore form a *single-valued representation of the group.*

If the parameter space is multiply connected there exist two or more paths $S_1(t), S_2(t), \cdots$ which cannot be deformed into one another continuously; the corresponding matrices $\overline{\mathbf{D}}(S)_{S_1(t)}, \overline{\mathbf{D}}(S)_{S_2(t)}, \cdots$ may also be different from

[8] H. Weyl. *Math. Z.* **23,** 271; **24,** 328, 377, 789 (1925); V. Schreier, *Abhandl. Math. Seminar Hamburg* **4,** 14 (1926); **5,** 233 (1927).

each other. The representation may thus be as multiply valued as there are paths from E to S which cannot be deformed into one another.

7. Equation (21.22) suggests that one consider in place of the original group a "covering group" which has as many elements $S_{S_1(t)}, S_{S_2(t)}, \cdots$ for each element S of the original group as there are paths $S_1(t), S_2(t), \cdots$ from E to S which cannot be deformed into one another.[9] The multiplication rule for this covering group is

$$S_{S_i(t)} R_{R_k(t)} = SR_{S_i(t), S \cdot R_k(t)}. \tag{21.22a}$$

According to (21.22) the matrices $\overline{\mathbf{D}}(S)_{S_i(t)}$ form a regular single-valued representation of the covering group. It follows that *the representation up*

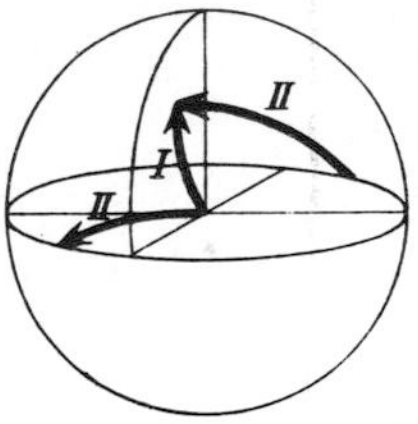

FIG. 12. Any element of the rotation group can be reached from the identity either (I) by a continuous path with no jumps, or (II) by a continuous path which includes a jump from some point to its antipode. These two kinds of paths cannot be deformed into one another.

to a factor of a continuous group can be transformed into a regular representation of the covering group by multiplication with appropriately chosen numbers. If all the representations of the covering group are known, then all the representations up to a factor of the original group are also known.

The parameter space (Fig. 1, page 90) of the three-dimensional pure rotation group is doubly connected. An arbitrary point can be reached from E either directly (Fig. 12) (I), or by a jump to the antipode (II), and these two paths cannot be deformed into one another. (A jump to the antipodes is not to be considered as a discontinuity in a line in parameter space, since the antipodes correspond to the same rotation.) On the other hand, a path with two jumps to antipodes can already be transformed into a path without jumps by choosing the deformation so that the two jumps coalesce into no jump at all (Fig. 13).

The covering group accordingly has twice as many elements as the rotation group; consequently it is isomorphic to the group of the $\mathfrak{D}^{(1/2)}(R)$. As a double-valued representation of the rotation group, this is certainly a regular representation of the covering group, and indeed a faithful one, since it assigns to each rotation two matrices $\pm\mathfrak{D}^{(1/2)}(R)$ which differ from one another and from all other $\mathfrak{D}^{(1/2)}(S)$.

The $\mathfrak{D}^{(1/2)}(R)$ constitute the unitary group; this is therefore the covering group of the three-dimensional rotation group. Its representations can be

[9] The group in question is also called Poincaré's group.

resolved into $\mathfrak{U}^{(0)}, \mathfrak{U}^{(1/2)}, \cdots$ and correspondingly the $\overline{\overline{\mathbf{D}}}(R) = c_R \mathbf{D}(R)$ can be broken down into $\pm \mathfrak{D}^{(0)}, \pm \mathfrak{D}^{(1/2)}, \pm \mathfrak{D}^{(1)}, \cdots$. If the $\mathbf{D}(R)$ are assumed to be in reduced form (this requires only a transformation to a new system of

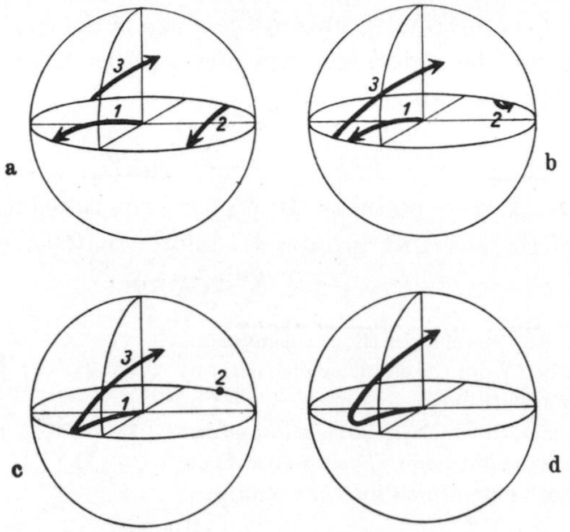

FIG. 13. A path which includes two jumps to antipodes can be continuously deformed into a path which includes no such jump by allowing the two jumps to coalesce as shown above.

linearly independent functions), we obtain for these functions

$$\mathbf{O}_R \Psi_\mu^{(j)} = \frac{1}{c_R} \sum_{\mu'} \mathfrak{D}^{(j)}(R)_{\mu'\mu} \Psi_{\mu'}^{(j)}, \tag{21.12b}$$

and j can be considered as the total quantum number of the eigenfunctions $\Psi_{-j}^{(j)}, \Psi_{-j+1}^{(j)}, \cdots, \Psi_{j-1}^{(j)}, \Psi_j^{(j)}$.

Although (21.12b) is not entirely equivalent with (21.12a), it permits the derivation of most of the rules for the total quantum number j.

22. The Fine Structure of Spectral Lines

1. In Chapter 18 we derived the selection rules for the orbital quantum number, parity, and multiplet system, as they apply in a theory which disregards spin. If the forces which arise from the spin magnetic moments of the electrons are taken into account, these rules are no longer strictly correct since they are based on the assumption that $\mathbf{P}_R\Psi$ is an eigenfunction of the energy operator with the same eigenvalue as Ψ. ($\mathbf{P}_R\Psi$ was assumed to be identical with the state Ψ, except for a rotation.)

We now know that if the spin is also considered, not $\mathbf{P}_R$, but $\mathbf{O}_R$ effects the rotation of the state; $\mathbf{P}_R$ rotates only the positional coordinates of the system. Correspondingly, $\mathbf{P}_R\Psi$ would only be an eigenfunction of $\mathbf{H}$ only if $\mathbf{H}$ were a "spin-free" quantity. In reality, terms arising from spin also appear in $\mathbf{H}$, and $\mathbf{P}_R\Psi$ is not an eigenfunction of $\mathbf{H}$ for the eigenvalue of Ψ and therefore cannot be written as a linear combination of the eigenfunctions belonging to this eigenvalue. Hence, when the spin is considered, the eigenfunctions do not belong to any representation of the rotation group with reference to the $\mathbf{P}_R$, and the concept of the orbital quantum number is not valid in the strict sense. Only as long as the terms arising from spin are small and one can obtain good approximations to the solutions of the actual Schrödinger equation even if one neglects them—which is usually a valid assumption—does the concept of the orbital quantum number (and the multiplet system) have a meaning, and only then are the selection rules of Chapter 18 valid. This will be developed more precisely in what follows.

The calculations carried out in Chapter 18 by means of the operators $\mathbf{P}$ can also be made with the $\mathbf{P}$ replaced by the $\mathbf{O}$. Since the invariance of the Hamiltonian under the operations $\mathbf{O}$ applies to *all* of its terms, the results so obtained will be rigorous. The operators $\mathbf{O}_R$, which correspond to rotations, commute with the operator $\mathbf{O}_I$ of inversion and both commute with the operators $\mathbf{O}_P$, which permute all *four* coordinates of two or more electrons

$$\mathbf{O}_P\Psi(x_{\alpha_1}, y_{\alpha_1}, z_{\alpha_1}, s_{\alpha_1}, \cdots, x_{\alpha_n}, y_{\alpha_n}, z_{\alpha_n}, s_{\alpha_n}) = \Psi(x_1, y_1, z_1, s_1, \cdots, x_n, y_n, z_n, s_n). \tag{22.1}$$

$\left[P \text{ is the permutation } \begin{pmatrix} 1\,2\cdots n \\ \alpha_1\alpha_2\cdots\alpha_n \end{pmatrix}\right]$. The total symmetry group is the direct product of the group of the $\mathbf{O}_R$, which describes rotations, with the reflection and permutation groups. The representations of this direct product, and hence the eigenvalues of the full Schrödinger equation, can be characterized by three quantum numbers, or three symbols. These specify the representations of the three groups whose direct product gives that representation of the full symmetry group to which the eigenfunctions of the eigenvalue in question belong. The representation $\mathfrak{D}^{(J)}$ of the group of the rotation operators was discussed in the preceding chapter; it gives J, the total angular momentum quantum number.[1] The representation of the reflection group $\mathbf{O}_E = 1$, $\mathbf{O}_I = \mathbf{P}_I$ gives the parity. We now turn to a more detailed discussion of the permutation operators $\mathbf{O}_P$. This discussion leads to Pauli's equivalence principle and will complete the discussion of those symmetry properties which apply rigorously. The remainder of the chapter will be devoted to the connection of these quantities with the approximate concepts of Chapter 18, in particular the orbital angular momentum quantum number L and the multiplet system S.

It is useful to decompose the permutations (22.1) of all four coordinates into two factors which correspond to the two factors $\mathbf{P}_R$ and $\mathbf{Q}_R$ which made up $\mathbf{O}_R$. We write therefore

$$\mathbf{O}_P = \mathbf{P}_P\mathbf{Q}_P = \mathbf{Q}_P\mathbf{P}_P, \tag{22.2}$$

where $\mathbf{Q}_P$ affects only the spin coordinates

$$\mathbf{Q}_P\Psi(x_1, y_1, z_1, s_{\alpha_1}, \cdots, x_n, y_n, z_n, s_{\alpha_n}) = \Psi(x_1, y_1, z_1, s_1, \cdots, x_n, y_n, z_n, s_n), \tag{22.2a}$$

and $\mathbf{P}_P$, only the cartesian coordinates

$$\begin{aligned}\mathbf{P}_P\Phi(x_{\alpha_1}, y_{\alpha_1}, z_{\alpha_1}, \sigma_1, \cdots, x_{\alpha_n}, y_{\alpha_n}, z_{\alpha_n}, \sigma_n)& \\ = \Phi(x_1, y_1, z_1, \sigma_1, \cdots, x_n, y_n, z_n, \sigma_n).&\end{aligned} \tag{22.2b}$$

For if we substitute $\mathbf{Q}_P\Psi$ for Φ in (22.2b), we obtain

$$\mathbf{P}_P\mathbf{Q}_P\Psi(\cdots, x_{\alpha_k}, y_{\alpha_k}, z_{\alpha_k}, \sigma_k, \cdots) = \mathbf{Q}_P\Psi(\cdots x_k, y_k, z_k, \sigma_k \cdots),$$

and further substitution of $\sigma_k = s_{\alpha_k}$ into this yields (22.2) directly by (22.2a) and (22.1).

2. An essential simplification of what follows results from the fact that the eigenfunctions of all *physical* states belong to the antisymmetric representation with reference to the $\mathbf{O}_P$:

$$\boxed{\mathbf{O}_P\Phi = \varepsilon_P\Phi;} \quad (\mathbf{O}_P - \varepsilon_P)\Phi = 0, \tag{22.3}$$

where ε_p is either $+1$ or -1 according to whether P is an even or an odd

[1] For the remainder of this book we shall use the letter J for this quantum number.

permutation. The functions which satisfy (22.3) are referred to as *antisymmetric functions*; the statement that all wave functions are antisymmetric is the content of the *Pauli principle.*[2]

The Pauli principle is not a consequence of the principles of quantum mechanics previously introduced; in contrast to the time-dependent Schrödinger equation, which plays the role of the equation of motion, it can be said to be an initial condition which is fulfilled in every system. If (22.3) is satisfied at some time, it is always satisfied, as we now show. From

$$i\hbar \frac{\partial \Phi}{\partial t} = \mathbf{H}\Phi,$$

since $\mathbf{H}$ is an operator symmetric under the $\mathbf{O}_P$, and thus commutes with them, it follows that

$$i\hbar \frac{\partial}{\partial t}(\mathbf{O}_P - \varepsilon_P)\Phi = (\mathbf{O}_P - \varepsilon_P) i\hbar \frac{\partial \Phi}{\partial t} = \mathbf{H}(\mathbf{O}_P - \varepsilon_P)\Phi. \quad (22.3a)$$

But from this it follows that $(\mathbf{O}_P - \varepsilon_P)\Phi$ always vanishes if it was zero at some time. From (22.3a) we conclude that the scalar product

$$((\mathbf{O}_P - \varepsilon_P)\Phi, (\mathbf{O}_P - \varepsilon_P)\Phi) \quad (22.E.1)$$

is constant in time; therefore it always remains zero if it was once zero. However, the vanishing of (22.E.1) implies the vanishing of $(\mathbf{O}_P - \varepsilon_P)\Phi$. We see that the Pauli principle is at least *consistent* with the quantum mechanical equation of motion.

An important consequence of the fact that all wave functions belong to an antisymmetric representation applies to the division of a system into several parts. Let us consider, for example, a system of two Helium atoms which have been interacting for some time and have afterwards separated from one another. The irreducible representation of the symmetric group of the fourth degree to which the wave function belonged before the separation shall be denoted by $\mathbf{D}(P)$. We can then pose the question: to which representations of the symmetric group of the second degree can the states of one Helium atom belong after the separation? If $\mathbf{D}(P)$ is the antisymmetric representation, the state of both Helium atoms is certainly also antisymmetric after the separation. The fact that one part of a system belongs to a specified representation is given uniquely by the fact that the total system belongs to the antisymmetric representation. The same holds if $\mathbf{D}(P)$ is the symmetric (identical) representation, *but not if it is any other representation.*

The reason for the antisymmetric character of all wave functions cannot be given on the basis of general considerations but must be looked upon as an experimental fact.[3]

[2] W. Heisenberg, *Z. Physik.* **38,** 411 (1926) and P. A. M. Dirac, *Proc. Roy. Soc.* **112,** 661 (1926).

[3] W. Pauli has shown meanwhile that relativistic field theories can be easily formulated for particles with half-integral spin only if they obey the Pauli principle [remark added in translation].

3. In the following we consider the Hamiltonian operator as divided into two parts:

$$\mathbf{H} = \mathbf{H}_0 + \mathbf{H}_1. \tag{22.4}$$

The first part is the ordinary Schrödinger operator, which contains the interactions of the charges and the kinetic energies:

$$\mathbf{H}_0 = -\hbar^2 \sum_k \frac{1}{2m_k}\left(\frac{\partial^2}{\partial x_k^2} + \frac{\partial^2}{\partial y_k^2} + \frac{\partial^2}{\partial z_k^2}\right) + V(x_1, \cdots, z_n). \tag{22.4a}$$

This is a spin-free operator. The second part, $\mathbf{H}_1$, contains the magnetic moments of the electrons; it will be considered small compared to $\mathbf{H}_0$ in this discussion and will be treated as a "perturbation." This perturbation is the cause of the fine structure. It results in a splitting of the eigenvalues of the simple Schrödinger equation (22.4a) (i.e., of the "gross structure levels") into several fine structure components.

The first step in the application of perturbation theory (Chapter 5) will be the determination of the "correct linear combinations." This is necessary since all the eigenvalues of the unperturbed problem, that is, of $\mathbf{H}_0$, are degenerate. This will be the major problem of this chapter. It can be assumed that the correct linear combinations belong to an irreducible representation of the symmetric group as regards the $\mathbf{O}_P$; because of the Pauli principle we use only representations which are antisymmetric. If the isotropy of space is not perturbed it can be further assumed that they belong to one row of an irreducible representation $\mathfrak{D}^{(J)}$ of the rotation group with regard to the $\mathbf{O}_R$. In the present case only one antisymmetric linear combination can be formed from the eigenfunctions of an eigenvalue of $\mathbf{H}_0$ which belongs to a certain row of a representation $\mathfrak{D}^{(J)}$, so that the correct linear combination for the perturbation procedure can be determined on the basis of this requirement alone.

Let E be an eigenvalue of $\mathbf{H}_0$, and $\psi(x_1, y_1, z_1, \cdots, x_n, y_n, z_n)$ an eigenfunction belonging to it, a function of the cartesian coordinates alone. We obtain an eigenfunction of $\mathbf{H}_0$ for the eigenvalue E, which is a function of all the coordinates $x_1, y_1, z_1, s_1, \cdots, x_n, y_n, z_n, s_n$ *by multiplying* ψ *with an arbitrary function* $f(s_1, \cdots, s_n)$ *of the spin coordinates.* Since $\mathbf{H}_0$ is a spin-free operator, $f(s_1, \cdots, s_n)$ can be treated like a constant factor.

$$\mathbf{H}_0\psi f = f\mathbf{H}_0\psi = fE\psi = E\psi f. \tag{22.5}$$

There exist in all 2^n linearly independent functions of the $s_1, s_2, \cdots, s_n$,

$$f_{\sigma_1\sigma_2\cdots\sigma_n} = \delta_{s_1\sigma_1}\delta_{s_2\sigma_2}\cdots\delta_{s_n\sigma_n} \quad (\sigma_1 = \pm 1, \sigma_2 = \pm 1, \cdots, \sigma_n = \pm 1), \tag{22.6}$$

in terms of which all functions of $s_1, s_2, \cdots, s_n$ can be expressed linearly, as we have already seen in Chapter 13 where the irreducible representations of the symmetric group were determined. Therefore, if

$$f_1, f_2, \cdots, f_{2^n} \tag{22.6a}$$

is a complete orthogonal system of functions of s (they may be the functions (22.6)), we can form the following 2^n eigenfunctions of $\mathbf{H}_0$ from ψ:

$$\psi f_1, \psi f_2, \cdots, \psi f_{2^n}. \tag{22.7}$$

If several functions of $x_1, y_1, z_1, \cdots, x_n, y_n, z_n$ are eigenfunctions of $\mathbf{H}_0$ with eigenvalue E, then according to (22.7), 2^n linearly independent eigenfunctions containing the spin coordinates as variables can be formed from each of them. By introducing the spin coordinates the multiplicity of the eigenvalues of the spin-free operators is increased 2^n times. This corresponds to the circumstances that $\mathbf{H}_0\psi = E\psi$ prescribes only the motion of the cartesian coordinates; for each of the n spins a choice can still be made between two opposite orientations.

4. We first consider a system which displays no symmetry other than the equivalence of the electrons, that is, one in which the spatial symmetry is removed by an external field. It can be assumed that the functions $\psi_1, \psi_2, \cdots$ of $x_1, y_1, z_1, \cdots, x_n, y_n, z_n$ are the eigenfunctions of a given eigenvalue of $\mathbf{H}_0$ which belong to an irreducible representation of the symmetric group of the nth degree,

$$\mathbf{P}_P\psi_\varkappa = \sum_{\varkappa'} \mathbf{D}(P)_{\varkappa'\varkappa}\psi_{\varkappa'}. \tag{22.8}$$

These equations also hold if the $\psi_\varkappa f_\lambda$ are substituted for the $\psi_\varkappa$, since a function of the spin coordinates can be considered as a constant factor with regard to the operators $\mathbf{P}_P$.

The eigenfunction $\psi_\varkappa f_\lambda$ of $\mathbf{H}_0$ must also belong to a representation of the group of the $\mathbf{O}_P$, since the electrons are also equivalent when spin is considered. The state $\mathbf{O}_P\psi_\varkappa f_\lambda$ in which the electrons have merely interchanged their roles in relation to $\psi_\varkappa f_\lambda$ must also be an eigenfunction of $\mathbf{H}_0$ with the same eigenvalue as $\psi_\varkappa f_\lambda$, and can therefore be expressed as a linear combination of the $\psi_{\varkappa'} f_{\lambda'}$. We can introduce the expression (22.8) for the $\mathbf{P}_P\psi_\varkappa$ into

$$\mathbf{O}_P\psi_\varkappa f_\lambda = \mathbf{P}_P\mathbf{Q}_P\psi_\varkappa f_\lambda = \mathbf{P}_P\psi_\varkappa \cdot \mathbf{Q}_P f_\lambda \tag{22.9}$$

and express the $\mathbf{Q}_P f_\lambda$ in terms of the $f_{\lambda'}$, since *every* function of s can be expressed in terms of the $f_{\lambda'}$. However, in order to have as simple a system of coefficients as possible we ought to begin from an orthogonal system (22.6a) whose functions belong to irreducible representations of the symmetric group with regard to the operators $\mathbf{Q}_P$.

5. We have determined such an orthogonal system for the s in Chapter 13. There we used the orthogonal system

$$s_1^{\gamma_1} s_2^{\gamma_2} \cdots s_n^{\gamma_n} \quad (\gamma_1, \gamma_2, \cdots, \gamma_n = 0 \text{ or } 1) \tag{22.6b}$$

rather than (22.6). We arranged these functions in such a way that all the functions of the kth row were of the kth degree $(\gamma_1 + \gamma_2 + \cdots + \gamma_n = k)$; there were $\binom{n}{k}$ such functions. It was then shown that for $k \leqslant n/2$, linear combinations of the functions of the kth degree can be formed each of which belongs to one row of one of the representations

$$\mathbf{D}^{(0)}, \mathbf{D}^{(1)}, \mathbf{D}^{(2)}, \cdots, \mathbf{D}^{(k)} \tag{22.E.2}$$

Since the dimension of $\mathbf{D}^{(i)}$ is

$$l_i = \binom{n}{i} - \binom{n}{i-1}, \tag{22.10}$$

the number of these functions is indeed $l_0 + l_1 + l_2 + \cdots + l_k = \binom{n}{k}$. For $k \geqslant \frac{1}{2}n$ the representations

$$\mathbf{D}^{(0)}, \mathbf{D}^{(1)}, \mathbf{D}^{(2)}, \cdots, \mathbf{D}^{(n-k)} \tag{22.E.3}$$

occur in place of the representations (22.E.2) (see the tabulation on page 133).

If we denote the functions of the kth degree which belong to the λth row of $\mathbf{D}^{(i)}$ by $g_{\lambda k}^{(i)}$, then

$$\mathbf{O}_P g_{\lambda k}^{(i)} = \sum_{\lambda'=1}^{l_i} \mathbf{D}^{(i)}(P)_{\lambda'\lambda} g_{\lambda' k}^{(i)} \quad (i = 0, 1, 2, \cdots, k \text{ or } n-k). \tag{22.11}$$

We have used the functions (22.6b) rather than the functions (22.6) because with these the factors $s_\rho^{\gamma_\rho}$, with $\gamma_\rho = 0$ can simply be omitted, with a consequent simplification of the formulas. Now, however, we will revert to the functions (22.6), substituting $\delta_{s_\rho, -1}$ for $s_\rho^0 = 1$, and $\delta_{s_\rho, 1}$ for $s_\rho^1 = s_\rho$, that is, $\delta_{s_\rho, 2\gamma-1}$ for s_ρ^γ throughout. Thus, the function

$$\mathbf{U}F(s_1 s_2 \cdots s_n) = \sum_{\gamma_\rho=0,1} c_{\gamma_1\gamma_2\cdots\gamma_n} \delta_{s_1, 2\gamma_1-1} \delta_{s_2, 2\gamma_2-1} \cdots \delta_{s_n, 2\gamma_n-1}, \tag{22.12a}$$

replaces the function

$$F(s_1 s_2 \cdots s_n) = \sum_{\gamma_\rho=0,1} c_{\gamma_1\gamma_2\cdots\gamma_n} s_1^{\gamma_1} s_2^{\gamma_2} \cdots s_n^{\gamma_n} \tag{22.12}$$

everywhere. This does not alter the transformation properties since the substitution of (22.12a) for (22.12) manifestly commutes with a permutation of the variables. Therefore, if we write

$$\mathsf{U} g^{(i)}_{\lambda k} = f^{(\frac{1}{2}n-i)}_{\lambda, k-\frac{1}{2}n}; \quad \mathsf{U} g^{(\frac{1}{2}n-S)}_{\lambda, \frac{1}{2}n+m} = f^{(S)}_{\lambda m} \tag{22.13}$$

and[4]

$$\mathbf{D}^{(i)}(P) = \mathbf{A}^{(\frac{1}{2}n-i)}(P)^*; \quad \mathbf{D}^{(\frac{1}{2}n-S)}(P) = \mathbf{A}^{(S)}(P)^* \tag{22.13a}$$

we shall have, according to (22.11),

$$\mathsf{Q}_P f^{(S)}_{\lambda m} = \sum_{\lambda'} \mathbf{A}^{(S)}(P)^*_{\lambda'\lambda} f^{(S)}_{\lambda' m}. \tag{22.11a}$$

For even n, both S and m are integral; for odd n, both are half-integral.

The function $g^{(\frac{1}{2}n-S)}_{\lambda, \frac{1}{2}n+m}$ is of degree $\frac{1}{2}n + m$, that is, if it is written in the form (22.12) only terms which contain $\frac{1}{2}n + m$ factors s^1_ρ (and $\frac{1}{2}n - m$ factors s^0_ρ) occur in it. Therefore, in $\mathsf{U} g^{(\frac{1}{2}n-S)}_{\lambda, \frac{1}{2}n+m} = f^{(S)}_{\lambda m}$, only those terms appear which contain $\frac{1}{2}n + m$ factors, $\delta_{s_\rho, 1}$ (and $\frac{1}{2}n - m$ factors, $\delta_{s_\rho, -1}$); the functions $f^{(S)}_{\lambda m}$ can be different from zero only for sets of values of the s_ρ in which exactly $\frac{1}{2}n + m$ of the s equal $+1$ (and $\frac{1}{2}n - m$ equal -1), so that the sum of the s_ρ's is $\frac{1}{2}n + m - (\frac{1}{2}n - m) = 2m$.

$$f^{(S)}_{\lambda m}(s_1 s_2 \cdots s_n) = 0 \quad \text{for} \quad s_1 + s_2 + \cdots + s_n \neq 2m. \tag{22.14}$$

If the functions

$$f^{(S)}_{\lambda m} \left\{ \begin{array}{l} \lambda = 1, 2, \cdots, \binom{n}{\frac{1}{2}n - S} - \binom{n}{\frac{1}{2}n - S - 1} \\ m = -S, -S+1, \cdots, S-1, S \\ S = \frac{1}{2}n, \frac{1}{2}n - 1, \frac{1}{2}n - 2, \cdots, \frac{1}{2} \text{ or } 0, \end{array} \right\} \tag{22.E.4}$$

are taken as the complete orthogonal system of functions of s, we obtain for (22.9) by (22.8) and (22.11a)

$$\mathsf{O}_P \psi_\varkappa f^{(S)}_{\lambda m} = \sum_{\varkappa'} \sum_{\lambda'} \mathbf{D}(P)_{\varkappa'\varkappa} \mathbf{A}^{(S)}(P)^*_{\lambda'\lambda} \psi_{\varkappa'} f^{(S)}_{\lambda' m}. \tag{22.9a}$$

Thus the $\psi_\varkappa f^{(S)}_{\lambda m}$ transform among themselves according to the direct product

$$\mathbf{D}(P) \times \mathbf{A}^{(S)}(P)^*.$$

6. It can be assumed that the eigenfunctions of the first approximation, the correct linear combinations,

$$\sum_{\substack{\varkappa S' \\ \lambda m}} a_{\varkappa S' \lambda m} \psi_\varkappa f^{(S')}_{\lambda m}, \tag{22.15}$$

for the perturbation procedure which serves to introduce the spin forces,

[4] Actually, the stars in (22.13a) have no significance since the $\mathbf{D}^{(i)}(P)$ are real. They are introduced only because they simplify the following calculations, inasmuch as they make it unnecessary to *use* the real nature of the $\mathbf{D}^{(i)}$.

belong to irreducible representations of the group of the $\mathbf{O}_P$. Since the Pauli principle requires that we use only eigenfunctions whose representation is antisymmetric, it is sufficient to determine the antisymmetric linear combinations (22.15); the first approximation to eigenfunctions which satisfy the Pauli principle must be a linear combination of these.

We therefore assume that (22.15) is antisymmetric. It then follows from (22.9a) and the linear independence of the $\psi_\varkappa f^{(S')}_{\lambda' m}$ that

$$\sum_{\varkappa\lambda} a_{\varkappa S'\lambda m} \mathbf{D}(P)_{\varkappa'\varkappa} \mathbf{A}^{(S')}(P)^*_{\lambda'\lambda} = \varepsilon_P a_{\varkappa' S'\lambda' m}. \tag{22.16}$$

If we denote the representation *associated* with $\mathbf{A}^{(S')}(P)$ by

$$\overline{\mathbf{A}}^{(S')}(P) = \varepsilon_P \mathbf{A}^{(S')}(P) \tag{22.17}$$

and multiply (22.16) by ε_P, it follows, since $\varepsilon_P^2 = 1$, that

$$\sum_{\varkappa\lambda} a_{\varkappa S'\lambda m} \mathbf{D}(P)_{\varkappa'\varkappa} \overline{\mathbf{A}}^{(S')}(P)^*_{\lambda'\lambda} = a_{\varkappa' S'\lambda' m}. \tag{22.18}$$

Summing this over all permutations P, we can infer from the orthogonality relations that the left side vanishes if $\mathbf{D}(P)$ and $\overline{\mathbf{A}}^{(S')}(P)$ are not equivalent. If $\mathbf{D}(P)$ is not equivalent to any of the representations $\overline{\mathbf{A}}^{(S')}(P)$, then all $a_{\varkappa' S'\lambda' m}$ vanish and no antisymmetric linear combination at all can be formed from the $\psi_\varkappa f^{(S')}_m$. An antisymmetric eigenfunction can be formed from the functions of s and the eigenfunctions of $\mathbf{H}_0$ which belong to an irreducible representation of the $\mathbf{P}_P$, only if this representation is equivalent to one of the represention $\overline{\mathbf{A}}^{(\frac{1}{2}n)}$, $\overline{\mathbf{A}}^{(\frac{1}{2}n-1)}$, $\overline{\mathbf{A}}^{(\frac{1}{2}n-2)}$, $\cdots$. Eigenfunctions and eigenvalues of $\mathbf{H}_0$ which belong to other representations are therefore excluded by the Pauli principle.

We will therefore assume that $\mathbf{D}(P)$ is equivalent to one of the $\overline{\mathbf{A}}^{(S')}(P)$, say, $\overline{\mathbf{A}}^{(S)}(P)$; actually, we assume that it is identical with it, since a similarity transformation of $\mathbf{D}(P)$ amounts only to a specific selection of the linearly independent eigenfunctions $\psi_\varkappa$. Let S be called the multiplet system of the eigenfunctions $\psi_\varkappa$ which belong to the representation $\overline{\mathbf{A}}^{(S)}$. If we substitute

$$\mathbf{D}(P) = \overline{\mathbf{A}}^{(S)}(P) \tag{22.19}$$

into (22.18) and then sum over all the permutations, we obtain (denoting the dimension of $\mathbf{A}^{(S)}(P)$ by g_S for the moment)

$$\begin{aligned} \sum_{\varkappa\lambda} a_{\varkappa S'\lambda m} \frac{n!}{g_S} \delta_{SS'} \delta_{\varkappa'\lambda'} \delta_{\varkappa\lambda} &= n!\, a_{\varkappa' S'\lambda' m}, \\ a_{\varkappa' S'\lambda' m} = \delta_{SS'} \delta_{\varkappa'\lambda'} \sum_{\varkappa} \frac{a_{\varkappa S\varkappa m}}{g_S} &= \delta_{SS'} \delta_{\varkappa'\lambda'} b_m, \end{aligned} \tag{22.20}$$

where b_m is independent of S', $\varkappa'$, and λ'. The antisymmetric linear combinations of the $\psi_\varkappa f^{(S)}_{\lambda m}$, Eq. (22.15), are therefore of the form:

$$\sum_{\substack{\varkappa S' \\ \lambda m}} \delta_{SS'}\delta_{\varkappa\lambda} b_m \psi_\varkappa f^{(S')}_{\lambda m} = \sum_m b_m \sum_\varkappa \psi_\varkappa f^{(S)}_{\varkappa m}. \tag{22.20a}$$

There are $2S + 1$ linearly independent antisymmetric functions

$$\Xi^S_m = \sum_\varkappa \psi_\varkappa f^{(S)}_{\varkappa m} \tag{22.20b}$$

corresponding to the $2S + 1$ values of m.

If we wish to form antisymmetric functions from the eigenfunctions ψ_1, $\psi_2, \psi_3, \cdots$ of an eigenvalue of $\mathbf{H}_0$, we must multiply the $\psi_\varkappa$ which belong to the $\varkappa$th row of $\overline{\mathbf{A}}^{(S)}$ with a function $f^{(S)}_{\varkappa m}$ of s which belongs to the $\varkappa$th row of the *associated* representation $\mathbf{A}^{(S)*}$, and add these products for all $\varkappa$ (for all partners). The other $g_S \cdot (2^n - 2S - 1)$ linear combinations of the $\psi_\varkappa f^{(S)}_{\lambda m}$ which are orthogonal to these functions belong to representations of the $\mathbf{O}_P$ other than the antisymmetric representation.

7. If the spin terms $\mathbf{H}_1$ are added to $\mathbf{H}_0$ as a perturbation, $\mathbf{H}$ is no longer a spin-free operator and the eigenvalue E splits into several eigenvalues which belong in general to irreducible representations of the group of the symmetry operators $\mathbf{O}_P$. Since the wave functions of all physically realizable states are antisymmetric, only those levels which belong to the antisymmetric representation are possible energy levels. If the eigenfunctions of $\mathbf{H}_0$ with the eigenvalue E, which are functions of $x_1, y_1, z_1, \cdots, x_n, y_n, z_n$, belong to the representation $\overline{\mathbf{A}}^{(S)}(P)$, then $2S + 1$ closely spaced levels will lie near the energy E. To each of these levels belongs, in the first approximation, one linear combination of the Ξ_m of (22.20b). The actual correct linear combination (i.e., the values of the b_m's in (22.20a)) cannot be determined without solving the $(2S + 1)$-dimensional secular equation for the matrix

$$(\mathbf{H}_1)_{m'm} = (\Xi_{m'}, \mathbf{H}_1 \Xi_m) \tag{22.20c}$$

since in the present case of assumed external fields, there is no symmetry which could be of assistance.

8. We now consider a system in which the full rotational symmetry is present, besides the equivalence of the electrons. The functions of $x_1, y_1, z_1, \cdots, x_n, y_n, z_n$ which are the eigenfunctions of $\mathbf{H}_0$ then have an orbital quantum number L besides the multiplet system S and can be chosen so that they satisfy the equations

$$\mathbf{P}_P \psi_{\varkappa\mu} = \sum_{\varkappa'} \overline{\mathbf{A}}^{(S)}(P)_{\varkappa'\varkappa} \psi_{\varkappa'\mu}; \quad \mathbf{P}_R \psi_{\varkappa\mu} = \sum_{\mu'} \mathfrak{D}^{(L)}(R)_{\mu'\mu} \psi_{\varkappa\mu'} \tag{22.21}$$

(P here is a permutation and R a rotation). From the functions $\psi_{\varkappa\mu}$ of the space coordinates one can form functions $\psi_{\varkappa\mu} f^{(S)}_{\lambda m}$ of all the coordinates which are also eigenfunctions of $\mathbf{H}_0$. The $\psi_{\varkappa\mu} f^{(S)}_{\lambda m}$ satisfy (22.21) as well as the $\psi_{\varkappa\mu}$; since $\mathbf{P}$ does not affect the spin coordinates, the spin function $f^{(S)}_{\lambda m}$ can be treated as a constant factor in Eq. (22.21).

The $\psi_{\varkappa\mu} f^{(S)}_{\lambda m}$ must belong to a representation of the rotation group under the $\mathbf{O}_R$ also, since the mere introduction of spin coordinates does not affect the equivalence of the spatial directions. In fact (see the analogous Eq. (22.9))

$$\mathbf{O}_R \psi_{\varkappa\mu} f^{(S)}_{\lambda m} = \mathbf{P}_R \psi_{\varkappa\mu} \cdot \mathbf{Q}_R f^{(S)}_{\lambda m}, \tag{22.22}$$

and in this equation the $\mathbf{P}_R \psi_{\varkappa\mu}$ can be expressed by means of (22.21) in terms of the original $\psi_{\varkappa\mu}$; also, $\mathbf{Q}_R f^{(S)}_{\lambda m}$ can be written in terms of the $f^{(S)}_{\lambda m}$—as can every function of the s. We now determine the coefficients.

If one expresses the $\mathbf{Q}_R f^{(S)}_{\lambda m}$ in terms of the $f^{(S')}_{\lambda' m'}$, only those $f^{(S)}_{\lambda m'}$ which also belong to the λth row of $\mathbf{A}^{(S)}$ need be used, since $\mathbf{Q}_R$ is an operator symmetric under permutations of the s, and (in contrast with $\mathbf{Q}_P$) does not change the transformation properties of the $f^{(S)}_{\lambda m'}$. Therefore we must have

$$\mathbf{Q}_R f^{(S)}_{\lambda m} = \sum_{m'=-S}^{S} \mathfrak{D}^{(S)}(R)_{m'm} f^{(S)}_{\lambda m'} \quad (m = -S, -S+1, \cdots, S-1, S). \tag{22.23}$$

Moreover, because $\mathbf{Q}_R \mathbf{Q}_{R'} = \pm \mathbf{Q}_{RR'}$, the matrices $\mathfrak{D}^{(S)}(R)$ form a $(2S+1)$-dimensional (single or double-valued) representation of the rotation group. This representation is the irreducible representation $\mathfrak{D}^{(S)}(R)$ as will be shown immediately.

Let R be a rotation about Z through an angle α. Then

$$\begin{aligned} \mathbf{Q}_R f^{(S)}_{\lambda m}(s_1, \cdots, s_n) &= \sum_{t_\rho = \pm 1} \cdots \mathfrak{D}^{(1/2)}(R)_{\frac{1}{2}s_\rho, \frac{1}{2}t_\rho} \cdots f^{(S)}_{\lambda m}(t_1, \cdots, t_n) \\ &= \sum_{t_\rho = \pm 1} \delta_{s_1 t_1} e^{i\frac{1}{2}s_1\alpha} \cdots \delta_{s_n t_n} e^{i\frac{1}{2}s_n\alpha} f^{(S)}_{\lambda m}(t_1, \cdots, t_n) \\ &= e^{i\frac{1}{2}(s_1 + \ldots + s_n)\alpha} f^{(S)}_{\lambda m}(s_1, \cdots, s_n), \end{aligned} \tag{22.24}$$

$$\mathbf{Q}_R f^{(S)}_{\lambda m}(s_1, \cdots, s_n) = e^{+im\alpha} f^{(S)}_{\lambda m}(s_1, \cdots, s_n)$$

where we substitute $m = \frac{1}{2}(s_1 + s_2 + \cdots + s_n)$, since according to (22.14), the function $f^{(S)}_{\lambda m}$ surely vanishes for other sets of values of the s. For $R = \{\alpha, 0, 0\}$, the representation in (22.23) is a diagonal matrix with diagonal elements $\exp(-iS\alpha)$, $\exp(-i(S-1)\alpha)$, $\cdots$, $\exp(+i(S-1)\alpha)$, $\exp(+iS\alpha)$, which establishes its equivalence with irreducible representation $\mathfrak{D}^{(S)}(R)$. In addition, (22.24) shows that $f^{(S)}_{\lambda m}$ belongs to the mth row of $\mathfrak{D}^{(S)}(R)$, so that $\mathfrak{D}^{(S)}(R)$ appears in (22.23) correctly. *The functions of $s_1, s_2, \cdots, s_n$, which belong to the representation $\mathbf{A}^{(S)*} = \mathbf{D}^{(\frac{1}{2}n-S)}$ with regard to the permutation of the variables, belong to the representation $\mathfrak{D}^{(S)}$ of the rotation group with* *regard to the rotations* $\mathbf{Q}_R$. They actually belong to the representation $\mathbf{A}^{(S)*} \times \mathfrak{D}^{(S)}$ of the direct product of the two groups. This follows from operating on (22.23) with $\mathbf{Q}_P$ and using (22.11a).

$$\mathbf{Q}_P\mathbf{Q}_R f^{(S)}_{\lambda m} = \sum_{m'} \mathfrak{D}^{(S)}(R)_{m'm}\mathbf{Q}_P f^{(S)}_{\lambda m'} = \sum_{m'}\sum_{\lambda'} \mathfrak{D}^{(S)}(R)_{m'm}\mathbf{A}^{(S)}(P)^*_{\lambda'\lambda} f^{(S)}_{\lambda' m'}, \tag{22.24a}$$

that is, $f^{(S)}_{\lambda m}$ belongs to the (λ, m)th row of $\mathbf{A}^{(S)}(P)^* \times \mathfrak{D}^{(S)}(R)$.

The results of this discussion can be nicely illustrated by means of the array on page 133. We can consider each $\mathbf{D}^{(i)}$ to be replaced by the functions which belong to this $\mathbf{D}^{(i)}$. Then the ith *column* will contain those functions which belong to $\mathbf{D}^{(i)} = \mathbf{A}^{(\frac{1}{2}n-i)}$ with regard to the permutation of variables, the $\mathbf{D}^{(i)}$ of the kth row being replaced by $g^{(i)}_{1k}, g^{(i)}_{2k}, \cdots$. If $f^{(\frac{1}{2}n-i)}_{\lambda,k-\frac{1}{2}n} = \mathbf{U}g^{(i)}_{\lambda k}$ of Eq. (22.13) is now substituted for $g^{(i)}_{\lambda k}$ then the $k = (\frac{1}{2}n + m)$th row will contain functions which belong to $\exp(+im\varphi)$ with regard to rotations about Z. From the fact that each $\mathbf{D}^{(i)} = \mathbf{A}^{(\frac{1}{2}n-i)}$ occurs at most once in each row, it is seen that there exists at most one function of s which belongs to a given row of $\mathbf{A}^{(\frac{1}{2}n-i)}$, and to $\exp(+im\varphi)$ with regard to rotations about Z. Since $\mathbf{A}^{(\frac{1}{2}n-i)}$ occurs in the rows $i, i+1, \cdots, n-i-1, n-i$, the expression $m = k - \frac{1}{2}n$ will assume in the ith column the values $-\frac{1}{2}n + i, -\frac{1}{2}n + i + 1, \cdots, \frac{1}{2}n - i - 1, \frac{1}{2}n - i$. The functions which appear in the different rows of the ith column belong, with regard to the three-dimensional rotations, to different rows of $\mathfrak{D}^{(\frac{1}{2}n-i)}$ and are partners.

If we had used the functions g of Chapter 13 directly instead of the functions $f = \mathbf{U}g$, we would have had only to say "rotations about X" instead of "rotations about Z"; nothing else would have been changed.

An antisymmetric function of the $x_1, y_1, z_1, s_1, \cdots, x_n, y_n, z_n, s_n$, which transforms according to the representation $\overline{\mathbf{A}}^{(S)}$ under permutations $\mathbf{P}_P$ of the Cartesian coordinates alone, and belongs to the multiplet system S, must transform (Eqs. (22.21) and (22.11a) according to the representation $\mathbf{A}^{(S)*}$ under permutations $\mathbf{Q}_P$ of the spin coordinates and (Eq. (22.24a)) according to $\mathfrak{D}^{(S)}$ under rotations of the spin coordinates. *Therefore the multiplet system is not merely a symmetry with regard to permutations of the variables* (either the Cartesian or the spin coordinates). *Rather, because of the special structure of the functions of s, it is also a symmetry with regard to the rotation of the spin coordinates,* just as the orbital quantum number is an expression of the symmetry with regard to rotation of the Cartesian coordinates. One important difference between the orbital quantum number and the multiplet system results from the fact that the most important quantities, like $\mathbf{H}_0$, are spin-free quantities which are invariant under all $\mathbf{Q}$, even if the isotropy of space is removed by an external field.

The fact that those functions, $f^{(S)}_{\lambda m}$, which belong to an irreducible representation $\mathbf{A}^{(S)}$ of the symmetric group, also belong to an irreducible representation $\mathfrak{D}^{(S)}$ of the rotation group, and conversely, is a property of functions of variables which are capable of assuming only two values. If s could assume several values, then a function which belongs to a certain representation of the symmetric group could still belong to various representations of the rotation group, and, conversely, a function which belongs to a given representation of the rotation group could also belong to various representations of the symmetric group. Only with a two-valued variable are the transformation properties under rotations and permutations linked in the way described above.

9. If we now form antisymmetric combinations of the $\psi_{\varkappa\mu} f_{\lambda m}^{(S)}$ by (22.20b), we obtain $(2S+1)(2L+1)$ of these, since the expression (22.20b) can be constructed for every μ:

$$\Xi_{m\mu}^{SL} = \sum_{\varkappa} \psi_{\varkappa\mu}^{SL} f_{\varkappa m}^{(S)} \quad (\mu = -L, \cdots, L;\ m = -S, \cdots, S). \tag{22.25}$$

If we apply a rotation to the states $\Xi_{m\mu}^{SL}$,

$$\begin{aligned}\mathbf{O}_R \Xi_{m\mu}^{SL} &= \sum_{\varkappa} \mathbf{P}_R \psi_{\varkappa\mu}^{SL} \cdot \mathbf{Q}_R f_{\varkappa m}^{(S)} \\ &= \sum_{\varkappa} \sum_{\mu' m'} \mathfrak{D}^{(L)}(R)_{\mu'\mu}\, \psi_{\varkappa\mu'}^{SL} \mathfrak{D}^{(S)}(R)_{m'm} f_{\varkappa m'}^{(S)} \\ &= \sum_{\mu' m'} \mathfrak{D}^{(L)}(R)_{\mu'\mu} \mathfrak{D}^{(S)}(R)_{m'm} \Xi_{m'\mu'}^{SL},\end{aligned}$$

they transform according to the direct product $\mathfrak{D}^{(L)} \times \mathfrak{D}^{(S)}$. The total quantum numbers J of the resulting antisymmetric eigenvalues are therefore obtained by the decomposition of $\mathfrak{D}^{(L)} \times \mathfrak{D}^{(S)}$. This decomposition has already been carried out in Chapter 17. The irreducible components have upper indices

$$J = |L - S|, |L - S| + 1, \cdots, L + S - 1, L + S, \tag{22.26}$$

while the corresponding linear combinations of $\Xi_{m\mu}^{SL}$ are, by Eq. (17.18a), page 192,

$$\Psi_m^J = \sum_{\mu} s_{J\mu, m-\mu}^{(LS)} \Xi_{m-\mu\,\mu}^{SL}. \tag{22.27}$$

The coefficients $s_{J\mu,m-\mu}^{(LS)}$ have been determined in Chapter 17, Eqs. (17.27), (17.27b).

A level with orbital quantum number L and multiplet system S splits upon introduction of the spin into $2L + 1$ or $2S + 1$ (whichever is smaller) "fine structure components" with the total quantum numbers (22.26). The corresponding eigenfunctions for the first approximation are given by (22.27).

Although under full spatial symmetry the number of eigenfunctions which belong to one eigenvalue is much greater than in the absence of the full symmetry, the correct linear combinations for the perturbation procedure can still be determined more easily with the full symmetry than they can without it. In the presence of full spatial symmetry, the coefficients of the correct linear combinations are merely the coefficients of the vector addition model, given explicitly in Chapter 17. Thus, full spatial symmetry more than makes up for the complications it introduces.

Equation (22.26) shows that the total quantum numbers J of the levels which arise upon the introduction of spin from a level with orbital quantum number L and multiplet system S, are given by the *vector addition model.* In this model the two vectors L and S must be combined according to Fig. 9

to obtain J, the resultant vector.[5] The vector L is interpreted as the angular momentum of the orbital motion, and S, as the angular momentum due to the spin of the electrons; J is the total angular momentum.

10. Let us determine, finally, the parity of the functions (22.27). If the parity of the function $\psi_{\varkappa\mu}$ is w (it is the same for all $\psi_{\varkappa\mu}$),

$$\mathbf{P}_I\psi_{\varkappa\mu} = w\psi_{\varkappa\mu}.$$

This also holds for the functions (22.27) since, considered as functions of the Cartesian coordinates, they are just linear combinations of the $\psi_{\varkappa\mu}$, and $\mathbf{O}_I = \mathbf{P}_I$. Thus, the parity does not change upon the introduction of the spin coordinates but is the same for all the fine structure components of a level as it was for the corresponding gross structure level before the introduction of the spin.

11. Let us estimate the "multiplet splitting," the separation in energy of the fine structure components from one another. Classically, the splitting is due to the energy of interaction of the spin magnetic dipoles with the current which results from the electrons circling the nucleus and with one another. The field strength which is generated by the circular current is $\sim ev/r^2c$, where e is the charge, v the velocity of the electron, and r its distance from the origin. For r we can substitute $\hbar^2/me^2$, the radius of the first Bohr orbit, which is the average separation of the inner electrons from the nucleus in quantum mechanics, and v can be estimated from $mvr \sim \hbar$. This gives for the magnetic field strength

$$\sim \frac{m^2e^7}{\hbar^5c}$$

and the energy of a magnetic dipole $e\hbar/2mc$ in this field is $me^8/2\hbar^4c^2$. (The exact calculation by Dirac's relativistic theory yields the value $me^8/32\hbar^4c^2$, for the energy difference between the two levels with $N = 2$, $l = 1$, $j = \frac{1}{2}$, and $j = 3/2$ in the hydrogen atom.) Thus the fine structure splitting is only about

$$\sim \left(\frac{e^2}{\hbar c}\right)^2 = \alpha^2 = \left(\frac{1}{137}\right)^2$$

of the gross structure, or of the difference between levels of the hydrogen atom with different principal quantum numbers ($\sim me^4/\hbar^2$). The constant α is *Sommerfeld's fine structure constant.*

We can obtain a crude estimate of the orders of magnitude of different physical effects by expanding the energy in powers of the fine structure constant. Practically every power introduces a new physical effect into the calculation. The zeroth power contains the rest energy of the electron mc^2.

[5] For this application, in Fig. 9 (page 187), l should be replaced by L, $\bar{l}$ by S, and L by J.

The first power has a zero coefficient. The second power is the energy given by the ordinary Schrödinger theory; it is proportional to $mc^2\alpha^2 = me^4/\hbar^2$ and is the only term in which the velocity of light does not appear. The coefficient of the third power is again zero. We have just seen that the fourth power term gives the energy of the magnetic moment of the spinning electron in the first approximation of the perturbation procedure. The fifth power contains the broadening of the levels due to dipole radiation.[6] The sixth term is the second approximation to the spin effects, and the seventh the broadening of the levels due to quadrupole radiation. The eighth term is the third approximation in the calculation of the spin energy, and the ninth power the level broadening by lines which are excluded by the intercombination prohibition, etc.

Naturally, a term in the expansion which contains a higher power of the fine structure constant can be larger than a term with a lower power if its coefficient is sufficiently large. However, as a rule, the term with the higher power of α is the smaller. Nevertheless, the coefficients of some of the terms (e.g., the fine structure splitting) ordinarily increase with increasing charge number of the atom, while for other terms (e.g., radiative level broadening) this is not the case, or not generally the case. Thus the second approximation for the fine structure splitting is—except for the first few elements—substantially larger than the radiative broadening. The lines which are excluded by the intercombination prohibition are almost always stronger than the quadrupole lines, so that the expansion in powers of α is sometimes not much more than a convention for grouping effects. If the term which occurs earlier in the series is larger than that which occurs later, we say that the coupling is *normal*.

12. If the eigenfunctions of $\mathbf{H}$ were given exactly by (22.27), they would belong to the irreducible representations $\mathbf{A}^{(S)}(P)$ and $\mathfrak{D}^{(L)}(R)$ of the groups of $\mathbf{P}_P$ and $\mathbf{P}_R$, respectively, and the selection rules for the multiplet system and the orbital quantum number would hold exactly. In reality (22.27) is only the first approximation to the eigenfunctions. If the second approximation

$$\Phi_m^{NJ} = \Psi_m^{NJ} + \sum_{N' \neq N} \sum_{J'm'} \left(\frac{(\Psi_{m'}^{N'J'}, \mathbf{H}_1 \Psi_m^{NJ})}{E_N - E_{N'}} \right) \Psi_{m'}^{N'J'} \tag{22.28}$$

[6] The sum of the broadening of two levels gives the natural width of the line for the transition between them. The width of a level is the $\hbar$ times the sum of the transition probabilities for all the transitions which are possible from this level. If in Eq. (18.1a), $mc^2\alpha^2 \sim \hbar\omega$ is substituted for $\hbar\omega$, and the radius of the first Bohr orbit is substituted for the matrix element of x, the transition probability becomes

$$\sim \frac{4}{3} \frac{e^2 m^3 c^6 \alpha^6}{\hbar c^3 \hbar^3} \cdot \frac{\hbar^4}{m^2 e^4} = \frac{1}{\hbar} \frac{4mc^3\hbar\alpha^6}{3e^2} \sim \frac{mc^2}{\hbar} \alpha^5.$$

It is proportional to the fifth power of the fine structure constant.

is essentially the same as the first, it can be assumed that the first approximation is almost correct.[7] In this case transitions which are excluded by the selection prohibitions for S or L cannot occur with notable intensity.

It is sufficient in (22.28) to sum over N'; since $\mathbf{H}_1$ is symmetric under the $\mathbf{O}_R$, $(\Psi_{m'}^{N'J'}, \mathbf{H}_1\Psi_m^{NJ})$ certainly vanishes for $J' \neq J$ or $m' \neq m$. Furthermore, $(\Psi_m^{N'J}, \mathbf{H}_1\Psi_m^{NJ})$ is of the same order of magnitude as $(\Psi_m^{NJ}, \mathbf{H}_1\Psi_m^{NJ})$ which gives the first approximation to the energy perturbation due to spin (i.e., the multiplet splitting). On the other hand $E_N - E_{N'}$ is the separation from the nearest gross structure level which has an eigenvalue with total quantum number J. If the first quantity is substantially smaller than the second, the approximation (22.27) is a good one; otherwise it is not. The validity of the approximation thus depends critically on the accidental proximity of levels with the same J, but different S and L. (If S and L of $\Psi_m^{N'J}$ are equal to S and L of Ψ_m^{NJ}, the corresponding term in (22.28) does not affect the transformation properties of Ψ_m^{NJ} with respect to the $\mathbf{P}$.)

[7] $E_{N'}$ runs over all the eigenvalues of the simple Schrödinger equation; the indices S and L, which give the multiplet system and the orbital quantum number, are included in N'.

23. Selection and Intensity Rules with Spin

The selection, intensity, and interval rules for the theory which includes the spin can be divided into two classes. The rules of the first class (numbered 1 to 4 below) follow from symmetry considerations, without any assumptions about the magnitude of the spin forces. These rules, in their content as well as in their bases, are very similar to the rules of the simple theory (Chapter 18), which also arise from the invariance of the energy operator under rotation and reflection. The isotropy of space alone does not suffice to derive the rules of the second class (5 to 7 below); to derive these it must also be assumed that the spin forces are small compared with the electrostatic forces of the simple theory, so that the eigenfunctions and eigenvalues of the simple theory are not essentially changed by the inclusion of the spin in the Hamiltonian.

1. The selection rule for the total quantum number is the same as the selection rule for the orbital quantum number in the simple theory. In a transition involving dipole radiation, J changes by ± 1 or 0, with the added restriction that transitions between two levels with $J = 0$ are forbidden. The matrix elements of vector operators (multiplication with $x_1 + x_2 + \cdots + x_n$, etc) are characteristic of dipole radiation, and these vanish if the conditions mentioned above are not fulfilled.

Also, the selection rule for the parity (Laporte's rule) is maintained because the operator $\mathbf{O}_I$ is identical with the operator $\mathbf{P}_I$ of the simple Schrödinger theory. All the matrix elements

$$(\Psi_F, \mathbf{V}_x\Psi_E), (\Psi_F, \mathbf{V}_y\Psi_E), (\Psi_F, \mathbf{V}_z\Psi_E) \tag{23.1}$$

of any *polar* vector operator vanish, unless the parities w_F and w_E of Ψ_F and Ψ_E are opposite. If one carries out an inversion of the axes, a polar vector retains its direction, so that its components change sign, i.e.,

$$\mathbf{O}_I\mathbf{V}_x\mathbf{O}_I^{-1} = -\mathbf{V}_x.$$

Because $\mathbf{O}_I\Psi_F = w_F\Psi_F$ and $\mathbf{O}_I\Psi_E = w_E\Psi_E$, the unitary character of $\mathbf{O}_I$ implies that

$$\begin{aligned}(\Psi_F, \mathbf{V}_x\Psi_E) &= (\mathbf{O}_I\Psi_F, \mathbf{O}_I\mathbf{V}_x\mathbf{O}_I^{-1} \cdot \mathbf{O}_I\Psi_E)\\ &= -w_Fw_E(\Psi_F, \mathbf{V}_x\Psi_E).\end{aligned}$$

Thus, (23.1) must vanish if Ψ_F and Ψ_E have the same parity. (In a corresponding manner, it can be shown that the matrix elements of an *axial* vector operator are zero if Ψ_F and Ψ_E have different parity.)

Since the parity of a gross structure level is retained in all its fine structure components, Laporte's rule applies to all the fine structure components of a gross structure level in the same way.

If a spectrum consists only of doublet levels with parity $w = (-1)^L$, as, for example, in every hydrogen-like spectrum, the selection rules for j and w also imply the validity of the selection rules for L. On account of Laporte's rule, L can change only by an odd number; a change of 1 is allowed, but not a change of 3 or more, because this would require that $j(= L \pm \frac{1}{2})$ change by 2 or more, which is not possible.

The rule that the transformation property does not change under a permutation of the electrons is already contained in the statement that the wave functions, all of which are antisymmetric, remain antisymmetric in spite of an *arbitrary* perturbation (not only under the influence of radiation).

2. In a magnetic field parallel to the Z-axis, levels with total quantum number j split into $2j + 1$ Zeeman components. The "correct linear combination" for treating the added magnetic energy as a perturbation are the Ψ^j_μ, themselves, just as in the simple theory. If the operator $\mathbf{O}_R$ is applied to a Ψ^j_μ, where R is a rotation about Z through an angle α, the wave function Ψ^j_μ is merely multiplied by $e^{i\mu\alpha}$. The magnetic field removes the degeneracy completely; in a magnetic field only one eigenfunction belongs to each eigenvalue.

Let the auxiliary operator $\mathbf{H}_2$ involving the magnetic field be expanded in a power series in the components $\mathscr{H}_x$, $\mathscr{H}_y$, $\mathscr{H}_z$ of the field strength.

$$\mathbf{H}_2 = (\mathscr{H}_x\mathbf{V}_x + \mathscr{H}_y\mathbf{V}_y + \mathscr{H}_z\mathbf{V}_z) + (\mathscr{H}_x^2\mathbf{V}_{xx} + \cdots) + \cdots. \tag{23.2}$$

Then the coefficients $\mathbf{V}_x$, $\mathbf{V}_y$, $\mathbf{V}_z$ of the first power must form an axial vector operator, since $\mathscr{H}$ itself is an axial vector and $\mathbf{H}_2$ as a whole must be a scalar. The first approximation to the energy perturbation due to a magnetic field in the Z-direction

$$\mathscr{H}_z(\Psi^j_\mu, \mathbf{V}_z\Psi^j_\mu)$$

is, according to the formula for the matrix elements of vector operators, proportional to μ (see the middle formula of Eq. (21.19b)). The splitting in a magnetic field is therefore proportional to the first power of the field strength for weak fields, and divides the original level into $2j + 1$ equidistant components. However, in contrast to the splitting of the simple theory, it is not equally large for all levels and cannot be calculated in general. Only in the case of "normal coupling," that is, if Eq. (22.27) is a good approximation for the eigenfunction, can it be given numerically.

The situation is different as far as the intensity relationships for the Zeeman components are concerned. The strength of the line which connects the μ-component of the higher level to the μ'-component of the lower level is, except for a constant universal factor, the square of the absolute value of

$$(\Psi^{Nj}_{\mu}, \sum_k z_k \Psi^{N'J'}_{\mu'}), \quad \frac{1}{\sqrt{2}}(\Psi^{Nj}_{\mu}, \sum_k (x_k + iy_k)\Psi^{N'j'}_{\mu'}),$$

$$\frac{1}{\sqrt{2}}(\Psi^{Nj}_{\mu}, -\sum_k (x_k - iy_k)\Psi^{N'j'}_{\mu'}),$$

according to whether the light is polarized in the Z-direction, or right- or left-circularly polarized about Z. These are the matrix elements of the three different components $(0, -1, +1)$ of a vector operator. Their ratios for different μ, μ', and polarizations can be obtained directly from Eq. (21.19). This formula also shows that the magnetic quantum number μ can change only by 0 (π-components) or ± 1 (σ-components). The relative intensities in a $j \rightarrow j - 1$ transition are, for example,

$$\begin{aligned} A_{\mu\rightarrow\mu-1} &= (j+\mu)(j+\mu-1) \\ A_{\mu\rightarrow\mu} &= 2(j+\mu)(j-\mu) \\ A_{\mu\rightarrow\mu+1} &= (j-\mu-1)(j-\mu). \end{aligned} \tag{23.3}$$

The sum of the three expressions in (23.3), the transition probability from the higher state with magnetic quantum number μ to all Zeeman levels of the lower level, is the same for all the Zeeman components of the upper level, i.e., it is independent of μ. The same holds for the sum of the transition probabilities of all the lines which have the same lower Zeeman level in common.

This *sum rule for transition probabilities* has a simple physical basis. The sum of the three expressions in (23.3) is the total probability for the transition from the states Ψ^{Nj}_{μ} into all states whose energies correspond to the lower level. But since the states Ψ^{Nj}_{μ} with different μ transform into linear combinations of one another upon rotation of the axes and thus differ only by a rotation, and since the total transition probability must be independent of a rotation, it cannot depend upon μ.

Mathematically, the sum rule can be derived most simply from Eq. (21.18a), by forming

$$|\mathbf{T}^{(\rho)}_{Nj\mu;N'j'\mu'}|^2 = \sum_{\nu\sigma\nu'}\sum_{\lambda\tau\lambda'} \mathfrak{D}^{(j)}(R)^*_{\nu\mu}\mathfrak{D}^{(j)}(R)_{\lambda\mu}\mathfrak{D}^{(\omega)}(R)^*_{\sigma\rho}\mathfrak{D}^{(\omega)}(R)_{\tau\rho}$$
$$\cdot\, \mathfrak{D}^{(j')}(R)_{\nu'\mu'}\mathfrak{D}'^{(j)}(R)^*_{\lambda'\mu'}\mathbf{T}^{(\sigma)}_{Nj\nu;N'j'\nu'}\mathbf{T}^{(\tau)*}_{Nj\lambda;N'j'\lambda'}.$$

If this is summed over μ and ρ, because of the unitary nature of $\mathfrak{D}^{(j)}$ and $\mathfrak{D}^{(\omega)}$, the first four factors on the right are replaced by $\delta_{\nu\lambda} \cdot \delta_{\sigma\tau}$.

Integration over all rotations then yields, because of the orthogonality relations,

$$\sum_{\mu\rho} |\mathbf{T}^{(\rho)}_{Nj\mu;N'j'\mu'}|^2 = \frac{1}{2j'+1}\sum_{\nu\sigma\nu'}|\mathbf{T}^{(\sigma)}_{Nj\nu;N'j'\nu'}|^2. \tag{23.E.1}$$

This establishes directly that the sum (23.E.1) is independent of μ'.

3. An electric field parallel to the Z-axis splits a level with total quantum number j into $j + 1$ components in the case of an even number of electrons—the same as in the simple theory discussed in Chapter 18. These belong to the representations

$$\mathfrak{Z}^{(j)}, \mathfrak{Z}^{(j-1)}, \cdots, \mathfrak{Z}^{(2)}, \mathfrak{Z}^{(1)}, \mathfrak{Z}^{(0)} \quad \text{or} \quad \mathfrak{Z}^{(0')}$$

of the two-dimensional rotation-reflection group. The last level belongs to $\mathfrak{Z}^{(0)}$ or to $\mathfrak{Z}^{(0')}$ according to whether $w(-1)^j$ is equal to $+1$ or -1. The selection rules of Chapter 18 can also be derived exactly as was done there, except that j must be substituted for L.

The Stark effect in the case of an odd number of electrons will be treated in more detail. Actually, the result itself could be obtained quite easily. However, a question of principle is involved which we wish to discuss.

The difficulty arises from the fact that two matrices, $\pm\mathfrak{D}^{(j)}(R)$, correspond to each rotation R. The same holds for improper rotations:

$$\mathfrak{D}^{(j,w)}(RI) = \pm w\mathfrak{D}^{(j)}(R).$$

Only to the inversion does a single matrix, $+w\mathbf{1}$, correspond. However, the electric field removes the inversion symmetry, and although many improper rotations remain, the corresponding matrices are, because of their double-valuedness, the same whether $w = +1$ or $w = -1$. This suggests that some essential element has been lost by the double-valuedness. For certain symmetries this would actually be the case. In the case of the symmetry group in an electric field, the more detailed analysis which follows does not lead to any results beyond those which are already evident.

In order to obtain single-valued representations we recall that for an odd number of electrons the rotational symmetry is expressed by means of the operators $\mathbf{O}_{\mathbf{u}}$ which form a group isomorphic to the two-dimensional unitary group. In order to express the invariance under improper rotations, we use the operators $\mathbf{O}_I\mathbf{O}_{\mathbf{u}}$. The set of operators $\mathbf{O}_{\mathbf{u}} = \mathbf{1}\mathbf{O}_{\mathbf{u}}$, $\mathbf{O}_I\mathbf{O}_{\mathbf{u}}$ is the direct product of the reflection group ($\mathbf{O}_E = \mathbf{1}$, $\mathbf{O}_I$) and the group of the $\mathbf{O}_{\mathbf{u}}$. If we denote the general element of the group of the direct product of the reflection group and the unitary group[1] by $\mathfrak{z}$, then the entire rotation-reflection symmetry can be expressed by means of the $\mathbf{O}_{\mathfrak{z}}$ which form a group isomorphic to the group of the $\mathfrak{z}$. The $\mathfrak{z}$ and $\mathbf{O}_{\mathfrak{z}}$ correspond either to pure rotations, in which case $\mathfrak{z}$ has the form $E\mathbf{u}$, or to improper rotations, for which $\mathfrak{z}$ has the form $I\mathbf{u}$. However, two $\mathfrak{z}$ or $\mathbf{O}_{\mathfrak{z}}$ correspond to each rotation, whether proper or improper.

[1] The $\mathfrak{z}$ are thus elements of an abstract group, not of matrices but of pairs $J\mathbf{u}$, where J is either E or I and $\mathbf{u}$ is an element of the unitary group. The law of multiplication is see Chapter 16) $J\mathbf{u} \cdot J_1\mathbf{u}_1 = JJ_1\mathbf{u}\mathbf{u}_1$.

If an external field is applied, only those $\mathfrak{z}$ remain symmetry operations[2] which correspond to rotations, proper or improper, belonging to the symmetry group of the system in the external field. The matrices $\mathbf{D}(\mathfrak{z})$ corresponding to these,

$$\mathbf{O}_{\mathfrak{z}}\Psi_{\mu} = \sum_{\mu'} \mathbf{D}(\mathfrak{z})_{\mu'\mu}\Psi_{\mu'}, \tag{23.4}$$

form a (single-valued) representation of the group of the corresponding $\mathfrak{z}$, and the different levels of the system in the field belong to the different representations of this group. The symmetry group of the system is not isomorphic to this group, but (doubly) homomorphic, since two $\mathfrak{z}$ correspond to each of its elements.

In the case of a homogeneous electric field parallel to the Z-axis, rotations about Z and the reflections in the planes through Z belong to the symmetry group. To the rotations about Z through an angle α, correspond the matrices

$$\mathfrak{z}_\alpha = E\begin{pmatrix} e^{-\frac{1}{2}i\alpha} & 0 \\ 0 & e^{\frac{1}{2}i\alpha} \end{pmatrix}; \ \mathfrak{z}'_\alpha = E\begin{pmatrix} -e^{-\frac{1}{2}i\alpha} & 0 \\ 0 & -e^{+\frac{1}{2}i\alpha} \end{pmatrix} \ (-\pi < \alpha \leqslant \pi). \tag{23.5}$$

(See Eq. (15.16).) The reflection in the ZX-plane is the product of an inversion and a rotation about Y through π. The corresponding $\mathfrak{z}$ are therefore

$$\mathfrak{z}_y = I\begin{pmatrix} 0 & -1 \\ 1 & 0 \end{pmatrix}; \ \mathfrak{z}'_y = I\begin{pmatrix} 0 & 1 \\ -1 & 0 \end{pmatrix}. \tag{23.5a}$$

Products of (23.5) and (23.5a) correspond to the reflections in the other planes. In the representation of the direct product of the reflection group and the unitary group which belongs to a level with parity w and total quantum number j, the matrices which correspond to the group elements (23.5) are

$$\mathbf{D}(\mathfrak{z}_\alpha) = \begin{pmatrix} e^{-ij\alpha} & \cdots & 0 \\ \vdots & \ddots & \vdots \\ 0 & \cdots & e^{ij\alpha} \end{pmatrix}; \ \mathbf{D}(\mathfrak{z}'_\alpha) = -\begin{pmatrix} e^{-ij\alpha} & \cdots & 0 \\ \vdots & \ddots & \vdots \\ 0 & \cdots & e^{ij\alpha} \end{pmatrix}. \tag{23.6}$$

Similarly, the matrices which correspond to the group elements (23.5a) are (substitute $a = 0$, $b = -1$ for $\mathfrak{z}_y$ and $a = 0$, $b = +1$ for $\mathfrak{z}'_y$ into Eq. (15.21a) and multiply by w):

$$\mathbf{D}(\mathfrak{z}_y) = \begin{pmatrix} 0 & 0 \cdots 0 & -w \\ 0 & 0 \cdots w & 0 \\ \vdots & \vdots \quad \vdots & \vdots \\ 0 & -w \cdots 0 & 0 \\ w & 0 \cdots 0 & 0 \end{pmatrix} = -\mathbf{D}(\mathfrak{z}'_y). \tag{23.6a}$$

[2] That is, only these still transform eigenfunctions of a given eigenvalue into eigenfunctions of the same eigenvalue.

The matrices (23.6) and (23.6a) and their products form a representation of that subgroup of the direct product of the reflection group and the unitary group whose elements correspond to the symmetry elements of the system which remain in the presence of the electric field. This representation can be reduced by interchanging the rows and columns so that their order becomes $-j, j, -j+1, j-1, \cdots, -\frac{1}{2}, \frac{1}{2}$ instead of $-j, -j+1, \cdots, j-1, j$. It then decomposes into a set of two-rowed irreducible representations

$$\mathbf{Z}^{(m)}(\mathfrak{z}_\alpha) = \begin{pmatrix} e^{-im\alpha} & 0 \\ 0 & e^{im\alpha} \end{pmatrix}; \quad \mathbf{Z}^{(m)}(\mathfrak{z}'_\alpha) = \begin{pmatrix} -e^{-im\alpha} & 0 \\ 0 & -e^{im\alpha} \end{pmatrix} \tag{23.7}$$

and

$$\mathbf{Z}^{(m)}(\mathfrak{z}_y) = (-1)^{j-m} \begin{pmatrix} 0 & -w \\ w & 0 \end{pmatrix}; \quad \mathbf{Z}^{(m)}(\mathfrak{z}'_y) = (-1)^{j-m} \begin{pmatrix} 0 & w \\ -w & 0 \end{pmatrix}, \tag{23.7a}$$

in which m assumes the values

$$m = j, j-1, j-2, \cdots, \tfrac{3}{2}, \tfrac{1}{2} \tag{23.8}$$

so that a level with total quantum number j splits into $j + \frac{1}{2}$ Stark-effect components whose electric quantum numbers appear in (23.8).

It happens in this case that the representations $\mathbf{Z}^{(m)}$ for $w = +1$ and $w = -1$ are equivalent, since they can be transformed into one another by the matrix

$$\begin{pmatrix} -1 & 0 \\ 0 & 1 \end{pmatrix}.$$

Thus, levels with the same electric quantum numbers which arise from even and odd levels have the same transformation properties; their selection rules will be the same. This result could have been anticipated from the fact that Laporte's rule is not valid in an electric field for an even number of electrons either, and the only difference between levels arising from even and odd levels is the appearance of 0 and 0′ levels, respectively. For an odd number of electrons even this characteristic of parity is eliminated, since no 0 or 0′ levels can appear.

4. If the perturbation operator for the electric field is expanded in a series like (23.2), it follows from the polar nature of the electric field vector that the coefficients $\mathbf{V}_x$, $\mathbf{V}_y$, $\mathbf{V}_z$ must be the components of a polar vector. Therefore, the matrix elements

$$(\Psi'^{Nj}_{\mu}, \mathbf{V}_z \Psi'^{Nj}_{\mu'}),$$

which might produce an effect proportional to the first power of the field strength, vanish, since Ψ'^{Nj}_{μ} and $\Psi'^{Nj}_{\mu'}$ have the same parity.

The splitting takes place in the second approximation, which is proportional to $\mathscr{E}^2$; it can be shown that in this approximation a displacement and a splitting proportional to μ^2 occur.

5. Most of the rules derived so far, insofar as they refer to the isotropic case, are special cases of Eq. (21.19),

$$\mathbf{T}^{(\rho)}_{Nj\mu;N'j'\mu'} = s^{(j\omega)}_{j'\mu\rho}\delta_{\mu+\rho,\mu'}T_{Nj;N'j'}. \tag{23.9}$$

This equation allows the determination of the ratio of the matrix elements

$$\frac{\mathbf{T}^{(\rho)}_{Nj\mu;N'j'\mu'}}{\mathbf{T}^{(\sigma)}_{Nj\nu;N'j'\nu'}} = \frac{(\Psi^{Nj}_{\mu}, \mathbf{T}^{(\rho)}\Psi^{N'j'}_{\mu'})}{(\Psi^{Nj}_{\nu}, \mathbf{T}^{(\sigma)}\Psi^{N'j'}_{\nu'})} \tag{23.9a}$$

if the corresponding eigenfunctions Ψ^{Nj}_{μ} and Ψ^{Nj}_{ν}, and $\Psi^{N'j'}_{\mu'}$ and $\Psi^{N'j'}_{\nu'}$ belong to the same eigenvalues E^{N}_{j} and $E^{N'}_{j'}$ (that is, if they are partners), and if the operators $\mathbf{T}^{(\rho)}$ and $\mathbf{T}^{(\sigma)}$ are components of the same *irreducible tensor operator*

$$\mathbf{O}_R^{-1}\mathbf{T}^{(\rho)}\mathbf{O}_R = \sum_{\sigma} \mathfrak{D}^{(\omega)}(R)_{\rho\sigma}\mathbf{T}^{(\sigma)}. \tag{23.9b}$$

Scalars corresponding to the representation $\mathfrak{D}^{(0)}$, and vectors (corresponding to $\mathfrak{D}^{(1)}$), etc., are irreducible tensors. The $T_{Nj;N'j'}$ in (23.9) are numbers which cannot be determined by general methods since they depend on the set of operators $\mathbf{T}$ and on the particular Hamiltonian operator used.

So far we have had only one formula which could not be written in the form (23.9). That is the formula for the normal Zeeman effect, Eq. (18.8). In its derivation it had to be noted that the vector-operator in question, $\mathbf{L}_z$, is given by (18.7)

$$\mathbf{L}_z = -i\hbar\frac{\partial}{\partial\varphi}\mathbf{P}_{\{\varphi 00\}} \tag{23.10}$$

evaluated at $\varphi = 0$. Otherwise, the derivation of rules which go beyond (23.9) is possible only on the basis of further assumptions or approximations.

The most important assumption of this kind is that of "normal," or Russell-Saunders, coupling between spin and orbital angular momentum. This was also assumed in the preceding chapter; it is characterized by a fine structure splitting which is small in comparison with the separation between adjacent levels of the gross structure. In this case not only can a total quantum number be defined, but the concepts of multiplet system and orbital quantum number are also meaningful. It is well to put this into evidence by substituting the triple symbol NSL for the simple running number N of levels with the same total quantum number J, where S represents the multiplet system, L the orbital quantum number, and N serves only to differentiate levels with equal S, L, and J.[3] The remainder of this chapter will be based on the assumption of "normal coupling."

[3] We again use the symbol J for the total quantum number, as always in the case of normal coupling.

The eigenfunctions have, according to Eq. (22.27), the form

$$\Psi_m^{NSLJ} = \sum_\mu s_{J\mu,m-\mu}^{(LS)} \Xi_{m-\mu,\mu}^{NSL}. \tag{23.11}$$

The $\Xi_{-S\mu}^{NSL}, \Xi_{-S+1,\mu}^{NSL}, \cdots, \Xi_{S,\mu}^{NSL}$ are partners under the $\mathbf{Q}_R$ and belong to the different rows of $\mathfrak{D}^{(S)}$; the same holds for the set $\Xi_{\nu,-L}^{NSL}, \Xi_{\nu,-L+1}^{NSL}, \cdots, \Xi_{\nu,L}^{NSL}$ with respect to the operators $\mathbf{P}_R$ and the representation $\mathfrak{D}^{(L)}$. If (23.11) holds, the ratio of the matrix elements

$$(\Psi_m^{NSLJ}, \mathbf{T}^{(\sigma\rho)}\Psi_{m'}^{N'S'L'J'}) = \mathbf{T}_{NSLJm;N'S'L'J'm'}^{(\sigma\rho)}, \tag{23.12}$$

with different $J, J', m, m', \sigma, \rho$, but identical NSL and $N'S'L'$ can be calculated if the $\mathbf{T}^{(\sigma\rho)}$ are the components of a tensor which is of degree q with regard to the $\mathbf{Q}_R$, of degree p with regard to the $\mathbf{P}_R$, and irreducible with regard to both:

$$\mathbf{Q}_R^{-1}\mathbf{T}^{(\sigma\rho)}\mathbf{Q}_R = \sum_{\sigma'} \mathfrak{D}^{(q)}(R)_{\sigma\sigma'}\mathbf{T}^{(\sigma'\rho)}, \tag{23.13a}$$

$$\mathbf{P}_R^{-1}\mathbf{T}^{(\sigma\rho)}\mathbf{P}_R = \sum_{\rho'} \mathfrak{D}^{(p)}(R)_{\rho\rho'}\mathbf{T}^{(\sigma\rho')}. \tag{23.13b}$$

With respect to the actual symmetry operators $\mathbf{O}_R$, the tensor $\mathbf{T}$ is in general not irreducible; it belongs to a direct product of two irreducible representations

$$\begin{aligned}\mathbf{O}_R^{-1}\mathbf{T}^{(\sigma\rho)}\mathbf{O}_R &= \mathbf{Q}_R^{-1}\mathbf{P}_R^{-1}\mathbf{T}^{(\sigma\rho)}\mathbf{P}_R\mathbf{Q}_R \\ &= \sum_{\rho'} \mathbf{Q}_R^{-1}\mathfrak{D}^{(p)}(R)_{\rho\rho'}\mathbf{T}^{(\sigma\rho')}\mathbf{Q}_R = \sum_{\sigma'\rho'} \mathfrak{D}^{(q)}(R)_{\sigma\sigma'}\mathfrak{D}^{(p)}(R)_{\rho\rho'}\mathbf{T}^{(\sigma'\rho')}.\end{aligned}$$

Under the operations $\mathbf{Q}_R$, the $\Xi_{\nu\mu}^{NSL}$ for $\nu = -S, \cdots, S$ belong to $\mathfrak{D}^{(S)}$ and are partners. It follows from (23.13a) that the equation analogous to (23.9) is

$$(\Xi_{\nu\mu}^{NSL}, \mathbf{T}^{(\sigma\rho)}\Xi_{\nu'\mu'}^{N'S'L'}) = \delta_{\nu+\sigma,\nu'}\, s_{S'\nu\sigma}^{(Sq)}\, t_{NSL\mu;N'S'L'\mu'}^{(\rho)}. \tag{23.14a}$$

Similarly, one has

$$(\Xi_{\nu\mu}^{NSL}, \mathbf{T}^{(\sigma\rho)}\Xi_{\nu'\mu'}^{N'S'L'}) = \delta_{\mu+\rho,\mu'}\, s_{L'\mu\rho}^{(Lp)}\, t_{NSL\nu;N'S'L'\nu'}^{(\sigma)} \tag{23.14b}$$

because of (23.13b) and because the $\Xi_{\nu\mu}^{NSL}$ for $\mu = -L, \cdots, L$ transform according to $\mathfrak{D}^{(L)}$ under the operations $\mathbf{P}_R$.

Combination of (23.14a) and (23.14b) gives

$$(\Xi_{\nu\mu}^{NSL}, \mathbf{T}^{(\sigma\rho)}\Xi_{\nu'\mu'}^{N'S'L'}) = \delta_{\nu+\sigma,\nu'}\,\delta_{\mu+\rho,\mu'}\, s_{S'\nu\sigma}^{(Sq)}\, s_{L'\mu\rho}^{(Lp)}\, t_{NSL;N'S'L'}, \tag{23.14}$$

or, on account of (23.11)

$$\begin{aligned}&(\Psi_m^{NSLJ}, \mathbf{T}^{(\sigma\rho)}\Psi_{m'}^{N'S'L'J'}) \\ &= \sum_{\mu\mu'} s_{J,\mu,m-\mu}^{(LS)}\, s_{J',\mu',m'-\mu'}^{(L'S')}\, \delta_{m-\mu+\sigma,m'-\mu'}\, \delta_{\mu+\rho,\mu'}\, s_{S',m-\mu,\sigma}^{(Sq)}\, s_{L'\mu\rho}^{(Lp)}\, t_{NSL;N'S'L'} \\ &= \sum_{\mu} s_{J,\mu,m-\mu}^{(LS)}\, s_{J',\mu+\rho,m-\mu+\sigma}^{(L'S')}\, \delta_{m+\sigma+\rho,m'}\, s_{S',m-\mu,\sigma}^{(Sq)}\, s_{L'\mu\rho}^{(Lp)}\, t_{NSL;N'S'L'}.\end{aligned} \tag{23.15}$$

These formulas determine the ratios of all the matrix elements (23.12) with the same NSL and $N'S'L'$.

In (23.15), as in (23.9), all $s_{J\mu\nu}^{(LS)}$ whose first lower index is larger than the sum of the two upper indices or smaller than the absolute value of their difference ($J > L + S$ or $J < |L - S|$) must be set equal to zero. The same holds for $|\mu| > L$, for $|\nu| > S$, or $|\mu + \nu| > J$.

6. It might seem as though the class of operators defined by (23.13a) and (23.13b) is rather an artificial one. However, almost all important operators are tensor components or sums of tensor components of this kind. In particular, the spin-free operators are all symmetric (i.e., scalars) with respect to the $\mathbf{Q}_R$, so that (23.13a) holds for these with $q = 0$. Therefore they transform under the $\mathbf{P}_R$ in the same way as under the $\mathbf{O}_R$, and are scalars, vectors, etc. under the former if they are these in reality.

Let us verify (23.15) in a few simple cases. For spin-free operators and all operators with $q = 0$ we see that the scalar product (23.15) vanishes if $S' \neq S$. This corresponds to the earlier rule that matrix elements between states which belong to different multiplicities vanish (rule A, page 196). If $p = 0$ as well (that is, if the operator is a scalar under the $\mathbf{P}_R$, and therefore under the $\mathbf{O}_R$), then $L' = L$ must also hold. Since $\rho = \sigma = 0$ (a scalar has only a 0-component), the sum in (23.15) can be evaluated by using the orthogonality relationships for the vector coupling coefficients (Eq. (17.28)),

$$\sum_{\mu} s_{J,\mu,m-\mu}^{(LS)} s_{J',\mu,m-\mu}^{(LS)} = \delta_{JJ'}, \tag{23.16}$$

and the fact that $s_{L\mu 0}^{(L0)} = s_{S,m-\mu,0}^{(S0)} = 1$. For an operator which is a scalar in both respects ($p = 0$, $q = 0$), we obtain the results that the matrix elements

$$(\Psi_m^{NSLJ}, \mathbf{T}\Psi_{m'}^{N'S'L'J'}) = \delta_{SS'}\delta_{LL'}\delta_{JJ'}\delta_{mm'} \cdot t_{NSL;N'S'L'} \tag{23.17}$$

(a) vanish for $J' \neq J$ or $m' \neq m$, and are independent of m for $J' = J$ and $m' = m$ — which is just the rule for operators which are symmetric under the $\mathbf{O}_R$ — and (b) that they are the same for all the fine structure components of a gross structure level, independent of J. For this it is not sufficient that $\mathbf{T}$ be a scalar under the $\mathbf{O}_R = \mathbf{P}_R\mathbf{Q}_R$; it must be a scalar under the $\mathbf{P}_R$ and the $\mathbf{Q}_R$ separately, and the coupling must be "normal."

One operator which is a scalar in both respects is, for example, the Hamiltonian operator $\mathbf{H}_0$ of the simple Schrödinger theory. In this case

$$(\Psi_m^{NSLJ}, \mathbf{H}_0\Psi_{m'}^{N'S'L'J'}) = E^{NSL}\delta_{NN'}\delta_{SS'}\delta_{LL'}\delta_{JJ'}\delta_{mm'}$$

where E^{NSL} is the eigenvalue of the simple Schrödinger equation; E^{NSL} is the same for all fine structure components, since this theory gives no fine structure splitting.

Work these out sometime!

The Hönl-Kronig Intensity Formulas

If $\mathbf{T}^{(\sigma\rho)} = \mathbf{V}^{(\rho)}$ is a scalar under the $\mathbf{Q}_R$, and a vector under the $\mathbf{P}_R$ (as, for example, the operator for multiplication by

$$\frac{1}{\sqrt{2}}\sum_k (x_k + iy_k), \qquad \sum_k z_k, \qquad -\frac{1}{\sqrt{2}}\sum_k (x_k - iy_k)$$

which determines the dipole transition probabilities), then $p = 1$, $q = 0$ and we can write

$$\mathbf{V}^{(\rho)}_{NSLJm;N'S'L'J'm'} = \delta_{SS'}\,\delta_{m+\rho,m'} \sum_{\mu} s^{(LS)}_{J,\mu,m-\mu}\, s^{(L'S)}_{J',\mu+\rho,m-\mu}\, s^{(L1)}_{L',\mu,\rho}\, v_{NSL;N'SL'} \tag{23.15a}$$

for (23.15). The matrix elements (23.15a) will vanish unless $S' = S$ and $L' = L$ or $L' = L \pm 1$ (and $J' = J$ or $J' = J \pm 1$). Since we already know the ratio of the matrix elements for different m, m', and ρ (Eq. (23.9)),

$$\mathbf{V}^{(\rho)}_{NSLJm;N'SL'J'm'} = s^{(J1)}_{J'm\rho}\,\delta_{m+\rho,m'}\,V_{NSLJ;N'SL'J'} \tag{23.18}$$

we can substitute particular values for these and calculate the ratios for different J and J' for these values. The formulas for the s will be simplest if we substitute $m = J$, $m' = J'$ and $\rho = m' - m = J' - J$. Then, for example, Eq. (17.27b) and Table IV on page 193 give for $L' = L - 1$, $J' = J + 1$, the following simplifying relationship:

$$s^{(LS)}_{J,\mu,J-\mu}\, s^{(L1)}_{L-1,\mu,1}$$

$$= \frac{(-1)^{L-\mu}\sqrt{(L+S-J)!(2J+1)!}}{\sqrt{(J+L+S+1)!(J+S-L)!(J-S+L)!}}$$

$$\times \sqrt{\frac{(L+\mu)!(S+J-\mu)!}{(L-\mu)!(S-J+\mu)!}}\,\frac{\sqrt{(L-\mu-1)(L-\mu)}}{\sqrt{2L(2L+1)}}$$

$$= \frac{(-1)^{L-1-(\mu+1)}\sqrt{(L-1+S-J-1)!(2J+3)!}}{\sqrt{(J+1+L-1+S+1)!(J+1+S-L+1)!(J+1-S+L-1)}}$$

$$\times \sqrt{\frac{(L+\mu)!(S+J-\mu)!}{(L-\mu-2)!(S-J+\mu)!}}$$

$$\times \sqrt{\frac{(L+S-J-1)(L+S-J)(J+S-L+1)(J+S-L+2)}{(2J+2)(2J+3)2L(2L+1)}}$$

$$= s^{(L-1,S)}_{J+1,\mu+1,J-\mu}$$

$$\times \sqrt{\frac{(L+S-J-1)(L+S-J)(J+S-L+1)(J+S-L+2)}{(2J+2)(2J+3)2L(2L+1)}}$$

By means of (23.16) and the equality above, we obtain

$$\mathbf{V}^{(1)}_{NSLJJ;N'SL-1J+1J+1}$$
$$= \sum_{\mu} s^{(LS)}_{J,\mu,J-\mu}\, s^{(L1)}_{L-1,\mu,1}\, s^{(L-1,S)}_{J+1,\mu+1,J-\mu}\, v_{N'SL;NSL-1}$$
$$= \sqrt{\frac{(L+S-J-1)(L+S-J)(J+S-L+1)(J+S-L+2)}{(2J+2)(2J+3)2L(2L+1)}}\, v_{NSL;N'SL-1}$$

for the sum of (23.15a). Hence, $s^{(J1)}_{J+1,J,1} = 1$ gives for the $V_{NSLJ;N'S'L'J'}$ in (23.18)

$$V_{NSLJ;N'SL-1J+1}$$
$$= \sqrt{\frac{(L+S-J-1)(L+S-J)(J+S-L+1)(J+S-L+2)}{(2J+2)(2J+3)(2L)(2L+1)}}\, v_{NSL;N'SL-1}. \tag{23.19a}$$

The analogous formulas

$$V_{NSLJ;N'SL-1J}$$
$$= \sqrt{\frac{(L+S-J)(J+S-L+1)(J-S+L)(J+L+S+1)}{2J(2J+2)(L)(2L+1)}}\, v_{NSL;N'SL-1} \tag{23.19b}$$

$$V_{NSLJ;N'SL-1J-1}$$
$$= \sqrt{\frac{(J-S+L-1)(J-S+L)(J+S+L)(J+L+S+1)}{2J(2J-1)(2L)(2L+1)}}\, v_{NSL;N'SL-1} \tag{23.19c}$$

can be derived in the same fashion. These equations, together with (23.18), express all the matrix elements of the dipole transition operators between the wave functions of two multiplets in terms of the same quantity, $v_{NSL,N'SL-1}$. The orbital quantum numbers of the two multiplets are L and $L' = L - 1$. A similar calculation gives for $L' = L$ the result

$$V_{NSLJ;N'SLJ+1}$$
$$= \sqrt{\frac{(L+S-J)(J-S+L+1)(J+S-L+1)(J+L+S+2)}{(2J+2)(2J+3)(2L)(L+1)}}\, v_{NSL;N'SL} \tag{23.19d}$$

$$V_{NSLJ;N'SLJ-1}$$
$$= -\sqrt{\frac{(L+S-J+1)(J-S+L)(J+S-L)(J+L+S+1)}{2J(2J-1)(2L)(L+1)}}\, v_{NSL;N'SL}. \tag{23.19e}$$

In this case the $s^{(L1)}_{L\mu J'-J}$ has been combined in part with the first and in part with the second factor in (23.15a). Only the derivation of the corresponding formula for $L' = L$ and $J' = J$ requires special handling: The coefficient $s^{(L1)}_{L\mu 0}$ must be decomposed into a sum of two parts

$$s^{(L1)}_{L\mu 0} = \frac{\mu}{\sqrt{L(L+1)}} = \frac{L}{\sqrt{L(L+1)}} - \frac{\sqrt{L-\mu}\sqrt{L-\mu}}{\sqrt{L(L+1)}}.$$

The summation over the first term in (23.15a) can be carried out directly using the orthogonality relations (23.16); in the sum over μ this gives

$$v_{NSL;N'SL} L/\sqrt{L(L+1)}.$$

The summation over the second term can be performed by using the fact that

$$s^{(LS)}_{J,\mu,J-\mu}\sqrt{L-\mu} = \frac{(-1)^{L-\mu}\sqrt{(L+S-J)!(2J+1)!}}{\sqrt{(J+S+L+1)!(J+S-L)!(J-S+L)!}} \times\sqrt{\frac{(L+\mu)!(J+S-\mu)!}{(L-\mu-1)!(S-J+\mu)!}}$$

$$= -\, s^{(L-\frac{1}{2},S)}_{J+\frac{1}{2},\mu+\frac{1}{2},J-\mu}\sqrt{\frac{(L+S-J)(J+S-L+1)}{2J+2}}$$

and the orthogonality relations (23.16). We thereby obtain for (23.15a)

$$\sum_{\mu} (s^{(LS)}_{J,\mu,J-\mu})^2\, s^{(L1)}_{L\mu 0} = \frac{L}{\sqrt{L(L+1)}} - \frac{(L+S-J)(J+S-L+1)}{(2J+2)\sqrt{L(L+1)}}$$

$$= \frac{J(J+1)+L(L+1)-S(S+1)}{2(J+1)\sqrt{L(L+1)}}$$

and, from this finally,

$$V_{NSLJ;N'SLJ} = \frac{J(J+1)+L(L+1)-S(S+1)}{2\sqrt{J(J+1)}\sqrt{L(L+1)}}\, v_{NSL;N'SL}. \qquad (23.19\text{f})$$

The ratios of the matrix elements for $L' = L + 1$ could be obtained by the same kind of direct calculation; alternatively, note that the Hermitian character of $\mathbf{V}^{(0)}$ implies

$$\mathbf{V}^{(0)}_{N'SL-1J'm';NSLJm} = \overset{*}{\mathbf{V}}{}^{(0)}_{NSLJm;N'SL-1J'm'}.$$

Hence the ratios can be calculated from the relations (23.19a) through (23.19c).

The formulas (23.19a) through (23.19f) contain the Hönl-Kronig intensity formulas for the ratios of the intensities of the fine structure components of a line. To obtain the total intensity of a fine structure component $NSLJ \rightarrow N'S'L'J'$ we must sum the intensities $|\mathbf{V}^{(\rho)}_{NSLJm;N'S'L'J'm'}|^2$ of the individual Zeeman components over all m, m', and ρ:

$$\sum_{m'm}\sum_{\rho} \left|\mathbf{V}^{(\rho)}_{NSLJm;N'SL'J'm'}\right|^2 = \sum_{mm'} \left|V_{NSLJ;N'SL'J'} s^{(J1)}_{J'm,m'-m}\right|^2$$

$$= \left|V_{NSLJ;N'SL'J'}\right|^2 \sum_{m'} 1 = (2J'+1)\left|V_{NSLJ;N'SL'J'}\right|^2.$$

The total intensity of the line $J \rightarrow J'$ is therefore essentially determined by the $V_{NSLJ;N'S'L'J'}$.

The Landé g-Formula

7. A second application of the formula (23.19f) is related to the Zeeman effect. The interaction of a magnetic field with an atom involves two added terms in the Hamiltonian operator. The first term is $\mathbf{V} = \eta \mathscr{H} \mathbf{L}_z$ where $\eta = e/2m_0c$, and m_0 is the electron mass. This term describes the interaction of the magnetic field with the currents generated by the motion of the electrons; it had the same form in the simple theory (Eqs. (18.6) and (18.7)). The effect of the operator $\mathbf{L}_z$ is simply to multiply the wave function by the Z-component of angular momentum:

$$\mathbf{L}_z \psi^{NSL}_{\varkappa\mu} = \mu\hbar\psi^{NSL}_{\varkappa\mu}. \tag{23.20}$$

Therefore, according to Eq. (22.25),

$$\mathbf{L}_z \Xi^{NSL}_{\nu\mu} = \sum_{\varkappa} \mathbf{L}_z \psi^{NSL}_{\varkappa\mu} f^{(S)}_{\varkappa\nu} = \hbar \sum_{\varkappa} \mu\psi^{NSL}_{\varkappa\mu} f^{(S)}_{\varkappa\nu} = \mu\hbar\Xi^{NSL}_{\nu\mu}$$

so that $v_{NSL;N'S'L'}$ become in this case

$$(\Xi^{NSL}_{\nu\mu}, \mathbf{L}_z \Xi^{NSL}_{\nu\mu}) = \mu\hbar = v_{NSL;NSL} \frac{\mu}{\sqrt{L(L+1)}},$$

as comparison with (23.14) shows. This gives, according to (23.19f),

$$V_{NSLJ;NSLJ} = \hbar \frac{J(J+1) + L(L+1) - S(S+1)}{2\sqrt{J(J+1)}}. \tag{23.20a}$$

Equation (23.18) then shows that the matrix elements of $\mathbf{L}_z$ are

$$(\Psi^{NSLJ}_m, \mathbf{L}_z \Psi^{NSLJ}_m) = m\hbar \frac{J(J+1) + L(L+1) - S(S+1)}{2J(J+1)}. \tag{23.21}$$

The second term, $\overline{\mathbf{V}}$, of the magnetic field operator in the Hamiltonian describes the interaction of the magnetic field with the spin magnetic moment of the electron; it is equal to the scalar product of the magnetic moment with the field strength, that is ($\eta = e/2m_0c$),

$$2\eta(\mathbf{S}_x\mathscr{H}_x + \mathbf{S}_y\mathscr{H}_y + \mathbf{S}_z\mathscr{H}_z), \tag{23.22}$$

or, for several electrons, a sum of terms of the form (23.22). If the magnetic field is in the Z direction, then $\overline{\mathbf{V}} = 2\eta\mathscr{H}\mathbf{S}_z$, where $\mathbf{S}_z$ is the Z-component of the total spin. The corresponding operator is multiplication by

$$\tfrac{1}{2}\hbar(s_1 + s_2 + \cdots + s_n) = \mathbf{S}_z \tag{23.22a}$$

since $\mathbf{s}_z$ is multiplication by s, according to Eq. (20.21). It will be shown that

$$\mathbf{S}_z\Psi = -i\hbar \frac{\partial}{\partial\alpha} \mathbf{Q}_{\{\alpha,0,0\}} \Psi \Big|_{\alpha=0}. \tag{23.23a}$$

This is the analogue of Eq. (18.7)

$$\mathbf{L}_z\Psi = -i\hbar \frac{\partial}{\partial\alpha} \mathbf{P}_{\{\alpha,0,0\}} \Psi \Big|_{\alpha=0}. \tag{23.23b}$$

The factor $\frac{1}{2}$ in (23.22a) is due to the fact that the spin has an angular momentum of only $\hbar/2$. Since $\mathfrak{D}^{(1/2)}(\alpha, 0, 0)_{\frac{1}{2}s,\frac{1}{2}t} = \delta_{st}e^{\frac{1}{2}is\alpha}$, the equation defining $\mathbf{Q}_R$ (Eq. (21.6b) takes the form

$$\begin{aligned}\mathbf{Q}_{\{\alpha 00\}}\Psi(\cdots, x_k, y_k, z_k, s_k, \cdots) &= \sum_{t_1\cdots t_n=\pm 1} \cdots \mathfrak{D}^{(1/2)}(\{\alpha 00\})_{\frac{1}{2}s_k,\frac{1}{2}t_k} \cdots \Psi(\cdots, x_k, y_k, z_k, t_k, \cdots) \\ &= \sum_{t_1\cdots t_n} \cdots \delta_{s_k t_k} e^{\frac{1}{2}is_k\alpha} \cdots \Psi(\cdots, x_k, y_k, z_k, t_k, \cdots) = e^{\frac{1}{2}i(s_1+\cdots+s_n)\alpha}\Psi,\end{aligned}$$

and from this, Eq. (23.23a) follows directly.

One has also, therefore,

$$(\Xi^{NSL}_{\nu\mu}, \mathbf{S}_z\Xi^{NSL}_{\nu\mu}) = \nu\hbar. \tag{23.22b}$$

Now $\mathbf{S}_z$ is a scalar under the $\mathbf{P}_R$ and a vector under the $\mathbf{Q}_R$, while $\mathbf{L}_z$ is a vector under the $\mathbf{P}_R$ and a scalar under the $\mathbf{Q}_R$. In the calculation of the expression $(\Psi^{NSLJ}_m, \mathbf{S}_z\Psi^{NSLJ}_m)$ from the quantities (23.22b), the roles of L and S must therefore be interchanged, and we obtain, instead of (23.21),

$$(\Psi^{NSLJ}_m, \mathbf{S}_z\Psi^{NSLJ}_m) = m\hbar \frac{J(J+1) + S(S+1) - L(L+1)}{2J(J+1)}. \tag{23.24}$$

The matrix elements of the whole operator for the interaction with the magnetic field, $\mathbf{V} + \overline{\mathbf{V}} = \eta\mathscr{H}\mathbf{L}_z + 2\eta\mathscr{H}\mathbf{S}_z$, can be calculated by adding (23.21) and twice (23.24). The displacement of the Zeeman component with magnetic quantum number m is found to be

$$\Delta E_m = \frac{e\hbar\mathscr{H}}{2m_0c} m \frac{3J(J+1) + S(S+1) - L(L+1)}{2J(J+1)}. \tag{23.25}$$

This is the familiar Landé g-formula. It states that because of the anomalous (twice the classical value) magnetic moment associated with the electron spin, different levels split differently in the magnetic field. The actual splitting is obtained if the splitting, $\eta\mathscr{H}m$, of the normal Zeeman effect is multiplied by

$$g = 1 + \frac{J(J+1) + S(S+1) - L(L+1)}{2J(J+1)}. \tag{23.25a}$$

The derivation of the formulas (23.19) and analogous formulas can be shortened by noting that the calculated ratios of the matrix elements must be, according to (23.15), independent of the particular mechanical problem, and of the particular form of the operators $\mathbf{T}^{(\rho\sigma)}$ and can depend only on their transformation properties. In fact, the ratios to be calculated are simply sums of products of the coefficients $s^{(LS)}_{J\mu\nu}$. However, the s are all pure numbers given by Eq. (17.27), so that these ratios are the same for all operators with the same transformation properties. Thus, they can be calculated for any tensor with the desired transformation properties (23.13a) and (23.13b), and the results carried over to all tensors with the same p and q.

The Interval Rule

8. As an example of this let us derive Landé's interval rule, i.e., the ratio of the level shifts

$$(\Psi_m^{NSLJ}, \mathbf{H}_1 \Psi_m^{NSLJ}) = \Delta E_J^{NSL}$$

for the different fine structure components of the same gross structure level. The operator $\mathbf{H}_1$ is the addition to the simple Schrödinger energy operator which describes the magnetic moments of the electrons.

The operator $\mathbf{H}_1$ consists of two parts. The first part gives the interaction of the magnetic moments of the electrons with the current generated by their motion; the second, the interaction of the magnetic moments with one another.

The first, and almost always the larger, part consists of a sum of n expressions $\mathbf{B} = \mathbf{B}_1 + \mathbf{B}_2 + \cdots + \mathbf{B}_n$ where $\mathbf{B}_k$ describes the interaction of the magnetic moment of the kth electron with the currents. Apart from the Cartesian coordinates, $\mathbf{B}_k$ acts only on the spin coordinate of the kth electron[4] so that

$$\mathbf{B}_k = \mathbf{s}_{kx}\mathbf{V}_{kx} + \mathbf{s}_{ky}\mathbf{V}_{ky} + \mathbf{s}_{kz}\mathbf{V}_{kz}, \tag{23.26}$$

[4] Each operator which acts only on the kth spin coordinate can be written in the form $\mathbf{S}_0 + \mathbf{s}_{kx}\mathbf{V}_{kx} + \mathbf{s}_{ky}\mathbf{V}_{ky} + \mathbf{s}_{kz}\mathbf{V}_{kz}$, where $\mathbf{S}_0$, $\mathbf{V}_{kx}$, $\mathbf{V}_{ky}$, and $\mathbf{V}_{kz}$ are spin-free operators. In (23.26) the term $\mathbf{S}_0$ does not occur. However, even if it did occur, it would have to be a scalar with respect to the $\mathbf{P}^R$ as well as with respect to the $\mathbf{Q}_R$. It would correspond, to the case $p = q = 0$ in (23.13a) and (23.13b) and would produce, according to (23.17) the same displacement for all fine structure components, without changing the splitting.

where the $\mathbf{V}_{kx}, \mathbf{V}_{ky}, \mathbf{V}_{kz}$ are spin-free operators. Since $\mathbf{B}_k$ must be a scalar under the $\mathbf{O}_R$, and since $\mathbf{s}_{kx}, \mathbf{s}_{ky}, \mathbf{s}_{kz}$ are the components of a vector operator, the operators $\mathbf{V}_{kx}, \mathbf{V}_{ky}, \mathbf{V}_{kz}$ must also be the components of a vector operator.

Instead of the ratios of all the matrix elements of $\mathbf{B}$,

$$(\Psi_m^{NSLJ}, \mathbf{B}\Psi_m^{NSLJ}) : (\Psi_m^{NSLJ'}, \mathbf{B}\Psi_m^{NSLJ'}),$$

which we want to calculate, we can simply calculate this ratio for one $\mathbf{B}_k$—these ratios are the same for all k. Furthermore, $\mathbf{s}_{kx}\mathbf{V}_{kx}, \mathbf{s}_{ky}\mathbf{V}_{ky}, \mathbf{s}_{kz}\mathbf{V}_{kz}$ are the xx, yy, and zz components of a tensor, which satisfies (23.13a) and (23.13b), and is a vector in both respects ($p = q = 1$). The ratio of any two of the expressions

$$(\Psi_m^{NSLJ}, \mathbf{s}_{kx}\mathbf{V}_{kx}\Psi_m^{NSLJ}); \ (\Psi_m^{NSLJ}, \mathbf{s}_{ky}\mathbf{V}_{ky}\Psi_m^{NSLJ}); \\ (\Psi_m^{NSLJ}, \mathbf{s}_{kz}\mathbf{V}_{kz}\Psi_m^{NSLJ}) \tag{23.27}$$

is therefore the same for all similar tensors, and this holds also for the ratio of these to similar expressions in which J' appears in place of J.

The same holds for the sum of the three expressions in (23.27) so that it is sufficient to calculate the ratios of the matrix elements

$$(\Psi_m^{NSLJ}, (\mathbf{T}^{(xx)} + \mathbf{T}^{(yy)} + \mathbf{T}^{(zz)})\,\Psi_m^{NSLJ}) \tag{23.28}$$

for different J, where $\mathbf{T}$ is an arbitrary vector operator in both respects. Naturally, these operators will be so chosen that the calculation of (23.28) becomes as simple as possible. Let

$$\mathbf{T}^{(xx)} = \mathbf{L}_x\mathbf{S}_x; \ \mathbf{T}^{(xy)} = \mathbf{L}_x\mathbf{S}_y; \ \mathbf{T}^{(xz)} = \mathbf{L}_x\mathbf{S}_z; \ \cdots. \tag{23.29}$$

Then first of all

$$\frac{\partial}{\partial\alpha}\,\mathbf{O}_{\{\alpha00\}} = \mathbf{Q}_{\{\alpha00\}}\,\frac{\partial}{\partial\alpha}\,\mathbf{P}_{\{\alpha00\}} + \mathbf{P}_{\{\alpha00\}}\,\frac{\partial}{\partial\alpha}\,\mathbf{Q}_{\{\alpha00\}}. \tag{23.30}$$

For $\alpha = 0$ this gives, according to (23.23a) and (23.23b),

$$\mathbf{L}_z + \mathbf{S}_z = -i\hbar\,\frac{\partial}{\partial\alpha}\,\mathbf{O}_{\{\alpha00\}}\bigg|_{\alpha=0}. \tag{23.30a}$$

From this it follows, since $\mathbf{O}_{\{\alpha00\}}\Psi = \exp(im\alpha)\Psi$, that

$$(\mathbf{L}_z + \mathbf{S}_z)\Psi_m = m\hbar\Psi_m \tag{23.31}$$

and

$$(\mathbf{L}_z + \mathbf{S}_z)^2\Psi_m = m^2\hbar^2\Psi_m. \tag{23.31a}$$

Thus we obtain

$$\sum_{m=-J}^{J}(\Psi_m^{NSLJ}, (\mathbf{L}_z + \mathbf{S}_z)^2\,\Psi_m^{NSLJ}) = \sum_{m=-J}^{J} m^2\hbar^2 = \frac{\hbar^2 J(J+1)(2J+1)}{3}. \tag{23.32}$$

In this expression z can be replaced by x or y since after summation over m, no axis can be distinguished. To verify this point, assume that $\mathbf{O}_R$ is a rotation which transforms Z into X, then (23.32) becomes

$$\begin{aligned}\sum_m (\mathbf{O}_{R^{-1}}\Psi'^{NSLJ}_m, \mathbf{O}_{R^{-1}}(\mathbf{L}_z + \mathbf{S}_z)^2\mathbf{O}_R \cdot \mathbf{O}_{R^{-1}}\Psi'^{NSLJ}_m) \\ = \sum_m \sum_{m'm''} \mathfrak{D}^{(J)}(R^{-1})^*_{m'm}\mathfrak{D}^{(J)}(R^{-1})_{m''m}(\Psi'^{NSLJ}_{m'}, (\mathbf{L}_x + \mathbf{S}_x)^2\,\Psi'^{NSLJ}_{m''}) \\ = \sum_{m'm''} \delta_{m'm''}(\Psi'^{NSLJ}_{m'}, (\mathbf{L}_x + \mathbf{S}_x)^2\,\Psi'^{NSLJ}_{m''}) \\ = \sum_m (\Psi'^{NSLJ}_m, (\mathbf{L}_x + \mathbf{S}_x)^2\,\Psi'^{NSLJ}_m).\end{aligned}$$

Therefore

$$\begin{aligned}\sum_m (\Psi'^{NSLJ}_m, [(\mathbf{L}_x + \mathbf{S}_x)^2 + (\mathbf{L}_y + \mathbf{S}_y)^2 + (\mathbf{L}_z + \mathbf{S}_z)^2]\Psi'^{NSLJ}_m) \\ = \hbar^2 J(J+1)(2J+1). \quad (23.33)\end{aligned}$$

But since $(\mathbf{L}_x + \mathbf{S}_x)^2 + (\mathbf{L}_y + \mathbf{S}_y)^2 + (\mathbf{L}_z + \mathbf{S}_z)^2$ is a scalar, i.e., an operator symmetric under the $\mathbf{O}_R$, the $2J + 1$ terms on the left in (23.33) are all the same, namely,

$$(\Psi'^{NSLJ}_m, [(\mathbf{L}_x+\mathbf{S}_x)^2+(\mathbf{L}_y+\mathbf{S}_y)^2+(\mathbf{L}_z+\mathbf{S}_z)^2]\Psi'^{NSLJ}_m) = \hbar^2 J(J+1). \quad (23.33a)$$

For the orbital angular momentum one can likewise infer from

$$\mathbf{L}_z \Xi^{NSL}_{\nu\mu} = \mu\hbar\Xi^{NSL}_{\nu\mu} \quad (23.34)$$

that

$$(\Xi^{NSL}_{\nu\mu}, (\mathbf{L}_x^2 + \mathbf{L}_y^2 + \mathbf{L}_z^2)\Xi^{NSL}_{\nu\mu}) = \hbar^2 L(L+1). \quad (23.35)$$

It then follows from (23.11) and the orthogonality relations (17.28)

$$(\Psi'^{NSLJ}_m, (\mathbf{L}_x^2 + \mathbf{L}_y^2 + \mathbf{L}_z^2)\Psi'^{NSLJ}_m) = \hbar^2 L(L+1), \quad (23.35a)$$

since $\mathbf{L}_x^2 + \mathbf{L}_y^2 + \mathbf{L}_z^2$ is a scalar in both respects. Similarly, for the spin

$$\mathbf{S}_z \Xi^{NSL}_{\nu\mu} = -i\hbar \frac{\partial}{\partial\alpha}\mathbf{Q}_{\{\alpha 00\}}\Xi^{NSL}_{\nu\mu} = \nu\hbar\Xi^{NSL}_{\nu\mu} \quad (\alpha = 0) \quad (23.36)$$

implies that

$$(\Psi'^{NSLJ}_m, (\mathbf{S}_x^2 + \mathbf{S}_y^2 + \mathbf{S}_z^2)\Psi'^{NSLJ}_m) = \hbar^2 S(S+1). \quad (23.36a)$$

By subtracting (23.35a) and (23.36a) from (23.33a), we obtain

$$\begin{aligned}(\Psi'^{NSLJ}_m, (\mathbf{L}_x\mathbf{S}_x + \mathbf{L}_y\mathbf{S}_y + \mathbf{L}_z\mathbf{S}_z)\Psi'^{NSLJ}_m) \\ = \tfrac{1}{2}\hbar^2[J(J+1) - L(L+1) - S(S+1)]. \quad (23.37)\end{aligned}$$

According to the preceding discussion the shifts of the fine structure components of the same gross structure level are in the proportion given by (23.37):

$$\Delta E_J^{NSL} = \varepsilon_{NSL}[J(J+1) - L(L+1) - S(S+1)]. \tag{23.37a}$$

The difference between the level displacements of two successive fine structure components

$$\Delta E_{J+1}^{NSL} - \Delta E_J^{NSL} = 2\varepsilon_{NSL}(J+1) \tag{23.37b}$$

is therefore proportional to the larger of the two total quantum numbers. This is *Landé's Interval Rule.*

The Landé interval rule is valid only in the case of normal coupling, i.e., when the fine structure splitting is small compared to the separation of the gross structure levels. Moreover, it involves the assumption that the interactions among the spin-magnetic moments can be neglected. This assumption fails for very light elements, especially He, as Heisenberg has shown.[5] The interval rule therefore holds best for elements with medium atomic numbers.

The interactions of the spin-magnetic moments among themselves consist of two parts. The first part is a scalar in both respects and therefore does not influence the fine structure at all. The second part belongs to $\mathfrak{D}^{(2)}$ in both respects. In all, a level displacement[6] is obtained which is proportional to $[J(J+1) - L(L+1) - S(S+1)]^2$, apart from a term of the form (23.37a), and a term independent of J. The ratio of the proportionality constant of this term to ε_{NSL} cannot be determined from general considerations, so that the interval formula contains *two undetermined* constants if the spin-spin interaction is included.

[5] See W. Heisenberg, *Z. Physik.* **39,** 499 (1926).

[6] The proof will be left to the reader. See also G. Araki, *Progr. Theoret. Phys.* (*Kyoto*), **3,** 152 (1948).

24. Racah Coefficients

The derivations of the Hönl-Kronig intensity formulas, and of Landé's interval rule, which were carried out in the preceding chapter, are particular cases of the evaluation of matrix elements of an irreducible tensor operator which has a definite transformation property not only as far as rotations of all coordinates are concerned but also under rotations of the spin coordinates, and of the positional coordinates, separately. Operators $\mathbf{T}^{(\sigma\rho)}$ of this kind were defined[1] in (23.13a) and (23.13b). Operators which are irreducible under simultaneous rotation of both spin and positional coordinates can be obtained from these by linear combination:

$$\mathbf{T}_{\omega}^{(\tau)} = \sum_{\rho} s_{\omega\rho\tau-\rho}^{(qp)} \mathbf{T}_{qp}^{(\rho,\tau-\rho)}. \tag{24.1}$$

It is easy to verify by (23.13a), (23.13b), (17.16b) and the orthogonality relations (17.28) for the s that

$$\mathbf{O}_R^{-1}\mathbf{T}_{\omega}^{(\tau)}\mathbf{O}_R = \mathbf{D}^{(\omega)}(R)_{\tau\tau'}\mathbf{T}_{\omega}^{(\tau')}. \tag{24.1a}$$

Actually, an operator of this nature has already been considered when Landé's interval rule was derived. The operator for the spin-orbit interaction is a scalar ($\omega = 0$), composed of operators which have vector character both as far as the rotation of spin ($q = 1$) and also as far as the rotation of positional coordinates ($p = 1$) are concerned.

Similarly, the wave functions Ψ_m^{NSLJ} and $\Psi_{m'}^{N'S'L'J'}$ which occur in the matrix element have a definite transformation property (specified by the quantum number J) with respect to rotations of all the coordinates. These wave functions also have definite transformation properties with respect to the rotation of the spin coordinates, and the positional coordinates, separately. The two corresponding quantum numbers are S and L. As a result, matrix elements of the form

$$(\Psi_{m'}^{N'S'L'J'}, \mathbf{T}_{\omega}^{(\tau)}\Psi_m^{NSLJ}) \tag{24.E.1}$$

can be expressed for all permissible values of J, J', ω, m, m', τ, in terms of a single constant. The permissible values are simply those for which the Ψ and $\mathbf{T}_{\omega}$ exist. The vector addition relation $|S - L| \leq J \leq S + L$ is the

[1] The reader will recall that $\mathbf{T}^{(\sigma\rho)}$ is the $\sigma\rho$-component of a tensor of degree q with respect to the spin rotations $\mathbf{Q}_R$ and of degree p with respect to the positional rotations $\mathbf{P}_R$. The operator $\mathbf{T}_{\omega}^{(\tau)}$ in (24.1) is the τth component of a tensor of degree ω with respect to the combined spin and positional rotations $\mathbf{O}_R = \mathbf{Q}_R\mathbf{P}_R$.

limitation on J; the limitation on m is $-J \leq m \leq J$, and so on. The difficulty which we encountered when carrying out the calculation was that the expression obtained by using the characteristics J, J', ω of the wave functions and operators with respect to rotations of all coordinates did not naturally match with the expression obtained when the transformation properties with respect to rotations of the spin and positional coordinates separately were used. An expression of the former kind is (23.18), an expression of the latter kind (23.15a). The calculation following (23.18) transforms (23.15a) into the form (23.18). The possibility of this transformation shows that there are important relations among the vector coupling coefficients s which have not been brought out so far. The rest of this chapter will be devoted to a more detailed study of the properties of the representations $\mathfrak{D}^{(J)}$ (particularly their reality conditions), of the symmetry of the vector coupling coefficients (already alluded to after (17.27)) and finally, of the general form of the relations which enabled us, for instance, to transform (23.15a) into the form (23.18).

The importance of explicit and general formulas for comparing matrix elements of the form (24.E.1) with different J, J', ω, m m', τ was clearly manifested in the book of Condon and Shortley.[2] General and explicit formulas for such a comparison were given first by Racah.[3] Lately, a number of monographs have been published on the subject,[4] which treat it much more elaborately than does the present chapter.

Conjugate Complex Representations

The reality conditions of the irreducible representations play an important role in the following analysis. The results to be obtained were first derived by two of the founders of the theory of representations;[5] they will be used also in Chapter 26.

Several ways of obtaining new representations from a given representation, or from a pair of representations, were described in the preceding chapters. To these, a new but rather obvious one will be added: the transition to the conjugate complex. If $\mathbf{D}(R)$ form a representation of a group, the same applies to $(\mathbf{D}(R))^*$, i.e., to the matrices whose elements are complex conjugate to the elements of $\mathbf{D}(R)$. Clearly, $\mathbf{D}(R)^*\mathbf{D}(S)^* = \mathbf{D}(RS)^*$ follows from $\mathbf{D}(R)\mathbf{D}(S) = \mathbf{D}(RS)$. Furthermore, if $\mathbf{D}(R)$ is irreducible, the same applies

[2] E. U. Condon and G. H. Shortley, "The Theory of Atomic Spectra." Cambridge University Press, 1935.

[3] G. Racah, *Phys. Rev.* **62,** 438 (1942); **63,** 367 (1943); also U. Fano and G. Racah, "Irreducible Tensorial Sets," Academic Press, New York, 1959.

[4] M. E. Rose, "Angular Momentum," John Wiley and Sons, New York, 1957. A. R. Edmonds, "Angular Momentum in Quantum Mechanics," Princeton University Press, 1957. Our $s^{(LS)}_{J\mu\nu}$ is denoted in the latter monograph by $(L\mu\, S\nu|LSJ\ \mu + \nu)$.

[5] G. Frobenius and I. Schur, *Berl. Ber.* 1906, p. 186.

for the conjugate complex representation $\mathbf{D}(R)^*$. If the transformation with $\mathbf{S}$ brings all $\mathbf{D}(R)$ into the reduced form shown on page 85, then $\mathbf{S}^*$ will bring $\mathbf{D}(R)^*$ into a similar form.

Complex conjugation leads to an important distinction between irreducible representations: the representation $\mathbf{D}(R)^*$ can either be equivalent or not equivalent to $\mathbf{D}(R)$. Since the character of $\mathbf{D}(R)^*$ is the conjugate complex of the character $\chi(R)$ of $\mathbf{D}(R)$, and since two representations are equivalent if their characters are identical (see page 86), $\mathbf{D}(R)$ *will be equivalent to the conjugate complex* $\mathbf{D}(R)^*$ *if its character is real*, that is, if all the numbers $\chi(R)$ are real. Otherwise $\mathbf{D}(R)$ and $\mathbf{D}(R)^*$ will be inequivalent.

The formulas (15.26) and (15.28) show that all irreducible representations of the three-dimensional rotation group, and of the two-dimensional unimodular unitary group, have real characters. The same is true for all groups in which every element is in the same class as its reciprocal. This can be seen most easily by considering the representation in the unitary form. It then follows from

$$\mathbf{D}(R^{-1}) = \mathbf{D}(R)^\dagger \tag{24.2}$$

that the characters of R and R^{-1} are conjugate complex. If R and R^{-1} are in the same class, the characters of R and R^{-1} are also equal. Hence, they are real. This is the situation with the three-dimensional rotation group, the two-dimensional unimodular unitary group, and also the group of *all* two-dimensional real orthogonal matrices. It is not true of the group of two-dimensional proper rotations and this has indeed representations with complex as well as representations with real characters (Chapter 14).

If $\mathbf{D}(R)$ is unitary and if it has a real character, there is a unitary matrix $\mathbf{C}$ which will transform $\mathbf{D}(R)^*$ into $\mathbf{D}(R)$. Then

$$\mathbf{C}\mathbf{D}(R) = \mathbf{D}(R)^*\mathbf{C}. \tag{24.3}$$

If $\mathbf{D}(R)$ is irreducible, $\mathbf{C}$ in (24.3) is uniquely determined except for a constant factor. *Furthermore,* $\mathbf{C}$ *is either symmetric or skew symmetric.* In order to prove this theorem, take the conjugate complex of (24.3) and multiply it with $\mathbf{C}$ on the left. This gives

$$\mathbf{C}\mathbf{C}^*\mathbf{D}(R)^* = \mathbf{C}\mathbf{D}(R)\mathbf{C}^* = \mathbf{D}(R)^*\mathbf{C}\mathbf{C}^*. \tag{24.3a}$$

The last member is obtained by using (24.3) again. If $\mathbf{D}(R)^*$ is irreducible, the matrix $\mathbf{C}\mathbf{C}^*$ which commutes with it must be a multiple of the unit matrix: $\mathbf{C}\mathbf{C}^* = c\mathbf{1}$. Since, furthermore, $\mathbf{C}$ is unitary, $\mathbf{C}'\mathbf{C}^* = \mathbf{1}$. It then follows that $\mathbf{C} = c\mathbf{C}'$. The transpose of this equation is $\mathbf{C}' = c\mathbf{C}$ so that $\mathbf{C} = c^2\mathbf{C}$; $c = \pm 1$. This gives

$$\mathbf{C} = \pm\mathbf{C}'. \tag{24.3b}$$

One easily convinces oneself, furthermore, that if $\mathbf{C}$ is symmetric for a representation $\mathbf{D}(R)$, it will be symmetric also for every equivalent representation $\mathbf{S}^{-1}\mathbf{D}(R)\mathbf{S}$. A similar statement applies if $\mathbf{C}$ is skew symmetric so that the alternative implied by (24.3b) provides a classification of irreducible representations with real character into those for which $\mathbf{C} = \mathbf{C}'$ and those for which $\mathbf{C} = -\mathbf{C}'$.

The preceding results can be summarized as follows. *If* $\mathbf{D}(R)$ *is a unitary, irreducible representation, the same applies to* $\mathbf{D}(R)^*$. *The representations* $\mathbf{D}(R)$ *and* $\mathbf{D}(R)^*$ *are inequivalent if* $\chi(R)$ *is complex for any* R. An irreducible representation of this nature will be called complex. *If* $\chi(R)$ *is real,* $\mathbf{D}(R)$ *and* $\mathbf{D}(R)^*$ *are equivalent. The unitary matrix* $\mathbf{C}$ *which transforms them into one another can be either symmetric or skew symmetric.* In the former case the representation will be called *potentially real,* in the second case *pseudoreal.*

The reason for this terminology is that $\mathbf{D}(R)$ can be actually given a real form if the $\mathbf{C}$ of (24.3) is symmetric. This follows from the lemma:[6] *If* $\mathbf{C}$ *is both symmetric and unitary, its eigenvectors can be assumed to be real*; it follows from

$$\mathbf{C}\mathfrak{v} = \omega\mathfrak{v} \tag{24.4}$$

by multiplication on the left with $\mathbf{C}^{-1} = \mathbf{C}^{\dagger} = \mathbf{C}^*$ that $\mathfrak{v} = \omega\mathbf{C}^*\mathfrak{v}$. Since the modulus of the characteristic value of a unitary matrix is 1, the conjugate complex of the last equation is

$$\mathbf{C}\mathfrak{v}^* = \omega\mathfrak{v}^*. \tag{24.4a}$$

If $\mathfrak{v}$ and $\mathfrak{v}^*$ are different, they can be replaced by their real *and* imaginary parts. If $\mathfrak{v}$ and $\mathfrak{v}^*$ differ only in a constant factor, they can be replaced by their real *or* by their imaginary parts. It now follows that a symmetric unitary matrix $\mathbf{C}$ can be written as

$$\mathbf{C} = \mathbf{r}^{-1}\boldsymbol{\omega}\mathbf{r}, \tag{24.4b}$$

where $\mathbf{r}$ is a real orthogonal matrix, $\mathbf{r}'\mathbf{r} = \mathbf{1}$, and $\boldsymbol{\omega}$ a diagonal matrix. We write $\boldsymbol{\omega}$ as the square of another diagonal matrix $\boldsymbol{\omega}_1$; the modulus of the diagonal elements of $\boldsymbol{\omega}_1$ is 1, and $\boldsymbol{\omega}_1^{-1} = \boldsymbol{\omega}_1^*$. Hence, (24.3) assumes the form

$$\mathbf{r}^{-1}\boldsymbol{\omega}_1^2\mathbf{r}\,\mathbf{D}(R) = \mathbf{D}(R)^*\mathbf{r}^{-1}\boldsymbol{\omega}_1^2\mathbf{r},$$

or, if one multiplies this by $\boldsymbol{\omega}_1^{-1}\mathbf{r} = \boldsymbol{\omega}_1^*\mathbf{r}$ from the left and by $\mathbf{r}^{-1}\boldsymbol{\omega}_1^{-1} = \mathbf{r}^{-1}\boldsymbol{\omega}_1^*$ from the right,

$$\boldsymbol{\omega}_1\mathbf{r}\mathbf{D}(R)\mathbf{r}^{-1}\boldsymbol{\omega}_1^* = \boldsymbol{\omega}_1^*\mathbf{r}\mathbf{D}(R)^*\mathbf{r}^{-1}\boldsymbol{\omega}_1. \tag{24.4c}$$

The left and right sides are conjugate complex, hence both sides are real. It follows that $\mathbf{D}(R)$ becomes real if it is transformed by $\mathbf{r}^{-1}\boldsymbol{\omega}_1^* = (\boldsymbol{\omega}_1\mathbf{r})^{-1}$. Conversely, if $\mathbf{D}(R)$ can be transformed into a real representation, $\mathbf{C}$ must be symmetric. $\mathbf{C}$ is obviously symmetric (namely a constant matrix) if $\mathbf{D}(R)$ is already real. Hence it is symmetric for any other form of this representation.

[6] This lemma plays an important role in the theory of the collision matrix.

It further follows that if $\mathbf{C}$ in (24.3) is skew symmetric, $\mathbf{D}(R)$ cannot be made real by a similarity transformation.

Let us determine, finally, the matrix $\mathbf{C}^{(j)}$ which transforms the irreducible representation $\mathfrak{D}^{(j)}$ of the three-dimensional rotation group into the conjugate complex $\mathfrak{D}^{(j)*}$. The matrices $\mathbf{C}^{(j)}$ play an important role also in quantum field theories. Since (24.3) must hold for every rotation, we apply it first to a rotation by α about Z. In this case, $\mathfrak{D}^{(j)}$ is a diagonal matrix and the nm element of the left and right sides of (24.3) are

$$\mathbf{C}^{(j)}_{nm} e^{im\alpha} = e^{-in\alpha} \mathbf{C}^{(j)}_{nm}. \tag{24.5}$$

Since this must be valid for every α, the matrix element $\mathbf{C}^{(j)}_{nm}$ vanishes unless $n + m = 0$

$$\mathbf{C}^{(j)}_{nm} = c^{(j)}_m \, \delta_{n,-m}. \tag{24.5a}$$

Next, we apply (24.3) to an arbitrary group element but write out only the $-j,\mu$ element of (24.3). The corresponding $\mathfrak{D}^{(j)}$ are particularly simple.

$$c^{(j)}_j \mathfrak{D}^{(j)}(\{\alpha\beta\gamma\})_{j\mu} = \mathfrak{D}^{(j)}(\{\alpha\beta\gamma\})^*_{-j-\mu} c^{(j)}_\mu, \tag{24.5b}$$

or, by (15.27a), (15.27b),

$$c^{(j)}_j \sqrt{\binom{2j}{j-\mu}}\, e^{ij\alpha} \cos^{j+\mu} \tfrac{1}{2}\beta \sin^{j-\mu} \tfrac{1}{2}\beta \, e^{i\mu\gamma}$$
$$= (-1)^{j-\mu} \sqrt{\binom{2j}{j+\mu}}\, e^{ij\alpha} \cos^{j+\mu} \tfrac{1}{2}\beta \sin^{j-\mu} \tfrac{1}{2}\beta \, e^{i\mu\gamma} c^{(j)}_\mu,$$

whence

$$c^{(j)}_\mu = c^{(j)}_j (-1)^{j-\mu}, \tag{24.5c}$$

as $j - \mu$ is always an integer.[7] Since $\mathbf{C}$ is determined by (24.3), only up to a factor, we choose $c^{(j)}_j = 1$ and obtain from (24.5a)

$$\mathbf{C}^{(j)}_{nm} = (-1)^{j-m} \delta_{n,-m} = (-1)^{j+n} \delta_{n,-m}. \tag{24.6}$$

All elements of $\mathbf{C}^{(j)}$ are zero except those on the skew diagonal. These elements are alternately $+1$ and -1, beginning with $+1$ in the upper right-hand corner and ending on the lower left-hand corner with $+1$ if j is an integer, and with -1 if j is a half-integer:

$$\mathbf{C}^{(j)} = \begin{pmatrix} 0 & \cdots & 0 & 0 & 1 \\ 0 & \cdots & 0 & -1 & 0 \\ 0 & \cdots & 1 & 0 & 0 \\ \cdot & & \cdot & \cdot & \cdot \\ \cdot & & \cdot & \cdot & \cdot \\ \cdot & \cdots & \cdot & \cdot & \cdot \end{pmatrix} \tag{24.6a}$$

[7] All exponents of (-1) in this book are integers.

Hence, $\mathbf{C}$ is symmetric for integral j and skew symmetric for half-integral j; the former representations are potentially real, the latter ones pseudoreal. We also note that the direct product of two potentially real representations, or of two pseudoreal representations, contains only potentially real irreducible components. The irreducible parts of the direct product of a potentially real representation and a pseudoreal representation are all pseudoreal.[8] The fact that the $\mathfrak{D}^{(j)}$ with integral j can be transformed into a real form could have been inferred from the fact that we could have used, in (15.5), real linear combinations $Y^l_m + Y^l_{-m}$ and $i(Y^l_m - Y^l_{-m})$, of the spherical harmonics. The corresponding form of $\mathfrak{D}^{(l)}$ would have been real. With the explicit form of $\mathbf{C}$ inserted Eq. (24.3) reads

$$\mathfrak{D}^{(j)}(R)^*_{m'm} = (-1)^{m-m'}\mathfrak{D}^{(j)}(R)_{-m'-m}. \tag{24.7}$$

which can also be proved directly. Naturally, the form of $\mathbf{C}^{(j)}$ depends on the form in which $\mathfrak{D}^{(j)}$ was assumed, but its symmetric or skew symmetric character does not.

Symmetric Form of the Vector Coupling Coefficients

The vector coupling coefficients were originally defined in (17.16) as the elements of a matrix $\mathbf{S}$ which transforms the direct product of two representations into the reduced form (17.15). They were recognized in (17.18) also—and this is their most important function—as the coefficients which permit the formation of functions belonging to a row m of an irreducible representation $\mathfrak{D}^{(L)}$ from products of functions ψ_μ and $\bar{\psi}_\nu$ which belong to the μ-row of $\mathfrak{D}^{(l)}$, and the ν-row of $\mathfrak{D}^{(\bar{l})}$, respectively. They perform the same function in (22.27) where the wave function with the quantum numbers J, m was obtained as

$$\Psi^J_m = \sum_\mu s^{(LS)}_{J\mu m-\mu}\Xi^{SL}_{m-\mu\mu} \tag{24.8}$$

from the wave functions Ξ which transform, under $\mathbf{Q}_R$ and $\mathbf{P}_R$, according to $\mathfrak{D}^{(S)}$ and $\mathfrak{D}^{(L)}$ and belong to the $m - \mu$ and μ-row of these representations, respectively. In neither of these cases do the three representations $\mathfrak{D}^{(L)}$, $\mathfrak{D}^{(l)}$, $\mathfrak{D}^{(\bar{l})}$; or $\mathfrak{D}^{(J)}$, $\mathfrak{D}^{(S)}$, $\mathfrak{D}^{(L)}$ enter symmetrically. The formula (17.22)

$$\int \mathfrak{D}^{(l)}(R)_{\mu'\mu}\mathfrak{D}^{(\bar{l})}(R)_{\nu'\nu}\mathfrak{D}^{(L)}(R)^*_{\mu'+\nu';\mu+\nu}\,dR = \frac{hs^{(l\bar{l})}_{L\mu'\nu'}s^{(l\bar{l})}_{L\mu\nu}}{2L+1} \tag{24.8a}$$

comes closest to this and this will be our starting point; $h = \int dR$ is the volume of the group. A somewhat more symmetric form of (24.8a) is

$$\int \mathfrak{D}^{(l)}(R)_{\mu'\mu}\mathfrak{D}^{(\bar{l})}(R)_{\nu'\nu}\mathfrak{D}^{(L)}(R)^*_{m'm}\,dR = \frac{h\mathbf{S}_{Lm';\mu'\nu'}\mathbf{S}_{Lm;\mu\nu}}{2L+1}, \tag{24.8b}$$

[8] See E. P. Wigner, *Am. Jour. Math.*, **63**, 57 (1941) for a further discussion of these relations and of other characteristics of irreducible representations; also S. W. Mackey, *ibid.* **73**, 576 (1951).

where $\mathbf{S}$ is the original matrix which transforms $\mathfrak{D}^{(l)} \times \mathfrak{D}^{(\bar{l})}$ into the reduced form. According to (17.20a) and (17.20b)

$$\mathbf{S}_{Lm;\mu\nu} = \delta_{m,\mu+\nu} s^{(l\bar{l})}_{L\mu\nu}. \tag{24.8c}$$

The integral (24.8b) vanishes unless $m' = \mu' + \nu'$ and $m = \mu + \nu$ and so do the coefficients $\mathbf{S}$. Since $\mathbf{C}^{\dagger}\mathfrak{D}^*\mathbf{C} = \mathbf{C}'\mathfrak{D}^*\mathbf{C} = \mathfrak{D}$, the left side of (24.8b) will be symmetric in l, $\bar{l}$, L if it is multiplied by $\mathbf{C}_{m'\lambda'}\mathbf{C}_{m\lambda}$ and summed over m' and m. On the right side the value of $\mathbf{C}$ can be introduced from (24.6);

$$\int \mathfrak{D}^{(l)}(R)_{\mu'\mu}\mathfrak{D}^{(\bar{l})}(R)_{\nu'\nu}\mathfrak{D}^{(L)}(R)_{\lambda'\lambda}\, dR = \frac{h(-)^{L-\lambda'}\mathbf{S}_{L,-\lambda';\mu'\nu'}(-)^{L-\lambda}\mathbf{S}_{L,-\lambda;\mu\nu}}{2L+1}. \tag{24.8d}$$

Hence, if we set

$$\frac{(-)^{L-\lambda}\mathbf{S}_{L,-\lambda;\mu\nu}}{\sqrt{2L+1}} \sim \begin{pmatrix} l & \bar{l} & L \\ \mu & \nu & \lambda \end{pmatrix},$$

l, $\bar{l}$, and L would enter symmetrically. For reasons which will become clear later, we set

$$\begin{pmatrix} l & \bar{l} & L \\ \mu & \nu & \lambda \end{pmatrix} = (-)^{l-\bar{l}-L}\frac{(-)^{L-\lambda}\mathbf{S}_{L,-\lambda;\mu\nu}}{\sqrt{2L+1}}. \tag{24.9}$$

The factor $(-)^{l-\bar{l}-L}$ disappears if this is introduced into (24.8b) because it appears in both matrix coefficients S and because $l - \bar{l} - L$ is necessarily an integer; L is integer or half-integer depending on whether $l + \bar{l}$, that is $l + \bar{l} - 2\bar{l} = l - \bar{l}$, is an integer or half-integer. The expression in (24.9) is called the three-j symbol, its definition in terms of the s and with a more symmetric notation is

$$\begin{pmatrix} j_1 & j_2 & j_3 \\ m_1 & m_2 & m_3 \end{pmatrix} = \frac{(-)^{j_1-j_2-m_3}}{\sqrt{2j_3+1}} s^{(j_1j_2)}_{j_3m_1m_2}\delta_{m_1+m_2+m_3,0}. \tag{24.9a}$$

Since the s are defined only if j_1, j_2, and j_3 form a vector triangle, that is, if their sum is an integer and if $|j_1 - j_2| \leq j_3 \leq j_1 + j_2$ (or, equivalently, if no j is larger than the sum of the other two), the three-j symbols are also defined only under these conditions. It simplifies later calculations if we stipulate that the value of the three-j symbols vanishes if the j do not form a vector triangle. Similarly, it eliminates the necessity of giving the limits on summations if one also assigns the value zero to those three-j symbols in which the absolute value of any m is larger than the corresponding j. These conventions will, therefore, be adopted.

The three-j symbol defined by (24.9a) are not entirely symmetric. Complete symmetry cannot be accomplished because, if, for instance, two of the j are equal, the s are not symmetric functions of the row indices m. However, the three-j symbols do satisfy the following relations:

$$(-)^{j_1+j_2+j_3}\begin{pmatrix} j_1 & j_2 & j_3 \\ m_1 & m_2 & m_3 \end{pmatrix} = \begin{pmatrix} j_1 & j_3 & j_2 \\ m_1 & m_3 & m_2 \end{pmatrix} = \begin{pmatrix} j_3 & j_2 & j_1 \\ m_3 & m_2 & m_1 \end{pmatrix} = \begin{pmatrix} j_2 & j_1 & j_3 \\ m_2 & m_1 & m_3 \end{pmatrix}, \tag{24.10}$$

i.e., if one interchanges two of the j, together with the corresponding m, ("interchanges two columns"), the value of the symbol remains unchanged if $j_1 + j_2 + j_3$ is even; it changes its sign if $j_1 + j_2 + j_3$ is odd. One can infer from this that the value of the symbol remains unchanged if the j, together with the corresponding m, are subjected to a cyclic permutation

$$\begin{pmatrix} j_1 & j_2 & j_3 \\ m_1 & m_2 & m_3 \end{pmatrix} = \begin{pmatrix} j_2 & j_3 & j_1 \\ m_2 & m_3 & m_1 \end{pmatrix} = \begin{pmatrix} j_3 & j_1 & j_2 \\ m_3 & m_1 & m_2 \end{pmatrix}. \tag{24.10a}$$

Finally, if all the row indices are replaced by their negatives, one obtains

$$\begin{pmatrix} j_1 & j_2 & j_3 \\ -m_1 & -m_2 & -m_3 \end{pmatrix} = (-1)^{j_1+j_2+j_3}\begin{pmatrix} j_1 & j_2 & j_3 \\ m_1 & m_2 & m_3 \end{pmatrix}. \tag{24.10b}$$

Thus, in general (that is, when all the three j's are different and at least one m is not zero) the value of eleven more symbols can be directly obtained from one. If some of the j are equal, or if all the m are zero, the value of the symbol may have to vanish as a result of the preceding equations.

Equations (24.10), (24.10a), and (24.10b) can be verified as follows. Introduction of the three-j symbols into (24.8d) gives

$$\int \mathfrak{D}^{(j_1)}(R)_{n_1m_1}\mathfrak{D}^{(j_2)}(R)_{n_2m_2}\mathfrak{D}^{(j_3)}(R)_{n_3m_3}\,dR = h\begin{pmatrix} j_1 & j_2 & j_3 \\ n_1 & n_2 & n_3 \end{pmatrix}\begin{pmatrix} j_1 & j_2 & j_3 \\ m_1 & m_2 & m_3 \end{pmatrix} \tag{24.11}$$

The left side remains unchanged if one interchanges any of the j, together with the indices n, m which go with them. This must be true also for the right side, and it must be true for any values of the n. If one sets all n equal to the corresponding m, the right side becomes the square of a three-j symbol and this must then be invariant if one interchanges any two j, together with the corresponding row index m. Except for the sign, the same holds then for the three-j symbols themselves. In order to determine the relation between the signs, one can set $n_1 = -j_1$, $n_2 = j_1 - j_3$, $n_3 = j_3$. This is a set for which the three-j symbol can be evaluated very easily because of the whole sum (17.27) for the corresponding s only one term, the $\varkappa = 0$ term, is different from zero. Actually, we need only the sign of

$$\begin{pmatrix} j_1 & j_2 & j_3 \\ -j_1 & j_1 - j_3 & j_3 \end{pmatrix} \tag{24.E.2}$$

and this has a $(-)^{j_1-j_2-j_3}$ from (24.9a) and a $(-)^{j_2+j_1-j_3}$ from (17.27). Hence, the sign of (24.E.2) is $(-)^{2j_1-2j_3}$. Similarly, the signs of

$$\begin{pmatrix} j_2 & j_1 & j_3 \\ j_1 - j_3 & -j_1 & j_3 \end{pmatrix} \quad \text{and} \quad \begin{pmatrix} j_1 & j_3 & j_2 \\ -j_1 & j_3 & j_1 - j_3 \end{pmatrix} \tag{24.E.3}$$

can be determined to be $(-)^{j_2-j_1-j_3}$ and $(-)^{-j_3-j_1+j_2}$. Hence interchange of the first two columns of (24.E.2) changes this symbol by the factor $(-)^{j_2-j_1-j_3}/(-)^{2j_1-2j_3} = (-)^{j_1+j_2+j_3}$. Since the product of the two symbols in (24.11) must remain unchanged under such an interchange, the second symbol also must change by the same factor if the first two columns are interchanged. Similarly, interchange of the last two columns gives the factor $(-)^{-j_3-j_1+j_2}/(-)^{2j_1-2j_3} = (-)^{-3j_1+j_2+j_3} = (-)^{j_1+j_2+j_3}$ since $(-)^{4j_1} = 1$. This shows that interchange of the last two columns also changes the three-j symbol by a factor $(-)^{j_1+j_2+j_3}$. This verifies the equality of the first, second, and last members of (24.10). The rest of (24.10), (24.10a) follows from this. The purpose of the factor $(-)^{j_1-j_2-m_3}$ was just to render the relations (24.10), (24.10a) valid.

In order to verify (24.10b), one notes that the right side of (24.11) is real. Hence, the left side can be replaced by its conjugate imaginary and the $\mathfrak{D}^*$ expressed again in terms of the $\mathfrak{D}$ by (24.7). This gives a factor $(-)^{n_1+n_2+n_3-m_1-m_2-m_3}$ which can be, however, omitted because both sides vanish unless $n_1 + n_2 + n_3 = 0$ and $m_1 + m_2 + m_3 = 0$. Hence

$$\begin{pmatrix} j_1 & j_2 & j_3 \\ -n_1 & -n_2 & -n_3 \end{pmatrix}\begin{pmatrix} j_1 & j_2 & j_3 \\ -m_1 & -m_2 & -m_3 \end{pmatrix} = \begin{pmatrix} j_1 & j_2 & j_3 \\ n_1 & n_2 & n_3 \end{pmatrix}\begin{pmatrix} j_1 & j_2 & j_3 \\ m_1 & m_2 & m_3 \end{pmatrix}. \tag{24.12}$$

If one again sets $n_1 = -j_1$, $n_2 = j_1 - j_3$, $n_3 = j_3$, the sign of the first symbol on the right becomes $(-)^{2j_1-2j_3}$. The symbol on the left also becomes of the form (24.E.2) if one interchanges the first and last column. Hence, its sign is $(-)^{j_1+j_2+j_3}(-)^{2j_3-2j_1} = (-)^{-j_1+j_2-j_3}$. The ratio of the first factors has, therefore, the sign $(-)^{j_1+j_2+j_3}$. This verifies the sign in (24.10b); replacement of the n by the corresponding m shows that the absolute values of both sides of (24.10b) are also equal. A more abstract derivation of these relations is given in the article of reference 8.

Covariant and Contravariant Vector Coupling Coefficients

The coupling of the orbital and spin angular momenta to a total angular momentum, given in (24.8), can be rewritten in terms of the three-j symbols:

$$\Psi^J_m = (-1)^{L+\mu+(m-\mu-S)}\sqrt{2J+1}\sum_\mu \begin{pmatrix} L & S & J \\ \mu & m-\mu & -m \end{pmatrix} \Xi^{SL}_{m-\mu\,\mu}. \tag{24.13}$$

The exponent of -1 is written in the way indicated because both $L + \mu$ and $m - \mu - S$ are integers. The limits of the summation over μ do not have to be indicated if one uses the convention that all three-j symbols are zero in which the absolute value of a row index exceeds the corresponding representation index. The first and last columns of the three-j symbol can be interchanged with the aid of (24.10). This involves no change if, at the same time, the sign of all row indices is changed. Furthermore, $m - \mu$ can be replaced by ν and the summation extended also over ν. The three-j symbol will vanish anyway if $\mu + \nu - m$ is not zero. In this way, (24.13) becomes

$$\Psi^J_m = \sum_{\nu\mu} (-)^{L+\mu+(\nu-S)}\sqrt{2J+1}\begin{pmatrix} J & S & L \\ m & -\nu & -\mu \end{pmatrix} \Xi^{SL}_{\nu\mu}. \tag{24.13a}$$

If one replaces, finally, Ψ_m^J by $(-)^{2L}\Psi_m^J$ and the exponents by their negative values—which is permissible because they are integers—one finds

$$\Psi_m^J = \sum_{\nu\mu} (-)^{L-\mu}(-)^{S-\nu}\sqrt{2J+1}\begin{pmatrix} J & S & L \\ m & -\nu & -\mu \end{pmatrix} \Xi_{\nu\mu}^{SL}. \tag{24.13b}$$

An additional improvement on the notation can be made by introducing the concept of covariant and contravariant components of the wave function and of the three-j symbols.[9] The covariant metric tensor which is naturally adapted for this is the $\mathbf{C}_{mn}^{(j)}$ defined in (24.3) and given explicitly in (24.6). Such a metric tensor permits the lowering of the indices of a vector to obtain the covariant components f_m^J of a vector from its contravariant components $f_J^{m'}$:

$$f_m^J = \sum_{m'} \mathbf{C}_{mm'}^{(J)} f_J^{m'}. \tag{24.14}$$

It should be noted that $\mathbf{C}_{mm'}^J = (-)^{J+m}\,\delta_{m',-m}$ is symmetric only for integral J so that the two indices m, m' cannot be interchanged. Similarly, the transition from covariant to contravariant components proceeds via

$$f_J^n = \sum_{n'} \mathbf{C}_J^{nn'} f_{n'}^J \tag{24.14a}$$

where[10]

$$\mathbf{C}_J^{nn'} = (-)^{J-n}\,\delta_{n,-n'} = (-)^{J+n'}\delta_{n,-n'}. \tag{24.14b}$$

We shall use only the covariant components of the wave functions but both covariant and contravariant components of the three-j symbols. For example, the component of the three-j symbol which is contravariant in the last index is

$$\begin{pmatrix} j_1 & j_2 & m \\ m_1 & m_2 & j \end{pmatrix} = \sum_{m'} \mathbf{C}_j^{mm'}\begin{pmatrix} j_1 & j_2 & j \\ m_1 & m_2 & m' \end{pmatrix} = (-)^{j-m}\begin{pmatrix} j_1 & j_2 & j \\ m_1 & m_2 & -m \end{pmatrix}. \tag{24.15}$$

Evidently, (24.13b) can be written in terms of this notation as

$$\Psi_m^J = \sqrt{2J+1}\begin{pmatrix} J & \nu & \mu \\ m & S & L \end{pmatrix} \Xi_{\nu\mu}^{SL} \tag{24.15a}$$

or, more concisely,

$$\Psi_m^J = \sqrt{2J+1}(J_m S^\nu L^\mu)\Xi_{\nu\mu}^{SL}. \tag{24.15b}$$

In (24.15a) and (24.15b) the usual summation convention of the general theory of relativity is implied with respect to row indices (that is, indices ν, μ, etc., which specify a row of a representation); repeated row indices are to

[9] This was originally suggested by C. Herring.

[10] A mnemotechnical rule to remember the sign in (24.14b) is that the first index (n) in the *con*travariant metric tensor appears with the *n*egative sign in the exponent.

be summed over. One index of each summation pair is always covariant (lower), the other contravariant (upper). Also, the free row indices, that is, the row indices which are not summed over, are covariant on both sides of the equation, or contravariant on both sides. Since covariant indices are raised on both sides with the same metric tensor, the free covariant indices can be replaced by free contravariant indices on both sides of any equation, and vice versa. As a result, the free indices can actually be omitted on both sides. An equation such as (24.15a) or (24.15b) which has a "relativistic form" remains valid even if the representations are not assumed in the form given in Chapter 15 but are only equivalent to those representations. It may be worth noting that the s of Chapter 17 are essentially mixed three-j symbols

$$s^{(l\bar{l})}_{L\mu\nu} = \sqrt{2L+1}(-)^{l-\bar{l}+L}\begin{pmatrix} l & \bar{l} & \mu+\nu \\ \mu & \nu & L \end{pmatrix}$$
$$= \sqrt{2L+1}(-)^{l-\bar{l}-L}\begin{pmatrix} L & \mu & \nu \\ \mu+\nu & l & \bar{l} \end{pmatrix}. \tag{24.16}$$

In spite of the similarity of the notation with that used in the theory of relativity, there are great conceptual differences. The indices of the vectors and tensors of relativity theory all run over the same values (0, 1, 2, 3); they refer to axes in the same space. The indices m, n, μ, etc., are all coupled with a representation, they refer to the various partners which belong to an irreducible representation. Each index can assume as many values as the representation to which it is coupled has rows and columns. The summation ("contraction") always takes place with respect to indices which are coupled with the same representation; the free indices on both sides of an equation—such as the m in (24.15b)—refer to the same representation ($\mathfrak{D}^{(J)}$ in this case). As a corollary to this, there is not one metric tensor but each representation has its own metric tensor. The difference between indices which are coupled with different representations finds its reflection also in the symmetric or antisymmetric nature of the tensors; these relations, given in (24.10), and (24.10a), are independent of the form of the representation only if the indices which are interchanged belong to the same representation. In this case, however, they *are* independent of the form of the representation and

$$\begin{pmatrix} J & j & j \\ m & \nu & \mu \end{pmatrix} = (-)^{J+2j}\begin{pmatrix} J & j & j \\ m & \mu & \nu \end{pmatrix} \tag{24.17}$$

is valid independent of the form in which the representation is used. It is this circumstance which suggested the sign convention for the three-j symbols which we adopted.

The relation (24.17) has an interesting and direct consequence: if one couples two particles, with wave functions which are partners to the same representation ("equivalent orbits"), to form a state with total angular momentum J,

$$\Psi^J_m(1, 2) = (J_m, j^\nu, j^\mu)\psi^j_\nu(1)\psi^j_\mu(2), \tag{24.17a}$$

(1 and 2 stand for the variables of the two particles), the resulting state will be symmetric under the interchange of the two particles if $J + 2j$ is even, antisymmetric if $J + 2j$ is odd. Thus, two $2p$ electrons give symmetric S and D states and an antisymmetric P state. This corresponds to the case $j = 1$ (called l in this case) and J (called L in this case) equal to 0 or 2 in the symmetric case and equal to 1 in the antisymmetric case. Similarly, two electron spins couple to give a symmetric $S = 1$ state and an antisymmetric $S = 0$ state.

Let us compute, finally, the fully contravariant form of the three-j symbol.

$$\begin{aligned}(J^m, S^\nu, L^\mu) &= \mathbf{C}_J^{mm'}\mathbf{C}_S^{\nu\nu'}\mathbf{C}_L^{\mu\mu'}(J_{m'}, S_{\nu'}, L_{\mu'}) \\ &= (-)^{J-m+S-\nu+L-\mu}(J_{-m}, S_{-\nu}, L_{-\mu}).\end{aligned} \tag{24.18}$$

The factor $(-)^{-m-\nu-\mu}$ can be omitted because the three-j symbol vanishes unless $m + \nu + \mu = 0$. Hence, (24.10b) gives

$$(J^m, S^\nu, L^\mu) = (J_m, S_\nu, L_\mu), \tag{24.18a}$$

the fully covariant and the fully contravariant three-j symbols are equal. This theorem depends on the form of the representations adopted in Chapter 15. However, it enables one to rewrite (24.11) in a covariant form. For this purpose, we first note that even though the indices of the representation coefficients are written as suffixes, the first index is, in reality, a contravariant index. This is already apparent from the basic formula

$$\mathbf{O}_R\psi^j_m = \sum_{m'} \mathfrak{D}^{(j)}(R)_{m'm}\psi^j_{m'}.$$

The summation over m' indicates that this should be an upper index. Hence, it seems natural to write, instead of (24.11),

$$\int \mathfrak{D}^{(j_1)}(R)_{n_1m_1}\mathfrak{D}^{(j_2)}(R)_{n_2m_2}\mathfrak{D}^{(j_3)}(R)_{n_3m_3}\,dR = h\begin{pmatrix} n_1 & n_2 & n_3 \\ j_1 & j_2 & j_3\end{pmatrix}\begin{pmatrix} j_1 & j_2 & j_3 \\ m_1 & m_2 & m_3\end{pmatrix}. \tag{24.18b}$$

Let us calculate the covariant-contravariant components of $\mathfrak{D}^{(j)}(R)_{nm}$

$$\mathbf{C}^j_{nn'}\mathbf{C}^{mm'}_j\mathfrak{D}^{(j)}(R)_{n'm'} = (\mathbf{C}\mathfrak{D}^{(j)}\mathbf{C}'^{-1})^m_n \tag{24.18c}$$

since the contravariant metric tensor is the reciprocal of the covariant metric tensor. Since $\mathbf{C}' = (-)^{2j}\,\mathbf{C}$, and since $\mathbf{C}^{-1}$ transforms $\mathfrak{D}$ into $\mathfrak{D}^*$, we find that the *covariant-contravariant n-m component of* $\mathfrak{D}^{(j)}(R)$ *is* $(-)^{2j}$ *times the complex conjugate* of the contravariant-covariant n-m component of $\mathfrak{D}^{(j)}(R)$ (which is the usual $\mathfrak{D}^{(j)}(R)_{nm}$). This gives for the original form of the integral over three representation coefficients

$$\int \mathfrak{D}^{(j_1)}(R)_{n_1m_1}\mathfrak{D}^{(j_2)}(R)_{n_2m_2}\mathfrak{D}^{(j)}(R)^*_{nm}\,dR = (-)^{2j}h\begin{pmatrix} n_1 & n_2 & j \\ j_1 & j_2 & n \end{pmatrix}\begin{pmatrix} j_1 & j_2 & m \\ m_1 & m_2 & j \end{pmatrix}. \tag{24.18d}$$

Naturally, (24.18d) could also have been obtained directly.

The theorem about the equality of the fully covariant and fully contravariant components of a three-j symbol gives the orthogonality relations (17.28) an invariant form

$$\begin{pmatrix} j_1 & j_2 & j \\ m_1 & m_2 & m \end{pmatrix}\begin{pmatrix} m_1 & m_2 & m' \\ j_1 & j_2 & j' \end{pmatrix} = \frac{\delta_{jj'}\,\delta_{mm'}}{2j+1}. \tag{24.19}$$

For $m = m'$, this is equivalent with the first equation (17.28); for $m \neq m'$ every term of the sum vanishes because $m_1 + m_2$ cannot be equal to both $-m$ and $-m'$. The other orthogonality relation becomes, in the form in which it is independent of the form of the representation

$$\sum_j \begin{pmatrix} j_1 & j_2 & j \\ m_1 & m_2 & m \end{pmatrix}\begin{pmatrix} m_1' & m_2' & m \\ j_1 & j_2 & j \end{pmatrix} = \frac{\delta_{m_1m'_1}\,\delta_{m_2m'_2}}{2j+1}. \tag{24.19a}$$

The summation over m is implied by the summation convention. The covariant notation is useful not only—and perhaps not principally—because it gives equations which are not changed if the representations are subjected to a similarity transformation. Its principal function may be to facilitate the memorizing of the equations. It also suggests a very condensed notation which will be introduced in the next section.

Racah Coefficients

The preceding calculations provide a more symmetric form of the vector coupling coefficients; they do not give the relations which would permit the formulas of the last chapter to be obtained effortlessly and with a minimum of computation. As was mentioned already in the first section, there must be some general relations between the vector coupling coefficients which, if fully exhibited, will make the calculation of the Hönl-Kronig formulas, of Landé's interval rule, and of other similar expressions, quite transparent. There are many ways to derive the formulas in question; the computations of the last chapter already imply some of the formulas.

The consideration of three particles moving in a spherically symmetric field leads to the aforementioned relations in the most natural way[11] The

[11] G. Racah, *loc. cit.* L. C. Biedenharn, J. M. Blatt and M. E. Rose, *Rev. Mod. Phys.* **24**, 249 (1952), A. R. Edmonds, *op. cit.* Chapter 6.

first particle has an energy value to which the wave functions $\psi_\varkappa$ correspond, with $\varkappa = -j_1, -j_1+1, \cdots, j_1-1, j_1$; the $\psi_\varkappa$ are partners and belong to the representation $\mathfrak{D}^{(j_1)}$. The wave functions which correspond to the energy of the second particle are φ_λ; these belong to the representation $\mathfrak{D}^{(j_2)}$. The analogous quantities for the third particle are χ_μ and $\mathfrak{D}^{(j_3)}$. The state of the whole system is a linear combination of the functions

$$\psi_\varkappa(1)\varphi_\lambda(2)\chi_\mu(3) \tag{24.E.4}$$

where 1, 2, and 3 stand for the coordinates of the three particles. Since the variables of ψ will always be the coordinates of the first particle, the (1) will be omitted henceforth. Similarly, φ_λ and χ_μ will be written instead of $\varphi_\lambda(2)$ and $\chi_\mu(3)$. The situation considered is highly schematic and does not describe any actual physical system. However, its consideration is useful for obtaining the relations which we seek.

We shall form linear combinations of the wave functions (24.E.4) which transform by an irreducible representation J when the coordinates of all three particles are subjected to a rotation. We can obtain such wave functions in three different ways. First, we can couple the angular momenta of the first two particles to a resultant angular momentum j according to (24.15a).

$$\mathrm{X}^j_m(1,2) = \sqrt{2j+1}\begin{pmatrix} j & \varkappa & \lambda \\ m & j_1 & j_2 \end{pmatrix}\psi_\varkappa\varphi_\lambda, \tag{24.20}$$

and couple then the third particle to the resulting angular momentum j to form a total angular momentum J,

$$\begin{aligned}\mathrm{X}^{jJ}_M(1,2,3) &= \sqrt{2J+1}\begin{pmatrix} J & \mu & m \\ M & j_3 & j \end{pmatrix}\chi_\mu \mathrm{X}^j_m(1,2) \\ &= \sqrt{2J+1}\sqrt{2j+1}\begin{pmatrix} J & \mu & m \\ M & j_3 & j \end{pmatrix}\begin{pmatrix} j & \varkappa & \lambda \\ m & j_1 & j_2 \end{pmatrix}\psi_\varkappa\varphi_\lambda\chi_\mu. \end{aligned} \tag{24.21}$$

The index j indicates the total angular momentum of the particles 1 and 2 from which the state X^{jJ}_M was obtained. The wave function (24.21) would be a natural one to consider if the interaction between particles 1 and 2 were stronger than the interaction of either particle with particle 3.

Alternatively, states of angular momentum J can be obtained by coupling first particles 2 and 3, and the resultant state to particle 1, or by coupling particles 1 and 3, and obtaining the final wave function by coupling the wave function obtained in this way to particle 2. These schemes correspond to the interaction being strongest between particles 2, 3 and between particles 1,

3, respectively, but we shall not be concerned with this motivation. The wave functions obtained are

$$\Psi_M^{jJ}(1, 2, 3) = \sqrt{2J+1}\sqrt{2j+1}\begin{pmatrix} J & \varkappa & m \\ M & j_1 & j \end{pmatrix}\begin{pmatrix} j & \lambda & \mu \\ m & j_2 & j_3 \end{pmatrix}\psi_\varkappa\varphi_\lambda\chi_\mu \quad (24.21a)$$

and

$$\Phi_M^{jJ}(1, 2, 3) = \sqrt{2J+1}\sqrt{2j+1}\begin{pmatrix} J & \lambda & m \\ M & j_2 & j \end{pmatrix}\begin{pmatrix} j & \varkappa & \mu \\ m & j_1 & j_3 \end{pmatrix}\psi_\varkappa\varphi_\lambda\chi_\mu. \quad (24.21b)$$

The index j in (24.21a) indicates the joint angular momentum of particles 2 and 3. Similarly, the j in (24.21b) gives the joint angular momentum of particles 1 and 3.

The three states Ψ_M^{jJ}, Φ_M^{jJ} and X_M^{jJ} are not identical even though the total angular momentum and its Z-component are $J\hbar$ and $M\hbar$ for each of them. However, since every state (24.E.4) can be expressed linearly in terms of all the $\Phi_{M'}^{j'J'}$, this holds also for Ψ_M^{jJ} or X_M^{jJ}. Furthermore, if one expresses, for instance,

$$X_M^{jJ} = \sum_{j'}\sum_{J'M'} c(jJM;\ j'J'M')\Phi_{M'}^{j'J'} \quad (24.22)$$

in terms of the Φ, the coefficients of the $\Phi_{M'}^{j'J'}$ with $J' \neq J$ or $M' \neq M$ will vanish because these Φ belong either to a representation which is different from the representation $\mathfrak{D}^{(J)}$ of X_M^{jJ}, or they belong to a different row of that representation. Hence, the summation over J', M' can be omitted in (24.22) and these indices can be replaced by J and M. Furthermore, the coefficients $c(jJM;\ j'JM)$ are independent of M because both the X_M^{jJ} and also the $\Phi_M^{j'J}$ are partners which belong to the same representation $\mathfrak{D}^{(J)}$. The scalar products $(X_M^{jJ}, \Phi_M^{j'J})$ are independent of M. Therefore, the coefficients c do not depend on M. Hence, (24.22) gives a relation of the form (omitting the $\sqrt{2J+1}$ throughout)

$$\sqrt{2j+1}\begin{pmatrix} J & \mu & m \\ M & j_3 & j \end{pmatrix}\begin{pmatrix} j & \varkappa & \lambda \\ m & j_1 & j_2 \end{pmatrix}\psi_\varkappa\varphi_\lambda\chi_\mu$$

$$= \sum_{j'} c^J(j;\ j')\sqrt{2j'+1}\begin{pmatrix} J & \lambda & m \\ M & j_2 & j' \end{pmatrix}\begin{pmatrix} j' & \varkappa & \mu \\ m & j_1 & j_3 \end{pmatrix}\psi_\varkappa\varphi_\lambda\chi_\mu. \quad (24.22a)$$

Both sides imply summation over m, $\varkappa$, λ, μ. However, because of the linear independence of the $\psi_\varkappa\varphi_\lambda\chi_\mu$, the coefficient of each $\psi_\varkappa\varphi_\lambda\chi_\mu$ is equal on the two sides.

$$\begin{pmatrix} J & \mu & m \\ M & j_3 & j \end{pmatrix}\begin{pmatrix} j & \varkappa & \lambda \\ m & j_1 & j_2 \end{pmatrix}$$

$$= \sum_{j'} (-)^{2j_1}(2j'+1)\begin{Bmatrix} J & j_2 & j' \\ j_1 & j_3 & j \end{Bmatrix}\begin{pmatrix} J & \lambda & m \\ M & j_2 & j' \end{pmatrix}\begin{pmatrix} j' & \varkappa & \mu \\ m & j_1 & j_3 \end{pmatrix}, \quad (24.23)$$

where

$$\begin{Bmatrix} J & j_2 & j' \\ j_1 & j_3 & j \end{Bmatrix} = \frac{(-)^{2j_1} c^J(j;\, j')}{\sqrt{2j+1}\sqrt{2j'+1}}. \tag{24.23a}$$

These are called the six-j symbols or Racah coefficients[12] or recoupling coefficients. The last name refers to the present derivation which is a transition from the wave functions X to the wave functions Φ. Particles 1 and 2 are strongly coupled in the former, particles 1 and 3 in the latter. It follows from the derivation that the six-j symbols are independent of $\varkappa$, λ, μ (these entered only at the transition from (24.22a) to (24.23)), and also independent of M (as was pointed out). This will be proved once more below. Hence, (24.23) is an identity in $\varkappa$, λ, μ and the six-j symbol is a universal function of the six j's which appear in it; it is completely (numerically) determined by these six numbers. Note that there is an implied summation over m on both sides of (24.23). Actually, since the last three-j symbol in (24.23) vanishes unless $m = \varkappa + \mu$, for every j' only one term is different from zero, and the right side contains, effectively, only a summation over j'. Furthermore, because of the three-j symbol on the right side, even the $m = \varkappa + \mu$ term vanishes unless $M = \lambda + m = \varkappa + \lambda + \mu$. The left side contains only one term—the $m = \varkappa + \lambda$ term—and vanishes unless $M = \mu + m = \varkappa + \lambda + \mu$. Thus, (24.23) is trivial unless $M = \varkappa + \lambda + \mu$. This is not surprising since both X_M^{jJ} and $\Phi_M^{j'J}$ contain only $\psi_\varkappa \varphi_\lambda \chi_\mu$ with $\varkappa + \lambda + \mu = M$ so that the comparison of the coefficients of the other $\psi_\varkappa \varphi_\lambda \chi_\mu$ cannot yield any information.

Equation (24.23) contains the relation which we sought. It will now be given various other forms and also written more symmetrically. For this purpose we first replace the contravariant indices $\varkappa$, λ, μ on both sides by covariant indices and carry out a cyclic permutation in the second three-j symbol on both sides. We also replace the various types of j by other symbols and obtain

$$\begin{pmatrix} j_1 & l_2 & \lambda \\ \mu_1 & \lambda_2 & l \end{pmatrix} \begin{pmatrix} l_1 & j_2 & l \\ \lambda_1 & \mu_2 & \lambda \end{pmatrix} = \sum_j (-)^{2l_1}(2j+1) \begin{Bmatrix} j_1 & j_2 & j \\ l_1 & l_2 & l \end{Bmatrix} \begin{pmatrix} j_1 & j_2 & \mu \\ \mu_1 & \mu_2 & j \end{pmatrix} \begin{pmatrix} l_1 & l_2 & j \\ \lambda_1 & \lambda_2 & \mu \end{pmatrix}. \tag{24.24}$$

There are four three-j symbols in this equation and there are, correspondingly, four triplets of j and l which must form a vector triangle. The three members of each triplet (for instance $l_1 j_2 l$) appear in different columns of the six-j

[12] Actually, Racah's W is not exactly equal to the six-j symbol; rather,

$$W(j_1 j_2 l_2 l_1;\, j_3 l_3) = (-)^{j_1+j_2+l_1+l_2} \begin{Bmatrix} j_1 & j_2 & j_3 \\ l_1 & l_2 & l_3 \end{Bmatrix}.$$

symbols and either all three are in the upper line, or two are in the lower line and one in the upper line. Conversely the six-j symbols have been defined only if these four triplets (that is $j_1 j_2 j$; $j_1 l_2 l$; $l_1 j_2 l$; $l_1 l_2 j$) form a vector triangle. We now set all other six-j symbols equal to zero. It would be rather difficult to remember the position of each j and l in the six-j symbol in (24.24) but it will be shown at once that all six-j symbols are equal which are composed of the same six j's and in which the same triplets have to form a vector triangle. As a result (except for the sign), (24.24) is rather easy to remember and shows clearly the transition from the coupling of j_1 to j_2 (and l_1 to l_2) to the coupling of j_1 to l_2 and l_1 to j_2. All of these can be integers or half-integers.

We now introduce the condensed notation mentioned at the end of the last section. It consists, essentially, of omitting all row indices. The *free* row indices are the same on both sides and can have any value—they need not be written out. Furthermore, it is not necessary to indicate whether they are covariant or contravariant as long as one remembers that they have the same character on both sides. The *contracted* indices need not be written out either because they are summed over anyway. However, in this case it is necessary to indicate which is the covariant and which the contravariant index, and this will be done by a lower or upper dot. *If one interchanges the two dots on the two j over the indices of which a summation has to be carried out, this introduces a factor* $(-)^{2j}$ because

$$f^j_\mu g^\mu_j = \mathbf{C}^j_{\mu\nu} f^\nu_j \mathbf{C}^{\mu\lambda}_j g^j_\lambda = (-)^{j+\mu} f^{-\mu}_j (-)^{j-\mu} g^j_{-\mu} = (-)^{2j} f^\mu_j g^j_\mu .$$

Hence, (24.24) can be written in the condensed form

$$(j_1 l_2 l^{\cdot})(l_1 j_2 l_{\cdot}) = (-)^{2l_1} \sum_j (2j+1) \begin{Bmatrix} j_1 & j_2 & j \\ l_1 & l_2 & l \end{Bmatrix} (j_1 j_2 j^{\cdot})(l_1 l_2 j_{\cdot}). \qquad (24.24a)$$

If one changes the position of the dots on the left, a factor $(-)^{2l} = (-)^{2l_1+2j_2}$ enters; if one changes them on the right, a factor $(-)^{2j} = (-)^{2j_1+2j_2}$ enters.

The orthogonality relations (24.19) in the condensed notation are

$$(j_{1\cdot} j_{2\cdot} j)(j_1^{\cdot} j_2^{\cdot} j') = (2j+1)^{-1}\, \delta(j_{\cdot}, j'^{\cdot}), \qquad (24.25)$$

where $\delta(j_{\cdot}, j'^{\cdot})$ is zero if $j \neq j'$ or if the corresponding indices are unequal; it is 1 if $j = j'$ and the corresponding indices are equal *and have the positions* on the left side which the dots indicate on the right. Hence

$$\delta(j_{\cdot}, j'^{\cdot}) = (-)^{2j}\, \delta(j^{\cdot}, j'_{\cdot}). \qquad (24.25a)$$

Naturally, the condensed notation cannot always be used, in particular, not if the same j occurs twice on the same side of the equation but there is no summation over its index. In this case, the same j occurs also twice on the other side of the equation and it remains ambiguous which index has to be identified with which j. It is for this reason that the condensed notation is not useful in relativistic calculations; all indices there refer to the same space. In the present instance, the use of the condensed notation does render many of the calculations more transparent.

Because of the summation over j on the right side, (24.24) does not give an explicit expression for the six-j symbol. Such an expression can be obtained by multiplying (24.24a) with $(l_1 l_2 j_3)$ and contracting over the indices of l_1 and l_2.

$$(j_1 l_{2\bullet} l^{\bullet})(l_{1\bullet} j_2 l_{\bullet})(l_1^{\bullet} l_2^{\bullet} j_3) = (-)^{2l_1} \sum_j (2j+1) \begin{Bmatrix} j_1 & j_2 & j \\ l_1 & l_2 & l \end{Bmatrix} (j_1 j_2 j^{\bullet})(l_{1\bullet} l_{2\bullet} j_{\bullet})(l_1^{\bullet} l_2^{\bullet} j_3).$$

The dots on the l_1 on the left side can be interchanged; this just cancels the $(-)^{2l_1}$ on the right. The last two factors on the right eliminate, by (24.25) the $2j+1$ and the summation; j has to be replaced by j_3 and its index, where it is free, will have the same position as the index of j_3. Hence,

$$(j_1 l_{2\bullet} l_3^{\bullet})(l_1^{\bullet} j_2 l_{3\bullet})(l_{1\bullet} l_2^{\bullet} j_3) = \begin{Bmatrix} j_1 & j_2 & j_3 \\ l_1 & l_2 & l_3 \end{Bmatrix} (j_1 j_2 j_3). \tag{24.24b}$$

This is probably the most important relation involving Racah coefficients; it will be used in the next section to calculate matrix elements of irreducible tensor operators. Because of the cyclic symmetry of the three-j symbols, it already shows that the columns of the six-j symbols can be interchanged cyclically. Similarly, interchanging j_1 with j_2 and l_1 with l_2 in (24.24) multiplies the left side by $(-)^{j_1+j_2+l_1+l_2}$, the right side by $(-)^{2l_2-2l_1+j_1+j_2+l_1+l_2+2j}$. The ratio of the three-j symbols on the two sides changes by $(-)^{2l_2-2l_1+2j}$ which is 1 because the vectors l_1, l_2, j must form a vector triangle. The combination of these two results shows that *the columns of a six-j symbol can be interchanged arbitrarily without changing its value*. Finally, interchange of j_1 with l_1, and of j_2 with l_2 changes the left side of (24.24) by $(-)^{2l}$ (because of the interchange of the covariant and contravariant λ), and changes the right side by $(-)^{2j_1-2l_1+2j}$. The ratio of these factors is also 1 because both pairs $j_1 j$ and $l_1 l$ form a vector triangle with j_2. Hence, the six-j symbol remains unchanged if the first two columns are inverted. Combination of this with the preceding result shows that *the six-j symbol remains unchanged if any two columns are inverted*. Altogether, there are 24 permutations of the j which leave the six-j symbol unchanged; these are all the permutations which interchange the four triples of vector triangles in an arbitrary way.[13] There are many further connections between six-j symbols. The symmetry relations, in particular, can be more explicitly exhibited by multiplying (24.24b)

[13] For further details, cf. A. R. Edmonds, *op. cit.*, and L. C. Biedenharn, J. M. Blatt and M. E. Rose, loc. cit.

with the fully contravariant three-j symbol of $j_1j_2j_3$ and contracting over all indices pertaining to these.

The simplest general formula for calculating the six-j symbol is implied in (24.24b). In order to evaluate it, one will use particular values for μ_1, μ_2, μ_3; the set $\mu_1 = -j_1$, $\mu_2 = j_1 - j_3$, $\mu_3 = j_3$ provides as simple expressions for the three-j symbols as can be obtained in general. A similar choice of the μ underlies the implicit computation of six-j symbols carried out at the derivation of the Hönl-Kronig formulas. A somewhat different expression was given by Racah in his original article.[14] Nevertheless, the computation remains tedious. There are, however, extensive tables for the six-j symbols or equivalent quantities. The table of Sharp, Kennedy, Sears, and Hoyle[15] is, perhaps, most accessible. We note only three rather trivial cases: if $j_2 = 0$, the vectors l_1, j_2, l_3 will form a vector triangle only for $l_3 = l_1$. Similarly, $j_1 = j_3$ follows from the triangle j_1, j_2, j_3. Hence, for $j_2 = 0$, all the non-vanishing six-j symbols have the form

$$\begin{Bmatrix} j_1 & 0 & j_1 \\ j_2 & j & j_2 \end{Bmatrix} = \frac{(-)^{j+j_1+j_2}}{\sqrt{2j_1+1}\sqrt{2j_2+1}}. \tag{24.26}$$

The symmetry of the six-j symbols permits one to shift the 0 to any one of the positions. For $j_2 = \frac{1}{2}$, one has two types

$$\begin{Bmatrix} j_1 - \frac{1}{2} & \frac{1}{2} & j_1 \\ j_2 & j & j_2 - \frac{1}{2} \end{Bmatrix} = (-)^J \left[\frac{(J+1)(J-2j)}{2j_1(2j_1+1)2j_2(2j_2+1)}\right]^{1/2} \tag{24.26a}$$

$$\begin{Bmatrix} j_1 - \frac{1}{2} & \frac{1}{2} & j_1 \\ j_2 - \frac{1}{2} & j & j_2 \end{Bmatrix} = (-)^{J-\frac{1}{2}} \left[\frac{(J-2j_1+\frac{1}{2})(J-2j_2+\frac{1}{2})}{2j_1(2j_1+1)2j_2(2j_2+1)}\right]^{1/2} \tag{24.26b}$$

where $J = j_1 + j_2 + j$.

Finally, for $j_2 = 1$, there are four types

$$\begin{Bmatrix} j_1 - 1 & 1 & j_1 \\ j_2 & j & j_2 - 1 \end{Bmatrix} = (-)^J \left[\frac{J(J+1)(J-2j-1)(J-2j)}{(2j_1-1)2j_1(2j_1+1)(2j_2-1)2j_2(2j_2+1)}\right]^{1/2} \tag{24.26c}$$

$$\begin{Bmatrix} j_1 - 1 & 1 & j_1 \\ j_2 - 1 & j & j_2 \end{Bmatrix} = (-)^{J-1} \left[\frac{(J-2j_1)(J-2j_1+1)(J-2j_2)(J-2j_2+1)}{(2j_1-1)2j_1(2j_1+1)(2j_2-1)2j_2(2j_2+1)}\right]^{1/2} \tag{24.26d}$$

[14] G. Racah, *loc. cit.*

[15] Tables of Coefficients for Angular Distribution Analysis, CRT-556, Atomic Energy of Canada, Ltd., 1954. Also, Simon, Van der Sluis, and Biedenharn, Oak Ridge National Laboratory Report 1679 (1954); Obi, Ishidzu, Horie, Yanagowa, Tanabe and Sato, *Ann. Tokyo Astron. Obs.*, 1953–55; and Rotenberg, Bivins, Metropolis, and Wooten, The 3-j and 6-j Symbols, Technology Press, Cambridge, Mass. (In press.) K. M. Howell, Tables of 6-j Symbols, University of Southampton.

$$\begin{Bmatrix} j_1 & 1 & j_1 \\ j_2 - 1 & j & j_2 \end{Bmatrix} = (-)^J \left[\frac{2(J+1)(J-2j)(J-2j_1)(J-2j_2+1)}{2j_1(2j_1+1)(2j_1+2)(2j_2-1)2j_2(2j_2+1)}\right]^{1/2} \tag{24.26e}$$

$$\begin{Bmatrix} j_1 & 1 & j_1 \\ j_2 & j & j_2 \end{Bmatrix} = (-)^J \frac{j(j+1) - j_1(j_1+1) - j_2(j_2+1)}{[j_1(2j_1+1)(2j_1+2)j_2(2j_2+1)(2j_2+2)]^{1/2}}, \tag{24.26f}$$

The last formula, with $j_1 = L$, $j_2 = S$, $j = J$ will turn out to be equivalent with Landé's interval rule.

Since the six-j symbols do not depend on the form in which the irreducible representations are assumed, it should be possible to calculate them in terms of the characters of the representations. This is not quite true because a number of sign conventions have been made in the definition of these symbols. There are, however, expressions in the six-j symbols which are independent of these sign conventions, such as the square of a six-j symbol. This can indeed be given as a triple integral over the group

$$\begin{Bmatrix} j_1 & j_2 & j_3 \\ l_1 & l_2 & l_3 \end{Bmatrix}^2 = h^{-3} \iiint \chi_1(R_1)\, \chi_2(R_2)\, \chi_3(R_3)\, \chi_1'(R_2 R_3^{-1})\, \chi_2'(R_3 R_1^{-1})\, \chi_3'(R_1 R_2^{-1})\, dR_1\, dR_2\, dR_3$$

where χ_i is the character of the representation $\mathfrak{D}^{(j_i)}$ and χ_i' is the character of $\mathfrak{D}^{(l_i)}$. The derivation of this formula will not be given in detail.

In addition to those mentioned, the six-j symbols satisfy a large number of other relations. In particular, one can show that the matrix

$$\mathbf{R}_{lj} = \sqrt{2l+1}\,\sqrt{2j+1} \begin{Bmatrix} j_1 & j_2 & j \\ l_1 & l_2 & l \end{Bmatrix}$$

is orthogonal. Because of the interchangeability of the columns of the six-j symbols each such symbol is, apart from the analogues of the factor $(2l+1)^{1/2}(2j+1)^{1/2}$, an element of three real orthogonal matrices.

Six-j symbols can be defined for a rather large variety of groups. They pose the mathematical problem of whether or not their values determine the group. This question has not been solved to date.

Matrix Elements of Spin-Free Tensor Operators

The formula (21.19) for the matrix elements of a tensor operator could be transcribed in terms of the three-j symbols but it is just as simple to rederive it. Since the operator to be considered is a scalar with respect to rotations of the spin coordinates, its rank ω with respect to rotations of all coordinates is equal to its rank p with respect to rotations of the positional coordinates. We suppress all other quantum numbers N, N', etc., which are not essential for the present and write

$$(\Psi_m^J, \mathbf{T}^\sigma \Psi_{m'}^{J'}) = (\mathbf{O}_R \Psi_m^J, \mathbf{O}_R \mathbf{T}^\sigma \mathbf{O}_R^{-1} \mathbf{O}_R \Psi_{m'}^{J'}). \tag{24.27}$$

The two sides of the equation are equal because $\mathbf{O}_R$ is unitary. Since $\Psi_M^{J'}$

and Ψ'^J_M belong to the representations $\mathfrak{D}^{(J')}$ and $\mathfrak{D}^{(J)}$, and because $\mathbf{T}^\sigma$ is a tensor operator of order p, (cf. (21.16b))

$$(\Psi'^J_m, \mathbf{T}^\sigma \Psi'^{J'}_{m'}) = \sum_\tau \sum_{\mu\mu'} \mathfrak{D}^{(J)}(R)^*_{\mu m} \mathfrak{D}^{(p)}(R^{-1})_{\sigma\tau} \mathfrak{D}^{(J')}(R)_{\mu' m'} (\Psi'^J_\mu, \mathbf{T}^\tau \Psi'^{J'}_{\mu'}).$$

Because of the unitary nature of the representations, $\mathfrak{D}^{(p)}(R^{-1})_{\sigma\tau} = \mathfrak{D}^{(p)}(R)^*_{\tau\sigma}$. The integral over the whole group gives a factor $\int dR = h$ on the left. It gives a twice-contravariant, once-covariant, and a once-contravariant, twice-covariant three-j symbol on the right. Hence,

$$(\Psi'^J_m, \mathbf{T}^\sigma \Psi'^{J'}_{m'}) = (J^m, p^\sigma, J'_{m'}) T_{JJ'} \tag{24.27a}$$

where

$$T_{JJ'} = \sum_\tau \sum_{\mu\mu'} (-)^{2J+2p} (J_\mu, p_\tau, J'^{\mu'}) (\Psi'^J_\mu, \mathbf{T}^\tau \Psi'^{J'}_{\mu'})$$

is independent of m, m' and σ. The formula requires only that J and J' be good quantum numbers and that $\mathbf{T}$ be an irreducible tensor operator of rank $\omega = p$ with respect to rotations of all coordinates. The $T_{JJ'}$ of (24.27a) is $(-)^{J-p-J'}\sqrt{2J'+1}$ times the corresponding quantity in (21.19), otherwise the two equations are entirely equivalent. Note that the covariant component as the first factor in a scalar product plays the role of a contravariant component. The reason for this is that the conjugate complex of the first factor has to be taken when the scalar product is calculated.

Let us assume now that Russell-Saunders coupling applies and that both Ψ'^J_m and $\Psi'^{J'}_{m'}$ can be represented by (24.15b) in terms of $\Xi^{SL}_{\nu\mu}$ and $\Xi^{S'L'}_{\nu'\mu'}$ which have proper spin and orbital angular quantum numbers. Since $\mathbf{T}^\sigma$ is a spin-free operator, or, at least, is a scalar under rotations of the spin coordinates, the matrix element (24.27) would vanish unless $S = S'$. Hence, we set $S = S'$ and obtain by (24.15b)

$$(\Psi'^J_m, \mathbf{T}^\sigma \Psi'^{J'}_{m'}) = \sqrt{2J+1}\sqrt{2J'+1}(J_m, S^\nu, L^\mu)(J'_{m'}, S^{\nu'}, L'^{\mu'})(\Xi^{SL}_{\nu\mu}, \mathbf{T}^\sigma \Xi^{SL'}_{\nu'\mu'}). \tag{24.28}$$

The scalar product on the right side is independent of J and J' so that this expression will enable us to compare not only the matrix elements between the states of a particular J and J' but also the matrix elements between all the states of two multiplets. The states referred to differ not only in the magnetic quantum numbers m and m' but also in the values of the total angular momentum; J can assume all values from $|S - L|$ to $S + L$, and J' all values from $|S - L'|$ to $S + L'$.

The first three-j symbol in (24.28) comes from the first factor of a scalar product. In order to have a "relativistic form" of the equation, we convert the covariant indices into contravariant indices and vice versa. A calculation similar to that leading to (24.18a) shows that

$$(J_m, S^\nu, L^\mu) = (-)^{2J}(J^m, S_\nu, L_\mu). \tag{24.28a}$$

(Instead of $(-)^{2J}$ one could have written $(-)^{2S+2L}$—either the covariant *or* the contravariant vectors appear in the exponent.) Since $\mathbf{T}^\sigma$ is also an irreducible tensor of rank p under rotations of the positional coordinates, Eq. (24.27a) applies to it as well. We write this in the form

$$(\Xi_{\nu\mu}^{SL}, \mathbf{T}^\sigma \Xi_{\nu'\mu'}^{SL'}) = \delta_{\nu\nu'}(L^\mu, p^\sigma, L'_{\mu'})T_{SL,SL'}. \tag{24.29}$$

$T_{SL,SL'}$ is not only independent of μ, σ, μ' as before, but also independent of ν, because $\mathbf{T}^\sigma$ is a scalar as far as the spin variables are concerned. Combination of (24.27a) and (24.29) with (24.28) gives

$$(J^m, p^\sigma, J'_{m'})T_{JJ'}$$
$$= (-)^{2J}\sqrt{2J+1}\sqrt{2J'+1}(J^m, S_\nu, L_\mu)(J'_{m'}, S^\nu, L'^{\mu'})(L^\mu, p^\sigma, L'_{\mu'})T_{SL,SL'}. \tag{24.29a}$$

This must be an identity in m, m', σ. It is indeed evident that the identity involved is (24.24b) and after some adjustment of signs, one finds

$$T_{JJ'} = (-)^{2J-L+S+J'+p}\begin{Bmatrix} J & p & J' \\ L' & S & L \end{Bmatrix}\sqrt{2J+1}\sqrt{2J'+1}T_{SL,SL'}. \tag{24.30}$$

This is the general formula, applicable in the case of Russell-Saunders coupling, which gives the ratio of the matrix elements between all states of two multiplets for an operator which is an irreducible tensor of rank p as far as rotation of the positional coordinates is concerned, but is invariant under rotations of the spin. It contains, for $p = 1$, the Hönl-Kronig formulas. A similar expression applies, with the roles of L and S interchanged, for an operator which is invariant under rotations of the positional coordinates but transforms like an irreducible tensor of rank q under rotations of the spin coordinates. The interaction between spin and external magnetic field is such an operator (with $q = 1$) and the factor in Landé's formula (23.24) is essentially a Racah coefficient or six-j symbol. The matter will not be pursued further because the most important results were obtained already in the preceding chapter, by more direct calculation.

General Two-Sided Tensor Operators

The properties of the six-j symbols are of considerable conceptual interest. Their practical usefulness must depend on the number of detailed problems which they simplify, on the interest in these problems, and in the facility with which these symbols can be handled. Tables for six-j symbols are bound to be more cumbersome than most mathematical tables because they depend on six variables. They are, in this regard, more cumbersome even than the vector coupling coefficients which depend, essentially, only on five variables. The problem of the present section leads to concepts often called nine-j symbols, which depend on nine variables, and the preceding remarks apply with even greater force to them.[16]

We shall now consider two-sided tensor operators $\mathbf{T}_{qp}^{\rho\sigma}$ or, rather, as indicated already in (24.1), an irreducible tensor[17]

$$\mathbf{T}_{\omega}^{\tau} = (\omega^{\tau}, q_{\rho}, p_{\sigma})\mathbf{T}_{qp}^{\rho\sigma} \tag{24.31}$$

which transforms by (24.1a) under the rotation of both spin and positional coordinates. Assuming Russell-Saunders coupling, we again express $\Psi_{m}^{\cdot J}$ and $\Psi_{m'}^{\cdot J'}$ in terms of the corresponding Ξ by means of (24.15b) and obtain, using the condensed notation,

$$(\Psi_{m}^{\cdot J}, \mathbf{T}_{\omega}^{\tau}\Psi_{m'}^{\cdot J'})$$
$$= \sqrt{2J+1}\sqrt{2J'+1}(J_{m}S^{\cdot}L^{\cdot})(\omega^{\tau}q_{\cdot}p_{\cdot})(J'_{m'}S'^{\cdot}L'^{\cdot})(\Xi_{\cdot\cdot}^{SL}, \mathbf{T}_{qp}^{\cdot\cdot}\Xi_{\cdot\cdot}^{S'L'}) \tag{24.32}$$

Since we have not defined contravariant components of wave functions, their indices are all lower. The last matrix element can be written as

$$(\Xi_{\nu\mu}^{SL}, \mathbf{T}_{qp}^{\rho\sigma}\Xi_{\nu'\mu'}^{S'L'}) = (S^{\nu}, q^{\rho}, S'_{\nu'})(L^{\mu}, p^{\sigma}, L'_{\mu'})T_{SL,S'L'} \tag{24.32a}$$

which is the analogue of (24.27a) or (24.29). We also write

$$(\Psi_{m}^{\cdot J}, \mathbf{T}_{\omega}^{\tau}\Psi_{m'}^{\cdot J'}) = (J^{m}, \omega^{\tau}, J'_{m'})T_{JJ'}. \tag{24.32b}$$

This equation continues to be valid since it depends only on the validity of J and J' as good quantum numbers. We again wish to calculate $T_{JJ'}$ in terms of $T_{SL,S'L'}$ and also to verify that the right sides of (24.32) and (24.32b) depend in the same way on m, m' and τ. In order to obtain a "relativistic" form of the equation which identifies (24.32) and (24.32b), the position of all the indices of the first three-j symbol of (24.32) has to be changed. This is always necessary with respect to symbols which come from the first factor of a scalar product; it introduces a factor $(-)^{2J}$ in the present case. We obtain

$$(J, \omega, J')T_{JJ'} = (-)^{2J}\sqrt{2J+1}\sqrt{2J'+1}\,(J\,S_{\cdot}L_{\cdot})(\omega\,q_{\cdot}p_{\cdot})$$
$$\times\,(J'S'^{\cdot}L'^{\cdot})(S^{\cdot}q^{\cdot}S'_{\cdot})(L^{\cdot}p^{\cdot}L'_{\cdot})T_{SL,S'L'}. \tag{24.33}$$

The ratio of the sum of the products of the five three-j symbols on the right

[16] Cf. however K. Smith and J. W. Stevenson, Argonne National Laboratory report 5776.

[17] Note that the operator of (24.31) differs from the operator (24.1) by the factor $(-)^{q-p-\omega}\sqrt{2\omega+1}$ which occurs in (24.16).

side to the three-j symbol on the left side is essentially the nine-j symbol

$$\begin{Bmatrix} J & S & L \\ \omega & q & p \\ J' & S' & L' \end{Bmatrix}. \tag{24.E.5}$$

The nine-j symbol vanishes unless the three vectors of each row and of each column form a vector triangle. The definition and properties of the nine-j symbols will not be discussed in detail. Rather, it will be shown how the expression on the right side of (24.33) can be condensed by means of six-j symbols into a single three-j symbol. The same procedure can be applied to all expressions which can give an invariant equation with a single three-j symbol.

The product of the first and the last three-j symbols on the right of (24.33) has the form of the product contained in (24.24a) except for a cyclic permutation of the j which can, however, be adjusted by (24.10a). Hence

$$(pL'L^{\bullet})(JSL_{\bullet}) = (-)^{2J} \sum_j (2j+1) \begin{Bmatrix} p & S & j \\ J & L' & L \end{Bmatrix} (pSj^{\bullet})(JL'j_{\bullet}). \tag{24.34}$$

We note that the second three-j symbol on the right of (24.33) contains p, the fourth contains S, and they both contain q. Hence, the p and S can be shifted into the same three-j symbol by a recoupling coefficient:

$$(S'Sq^{\bullet})(p\omega q_{\bullet}) = (-)^{2p} \sum_j (2j+1) \begin{Bmatrix} S' & \omega & j \\ p & S & q \end{Bmatrix} (S'\omega j^{\bullet})(pSj_{\bullet}). \tag{24.34a}$$

The product of the last two equations, if properly summed over the indices of p and S, can be contracted by means of the orthogonality relation (24.25):

$$(p^{\bullet}L'L^{\bullet})(JS^{\bullet}L_{\bullet})(S'S_{\bullet}q^{\bullet})(p_{\bullet}\omega q_{\bullet})$$
$$= (-)^{2J+2p} \sum_j (2j+1) \begin{Bmatrix} p & S & j \\ J & L' & L \end{Bmatrix} \begin{Bmatrix} S' & \omega & j \\ p & S & q \end{Bmatrix} (JL'j_{\bullet})(S'\omega j^{\bullet}). \tag{24.35}$$

If this is to be identified with the right side of (24.33), the position of the indices on S has to be changed. This merely introduces a factor $(-)^{2S}$. After that, multiplication with $(J'S'L') = (S'L'J')$ and proper contraction over the indices of S' and L' gives for the product of the five three-j symbols in (24.33)

$$(-)^{2J+2p+2S} \sum_j (2j+1) \begin{Bmatrix} p & S & j \\ J & L' & L \end{Bmatrix} \begin{Bmatrix} S' & \omega & j \\ p & S & q \end{Bmatrix} (JL'_{\bullet}j_{\bullet})(S'_{\bullet}\omega j^{\bullet})(S'^{\bullet}L'^{\bullet}J').$$

This now has the form of (24.24b) and is equal to

$$(-)^{2J+2\omega} \sum (-)^{2j}(2j+1) \begin{Bmatrix} p & S & j \\ J & L' & L \end{Bmatrix} \begin{Bmatrix} S' & \omega & j \\ p & S & q \end{Bmatrix} \begin{Bmatrix} J & \omega & J' \\ S' & L' & j \end{Bmatrix} (J\omega J').$$

The position of the indices of j and S' had to be shifted and this introduced a factor $(-)^{2j+2S'}$. However, the exponent could be simplified by the various conditions for the quantum numbers to form a vector triangle. We obtain finally

$$T_{JJ'} = (-)^{2\omega}\sqrt{2J+1}\sqrt{2J'+1}$$
$$\times \sum_j (-)^{2j}(2j+1)\begin{Bmatrix} p & S & j \\ J & L' & L \end{Bmatrix}\begin{Bmatrix} S' & \omega & j \\ p & S & q \end{Bmatrix}\begin{Bmatrix} J & \omega & J' \\ S' & L' & j \end{Bmatrix} T_{SL,S'L'}. \quad (24.36)$$

It should be noted that there are three essentially different ways of grouping the factors of the right side of (24.33) and that there are, correspondingly, three different ways to represent the nine-j symbol as a sum of products of three six-j symbols. The present grouping was selected here because it simplifies the following calculation.

An interesting special case obtains if $\omega = 0$, that is, if the operator **T** is an invariant with respect to the simultaneous rotation of spin and positional coordinates. This is the case, for instance, for the energy of interaction between spin and orbital motion. If $\omega = 0$, one must have $p = q$ and $J = J'$. Furthermore, since the second six-j symbol vanishes unless S', ω, and j form a vector triangle, only the $j = S'$ term contributes to the sum. With the expression (24.26) for the second and third six-j symbols, one obtains, after rearranging the six-j symbol,

$$T_{JJ'} = (-)^{J+L'+S+p}\frac{\sqrt{2J+1}}{\sqrt{2p+1}}\begin{Bmatrix} L & J & S \\ S' & p & L' \end{Bmatrix} T_{SL,S'L'}, \quad (24.36a)$$

again, essentially a six-j symbol. With $p = 1$, this gives Landé's interval rule, the case of $p = 2$ corresponds to spin-spin interaction. The six-j symbols turn up also in other parts of spectroscopy, such as determination of the wave function in complex spectra. They play an important role also in the theory of nuclei, in β-decay, in angular correlations between particles or quanta emitted successively, in the theory of nuclear reactions, and, last but not least, in the determination of nuclear wave functions. More comprehensive accounts were mentioned earlier in the present chapter.

25. The Building-Up Principle

1. The building-up[1] principle makes it possible to estimate the positions of the energy levels of atoms. By observing their selection rules, splitting in external fields etc., the characteristics of the individual levels such as the orbital angular momentum quantum number can, in principle, be determined. However, some indication concerning the region of the spectrum where a level of a given type should be sought, is also most helpful. The building-up principle fills this need.

However, the prime significance of the building-up principle does not lie in its applicability to the analysis of complicated spectra, but in the fact that the positions of the energy levels determine the most important physical and chemical properties of the atoms. Thus, for example, the strong electropositive character of the alkalis results from their ability to release an electron with the absorption of relatively little energy, i.e., the ground state does not lie very far below the lowest ionized state. Conversely, the inertia of the noble gases to chemical reaction is explained by the particularly great energy difference between the excited states and ionized states, and the ground state. The initiation of this line of thinking, which dominates so much of atomic physics, was N. Bohr's explanation of the most important features of the periodic system of the elements. The most important steps in the discovery of the building-up principle were, perhaps, the Landé-Sommerfeld vector model, the formulation of the normal coupling case by Russell and Saunders, and Pauli's principle of exclusion of identical orbits. The definitive formulation of the building-up principle was a result of the investigations of F. Hund.

To obtain an estimate of the positions of the energy levels, that is, of the eigenvalues of the Schrödinger equation,

$$\sum_k \left\{ -\frac{\hbar^2}{2m_k} \left(\frac{\partial^2}{\partial x_k^2} + \frac{\partial^2}{\partial y_k^2} + \frac{\partial^2}{\partial z_k^2} \right) - \frac{Ze^2}{r_k} \right\} \psi + \tfrac{1}{2} \sum_{i \neq k} \frac{e^2}{r_{ik}} \psi = E\psi, \quad (25.1)$$

one starts from a simplified equation,

$$\left.\begin{aligned} \mathbf{H}_0\psi &= (\mathbf{H}_1 + \mathbf{H}_2 + \cdots + \mathbf{H}_n)\psi = E\psi \\ \mathbf{H}_k &= -\frac{\hbar^2}{2m_k} \left(\frac{\partial^2}{\partial x_k^2} + \frac{\partial^2}{\partial y_k^2} + \frac{\partial^2}{\partial z_k^2} \right) - \frac{Ze^2}{r_k} \end{aligned}\right\} \quad (25.1a)$$

[1] See footnote[10] on page 184.

(Z is the nuclear charge) in which the interaction energy of the electrons,

$$\mathbf{W} = \sum_{k=2}^{n} \sum_{i=1}^{k-1} \frac{e^2}{r_{ik}}, \tag{25.1b}$$

is first neglected.[2] One then attempts to include this effect by a perturbation procedure (see Chapter 17).

This procedure is only valid when the potential energy of the nucleus is large in comparison with the interaction energy $\mathbf{W}$. This condition is best fulfilled when the nuclear charge number Z is large and the number of electrons is small, i.e., for strongly ionized atoms. The approximation procedure which will be applied here differs fundamentally from the approximation procedure used in chapters 22 and 23: it has nothing to do with the smallness of the fine structure constant,

$$\alpha = \frac{e^2}{\hbar c} = \frac{1}{137.0}$$

which was crucial for the validity of the approximations made earlier. The fundamental constants e, $\hbar$, and m appear in the eigenvalues of (25.1), and of all approximations to it, in the combination

$$\frac{me^4}{\hbar^2} \tag{25.E.1}$$

as can be seen at once from dimensional considerations: it is the only expression with the dimension of energy that can be obtained from m, e, and $\hbar$ (the velocity of light c does not occur in the simple Schrödinger equation). The approximation to be considered here does not form, therefore, an expansion of the energy in powers of the fine structure constant or any other small constant of nature, except possibly in the case of strongly ionized atoms when it can be considered to be an expansion in terms of $1/Z$.

The problem of the simple Schrödinger equation (25.1), which the theory discussed in the present chapter aims to solve, is the starting point for the considerations of the preceding chapters; it forms their "unperturbed problem" or gross structure. In view of this, the conditions under which (25.1a) can be expected to give a good approximation to (25.1) are even opposite to the conditions which make the treatment of the *modifications* of (25.1), described in preceding chapters, accurate. The solutions of (25.1a) will form a good basis for obtaining the solutions of (25.1) if the perturbation $\mathbf{W}$ of (25.1b) is small. If this is the case, the eigenvalues of (25.1) into which the eigenvalues of (25.1a) split, will lie close to each other. The calculation of the fine structure of splitting, on the other hand, becomes most accurate if the eigenvalues of (25.1) lie far from one another.

[2] As will be pointed out below, this is an oversimplification.

These statements about the relation between the approximation of the last chapters and that of the present one are only indicative of a trend and there must be many cases in which neither, and many cases in which both, approximations are useful and valid.

One circumstance which is very advantageous for the calculation of levels with the help of the building-up principle is the fact that a great part of the interaction energy of the electrons can be taken into account by modifying the nuclear potential. For example, if in a Li atom two so-called K-electrons ($N = 1$) and a more highly excited electron are to be considered, the latter will move almost entirely under the influence of a nuclear potential e/r since the actual nuclear potential $3e/r$ will be "screened off" by the two K-electrons which are almost certainly in the neighborhood of the nucleus. It is thus an improvement to use a modified potential in place of the *Coulomb* potential Ze^2/r in (25.1a). Naturally, if this substitution is made in (25.1a), then Eq. (25.1b) must also be changed correspondingly so that in combination with (25.1a) it again gives (25.1). The theory of screening was first fitted into quantum mechanics by *Hartree*. It gives surprisingly good values for the energy levels and other atomic properties.[3]

The derivation of the building-up principle which we present now is due to Slater.[4] Although neither the unperturbed problem (25.1a) nor the perturbation (25.1b) contain the spin coordinates in any way, Slater introduces the spin coordinates from the very beginning. This apparent complication actually simplifies the considerations a great deal, since one is restricted to the antisymmetric eigenfunctions from the outset. In this way one obtains as eigenfunctions not the spin-free eigenfunctions $\psi^{SL}_{\varkappa\mu}$ (which belong to a certain row of a representation $\bar{\mathbf{A}}^{(S)}$ of the symmetric group under permutations of the cartesian coordinates of the electrons), but the $\Xi^{SL}_{\nu\mu}$ derived in Chapter 22, which involve also the spin coordinates and which are antisymmetric under permutations of all coordinates of the electrons. The multiplet system of the $\Xi^{SL}_{\nu\mu}$ is manifested in rotations $\mathbf{Q}_R$ of the spin coordinates: $\Xi^{SL}_{\nu\mu}$ belongs to the νth row of $\mathfrak{D}^{(S)}$ under the $\mathbf{Q}_R$.

2. Let the eigenfunctions of the operator $\mathbf{H}_k$ (see Chapter 17, Section 2) be labeled by a single index b;

$$\mathbf{H}_k\psi_b(x_k, y_k, z_k) = E_b\psi_b(x_k, y_k, z_k). \tag{25.2}$$

The "orbit" b then denotes the combination of the principal quantum number N, the orbital angular momentum and magnetic quantum numbers l and μ. It is assumed that accidental degeneracies, coincidences of eigenvalues

[3] D. R. Hartree, *Proc. Cambridge Phil. Soc.* **24,** 89 (1928); see also J. C. Slater, *Phys. Rev.* **35,** 210 (1930); V. Fock, *Z. Physik.* **61,** 126 (1930); and D. R. Hartree, "The Calculation of Atomic Structures," Wiley, New York, 1957.

[4] J. C. Slater, *Phys. Rev.* **34,** 1293 (1929).

with the same N but different l, which occur in the pure Coulomb central field for the hydrogen atom, are removed by the screening. Then levels with different l are separated even for the same N; both the detailed theory and experiment show that levels with the same N lie lower for smaller l than for larger l. Since the $\mathbf{H}_1, \mathbf{H}_2, \cdots, \mathbf{H}_n$ differ only in that they act on different variables, the eigenvalues of all $\mathbf{H}_k$ are numerically the same; their eigenfunctions are also the same, except that they involve different variables.

When the spin coordinate s is introduced, two eigenfunctions

$$\psi_{b\sigma}(x_k, y_k, z_k, s_k) = \psi_b(x_k, y_k, z_k)\, \delta_{s_k\sigma} \qquad (\sigma = \pm 1) \tag{25.3}$$

result from each eigenfunction $\psi_b(x_k, y_k, z_k)$. Hence, the eigenfunctions of $\mathbf{H}_0$, as functions of all coordinates $x_1, y_1, z_1, s_1, \cdots, x_n, y_n, z_n, s_n$ are the products

$$\psi_{b_1\sigma_1 b_2\sigma_2\cdots b_n\sigma_n} = \psi_{b_1\sigma_1}(x_1, y_1, z_1, s_1)\psi_{b_2\sigma_2}(x_2, y_2, z_2, s_2) \cdots \psi_{b_n\sigma_n}(x_n, y_n, z_n, s_n) \tag{25.4}$$

of the eigenfunctions of the $\mathbf{H}_k$. Every pair of eigenfunctions $\psi_{b_1\sigma_1\cdots b_n\sigma_n}$ and $\psi_{b_1'\sigma_1'\cdots b_n'\sigma_n'}$ are orthogonal if they differ at all; if $b_i \neq b_i'$ then the scalar product vanishes after integration over x_i, y_i, z_i, and if $\sigma_i \neq \sigma_i'$ it vanishes because the summation over s_i vanishes. The eigenfunctions (25.4) for all 2^n systems of values of the $\sigma_1, \sigma_2, \sigma_3, \cdots, \sigma_n$ belong to the eigenvalue

$$E = E_{b_1} + E_{b_2} + \cdots + E_{b_n}. \tag{25.4a}$$

Moreover, since the Hamiltonian operator is invariant under permutations $\mathbf{O}_P$ of the electrons, all the eigenfunctions which are obtained from $\psi_{b_1\sigma_1\cdots b_n\sigma_n}$ by applying the operators $\mathbf{O}_P$ still belong to the eigenvalue (25.4a):

$$\mathbf{O}_P\psi_{b_1\sigma_1\cdots b_n\sigma_n}(1', 2', \cdots, n') = \psi_{b_1\sigma_1}(1) \cdots \psi_{b_n\sigma_n}(n), \tag{25.5}$$

where P is the permutation $\begin{pmatrix} 1 & 2 & \cdots & n \\ 1' & 2' & \cdots & n' \end{pmatrix}$ and k stands for the four variables x_k, y_k, z_k, s_k. The re-ordering of the factors transforms the right side of (25.5) into $\psi_{b_{1'}\sigma_{1'}}(1') \cdots \psi_{b_{n'}\sigma_{n'}}(n')$. Thus, if we resubstitute $1, 2, \cdots, n$ for $1', 2', \cdots, n'$, we obtain

$$\mathbf{O}_P\psi_{b_1\sigma_1\cdots b_n\sigma_n}(1, 2, \cdots, n) = \psi_{b_{1'}\sigma_{1'}\cdots b_{n'}\sigma_{n'}}(1, 2, \cdots, n). \tag{25.5a}$$

It is clear that the eigenvalue of (25.5a),

$$E_{b_{1'}} + E_{b_2} + \cdots + E_{b_{n'}}$$

is identical with the eigenvalue (25.4a).

We can collect all the eigenfunctions of the eigenvalue (25.4a) which result from one another by permutations of the electrons,

$$\psi_{b_1\sigma_1\cdots b_n\sigma_n},\ \mathbf{O}_{P_1}\psi_{b_1\sigma_1\cdots b_n\sigma_n},\ \mathbf{O}_{P_2}\psi_{b_1\sigma_1\cdots b_n\sigma_n},\ \cdots, \tag{25.6}$$

into a set; this set will be called a *configuration*. A configuration is thus characterized by n symbols $(b_k\ \sigma_k)$,

$$(b_1\sigma_1)(b_2\sigma_2)\cdots(b_n\sigma_n) = (N_1l_1\mu_1\sigma_1)(N_2l_2\mu_2\sigma_2)\cdots(N_nl_n\mu_n\sigma_n), \tag{25.E.2}$$

without regard to their order. It is clear that from any eigenfunction (25.5a) to which a permutation has already been applied, exactly the same eigenfunctions will be obtained by permutation of the variables as would be obtained from $\psi_{b_1\sigma_1\cdots b_n\sigma_n}$. Therefore, in the symbol (25.E.2) for the configuration any order of the b can be prescribed, e.g., that which is given by

$$\begin{aligned} &N_i \leqslant N_{i+1} \\ &l_i \leqslant l_{i+1} \quad \text{for} \quad N_i = N_{i+1} \\ &\mu_i \leqslant \mu_{i+1} \quad \text{for} \quad N_i = N_{i+1},\ l_i = l_{i+1} \end{aligned} \tag{25.7}$$

and

$$\sigma_i \leqq \sigma_{i+1} \quad \text{for} \quad N_i = N_{i+1},\ l_i = l_{i+1},\ \mu_i = \mu_{i+1}. \tag{25.7a}$$

Every eigenfunction belongs to one and only one configuration, and eigenfunctions of different configurations are orthogonal, since all distinct functions of the form (25.4) are orthogonal.

If an operator $\mathbf{O}_P$ is applied to the functions of a given configuration, the resulting functions can be expressed as linear combinations of the original functions of the configuration; in fact, they are themselves functions of the configuration. Therefore, a representation of the group of the $\mathbf{O}_P$, the symmetric group of the nth degree, belongs to the functions (25.6). By means of the matrix which reduces this representation, linear combinations of the functions (25.6) can be formed which belong to the irreducible representations of the group of $\mathbf{O}_P$. Conversely, the functions (25.6) can be written as linear combinations of these "irreducible" functions. Because of the Pauli principle, we need only the *antisymmetric* ones among these irreducible linear combinations, i.e., the antisymmetric components of $\mathbf{O}_{P_\varkappa}\psi_{b_1\sigma_1\cdots b_n\sigma_n}$; Eq. (12.6) shows that these are given by

$$\sum_P \varepsilon_P \mathbf{O}_P \mathbf{O}_{P_\varkappa}\psi_{b_1\sigma_1\cdots b_n\sigma_n} = \sum_P \varepsilon_P \mathbf{O}_{PP_\varkappa}\psi_{b_1\sigma_1\cdots b_n\sigma_n}, \tag{25.8}$$

where ε_P is equal to $+1$ for even permutations and -1 for odd permutations; it is the $\mathbf{D}(R)^*_{\varkappa\varkappa}$ of (12.6) for the antisymmetric representation.

The antisymmetric components (25.8) of all functions of the same configuration are identical except for sign: for $P_\varkappa = E$, the function (25.8) is, in fact, just the determinant[5]

$$\sqrt{n!}\cdot\chi_{b_1\sigma_1\cdots b_n\sigma_n} = \begin{vmatrix} \psi_{b_1\sigma_1}(1) & \psi_{b_1\sigma_1}(2) & \cdots & \psi_{b_1\sigma_1}(n) \\ \psi_{b_2\sigma_2}(1) & \psi_{b_2\sigma_2}(2) & \cdots & \psi_{b_2\sigma_2}(n) \\ \cdot & \cdot & & \cdot \\ \cdot & \cdot & & \cdot \\ \cdot & \cdot & & \cdot \\ \psi_{b_n\sigma_n}(1) & \psi_{b_n\sigma_n}(2) & \cdots & \psi_{b_n\sigma_n}(n) \end{vmatrix}. \tag{25.8a}$$

Since the function $\mathbf{O}_P\psi_{b_1\sigma_1\cdots b_n\sigma_n}$ differs from the function $\psi_{b_1\sigma_1\cdots b_n\sigma_n}$ only in that the variables are interchanged, the corresponding antisymmetric linear combination differs from (25.8a) only in that the functions of the variables x_k, y_k, z_k, s_k occur in some column other than the kth. We can therefore revert to the original function merely by rearranging the columns, which effects, at most, a change in sign.

Conversely, it follows that the antisymmetric linear combinations (25.8a) are the only ones which can be formed from the functions (25.6). If F is antisymmetric, it follows by equating the antisymmetric components on the two sides of the equation

$$F = \sum_P c_P \mathbf{O}_P \psi_{b_1\sigma_1\cdots b_n\sigma_n},$$

that except for a constant, F is equal to $\chi_{b_1\sigma_1\cdots b_n\sigma_n}$ since the antisymmetric component of every term on the right side is $\chi_{b_1\sigma_1\cdots b_n\sigma_n}$.

Thus, at most one antisymmetric linear combination can be formed from the functions of a given configuration, and not even one can be formed if, in the set (25.E.2), one has $\sigma_i = \sigma_k$ for any pair i, k for which $b_i = b_k$ (i.e., $N_i = N_k, l_i = l_k, \mu_i = \mu_k$). In this case, two rows of the determinant (25.8a) would be equal and it would vanish.

Thus every configuration in which $b_i = b_k$ and $\sigma_i = \sigma_k$ do not hold simultaneously for any pair i, k, gives one state which is allowed by the Pauli principle; a configuration in which $b_i = b_k$, $\sigma_i = \sigma_k$, for any pair i, k, is excluded by the Pauli principle. This is the original formulation of Pauli's principle of equivalence, which prior to quantum mechanics could be formulated only for our "unperturbed problem" (25.1a), that is, for a Hamiltonian which neglects the interactions of the electrons and ascribes an orbit to each electron. In quantum mechanics, the Pauli principle in its original form is a special case of the general requirement of antisymmetry for the wave function,[6] which is valid for *all* systems of electrons.

[5] The factor $\sqrt{n!}$ is prefixed in order to maintain the normalization of $\chi_{b_1\sigma_1\ldots b_n\sigma_n}$. Expressions of the form (25.8a) are often referred to as Slater determinants.

[6] W. Heisenberg and P. A. M. Dirac were the first to note this; their observation was the point of departure for the group theoretical treatment of spectral theory.

The original form of Pauli's principle implies in particular that those combinations $b_1, b_2, \cdots, b_n$ in which three orbits $b_i = b_j = b_k$ are identical, cannot describe "allowed" configurations. In an allowed configuration we would have to have $\sigma_i \neq \sigma_k$ and $\sigma_j \neq \sigma_k$ which is not possible, since the σ can have only two values, -1 and $+1$. *An orbit can be occupied, at most, by two electrons.*

3. We are now in a position to determine the number of allowed states whose energy would be (25.4a) if the interactions among electrons were zero. If the eigenvalues E_k of the $\mathbf{H}_k$ (considered only as functions of the x_k, y_k, z_k) were all simple, we would have to count only the allowed configurations among the 2^n configurations given by the different sets of values for the σ. If several functions belong to one eigenvalue E_k, then we must include every possible combination of the b with the energy $E_{b_1} + E_{b_2} + E_{b_3} + \cdots + E_{b_n} = E$.[7]

We are interested not only in the number of states which result from a state with energy (25.4a) because of interactions among the electrons, but also in their character, i.e., their multiplet systems and their orbital quantum numbers. This last is meaningful if the system has rotational symmetry, which is the case in the atoms which are of primary concern to us.

The following consideration uses only the symmetry under rotations of the spin coordinates and of the cartesian coordinates $\mathbf{Q}_R$ and $\mathbf{P}_R$; the symmetry under permutations of the electrons need not be considered. The rotation of the cartesian coordinates is a symmetry operation only in the spherically symmetric case, while that of the spin coordinates is always a symmetry operation since neither the initial problem (25.1a) nor the perturbation (25.1b) contain the spin coordinates. Therefore, the whole problem is invariant under all operators which act only on the spin coordinates. We can limit ourselves to the rotations $\mathbf{Q}_R$ since these already suffice to determine the multiplet systems of the individual perturbed levels. The entire symmetry which has to be considered is the direct product of the $\mathbf{O}_P$ with the $\mathbf{Q}_R$, and, in the isotropic case, with the $\mathbf{P}_R$ as well.

4. We consider first the anisotropic case. If we apply the operator $\mathbf{Q}_R$ to the antisymmetric linear combinations $\chi_{b_1\sigma_1\cdots b_n\sigma_n}$ of an unperturbed level E, we again obtain antisymmetric eigenfunctions with the same eigenvalue; these can therefore be expressed as a linear combination of the original eigenfunctions. The coefficients form a representation of the rotation group. If the irreducible representation $\mathfrak{D}^{(S)}$ of the group of the $\mathbf{Q}_R$ is contained

[7] It is ordinarily assumed that only those combinations of the b give the same energy

$$E_{b_1} + E_{b_2} + \cdots + E_{b_n} = E_{c_1} + E_{c_2} + \cdots + E_{c_n} \tag{25.E.3}$$

in which *the individual energies*—on the left and right sides of (25.E.3)—are already equal in pairs.

in this representation A_S times, A_S is also the number of antisymmetric levels of the multiplet system S which the perturbation creates from the level at $E = E_{b_1} + \cdots + E_{b_n}$. The irreducible components of a representation of the rotation group can be determined just from the matrices which correspond to rotations about Z. If the representation $(\exp(im\phi))$ of the two-dimensional rotation group occurs a_m times among these matrices, then the irreducible representation $\mathfrak{D}^{(S)}$ is contained in the whole representation $A_S = a_S - a_{S+1}$ times (see Section 1, Chapter 15).

If R is a rotation about Z through an angle φ, then the operator $\mathbf{Q}_R$ merely multiplies the functions of the configuration (25.6) by $\exp[\frac{1}{2}i(\sigma_1 + \cdots + \sigma_n)\varphi]$. The same holds also for the antisymmetric linear combination $\chi_{b_1\sigma_1\cdots b_n\sigma_n}$, so that this belongs to the representation of the rotations about Z with the magnetic quantum number $m = \frac{1}{2}(\sigma_1 + \sigma_2 + \cdots + \sigma_n)$. If the eigenvalue E has in all a_m allowed configurations with the sum $\sigma_1 + \sigma_2 + \cdots + \sigma_n = 2m$, then the perturbation splits it into $a_S - a_{S+1}$ levels belonging to $\mathfrak{D}^{(S)}$ under rotations of the spin coordinates.

Since the preceding paragraphs deal with the anisotropic case, let us consider an example in which the eigenvalues E_k of the $\mathbf{H}_k$ are all simple. In the case of four electrons, in one doubly occupied and two singly occupied orbits,

$$b_1 = b_2 \neq b_3 \neq b_4; \quad b_1 \neq b_4,$$

the following combinations of the σ each give one antisymmetric eigenfunction.

TABLE VII*

Example of Antisymmetric Combinations of Four Electrons

σ_1	σ_2	σ_3	σ_4	$\frac{1}{2}(\sigma_1 + \sigma_2 + \sigma_3 + \sigma_4)$
-1	$+1$	-1	-1	-1
-1	$+1$	-1	$+1$	0
-1	$+1$	$+1$	-1	0
-1	$+1$	$+1$	$+1$	$+1$

* Since $b_1 = b_2$, we can assume in counting the configurations that $\sigma_1 \leqslant \sigma_2$; (see (25.7a). But $\sigma_1 = \sigma_2$ is forbidden by the Pauli principle, so that only $\sigma_1 < \sigma_2$ can occur.

Thus

$$a_0 = 2; \; a_1 = 1; \; a_2 = a_3 = \cdots = 0$$

and there is $a_1 = 1$ level with the representation $\mathfrak{D}^{(1)}$, and $a_0 - a_1 = 1$ level with the representation $\mathfrak{D}^{(0)}$.

A level which has $2S + 1$ antisymmetric eigenfunctions belonging to $\mathfrak{D}^{(S)}$ under the $\mathbf{Q}_R$ belongs to the multiplet system S. For if we introduce the spin interaction, they split in general (in the anisotropic case!) into $2S + 1$ fine structure components. It can easily be verified that this definition of the multiplet system is identical with that used earlier. *According to Chapter 22, every function of the s which belongs to $\mathfrak{D}^{(S)}$ under the $\mathbf{Q}_R$ belongs to $\mathbf{A}^{(S)*}$ under the $\mathbf{Q}_P$.* Moreover, for every antisymmetric eigenfunction F which belongs to $\mathbf{A}^{(S)*}$ under the $\mathbf{Q}_P$ (cf. Eq (12.10)),

$$\sum_P \sum_\varkappa \mathbf{A}^{(S)}(P)_{\varkappa\varkappa} \mathbf{Q}_P F = \frac{n!}{g_S} F, \tag{25.9}$$

belongs to $\bar{\mathbf{A}}^{(S)}$ under the $\mathbf{P}_P$, and this is just the definition of the multiplet system. The last statement follows from (25.9) by the antisymmetry of F (that is, $\mathbf{O}_P F = \varepsilon_P F$), by the identity $\mathbf{Q}_P = \mathbf{P}_{P^{-1}} \mathbf{O}_P$, and by Eq. (22.17). Thus

$$\sum_P \sum_\varkappa \mathbf{A}^{(S)}(P)_{\varkappa\varkappa} \mathbf{P}_{P^{-1}} \mathbf{O}_P F = \sum_P \sum_\varkappa \mathbf{A}^{(S)}(P^{-1})^*_{\varkappa\varkappa} \mathbf{P}_{P^{-1}} \varepsilon_P F$$

$$= \sum_P \sum_\varkappa \bar{\mathbf{A}}^{(S)}(P^{-1})^*_{\varkappa\varkappa} \mathbf{P}_{P^{-1}} F, \tag{25.9a}$$

since $\varepsilon_P = \varepsilon_{P^{-1}}$ and $\mathbf{A}^{(S)}$ is unitary.

Under the influence of the perturbation $\mathbf{W}$, the correct linear combinations of the $\chi_{b_1\sigma_1 \cdots b_n\sigma_n}$ become simply the functions Ξ^S_m of Chapter 22, which were formed from the ready-made spin-free eigenfunctions of the Schrödinger equation (25.1).

The significant feature of the Slater method is that *it makes it possible to avoid entirely the consideration of the symmetry of the Schrödinger equation (25.1) under permutation of the Cartesian coordinates alone*, by considering instead the invariance under rotations $\mathbf{Q}_R$ of the spin coordinates. Consider for example, the selection rule which concerns the multiplet systems of levels in optical transitions (the intercombination prohibition). This rule follows from the fact that eigenfunctions of different multiplet systems belong to different representations under the $\mathbf{Q}_R$, and that multiplication by $(x_1 + x_2 + x_3 + \cdots + x_n)$ is symmetric under the $\mathbf{Q}_R$, since it does not act on the spin coordinates at all. (Previously, we deduced the intercombination prohibition from the fact that the eigenfunctions of different multiplet systems belong to different representations of the group of permutations $\mathbf{P}_P$ of the Cartesian coordinates.) We have not used the Slater method in the extreme form indicated since we are interested in all the symmetry properties and in using them all when possible.

Although there must exist situations in which more extensive conclusions can be obtained by considering the permutations $\mathbf{P}_P$ of the Cartesian coordinates than by means of the $\mathbf{Q}_R$ alone, it is surprising to what extent the group of the $\mathbf{Q}_R$ can be used to derive the results which follow, more directly, from the invariance under the group of the $\mathbf{P}_P$.

An essential requirement for the applicability of Slater's method is that the internal coordinates of the particles considered can assume only two values. If one were dealing with particles which had three possible orientations (spin angular momentum equal to $\hbar$, instead of $\frac{1}{2}\hbar$, as is the case for, say, a nitrogen nucleus), then $\mathfrak{D}^{(1)}$ would appear in the defining equation for the operators $\mathbf{Q}_R$ (Eq. (21.6b)) in place of $\mathfrak{D}^{(1/2)}$. This would have very little effect on the considerations of the present chapter. However, the conclusions which one could derive in such a theory from the rotational invariance (invariance with respect to the $\mathbf{Q}_R$) would be more restricted than the consequences of the invariance with respect to the $\mathbf{P}_P$. In fact, in this case several levels of the Schrödinger equation coincide, and this coincidence could not be explained by consideration of the $\mathbf{Q}_R$ alone. It would then be necessary either to introduce further operators, thereby losing the simplicity of the theory, or to use the symmetry under the operators $\mathbf{P}_P$ as was done in the first derivation of the building-up principle.[8] This is the reason why the permutations of the cartesian coordinates of the particles and the representations of the symmetric group were discussed in this book, and why the equivalence of the $\mathbf{Q}_R$ with the $\mathbf{P}_P$ for electrons was proven explicitly.

5. The principal difference between the *spherically symmetric case* and the asymmetric case is that in the spherically symmetric case the eigenvalues $E_{l_k}^{N_k}$ of the $\mathbf{H}_k$, considered as functions of the x_k, y_k, z_k alone, are not simple, but $(2l_k + 1)$-fold[9] and that we must determine not only the multiplet system but also the orbital angular momentum quantum numbers of the levels of the whole Hamiltonian. The unperturbed levels are specified by stating the principal and orbital angular momentum quantum numbers of the orbits

$$N_1 l_1, N_2 l_2, \cdots, N_n l_n. \tag{25.E.4}$$

To obtain all the configurations of the unperturbed levels (25.E.4), we must allow the μ and the σ in the symbols for the configurations

$$(N_1 l_1 \mu_1 \sigma_1)(N_2 l_2 \mu_2 \sigma_2) \cdots (N_n l_n \mu_n \sigma_n) = (b_1 \sigma_1)(b_2 \sigma_2) \cdots (b_n \sigma_n) \tag{25.E.2}$$

to assume all possible values ($|\mu_k| < l_k$; $\sigma_k = \pm 1$). In (25.E.2) we can restrict the N_k, l_k, and μ_k by (25.7) and, since we wish to calculate only with the allowed configurations, (25.7a) can be replaced by

$$\sigma_i < \sigma_{i+1} \quad \text{for} \quad N_i = N_{i+1},\ l_i = l_{i+1},\ \mu_i = \mu_{i+1}. \tag{25.7b}$$

For each allowed configuration there exists one antisymmetric eigenfunction (25.8a).

If the operators $\mathbf{Q}_R \mathbf{P}_{R'}$ are applied to these antisymmetric linear combinations of the eigenfunctions (25.E.4) and the resulting functions expressed in terms of the original functions

$$\mathbf{Q}_R \mathbf{P}_{R'} \chi_{N_1 l_1 \mu_1 \sigma_1 \cdots N_n l_n \mu_n \sigma_n} = \sum_{\mu' \sigma'} \mathbf{\Delta}(R, R')_{\mu_1' \sigma_1' \cdots \mu_n' \sigma_n'; \mu_1 \sigma_1 \cdots \mu_n \sigma_n} \chi_{N_1 l_1 \mu_1' \sigma_1' \cdots N_n l_n \mu_n' \sigma_n'} \tag{25.10}$$

the matrices $\mathbf{\Delta}(R, R')$ will form a representation of the direct product of the

[8] See E. Wigner, *Z. Physik.* **43,** 624 (1927); §§21 to 25. M. Delbrück, *ibid.* **51,** 181 (1928). Actually, the levels arising from a configuration can be determined more quickly by the methods of these articles than by the method described in the text. The method of the text (due to Slater) is, however, easier to visualize and to remember.

[9] If $\mathbf{H}_k$ actually had the form given in (25.1), all the eigenvalues $E(N_k, l_k)$ ($l_k = 0, 1, 2, \cdots, N_k - 1$) with the same N_k would coincide. However, it was assumed that the Coulomb field is sufficiently modified by the screening so that the eigenvalues are all separated.

groups of $\mathbf{Q}_R$ and $\mathbf{P}_{R'}$. If the irreducible representation $\mathfrak{D}^{(S)}(R) \times \mathfrak{D}^{(L)}(R')$ is contained A_{SL} times in $\mathbf{\Delta}(R, R')$ this will also be the number of levels with multiplet system S and orbital quantum number L which the perturbation $\mathbf{W}$ creates from a level (25.E.4). The corresponding linear combinations of the χ again form the first approximation functions for the calculation of the quantities which were denoted in Chapter 22 by $\Xi_{\nu\mu}^{SL}$.

To determine the numbers A_{SL}, it again suffices—as will be shown—to determine the matrices $\mathbf{\Delta}(R, R')$ in which R and R' are rotations about Z. If R is a rotation about Z through α, then one has

$$\mathbf{Q}_{\{\alpha 00\}}\, \chi_{N_1 l_1 \mu_1 \sigma_1 \cdots N_n l_n \mu_n \sigma_n} = e^{\frac{1}{2}i(\sigma_1 + \cdots + \sigma_n)\alpha} \chi_{N_1 l_1 \mu_1 \sigma_1 \cdots N_n l_n \mu_n \sigma_n}. \tag{25.11}$$

In the calculation of $\mathbf{P}_{\{\alpha' 00\}} \psi_{\mu_1 \sigma_1}^{N_1 l_1}, \cdots, \psi_{\mu_n \sigma_n}^{N_n l_n}$, the $\mathbf{P}_{\{\alpha' 00\}}$ can be applied separately to the individual factors; in this process the factors with magnetic quantum number μ_k are reproduced except for a factor $\exp(i\mu_k\alpha')$. Therefore one has

$$\mathbf{P}_{\{\alpha' 00\}} \chi_{N_1 l_1 \mu_1 \sigma_1 \cdots N_n l_n \mu_n \sigma_n} = e^{i(\mu_1 + \cdots + \mu_n)\alpha'} \chi_{N_1 l_1 \mu_1 \sigma_1 \cdots N_n l_n \mu_n \sigma_n} \tag{25.11a}$$

since this holds for all eigenfunctions of the configuration

$$(N_1 l_1 \mu_1 \sigma_1)(N_2 l_2 \mu_2 \sigma_2) \cdots (N_n l_n \mu_n \sigma_n),$$

and thus also for all linear combinations of them. Equation (25.11a) expresses the fact that the Z-components of the angular momentum of individual electrons are simply additive. From (25.11) and (25.11a) it follows that

$$\mathbf{Q}_{\{\alpha 00\}} \mathbf{P}_{\{\alpha' 00\}} \chi_{N_1 l_1 \mu_1 \sigma_1 \cdots N_n l_n \mu_n \sigma_n}$$
$$= e^{\frac{1}{2}i(\sigma_1 + \sigma_2 + \cdots + \sigma_n)\alpha} e^{i(\mu_1 + \mu_2 + \cdots + \mu_n)\alpha'} \chi_{N_1 l_1 \mu_1 \sigma_1 \cdots N_n l_n \mu_n \sigma_n}. \tag{25.12}$$

The matrices $\mathbf{\Delta}(R, R')$ which correspond to the rotation of the spin coordinates about Z through α and of the Cartesian coordinates through α', are diagonal matrices; the diagonal element which corresponds to the eigenfunction, $\chi_{N_1 l_1 \mu_1 \sigma_1 \cdots N_n l_n \mu_n \sigma_n}$ is $\exp[i(\nu\alpha + \mu\alpha')]$, where

$$\nu = \tfrac{1}{2}(\sigma_1 + \sigma_2 + \cdots + \sigma_n) \quad \text{and} \quad \mu = (\mu_1 + \mu_2 + \cdots + \mu_n).$$

The trace of this matrix is therefore obtained by the addition of the $\exp[i(\nu\alpha + \mu\alpha')]$ for all allowed configurations. The characters of $\mathbf{\Delta}(R, R')$ (R and R' are rotations about Z) obtained in this way can be summarized in a table like that on page 186, by assigning a row to each ν and a column to each μ, and placing in the intersecting squares as many crosses as there are allowed configurations with $\frac{1}{2}(\sigma_1 + \sigma_2 + \cdots + \sigma_n) = \nu$ and $\mu_1 + \mu_2 + \cdots + \mu_n = \mu$.

We take as an example two electrons whose unperturbed energies are equal and correspond to a p-state ($l = 1$). The allowed configurations are presented in Table VIII.

TABLE VIII*

Allowed Configurations of Two Electrons in Degenerate p-States

Configuration	μ_1 σ_1 μ_2 σ_2	μ	ν
1	$(-1\ -1)\ (-1\ \ 1)$	-2	0
2	$(-1\ -1)\ (\ 0\ -1)$	-1	-1
3	$(-1\ -1)\ (\ 0\ \ 1)$	-1	0
4	$(-1\ -1)\ (\ 1\ -1)$	0	-1
5	$(-1\ -1)\ (\ 1\ \ 1)$	0	0
6	$(-1\ \ 1)\ (\ 0\ -1)$	-1	0
7	$(-1\ \ 1)\ (\ 0\ \ 1)$	-1	1
8	$(-1\ \ 1)\ (\ 1\ -1)$	0	0
9	$(-1\ \ 1)\ (\ 1\ \ 1)$	0	1
10	$(\ 0\ -1)\ (\ 0\ \ 1)$	0	0
11	$(\ 0\ -1)\ (\ 1\ -1)$	1	-1
12	$(\ 0\ -1)\ (\ 1\ \ 1)$	1	0
13	$(\ 0\ \ 1)\ (\ 1\ -1)$	1	0
14	$(\ 0\ \ 1)\ (\ 1\ \ 1)$	1	1
15	$(\ 1\ -1)\ (\ 1\ \ 1)$	2	0

* The principal and orbital quantum numbers are omitted from the symbols for the configurations since they are 2 and 1 respectively for both electrons. Therefore $(\mu_k\ \sigma_k)$ stands for $(2\ 1\ \mu_k\ \sigma_k)$.

The last two columns contain $\mu_1 + \mu_2 = \mu$ and $\frac{1}{2}(\sigma_1 + \sigma_2) = \nu$, respectively. In Table IX a cross is entered in the appropriate square for each row of Table VIII.

This table summarizes the characters of the group elements $\mathbf{Q}_{\{\alpha 00\}}\mathbf{P}_{\{\alpha' 00\}}$

TABLE IX

Allowed Z-components of Spin and Orbital Angular Momentum for Two Equivalent p-Electrons

ν	μ = -2	-1	0	1	2
-1		+	+	+	
0	+	+ +	+ + +	+ +	+
1		+	+	+	

in the representation $\Delta(R, R')$. On the other hand, the character of this element in the irreducible representation $\mathfrak{D}^{(S)} \times \mathfrak{D}^{(L)}$ is

$$\sum_{\nu\mu} [\mathfrak{D}^{(S)}(\{\alpha 00\}) \times \mathfrak{D}^{(L)}(\{\alpha' 00\})]_{\nu\mu;\nu\mu} = \sum_{\mu=-L}^{L} \sum_{\nu=-S}^{S} e^{i(\nu\alpha+\mu\alpha')}. \quad (25.13)$$

This would be represented in Table IX by a rectangle of single crosses extending for ν from $-S$ to $\nu = S$ and for μ from $-L$ to $\mu = L$. If the character represented in Table IX is considered as a sum of irreducible characters, that is, as a sum of rectangular fields of crosses, the number $a_{\nu\mu}$ of crosses in the $\nu\mu$ square will be the sum of the numbers A_{SL} of representations $\mathfrak{D}^{(S)} \times \mathfrak{D}^{(L)}$ with $S \geqslant |\nu|$ and $L \geqslant |\mu|$ contained in $\Delta(R, R')$:

$$a_{\nu\mu} = A_{S,L} + A_{S+1,L} + A_{S+2,L} + \cdots$$
$$+ A_{S,L+1} + A_{S+1,L+1} + \cdots + A_{S,L+2} + A_{S+1,L+2} + \cdots. \quad (25.14)$$

Here A_{SL} is also the number of levels with multiplet system S and orbital quantum number L which result from the level (25.E.4) as a result of applying the perturbation. According to (25.14)

$$A_{SL} = a_{SL} - a_{S+1,L} - a_{S,L+1} + a_{S+1,L+1}. \quad (25.14a)$$

This shows that the irreducible components of the representation $\Delta(R, R')$ are, in fact, completely determined by the characters of those elements in which R and R' are rotations about Z, since these characters can be resolved into irreducible characters (25.13) in only one way.[10]

For the levels of Table VIII, Eq. (25.14a) gives $A_{11} = 1$; $A_{02} = 1$; $A_{00} = 1$, and all other A_{SL} are zero. Two equivalent p-electrons[11] therefore give a ^3P, a ^1D, and a ^1S level. In Table X the symbol for the level whose representation character involves the term $\exp[i(\nu\alpha + \mu\alpha')]$ is inserted for the cross representing this term.

6. We can also determine the parity of the levels obtained. For the eigenfunctions of a one-electron problem the parity is given by the orbital

[10] This is due to the fact that every class of the group of the direct product of $\mathbf{Q}_R$ and $\mathbf{P}_{R'}$ contains an element in which R and R' are both rotations about Z. Since in any representation all elements of the same class have the same character, the characters of these elements determine the entire character.

[11] Orbits with orbital quantum numbers $l = 0, 1, 2, 3, \cdots$ are called $s, p, d, f, \cdots$ orbits. Two orbits are equivalent if their principal quantum numbers are the same. Hence, the configuration considered in Table IX is an (Np, Np) or an $(Np)^2$ configuration. The levels of the system as a whole are denoted by $S, P, D, \cdots$ corresponding to $L = 0, 1, 2, \cdots$, with the value of $2S + 1$ given as a left superscript to denote the multiplet system, and the value of J as a right subscript; for example, $^3P_0$, $^3P_1$, or $^3P_2$, etc. See also Chapter 8.

angular momentum quantum number l (Eq. (19.17)): $w = (-1)^l$. Therefore, we have ($\mathbf{O}_I = \mathbf{P}_I$ denotes the inversion)

$$\mathbf{O}_I \psi^{N_1 l_1}_{\mu_1 \sigma_1}(1) \cdots \psi^{N_n l_n}_{\mu_n \sigma_n}(n) = \mathbf{P}_I \psi^{N_1 l_1}_{\mu_1 \sigma_1}(1) \cdots \mathbf{P}_I \psi^{N_n l_n}_{\mu_n \sigma_n}(n)$$
$$= (-1)^{l_1 + l_2 + \cdots + l_n} \psi^{N_1 l_1}_{\mu_1 \sigma_1}(1) \psi^{N_2 l_2}_{\mu_2 \sigma_2}(2) \cdots \psi^{N_n l_n}_{\mu_n \sigma_n}(n) \quad (25.15)$$

independent of μ_k and σ_k. The parity of all eigenfunctions of the eigenvalue

TABLE X

Allowed Levels for Two p-Electrons

ν	μ				
	-2	-1	0	1	2
-1		^3P	^3P	^3P	
0	^1D	$^1D\,^3P$	$^1S\,^1D\,^3P$	$^1D\,^3P$	^1D
1		^3P	^3P	^3P	

(25.E.4) is equal to $(-1)^{l_1 + l_2 + \cdots + l_n}$ and this is also the parity of all the perturbed levels. Thus, the parity of the levels arising from (25.E.4) is positive if the sum of the orbital quantum numbers for the individual orbits $l_1 + l_2 + \cdots + l_n$ is even, and negative if it is odd. This implies, among other things that electric dipole transitions between levels which result from the same unperturbed level (25.E.4) are forbidden by Laporte's rule.

7. In conclusion let us outline the calculation of the first approximation to the energy perturbation.

We denote the functions $\chi_{N_1 l_1 \mu_1 \sigma_1 \cdots N_n l_n \mu_n \sigma_n}$ with $\mu_1 + \mu_2 + \cdots + \mu_n = \mu$ and $\sigma_1 + \sigma_2 + \cdots + \sigma_n = 2\nu$, whose crosses occur in the $\nu\mu$ rectangle of Table IX, by $\chi_{\nu\mu 1}, \chi_{\nu\mu 2}, \chi_{\nu\mu 3}, \cdots$. The correct linear combinations $f_{\nu\mu 1}$, $f_{\nu\mu 2}, \cdots$, which belong to the $\nu\mu$th row of some representation $\mathfrak{D}^{(S)} \times \mathfrak{D}^{(L)}$, can all be written as linear combinations of the $\chi_{\nu\mu 1}, \chi_{\nu\mu 2}, \chi_{\nu\mu 3}, \cdots$ alone:

$$f_{\nu\mu\varkappa} = \sum_\lambda \mathbf{u}_{\varkappa\lambda} \chi_{\nu\mu\lambda}. \quad (25.16)$$

The transformation matrix is unitary since both the $\chi_{\nu\mu}$ and $f_{\nu\mu}$ are orthogonal sets:

$$\left.\begin{aligned} \delta_{\varkappa\varkappa'} &= (f_{\nu\mu\varkappa}, f_{\nu\mu\varkappa'}) = \sum_{\lambda\lambda'} (\mathbf{u}_{\varkappa\lambda}\chi_{\nu\mu\lambda}, \mathbf{u}_{\varkappa'\lambda'}\chi_{\nu\mu\lambda'}) \\ &= \sum_{\lambda\lambda'} \mathbf{u}^*_{\varkappa\lambda}\mathbf{u}_{\varkappa'\lambda'}\delta_{\lambda\lambda'} = \sum_\lambda \mathbf{u}^*_{\varkappa\lambda}\mathbf{u}_{\varkappa'\lambda}. \end{aligned}\right\} \quad (25.17)$$

The first approximation to the perturbation energy of the eigenvalue of $f_{\nu\mu}$

is $(f_{\nu\mu}, \mathbf{W}f_{\nu\mu})$. The sum of the perturbation energies for all $\varkappa$, that is, for all levels with $S \geqslant |\nu|$, $L \geqslant |\mu|$ can be calculated without first obtaining $\mathbf{u}$:

$$\left.\begin{aligned}\sum_{\varkappa} (f_{\nu\mu\varkappa}, \mathbf{W}f_{\nu\mu\varkappa}) &= \sum_{\varkappa}\sum_{\lambda\lambda'} \mathbf{u}^*_{\varkappa\lambda}\mathbf{u}_{\varkappa\lambda'}(\chi_{\nu\mu\lambda}, \mathbf{W}\chi_{\nu\mu\lambda'}) \\ &= \sum_{\lambda\lambda'} \delta_{\lambda\lambda'}(\chi_{\nu\mu\lambda}, \mathbf{W}\chi_{\nu\mu\lambda'}) = \sum_{\lambda} (\chi_{\nu\mu\lambda}, \mathbf{W}\chi_{\nu\mu\lambda}).\end{aligned}\right\} \tag{25.18}$$

For the sum of the perturbation energies of levels with multiplet system S and orbital quantum number L, which arise from (25.E.4), this implies

$$\begin{aligned}\sum_{\varkappa} \Delta E_{SL\varkappa} = \sum_{\lambda} [&(\chi_{SL\lambda}, \mathbf{W}\chi_{SL\lambda}) - (\chi_{S+1L\lambda}, \mathbf{W}\chi_{S+1L\lambda}) \\ &- (\chi_{SL+1\lambda}, \mathbf{W}\chi_{SL+1\lambda}) + (\chi_{S+1L+1\lambda}, \mathbf{W}\chi_{S+1L+1\lambda})],\end{aligned} \tag{25.18a}$$

in analogy to (25.14a).

If the level (25.E.4) of the unperturbed problem yields only one level with multiplet system S and orbital quantum number L, then its energy is given directly by (25.18a); in this case (25.18a) reduces the problem to quadratures.

In the calculation of the scalar products for (25.18a),

$$\begin{aligned}&(\chi_{N_1l_1\mu_1\sigma_1\cdots N_nl_n\mu_n\sigma_n}, \mathbf{W}\chi_{N_1l_1\mu_1\sigma_1\cdots N_nl_n\mu_n\sigma_n}) \\ &\quad = \frac{1}{n!}\sum_{PP'}(\varepsilon_P\mathbf{O}_P\psi^{N_1l_1}_{\mu_1\sigma_1}(1)\cdots\psi^{N_nl_n}_{\mu_n\sigma_n}(n), \mathbf{W}\varepsilon_{P'}\mathbf{O}_{P'}\psi^{N_1l_1}_{\mu_1\sigma_1}(1)\cdots\psi^{N_nl_n}_{\mu_n\sigma_n}(n)),\end{aligned} \tag{25.19}$$

the unitary operator $\varepsilon_P\mathbf{O}_P$ can be brought over to the second factor as $\varepsilon_P\mathbf{O}_P^{-1}$; since it commutes with $\mathbf{W}$, it can then be combined with $\varepsilon_{P'}\mathbf{O}_{P'}$. The summation can now be taken over $P^{-1}P' = T$ instead of over P', yielding simply $n!$. Thus the right side of (25.19) becomes

$$\tfrac{1}{2}(\psi^{N_1l_1}_{\mu_1\sigma_1}(1)\cdots\psi^{N_nl_n}_{\mu_n\sigma_n}(n), \sum_{i\neq k}\mathbf{W}_{ik}\sum_{T}\varepsilon_T\mathbf{O}_T\psi^{N_1l_1}_{\mu_1\sigma_1}(1)\cdots\psi^{N_nl_n}_{\mu_n\sigma_n}(n)),$$

where $\mathbf{W}$ is resolved into a sum of terms $\mathbf{W}_{ik}$ which correspond to the interactions between the individual pairs of electrons.

We consider the term for one particular $\mathbf{W}_{ik}$. When written out in detail it is

$$\begin{aligned}\sum_{T}\sum_{s_1\cdots s_n}\int\cdots\int &\psi^{N_1l_1}_{\mu_1\sigma_1}(1)^*\cdots\psi^{N_nl_n}_{\mu_n\sigma_n}(n)^* \\ &\cdot\mathbf{W}_{ik}\varepsilon_T\mathbf{O}_T\psi^{N_1l_1}_{\mu_1\sigma_1}(1)\cdots\psi^{N_nl_n}_{\mu_n\sigma_n}(n)\,dx_1\cdots dz_n.\end{aligned} \tag{25.20}$$

If T in this affects not only the ith and the kth electrons (i.e., T is neither the identity nor the transposition (ik)) but transforms, say, j into j', then (25.20) vanishes upon integration over x_j, y_j, z_j and summation over s_j because of the orthogonality of the eigenfunctions $\psi^{N_jl_j}_{\mu_j\sigma_j}$ and $\psi^{N_{j'}l_{j'}}_{\mu_{j'}\sigma_{j'}}$, since in an *allowed* configuration one cannot have $N_j = N_{j'}$; $l_j = l_{j'}$, $\mu_j = \mu_{j'}$, and

$\sigma_j = \sigma_{j'}$ all at the same time. Thus when calculating the $\mathbf{W}_{ik}$ term, it suffices to let T become equal to the identity and the transposition (ik). In both cases integration over the Cartesian coordinates and summation over the spin coordinates of all electrons different from i and k gives a factor 1, and (25.20) becomes

$$\sum_{s_i, s_k} \int \cdots \int \psi^{N_i l_i}_{\mu_i \sigma_i}(i) \psi^{N_k l_k}_{\mu_k \sigma_k}(k) \mathbf{W}_{ik} \Big[\psi^{N_i l_i}_{\mu_i \sigma_i}(i) \psi^{N_k l_k}_{\mu_k \sigma_k}(k) - \psi^{N_k l_k}_{\mu_k \sigma_k}(i) \psi^{N_i l_i}_{\mu_i \sigma_i}(k) \Big] dx_i dy_i dz_i dx_k dy_k dz_k. \tag{25.20a}$$

If we substitute $\psi^{N_i l_i}_{\mu_i \sigma_i}(i) = \psi^{N_i l_i}_{\mu_i}(\mathfrak{r}_i) \delta_{s_i \sigma_i}$, etc., into this ($\mathfrak{r}_i$ stands for the cartesian coordinates x_i, y_i, z_i of the ith electron), the summation over s_i, s_k can be carried out, and we obtain

$$\int \cdots \int \psi^{N_i l_i}_{\mu_i}(\mathfrak{r}_i) \psi^{N_k l_k}_{\mu_k}(\mathfrak{r}_k) \mathbf{W}_{ik} \Big[\psi^{N_i l_i}_{\mu_i}(\mathfrak{r}_i) \psi^{N_k l_k}_{\mu_k}(\mathfrak{r}_k) - \delta_{\sigma_i \sigma_k} \psi^{N_k l_k}_{\mu_k}(\mathfrak{r}_i) \psi^{N_i l_i}_{\mu_i}(\mathfrak{r}_k) \Big] dx_i dy_i dz_i dx_k dy_k dz_k. \tag{25.21}$$

By adding the integrals (25.21) for all $\binom{n}{2}$ pairs ik and all allowed configurations $(N_1 l_1 \mu_1 \sigma_1)$ $(N_2 l_2 \mu_2 \sigma_2) \cdots (N_n l_n \mu_n \sigma_n)$ for which $\mu_1 + \mu_2 + \cdots + \mu_n = \mu$ and $\sigma_1 + \sigma_2 + \cdots \sigma_n = 2\nu$, we obtain the sums (25.18) of the perturbation energies of all levels arising from (25.E.4) for which $S \geq |\nu|$ and $L \geq |\mu|$. Then (25.18a) gives the first approximation to the energy change, summed for all levels with a given S and L.

Regarding further details of the calculation, in particular the evaluation of the integrals (25.21), which can be done without explicit calculation in certain cases, the reader must refer to the original work of Slater.[4] He will also find interesting numerical examples presented there.

26. Time Inversion

Time Inversion and Antiunitary Operators

The symmetry group of an isolated system contains, in addition to the rotations and reflections considered in the previous chapters, displacements in space and time as well as transitions to a moving coordinate system.[1] The number of the states of such a system is infinitely large and the energy operator has a continuous spectrum. This point was brought out earlier in Chapter 17. From the infinite set of all states a finite manifold of states can be selected: those with zero linear momentum and definite energy. The restriction to states with zero linear momentum corresponds to the point of view of spectroscopy, where one is concerned only with the *internal energy* of atomic or molecular systems, not with their kinetic energy. As a matter of fact, the accuracy of spectroscopic measurements is frequently limited by the motion of the atoms or molecules; in such cases every effort is made to reduce the velocity of motion as much as possible.

The restriction to zero linear momentum eliminates the transformations to moving coordinate systems. It also effectively eliminates the displacement operators: the wave function of a particle with zero linear momentum is invariant under spatial displacements and a displacement in time by t multiplies it by the rather trivial factor $\exp(-iEt/\hbar)$ where E is the energy of the state. Alternately, as was mentioned before, the postulate of zero linear momentum can be replaced by the assumption of a static external field, such as the field of a fixed nucleus. This also eliminates the translational symmetry and the transition to moving coordinate systems as symmetry elements. In any case, it appears that our problem has no relevant symmetry elements apart from those already considered. This, however, is not entirely true: the transformation $t \rightarrow -t$ remains an additional symmetry element. It transforms a state φ into the state $\boldsymbol{\theta}\varphi$ in which all velocities (including the "spinning" of the electrons) have opposite directions to those in φ. (Hence, "reversal of the direction of motion" is perhaps a more felicitous, though longer, expression than "time inversion.") The relation between time inversion and the change which the lapse of time induces in a system is of great importance. The time behavior is described by the second Schrödinger equation

$$\partial\varphi/\partial t = -(i/\hbar)\mathbf{H}\varphi. \tag{26.1}$$

[1] The discussion of this and of the following section largely follows the author's article in *Göttinger Nachrichten, Math-Phys.* p. 546 (1932). See also G. Lüders, *Z. Physik.* **133,** 325 (1952).

Let us denote the stationary states and the corresponding energy values by Ψ_k and E_k. Then, in the course of the time interval t the state $\varphi_0 = \sum_k a_k \Psi_k$ changes into

$$\varphi_0 = \sum_k a_k \Psi_k \rightarrow \varphi_t = \sum_k a_k e^{-iE_k t/\hbar} \Psi_k. \tag{26.1a}$$

The transformation described by (26.1a) will be called "time displacement by t." It is a unitary operation.

The following four operations, carried out in succession on an arbitrary state, will result in the system returning to its original state. The first operation is time inversion, the second time displacement by t, the third again time inversion, and the last one again time displacement by t. The four operations, taken together, restore the system to its original state because the lapse of time, after a time inversion, actually pushes the system back in time. The two time inversions, on the other hand, compensate as far as direction of velocities is concerned. We can say, therefore, that

(time displacement by t) $\times$ (time inversion) $\times$ (time displacement by t) $\times$ (time inversion)

is equivalent to the unit operation. Alternatively,

(time displacement by t) $\times$ (time inversion)
= (time inversion) $\times$ (time displacement by $-t$) (26.1b)

and the operators which correspond to the two sides of (26.1b) can differ, at most, by a numerical factor of modulus 1 which has no physical significance.

Since $\mathbf{\theta}$ is a symmetry operator, it leaves the transition probability between any two states Ψ and Φ invariant:

$$|(\Psi, \Phi)| = |(\mathbf{\theta}\Psi, \mathbf{\theta}\Phi)|. \tag{26.2}$$

It then follows from the Appendix to Chapter 20 that $\mathbf{\theta}$ can be so normalized that it satisfies one of the two equations (20.29). The discussion of the Appendix to Chapter 20 already indicates that it satisfies the *second* alternative, the one which could be excluded for all purely spatial symmetry operations. This can be inferred also from (26.1a) but can be seen more directly by pursuing the trend of thought of the Appendix. The demonstration becomes simplest if the set of orthogonal functions $\Psi_1, \Psi_2, \cdots$ is identified with the eigenfunctions of the Hamiltonian; the Ψ_i are then the stationary states. The $\mathbf{\theta}\Psi_i$ are also stationary states and Ψ_i and $\mathbf{\theta}\Psi_i$ are associated with the same energy value.

If the first alternative of (20.29) also applied for $\mathbf{\theta}$, it would be a linear operator. This leads to a contradiction, and it follows that the second alternative of (20.29) applies for $\mathbf{\theta}$. In order to arrive at the contradiction, let us consider again an arbitrary state Φ_0 and expand it in terms of the stationary states.

$$\Phi_0 = \Sigma\, a_\varkappa \Psi_\varkappa. \tag{26.3}$$

The assumed linear character of $\boldsymbol{\theta}$ leads to

$$\boldsymbol{\theta}\Phi_0 = \Sigma\, a_\varkappa \boldsymbol{\theta}\Psi_\varkappa, \tag{26.3a}$$

and since $\boldsymbol{\theta}\Psi_\varkappa$ is also a stationary state whose energy is $E_\varkappa$, it will go over in the time interval t into $\exp(-iE_\varkappa t/\hbar)\boldsymbol{\theta}\Psi_\varkappa$. Hence, the state $\boldsymbol{\theta}\Phi_0$ will become after a time t the state

$$\Sigma\, a_\varkappa e^{-iE_\varkappa t/\hbar}\boldsymbol{\theta}\Psi_\varkappa. \tag{26.3b}$$

This must be the same state which is obtained by $\boldsymbol{\theta}$ from

$$\Phi_{-t} = \Sigma\, a_\varkappa e^{iE_\varkappa t/\hbar}\Psi_\varkappa.$$

If $\boldsymbol{\theta}$ is linear this state is

$$\boldsymbol{\theta}\Phi_{-t} = \Sigma\, a_\varkappa e^{iE_\varkappa t/\hbar}\boldsymbol{\theta}\Psi_\varkappa \tag{26.3c}$$

and this is, in general, not a constant multiple of (26.3b) because the exponents have the wrong sign. Hence, the assumption that $\boldsymbol{\theta}$ is linear leads to a contradiction and $\boldsymbol{\theta}$ must satisfy the second alternative of (20.29); that is, $\boldsymbol{\theta}\Phi_0$ must be, apart from a constant factor, equal to

$$\frac{a_1}{a_1^*}(a_1^*\boldsymbol{\theta}\Psi_1 + a_2^*\boldsymbol{\theta}\Psi_2 + a_3^*\boldsymbol{\theta}\Psi_3 + \cdots).$$

Since we can freely dispose of a constant factor in the definition of $\boldsymbol{\theta}\Phi_0$, we choose this equal to a_1^*/a_1 so that

$$\boldsymbol{\theta}\Phi_0 = \boldsymbol{\theta}(\Sigma\, a_\varkappa\Psi_\varkappa) = \Sigma\, a_\varkappa^*\boldsymbol{\theta}\Psi_\varkappa. \tag{26.4}$$

An operator which satisfies (26.4) for any set of $a_1, a_2, \cdots$ and a given complete orthogonal set $\Psi_\varkappa$ will be called *antilinear*. It will then satisfy a similar equation with respect to any set of functions. In particular, if $\Phi_1 = \Sigma\, b_\varkappa \Psi_\varkappa$, we have

$$\alpha\Phi_0 + \beta\Phi_1 = \alpha\Sigma\, a_\varkappa\Psi_\varkappa + \beta\,\Sigma\, b_\varkappa\Psi_\varkappa = \Sigma\,(\alpha a_\varkappa + \beta b_\varkappa)\Psi_\varkappa$$

so that

$$\begin{aligned}\boldsymbol{\theta}(\alpha\Phi_0 + \beta\Phi_1) &= \boldsymbol{\theta}(\Sigma\,(\alpha a_\varkappa + \beta b_\varkappa)\Psi_\varkappa) = \Sigma\,(\alpha a_\varkappa + \beta b_\varkappa)^*\boldsymbol{\theta}\Psi_\varkappa \\ &= \alpha^*\,\Sigma\, a_\varkappa^*\boldsymbol{\theta}\Psi_\varkappa + \beta^*\,\Sigma\, b_\varkappa^*\boldsymbol{\theta}\Psi_\varkappa = \alpha^*\boldsymbol{\theta}\Phi_0 + \beta^*\boldsymbol{\theta}\Phi_1.\end{aligned}$$

This last equation,

$$\boldsymbol{\theta}(\alpha\Phi_0 + \beta\Phi_1) = \alpha^*\boldsymbol{\theta}\Phi_0 + \beta^*\boldsymbol{\theta}\Phi_1, \tag{26.5}$$

which is valid for any Φ_0, Φ_1 and any two numbers α, β, is the usual definition of an antilinear operator. It follows from the fact that the second alternative of (20.29) is valid for the time inversion operator $\boldsymbol{\theta}$, and from the normalization (26.4) adopted for $\boldsymbol{\theta}(\sum a_\varkappa \Psi_\varkappa)$. In addition to being antilinear, $\boldsymbol{\theta}$ satisfies (26.2) for any pair of functions. An operator which satisfies (26.2) and (26.5) will be called *antiunitary* and a normal form for antiunitary operators will be derived.

The simplest antiunitary operation is the transition to the conjugate complex. This operation will be denoted by $\mathbf{K}$. The effect of $\mathbf{K}$ is to replace the expression following it by its conjugate complex

$$\mathbf{K}\varphi = \varphi^*. \tag{26.6}$$

The operator $\mathbf{K}$ is clearly antilinear. Since

$$(\mathbf{K}\Psi, \mathbf{K}\Phi) = (\Psi^*, \Phi^*) = (\Psi, \Phi)^*, \tag{26.6a}$$

$\mathbf{K}$ also satisfies (26.2). It is, therefore, antiunitary. It has one further important property;

$$\mathbf{K}^2 = 1. \tag{26.6b}$$

Indeed,

$$\mathbf{K}^2\Phi = \mathbf{K}(\mathbf{K}\Phi) = \mathbf{K}\Phi^* = (\Phi^*)^* = \Phi.$$

Let us consider the product $\mathbf{U} = \boldsymbol{\theta}\mathbf{K}$ of an antiunitary operator $\boldsymbol{\theta}$, and $\mathbf{K}$. This is linear.

$$\begin{aligned}\mathbf{U}(\alpha\Phi_0 + \beta\Phi_1) &= \boldsymbol{\theta}\mathbf{K}(\alpha\Phi_0 + \beta\Phi_1) = \boldsymbol{\theta}(\alpha^*\Phi_0^* + \beta^*\Phi_1^*) \\ &= \alpha\boldsymbol{\theta}\Phi_0^* + \beta\boldsymbol{\theta}\Phi_1^* = \alpha\boldsymbol{\theta}\mathbf{K}\Phi_0 + \beta\boldsymbol{\theta}\mathbf{K}\Phi_1 = \alpha\mathbf{U}\Phi_0 + \beta\mathbf{U}\Phi_1.\end{aligned}$$

Furthermore, $\boldsymbol{\theta}\mathbf{K}$ leaves the absolute value of a scalar product invariant because both its factors have this property. It therefore satisfies the assumptions of the appendix to Chapter 20 with the *first* alternative in (20.29) and hence is unitary. It follows that *every antiunitary operator*, in particular also $\boldsymbol{\theta}$, *can be written as the product of a unitary operator and the operator* $\mathbf{K}$ *of complex conjugation*

$$\boldsymbol{\theta}\mathbf{K} = \mathbf{U}; \quad \boldsymbol{\theta} = \mathbf{U}\mathbf{K}. \tag{26.7}$$

This is the normal form of antiunitary operators. It implies that $\boldsymbol{\theta}$ satisfies (26.4) and (26.5) and also that

$$(\boldsymbol{\theta}\Phi, \boldsymbol{\theta}\Psi) = (\mathbf{U}\mathbf{K}\Phi, \mathbf{U}\mathbf{K}\Psi) = (\mathbf{K}\Phi, \mathbf{K}\Psi)$$

so that (26.6a) is valid for any antiunitary operator

$$(\boldsymbol{\theta}\Phi, \boldsymbol{\theta}\Psi) = (\Phi, \Psi)^* = (\Psi, \Phi). \tag{26.8}$$

Let us note next that the product of two antiunitary operators is unitary

$$\mathbf{U}_1\mathbf{K}\mathbf{U}_2\mathbf{K}\Phi = \mathbf{U}_1\mathbf{K}\mathbf{U}_2\Phi^* = \mathbf{U}_1(\mathbf{U}_2\Phi^*)^* = \mathbf{U}_1\mathbf{U}_2^*\Phi$$

or

$$\mathbf{U}_1\mathbf{K}\mathbf{U}_2\mathbf{K} = \mathbf{U}_1\mathbf{U}_2^*. \tag{26.9}$$

Similarly, the product of a unitary and an antiunitary operator is antiunitary.

The operator of time inversion has an additional important property: though $\mathbf{\theta}\Phi$ is, in general, not the same state as Φ, the state $\mathbf{\theta}^2\Phi = \mathbf{\theta\theta}\Phi$ is the same state as Φ. Hence, $\mathbf{\theta}^2\Phi$ can differ from Φ only by a constant factor. This factor will be shown to be either $+1$ or -1. If one writes $\mathbf{\theta} = \mathbf{UK}$,

$$\mathbf{\theta}^2 = \mathbf{UKUK} = \mathbf{UU}^* = c\mathbf{1}. \tag{26.10}$$

Because of the unitary nature of $\mathbf{U}$, we have $\mathbf{UU}^\dagger = \mathbf{1}$ so that (26.10) implies $\mathbf{U}^* = c\mathbf{U}^\dagger$ or $\mathbf{U} = c\mathbf{U}'$. The transpose of this is $\mathbf{U}' = c\mathbf{U}$ so that $\mathbf{U} = c\mathbf{U}' = c^2\mathbf{U}$. This again gives $c = \pm 1$, so that $\mathbf{U}$ can be either symmetric or skew symmetric and

$$\mathbf{\theta}^2 = \pm\mathbf{1}. \tag{26.10a}$$

The reader will recognize the argument used before, at (24.3b). We shall find later that the upper sign applies in the simple Schrödinger theory and in the theory which takes the spin into account if the number of electrons is even. The lower sign applies in the theory which takes the spin into account if the number of electrons, or more generally, the number of particles with half-integral spin, is odd.

The relation (26.10a) holds only for the time inversion itself, not for the product of the time inversion with another symmetry operation. It is a consequence of the involutional nature[2] of the physical operation of time inversion that the succession of two time inversions restores the original state. The equation $\mathbf{\theta}^2 = c\mathbf{1}$ expresses this fact. However, the fact that c can be only 1 or -1 is a mathematical consequence of the antiunitary nature of $\mathbf{\theta}$. The situation is quite different from the one encountered for rotations. If R is a rotation by π, it is involutional as a physical operation. Nevertheless, $\mathbf{O}_R^2$ could be any multiple of the unit matrix of modulus 1. Since a factor is free in $\mathbf{O}_R$, it would be possible to normalize it so that $\mathbf{O}_R^2 = 1$. Actually, the normalization carried out in Chapter 20 renders $\mathbf{O}_R^2 = 1$ if the number of electrons is even, $\mathbf{O}_R^2 = -1$ if the number of electrons is odd. However, this is a result of normalization while Eq. (26.10a) is automatically fulfilled. In fact, the replacement of $\mathbf{\theta}$ by $\omega\mathbf{\theta}$ with $|\omega| = 1$ (which is quite permissible) does not change $\mathbf{\theta}^2$ at all; $\omega\mathbf{\theta}\omega\mathbf{\theta} = \omega\omega^*\mathbf{\theta\theta} = \mathbf{\theta}^2$.

Determination of the Time Inversion Operator

There are, from the point of view of time inversion, two important classes of physical quantities. The position coordinates, the total energy, and the kinetic energy belong to the first class. The probability for a certain value λ of any of these quantities is the same for φ and for $\mathbf{\theta}\varphi$, no matter what φ is. These quantities are either unrelated to time or contain an even power of the

[2] We call an operation an involution if its square is the unit operation.

time variable. As a result, the reversal of the direction of motion has no effect on these quantities. The velocity, linear and angular momenta, and the components of the spin in a given direction, belong to the second class of operators. If one of these has the value λ for φ, it has the value $-\lambda$ for $\boldsymbol{\theta}\varphi$. These quantities contain an odd power of the time variable. Naturally, there are physical quantities, such as a coordinate plus a velocity, which do not belong to either class. However, we shall not be concerned now with quantities of this nature.

The operators which correspond to quantities of the first class commute with $\boldsymbol{\theta}$. In fact, if $\mathbf{q}$ is such an operator, and $\varphi_\varkappa$ a state for which $\mathbf{q}$ has the value $\lambda_\varkappa$, then $\mathbf{q}\psi_\varkappa = \lambda_\varkappa\psi_\varkappa$. *Since* $\mathbf{q}$ *has the value* $\lambda_\varkappa$ *also for* $\boldsymbol{\theta}\psi_\varkappa$, *we have also* $\mathbf{q}\boldsymbol{\theta}\psi_\varkappa = \lambda_\varkappa\boldsymbol{\theta}\psi_\varkappa$. Hence, if φ is an arbitrary wave function $\varphi = \Sigma\, a_\varkappa\psi_\varkappa$, we have, since $\mathbf{q}$ is linear,

$$\boldsymbol{\theta}\mathbf{q}\varphi = \boldsymbol{\theta}\mathbf{q}\,\Sigma\, a_\varkappa\psi_\varkappa = \boldsymbol{\theta}\,\Sigma\, a_\varkappa\lambda_\varkappa\psi_\varkappa = \Sigma\, a_\varkappa^*\lambda_\varkappa\boldsymbol{\theta}\psi_\varkappa, \tag{26.11a}$$

since the $\lambda_\varkappa$ are real. On the other hand

$$\mathbf{q}\boldsymbol{\theta}\varphi = \mathbf{q}\boldsymbol{\theta}\,\Sigma\, a_\varkappa\psi_\varkappa = \mathbf{q}\,\Sigma\, a_\varkappa^*\boldsymbol{\theta}\psi_\varkappa = \Sigma\, a_\varkappa^*\mathbf{q}\boldsymbol{\theta}\psi_\varkappa = \Sigma\, a_\varkappa^*\lambda_\varkappa\boldsymbol{\theta}\psi_\varkappa. \tag{26.11b}$$

It follows that if $\mathbf{q}$ is an operator of the first class

$$\boxed{\boldsymbol{\theta}\mathbf{q} = \mathbf{q}\boldsymbol{\theta}.} \tag{26.11}$$

On the other hand, if $\mathbf{p}$ is an operator of the second class, the same argument leads to

$$\boxed{\boldsymbol{\theta}\mathbf{p} = -\mathbf{p}\boldsymbol{\theta},} \tag{26.12}$$

and $\boldsymbol{\theta}$ anticommutes with these operators. The foregoing argument is rigorous only if $\mathbf{q}$ and $\mathbf{p}$ have point spectra, but (26.11) and (26.12) can be shown to be valid for all operators of the first and second class, respectively.

Let us consider first the simple Schrödinger theory which disregards the spin. If we write $\boldsymbol{\theta} = \mathbf{UK}$, we have from $\boldsymbol{\theta}x = x\boldsymbol{\theta}$ where x is any one of the positional coordinates

$$\mathbf{UK}x\varphi = \mathbf{U}x\varphi^* = x\mathbf{UK}\varphi = x\mathbf{U}\varphi^* \tag{26.13}$$

so that $\mathbf{U}$ commutes with the operation of *multiplication* with any of the positional coordinates. Since the momentum operators $(\hbar/i)\;\partial/\partial x$ belong in the second class of operators, we have from (26.12)

$$\begin{aligned}\mathbf{UK}(\hbar/i)\;\partial\varphi/\partial x &= -(\hbar/i)\mathbf{U}\;\partial\varphi^*/\partial x\\ &= -(\hbar/i)(\partial/\partial x)\mathbf{UK}\varphi = -(\hbar/i)\;\partial(\mathbf{U}\varphi^*)/\partial x.\end{aligned} \tag{26.13a}$$

The i in the operator for the momenta compensates the minus sign in (26.12) and $\mathbf{U}$ commutes also with the operation of *differentiation* with respect to any of the positional coordinates. One can conclude from this that $\mathbf{U}$ must be simply multiplication with a constant of modulus 1. Since this constant can be chosen arbitrarily, we set it equal to 1 and obtain for the theory which disregards the spin

$$\mathbf{\theta} = \mathbf{K}; \quad \mathbf{\theta}\varphi = \varphi^*. \tag{26.14}$$

This shows that the wave functions of the stationary states can all be chosen to be real—a rather obvious conclusion in this case since the Hamiltonian operator is real. It may be well to note, however, that (26.14) applies only if the positional and momentum operators are assumed in the form x and $(\hbar/i)\partial/\partial x$ (see Chapter 4). If one uses "momentum coordinates" and substitutes $i\hbar\ \partial/\partial p$ for the positional coordinates and multiplication with the variables p in the wave function for the momentum coordinates, $\mathbf{\theta}$ becomes $\mathbf{UK}$ where $\mathbf{U}$ is not the unit operator but substitution of $-p$ for p

$$\mathbf{U}\varphi(-p_1, -p_2, \cdots, -p_f) = \varphi(p_1, p_2, \cdots, p_f). \tag{26.14a}$$

Let us now consider the theory which takes the spin into account. The operator $\mathbf{U}$ must satisfy (26.13) and (26.13a) in this case also, but these equations do not suffice to determine $\mathbf{U}$ completely; they only show that $\mathbf{U}$ does not act on the cartesian (positional) coordinates; it may yet act on the spin coordinates. It has, in this regard, a character opposite to that of the spin-free operators of Chapter 20. In order to determine $\mathbf{\theta} = \mathbf{UK}$ completely, it is necessary to consider the behavior of the spin variables $\mathbf{s}_{1x}, \mathbf{s}_{1y}, \mathbf{s}_{1z}, \cdots,$ $\mathbf{s}_{nx}, \mathbf{s}_{ny}, \mathbf{s}_{nz}$ under time inversion. The spin variables belong, as angular momenta, to the second class of operators so that they anticommute with $\mathbf{\theta}$. Since the $\mathbf{s}_{ix}$ are all real, we have for all $i = 1,2, \cdots n$,

$$\mathbf{\theta}\mathbf{s}_{ix} = \mathbf{UK}\mathbf{s}_{ix} = \mathbf{U}\mathbf{s}_{ix}\mathbf{K}.$$

This must be equal to $-\mathbf{s}_{ix}\mathbf{\theta} = -\mathbf{s}_{ix}\mathbf{UK}$ so that $\mathbf{s}_{ix}$ *anticommutes* with $\mathbf{U}$. The same is true of the $\mathbf{s}_{iz}$ which are also real. On the other hand, the imaginary $\mathbf{s}_{iy}$ *commute* with $\mathbf{U}$. Hence

$$\mathbf{U}\mathbf{s}_{ix} = -\mathbf{s}_{ix}\mathbf{U}, \quad \mathbf{U}\mathbf{s}_{iy} = \mathbf{s}_{iy}\mathbf{U}, \quad \mathbf{U}\mathbf{s}_{iz} = -\mathbf{s}_{iz}\mathbf{U}. \tag{26.13b}$$

An operator which satisfies these requirements is the product of all the imaginary spin operators,

$$\mathbf{U} = \mathbf{s}_{1y}\mathbf{s}_{2y} \cdots \mathbf{s}_{ny}. \tag{26.15}$$

This is, in fact, except for multiples of $\mathbf{U}$, the only spin-free operator which satisfies any two of the equations (26.13b). Let us assume that there is a second solution $\mathbf{U}_1\mathbf{U}$ of these equations. It then follows that $\mathbf{U}_1$ must commute with all $\mathbf{s}_{ix}, \mathbf{s}_{iy}, \mathbf{s}_{iz}$ and hence also with

$$c_1\mathbf{s}_{1z} + c_2\mathbf{s}_{2z} + \cdots + c_n\mathbf{s}_{nz} \tag{26.E.1}$$

for all values of c. A matrix which commutes with all these matrices is, however, a diagonal matrix since, for a proper choice of the c, no two diagonal elements of (26.E.1) are equal. On the other hand, no matrix element of

$$(\mathbf{s}_{1y} + \mathbf{s}_{1z})(\mathbf{s}_{2y} + \mathbf{s}_{2z}) \cdots (\mathbf{s}_{ny} + \mathbf{s}_{nz}) \tag{26.E.2}$$

vanishes so that only a constant matrix commutes with both (26.E.1) and (26.E.2). Since a constant is yet free in $\boldsymbol{\theta}$, we can write

$$\boldsymbol{\theta} = \mathbf{s}_{1y}\, \mathbf{s}_{2y} \cdots \mathbf{s}_{ny}\mathbf{K}, \tag{26.15a}$$

or

$$\boldsymbol{\theta}\Phi(x_1, y_1, z_1, s_1, \cdots, x_n, y_n, z_n, s_n)$$
$$= i^{-s_1-s_2\cdots-s_n}\Phi(x_1, y_1, z_1, -s_1, \cdots, x_n, y_n, z_n, -s_n)^* \tag{26.15b}$$

One easily verifies the fact that $\boldsymbol{\theta}^2 = 1$ if n is even, $\boldsymbol{\theta}^2 = -1$ if n is odd. There is an alternative form for the operator $\boldsymbol{\theta}$ which follows from the remark that $\mathfrak{D}^{(1/2)}(\{0, \pi, 0\}) = i\mathbf{s}_y$. Since $\mathbf{Q}_{\{0,\pi,0\}}$ consists of the application of $\mathfrak{D}^{(1/2)}(\{0, \pi, 0\})$ to every spin variable, comparison with (26.15a) shows that

$$\boldsymbol{\theta} = (-i)^n \mathbf{Q}_{\{0,\pi,0\}}\mathbf{K}. \tag{26.15c}$$

Finally, let us derive the relations between products of the time inversion operator $\boldsymbol{\theta}$ and the unitary operators $\mathbf{O}_R$ or $\mathbf{O}_\mathbf{u}$ which correspond to rotations of the coordinate system. Since rotations and time inversion commute as physical operations, $\mathbf{O}_R\boldsymbol{\theta}$ and $\boldsymbol{\theta}\mathbf{O}_R$ can differ only by a constant factor c_R which may, however, depend on R. Hence

$$\boldsymbol{\theta}^{-1}\mathbf{O}_R\boldsymbol{\theta} = c_R\mathbf{O}_R \quad \text{or} \quad \boldsymbol{\theta}^{-1}\mathbf{O}_\mathbf{u}\boldsymbol{\theta} = c_\mathbf{u}\mathbf{O}_\mathbf{u}. \tag{26.16}$$

The product of two of these equations gives, because of $\mathbf{O}_R\mathbf{O}_S = \mathbf{O}_{RS}$,

$$c_Rc_S\mathbf{O}_{RS} = \boldsymbol{\theta}^{-1}\mathbf{O}_R\boldsymbol{\theta}\boldsymbol{\theta}^{-1}\mathbf{O}_S\boldsymbol{\theta} = \boldsymbol{\theta}^{-1}\mathbf{O}_{RS}\boldsymbol{\theta} = c_{RS}\mathbf{O}_{RS}. \tag{26.16a}$$

Hence, the numbers c_R form a representation of the rotation group (or of the two-dimensional unimodular unitary group of the $\mathbf{u}$). Since the only one-dimensional representation of the proper rotation group or of the unitary group is the identical representation $c_R = 1$,

$$\mathbf{O}_R\boldsymbol{\theta} = \boldsymbol{\theta}\mathbf{O}_R \quad \text{or} \quad \mathbf{O}_\mathbf{u}\boldsymbol{\theta} = \boldsymbol{\theta}\mathbf{O}_\mathbf{u} \tag{26.17}$$

for all proper rotations. This equation can be verified also by direct calculation; it is equivalent with the equation

$$\mathfrak{D}^{(1/2)}(R)\mathbf{s}_y - \mathbf{s}_y\mathfrak{D}^{(1/2)}(R)^*. \tag{20.17a}$$

The preceding argument does not exclude the possibility that the two sides of (26.17) are equal in magnitude but have opposite signs if R is an improper rotation. In the corresponding representation (c_R) of the full rotation group, (1) corresponds to all proper rotations, (—1) to rotations with determinant —1. However, one easily verifies that (26.17) is valid also for the operator $\mathbf{O}_I$ of space inversion. It is, therefore, valid for all symmetry operations considered before.

Naturally, the considerations of this section do not prove that the quantum mechanical equations are invariant under the operation of time inversion. They do show, however, that if they are, the time inversion operator $\boldsymbol{\theta} = \mathbf{UK}$ must be given, within a constant factor, by (26.14) or (26.15a) in the framework of the simple theory, or that given in Chapter 20, respectively.

Transformation of the Eigenfunctions under Antiunitary Operators

Time inversion symmetry has no far-reaching consequences in the theory of atomic spectra. It provides a much more powerful tool in the investigation of systems of lower symmetry, such as polyatomic molecules or atoms in a crystal. As a matter of fact, the transformation (26.15) was first recognized in the course of an investigation of the rotation of the plane of polarization,[3] a phenomenon exhibited by systems without any symmetry plane. It is important, however, to recognize that the theory of group representations by linear transformations does not provide the complete mathematical framework for the treatment of a symmetry group which contains antiunitary operators, and it will be necessary to repeat some of the considerations of Chapter 11.

As was pointed out before, most explicitly when dealing with the Stark effect in Chapter 23, the group to be considered when deriving the consequences of the symmetry of a problem is not the group of the physical transformations, but the group of the quantum mechanical operators which correspond to these transformations. If the number of electrons is odd, the quantum mechanical operators which correspond to rotations are isomorphic to the group of two-dimensional unimodular unitary transformations $\mathbf{u}$ and only homomorphic to the group of rotations. Similarly, $\boldsymbol{\theta}^2$ corresponds, in this case, not to $\mathbf{u} = \mathbf{1}$ but to $\mathbf{u} = -\mathbf{1}$. The whole group consists of the transformations $\mathbf{O}_{\mathbf{u}}$ and $\boldsymbol{\theta}\mathbf{O}_{\mathbf{u}}$, the former unitary, the latter antiunitary. The multiplication rules are

$$\mathbf{O}_{\mathbf{v}}\mathbf{O}_{\mathbf{u}} = \mathbf{O}_{\mathbf{vu}}, \qquad \boldsymbol{\theta}\mathbf{O}_{\mathbf{v}} \cdot \mathbf{O}_{\mathbf{u}} = \boldsymbol{\theta}\mathbf{O}_{\mathbf{vu}},$$
$$\mathbf{O}_{\mathbf{v}} \cdot \boldsymbol{\theta}\mathbf{O}_{\mathbf{u}} = \boldsymbol{\theta}\mathbf{O}_{\mathbf{vu}}, \qquad \boldsymbol{\theta}\mathbf{O}_{\mathbf{v}} \cdot \boldsymbol{\theta}\mathbf{O}_{\mathbf{u}} = \mathbf{O}_{\pm\mathbf{vu}}. \tag{26.18}$$

The last two equations follow from (26.17) and the upper or lower sign holds in the last equation for even and odd electron numbers, respectively. The

[3] H. A. Kramers, *Koninkl. Ned. Akad. Wetenschap., Proc.* **33,** 959 (1930). The full significance of time inversion symmetry in classical theory was recognized only lately by H. Zocher and C. Török, *Proc. Natl. Acad. Sci. U.S.* **39,** 681 (1953).

multiplication rules (26.18) show that the unitary operators form a subgroup, in fact a normal subgroup of index 2, and that the antiunitary operators constitute the coset of this subgroup. The same is true of all groups which contain both unitary and antiunitary operators.

Let us review now the developments of Chapter 11 starting with Section 5. Equation (11.23) will be valid also for the antiunitary operators $\mathbf{\theta O_u}$ as it only expresses the fact that $\mathbf{\theta O_u}\psi_\varkappa$ is an eigenfunction if $\psi_\varkappa$ is:

$$\mathbf{\theta O_u}\psi_\varkappa = \sum_\lambda \mathbf{D}(\mathbf{\theta O_u})_{\lambda\varkappa}\psi_\lambda. \tag{26.19}$$

It will be true, furthermore, that $\mathbf{D}(\mathbf{\theta O_u})$ will be unitary if the $\psi_\varkappa$ are orthonormal. This is a consequence of the fact that, as a result of (26.8),

$$(\mathbf{\theta O_u}\psi_\varkappa, \mathbf{\theta O_u}\psi_\lambda) = (\mathbf{O_u}\psi_\lambda, \mathbf{O_u}\psi_\varkappa) = (\psi_\lambda, \psi_\varkappa) = \delta_{\lambda\varkappa} \tag{26.20}$$

holds, just as for unitary operators. The unitary character of $\mathbf{D}$, (Eq. (11.32)) was a direct consequence of the corresponding equation for unitary operators.

The product of the matrices $\mathbf{D}(\mathbf{\theta O_v})$ and $\mathbf{D}(\mathbf{O_u})$ or $\mathbf{D}(\mathbf{\theta O_u})$ will not be $\mathbf{D}(\mathbf{\theta O_v O_u}) = \mathbf{D}(\mathbf{\theta O_{vu}})$ or $\mathbf{D}(\mathbf{\theta O_v \theta O_u}) = \mathbf{D}(\mathbf{O_{\pm uv}})$ any more. In particular, if one applies $\mathbf{\theta O_v}$ to (26.19), one has, because of its antiunitary nature,

$$\mathbf{\theta O_v \theta O_u}\psi_\varkappa = \sum_\lambda \mathbf{\theta O_v D}(\mathbf{\theta O_u})_{\lambda\varkappa}\psi_\lambda = \sum_\lambda \mathbf{D}(\mathbf{\theta O_u})^*_{\lambda\varkappa}\mathbf{\theta O_v}\psi_\lambda$$
$$= \sum_{\lambda\mu} \mathbf{D}(\mathbf{\theta O_u})^*_{\lambda\varkappa}\mathbf{D}(\mathbf{\theta O_v})_{\mu\lambda}\psi_\mu,$$

so that

$$\mathbf{D}(\mathbf{\theta O_v})\mathbf{D}(\mathbf{\theta O_u})^* = \mathbf{D}(\mathbf{\theta O_v \theta O_u}) = \mathbf{D}(\mathbf{O_{\pm vu}}). \tag{26.21a}$$

Similarly,

$$\mathbf{D}(\mathbf{\theta O_v})\mathbf{D}(\mathbf{O_u})^* = \mathbf{D}(\mathbf{\theta O_v O_u}) = \mathbf{D}(\mathbf{\theta O_{vu}}) \tag{26.21b}$$

so that the matrices $\mathbf{D}(\mathbf{O_u})$, $\mathbf{D}(\mathbf{\theta O_u})$ do not form a representation of the group of the operators any more. The product relations which are valid for representations

$$\mathbf{D}(\mathbf{O_v})\mathbf{D}(\mathbf{O_u}) = \mathbf{D}(\mathbf{O_v O_u}) = \mathbf{D}(\mathbf{O_{vu}}) \tag{26.21c}$$

$$\mathbf{D}(\mathbf{O_v})\mathbf{D}(\mathbf{\theta O_u}) = \mathbf{D}(\mathbf{O_v \theta O_u}) = \mathbf{D}(\mathbf{\theta O_{vu}}) \tag{26.21d}$$

hold only if the first factor corresponds to a unitary operator. Otherwise, the conjugate complex of the second $\mathbf{D}$ appears. A particular consequence of this is that

$$\mathbf{D}((\mathbf{\theta O_u})^{-1}) = (\mathbf{D}(\mathbf{\theta O_u})^*)^{-1} = \mathbf{D}(\mathbf{\theta O_u})'. \tag{26.22}$$

In particular, $\mathbf{D}(\mathbf{\theta O_u})$ is symmetric if $\mathbf{\theta O_u}$ is an antiunitary involution $(\mathbf{\theta O_u})^2 = \mathbf{1}$. This is true of the time inversion operator $\mathbf{\theta}$ itself if the number of electrons is even; it is true of $\mathbf{\theta O_u}$ for an odd number of electrons if $\mathbf{u}$ corresponds to a rotation by π so that $\mathbf{u}^2 = -1$.

If the ψ are replaced by new linear combinations

$$\psi'_\mu = \sum_\nu \boldsymbol{\alpha}_{\nu\mu}\psi_\nu, \qquad \psi_\varkappa = \sum_\lambda \boldsymbol{\beta}_{\lambda\varkappa}\psi'_\lambda$$

by means of a transformation $\boldsymbol{\alpha} = \boldsymbol{\beta}^{-1}$, the matrices $\mathbf{D}(\mathbf{O_u})$ which correspond to the unitary transformation $\mathbf{O_u}$ will be replaced, according to (11.30), by

$$\overline{\mathbf{D}}(\mathbf{O_u}) = \boldsymbol{\alpha}^{-1}\mathbf{D}(\mathbf{O_u})\boldsymbol{\alpha}. \tag{26.23a}$$

On the other hand

$$\boldsymbol{\theta}\mathbf{O_u}\psi'_\mu = \boldsymbol{\theta}\mathbf{O_u}\sum_\nu \boldsymbol{\alpha}_{\nu\mu}\psi_\nu = \sum_\nu \boldsymbol{\alpha}^*_{\nu\mu}\boldsymbol{\theta}\mathbf{O_u}\psi_\nu$$
$$= \sum_\nu\sum_\varkappa \boldsymbol{\alpha}^*_{\nu\mu}\mathbf{D}(\boldsymbol{\theta}\mathbf{O_u})_{\varkappa\nu}\psi_\varkappa = \sum_\nu\sum_\varkappa\sum_\lambda \boldsymbol{\alpha}^*_{\nu\mu}\mathbf{D}(\boldsymbol{\theta}\mathbf{O_u})_{\varkappa\nu}\boldsymbol{\beta}_{\lambda\varkappa}\psi'_\lambda$$

so that $\mathbf{D}(\boldsymbol{\theta}\mathbf{O_u})$ is replaced by

$$\overline{\mathbf{D}}(\boldsymbol{\theta}\mathbf{O_u}) = \boldsymbol{\alpha}^{-1}\mathbf{D}(\boldsymbol{\theta}\mathbf{O_u})\boldsymbol{\alpha}^*. \tag{26.23b}$$

This could have been inferred from (26.21a) or (26.21b) since the $\overline{\mathbf{D}}$ satisfies these equations only if the $\boldsymbol{\alpha}$ is replaced by $\boldsymbol{\alpha}^*$ in the transformation of the matrices which correspond to antiunitary transformations.

The sets of equations (26.21) and (26.23) show that the matrices which transform the eigenfunctions under the operations of a group do not form a representation of this group if the group contains antiunitary operators. The solutions of the equations (26.21) are not furnished directly by the theory of representations but must be obtained by a special calculation. In particular, it is not possible to eliminate the conjugate complex sign in (26.21a) and (26.21b) by a redefinition of the matrices $\mathbf{D}(\boldsymbol{\theta}\mathbf{O_u})$. By separating the real and imaginary parts—both in the wave functions and in the transformations—one could give these equations a more natural form. However, they can be handled more easily in the form given.

A matrix system $\mathbf{D}$ which satisfies the equations (26.21) is not a representation of the group of unitary and antiunitary operators $\mathbf{O_u}$ and $\boldsymbol{\theta}\mathbf{O_u}$ in the usual sense. Nevertheless, these are the equations which arise in the consideration of the invariance with respect to operations connected with time inversion. They will be called *corepresentations* to remind one of the conjugate complex signs in (26.21). Naturally the concept of corepresentations applies only to a group of operators some of which are antiunitary.

Reduction of Corepresentations

The present section constitutes the first step in the determination of the corepresentations, that is the solution of the equations (26.21). The problem will be treated in this and the next section as a mathematical one. In particular, it will not be assumed that the unitary operators $\mathbf{O_u}$ correspond to rotations nor that the antiunitary operators contain the time inversion. In order to simplify the notation, the unitary operators $\mathbf{O_u}$ will be denoted by $\mathbf{u}, \mathbf{u}_1, \mathbf{u}_2, \cdots$. They form an invariant subgroup which will be called *the unitary subgroup*. The irreducible representations of this subgroup will be assumed to be known; a typical irreducible representation, assumed to be in unitary form, will be denoted by $\mathbf{\Delta}(\mathbf{u})$. The antiunitary operators $\boldsymbol{\theta}\mathbf{O_u}$ will be denoted, more briefly, by $\mathbf{a}, \mathbf{a}_1, \mathbf{a}_2, \cdots$. The four equations (26.21) then read

$$\mathbf{D}(\mathbf{u}_1)\mathbf{D}(\mathbf{u}_2) = \mathbf{D}(\mathbf{u}_1\mathbf{u}_2), \qquad \mathbf{D}(\mathbf{u})\mathbf{D}(\mathbf{a}) = \mathbf{D}(\mathbf{ua}),$$
$$\mathbf{D}(\mathbf{a})\mathbf{D}(\mathbf{u})^* = \mathbf{D}(\mathbf{au}), \qquad \mathbf{D}(\mathbf{a}_1)\mathbf{D}(\mathbf{a}_2)^* = \mathbf{D}(\mathbf{a}_1\mathbf{a}_2). \tag{26.21}$$

Two solutions of (26.21) will be called equivalent if they can be transformed into each other by a unitary matrix α so that

$$\overline{\mathbf{D}}(\mathbf{u}) = \boldsymbol{\alpha}^{-1}\mathbf{D}(\mathbf{u})\boldsymbol{\alpha}$$
$$\overline{\mathbf{D}}(\mathbf{a}) = \boldsymbol{\alpha}^{-1}\mathbf{D}(\mathbf{a})\boldsymbol{\alpha}^* \tag{26.23}$$

and a solution of (26.21) will be called irreducible if it cannot be brought into the reduced form (9.E.2) by a transformation (26.23). A matrix $\mathbf{D}(\mathbf{u})$ remains unchanged if $\boldsymbol{\alpha} = \omega\mathbf{1}$ is a multiple of the unit matrix; $\mathbf{D}(\mathbf{a})$ however is multiplied by $\omega^{-1}\omega^* = \omega^{*2}$. Hence, two solutions of (26.21) are surely equivalent if their $\mathbf{D}(\mathbf{u})$ are the same and their $\mathbf{D}(\mathbf{a})$ differ by a common numerical factor. By fixing the common phase factor of the $\mathbf{D}(\mathbf{a})$, one fixes the phase factor of the wave functions which transform by $\mathbf{D}(\mathbf{a})$; a joint phase factor of all the wave functions which belong to the different rows of a representation remains free as far as the unitary symmetry operations are concerned. The calculations which follow can be made more transparent by assuming the existence of wave functions $\psi_1, \psi_2, \psi_3, \cdots, \psi_f$ which transform, under suitable operators $\mathbf{u}$ and $\mathbf{a}$, according to the equations

$$\mathbf{u}\psi_\varkappa = \sum_1^f \mathbf{D}(\mathbf{u})_{\lambda\varkappa}\psi_\lambda$$
$$\mathbf{a}\psi_\varkappa = \sum_1^f \mathbf{D}(\mathbf{a})_{\lambda\varkappa}\psi_\lambda. \tag{26.19a}$$

In the physical problem, these are the wave functions in which we are principally interested. If one is interested in the purely mathematical problem of the solutions of (26.21), the wave functions $\psi_\varkappa$ can be replaced by vectors in a "representation space." This representation space has f dimensions where f is the number of rows and columns of $\mathbf{D}$. The matrices $\mathbf{D}$ can then be considered to act on the vectors in this representation space, $\mathbf{D}(\mathbf{u})$

and $\mathbf{D}(\mathbf{a})$ transforming the $\varkappa$th unit vector into the vector with the λ component $\mathbf{D}(\mathbf{u})_{\varkappa\lambda}$ and $\mathbf{D}(\mathbf{a})_{\varkappa\lambda}$, respectively. Thus, the unit vectors in the representation space can be made to assume the roles of the wave functions ψ. However, the use of the concept of wave functions is expected to render the following analysis less abstract than an analysis based on representation space.

The matrices $\mathbf{D}(\mathbf{u})$, which correspond to unitary transformations, form a representation of the unitary subgroup. Let us assume that $\mathbf{D}(\mathbf{u})$ as a representation of the unitary subgroup has been completely reduced and that the dimension l of the first irreducible part $\mathbf{\Delta}(\mathbf{u})$ does not exceed the dimension of any other irreducible part of $\mathbf{D}(\mathbf{u})$. This can be accomplished by choosing proper linear combinations of the wave functions (by using a proper coordinate system in representation space). Hence, we have

$$\mathbf{u}\psi_\varkappa = \sum_1^l \mathbf{\Delta}(\mathbf{u})_{\lambda\varkappa}\psi_\lambda \qquad \text{for } \varkappa \leq l. \tag{26.24}$$

Note that $\mathbf{\Delta}$ is defined only for unitary operators and $\mathbf{\Delta}(\mathbf{a})$, for instance, is meaningless. However, since $\mathbf{a}_1\mathbf{a}_2$ or $\mathbf{a}^{-1}\mathbf{u}\mathbf{a}$ are in the unitary subgroup, expressions like $\mathbf{\Delta}(\mathbf{a}_1\mathbf{a}_2)$ or $\mathbf{\Delta}(\mathbf{a}^{-1}\mathbf{u}\mathbf{a})$ are well defined.

Let us consider, next, the l wave functions

$$\psi'_\varkappa = \mathbf{a}_0\psi_\varkappa = \sum_1^f \mathbf{D}(\mathbf{a}_0)_{\lambda\varkappa}\psi_\lambda \qquad (\varkappa \leq l). \tag{26.25}$$

The summation on the right side has to be extended over all wave functions as we have made no assumptions about $\mathbf{D}(\mathbf{a})$. The $\mathbf{a}_0$ in (26.25) is an arbitrary but fixed antiunitary operator. We shall show that the $\psi'_\varkappa$ belong to an irreducible representation of the unitary subgroup. Consider

$$\begin{aligned}\mathbf{u}\psi'_\varkappa &= \mathbf{u}\sum_\lambda \mathbf{D}(\mathbf{a}_0)_{\lambda\varkappa}\psi_\lambda = \sum_\lambda\sum_\mu \mathbf{D}(\mathbf{a}_0)_{\lambda\varkappa}\mathbf{D}(\mathbf{u})_{\mu\lambda}\psi_\mu \\ &= \sum_\mu [\mathbf{D}(\mathbf{u})\mathbf{D}(\mathbf{a}_0)]_{\mu\varkappa}\psi_\mu.\end{aligned} \tag{26.26}$$

However, according to (26.21)

$$\mathbf{D}(\mathbf{u})\mathbf{D}(\mathbf{a}_0) = \mathbf{D}(\mathbf{u}\mathbf{a}_0) = \mathbf{D}(\mathbf{a}_0)\mathbf{D}(\mathbf{a}_0^{-1}\mathbf{u}\mathbf{a}_0)^* \tag{26.26a}$$

so that

$$\mathbf{u}\psi'_\varkappa = \sum_{\mu\lambda} \mathbf{D}(\mathbf{a}_0)_{\mu\lambda}\mathbf{D}(\mathbf{a}_0^{-1}\mathbf{u}\mathbf{a}_0)^*_{\lambda\varkappa}\psi_\mu = \sum_\lambda \mathbf{D}(\mathbf{a}_0^{-1}\mathbf{u}\mathbf{a}_0)^*_{\lambda\varkappa}\psi'_\lambda. \tag{26.26b}$$

Note that we have used only the relations (26.21), not the multiplication laws of the operators $\mathbf{u}$ and $\mathbf{a}$.

Since $\mathbf{a}_0^{-1}\mathbf{u}\mathbf{a}_0$ is in the unitary subgroup for $\varkappa \leq l$, one has $\mathbf{D}(\mathbf{a}_0^{-1}\mathbf{u}\mathbf{a}_0)_{\lambda\varkappa} = \mathbf{\Delta}(\mathbf{a}_0^{-1}\mathbf{u}\mathbf{a}_0)_{\lambda\varkappa}$ for $\lambda \leq l$ and $\mathbf{D}(\mathbf{a}_0^{-1}\mathbf{u}\mathbf{a}_0)_{\lambda\varkappa} = 0$ for $\lambda > l$. Thus

$$\mathbf{u}\psi'_\varkappa = \sum_1^l \mathbf{\Delta}(\mathbf{a}_0^{-1}\mathbf{u}\mathbf{a}_0)^*_{\lambda\varkappa}\psi'_\lambda \qquad (\varkappa \leq l) \tag{26.27}$$

and the $\psi'_\varkappa$, which are linear combinations of the ψ, belong to the l-dimensional representation

$$\bar{\mathbf{\Delta}}(\mathbf{u}) = \mathbf{\Delta}(\mathbf{a}_0^{-1}\mathbf{u}\mathbf{a}_0)^*. \tag{26.27a}$$

That these matrices form a representation of the unitary subgroup follows from (26.27). It also follows from the fact that $\mathbf{\Delta}$ is such a representation and that $\mathbf{a}_0^{-1}\mathbf{u}\mathbf{a}_0$ is unitary. Furthermore, $\bar{\mathbf{\Delta}}$ must be irreducible because it is contained in $\mathbf{D}(\mathbf{u})$ and because this contains no representation of lower dimensionality than l.

The relation of the representation $\bar{\mathbf{\Delta}}$ to $\mathbf{\Delta}$ will be discussed below. But first it will be shown that the wave functions

$$\mathbf{a}\psi_\varkappa = \Sigma\, \mathbf{D}(\mathbf{a})_{\mu\varkappa}\psi_\mu \tag{26.28a}$$

$$\mathbf{a}\psi'_\varkappa = \Sigma\, \mathbf{a}\mathbf{D}(\mathbf{a}_0)_{\lambda\varkappa}\psi_\lambda = \Sigma\,\Sigma\, \mathbf{D}(\mathbf{a}_0)^*_{\lambda\varkappa}\mathbf{D}(\mathbf{a})_{\mu\lambda}\psi_\mu \tag{26.28b}$$

for $\varkappa \leq l$ can be expressed linearly in terms of the $\psi_\varkappa$, $\psi'_\varkappa$, again with $\varkappa \leq l$. Because of $\mathbf{D}(\mathbf{a}) = \mathbf{D}(\mathbf{a}_0)\mathbf{D}(\mathbf{a}_0^{-1}\mathbf{a})^*$, (26.28a) is simply

$$\begin{aligned}\mathbf{a}\psi_\varkappa &= \Sigma\, \mathbf{D}(\mathbf{a})_{\mu\varkappa}\psi_\mu = \Sigma\,\Sigma\, \mathbf{D}(\mathbf{a}_0)_{\mu\nu}\mathbf{D}(\mathbf{a}_0^{-1}\mathbf{a})^*_{\nu\varkappa}\psi_\mu \\ &= \sum_1^l \mathbf{\Delta}(\mathbf{a}_0^{-1}\mathbf{a})^*_{\nu\varkappa}\psi'_\nu. \qquad (\varkappa \leq l)\end{aligned} \tag{26.29a}$$

The last step follows because $\mathbf{a}_0^{-1}\mathbf{a}$ is in the unitary subgroup and $\varkappa \leq l$ so that $\mathbf{D}(\mathbf{a}_0^{-1}\mathbf{a})_{\nu\varkappa} = \mathbf{\Delta}(\mathbf{a}_0^{-1}\mathbf{a})_{\nu\varkappa}$ for $\nu \leq l$ and vanishes otherwise. Similarly, it follows from $\mathbf{D}(\mathbf{a})\mathbf{D}(\mathbf{a}_0)^* = \mathbf{D}(\mathbf{a}\mathbf{a}_0)$ that (26.28b) is for $\varkappa \leq l$

$$\mathbf{a}\psi'_\varkappa = \sum \mathbf{D}(\mathbf{a}\mathbf{a}_0)_{\mu\varkappa}\psi_\mu = \sum_1^l \mathbf{\Delta}(\mathbf{a}\mathbf{a}_0)_{\mu\varkappa}\psi_\mu\,. \tag{26.29b}$$

We shall prove, next, the lemma that *the* $\psi'_\varkappa = \mathbf{a}_0\psi_\varkappa$ (for $\varkappa \leq l$) *either can all be expressed linearly in terms of the* $\psi_1, \psi_2, \cdots, \psi_l$ *or are all linearly independent of these and each other.* In the course of proving this lemma, we shall refer frequently to the $\psi_\varkappa$ and $\psi'_\varkappa = \mathbf{a}_0\psi_\varkappa$ with $\varkappa \leq l$. It is convenient, therefore, to stipulate that, for the rest of this section, $\varkappa$ is between 1 and l. We note, first, that the $\psi'_\varkappa$ are orthogonal to each other because they belong to different rows of an irreducible representation $\bar{\mathbf{\Delta}}$. Hence, any linear relationship between the $\psi'_\varkappa$ and $\psi_\varkappa$ could be given the form

$$\Sigma\, \alpha'_\varkappa\psi'_\varkappa = \varphi_1, \qquad \varphi_1 = \Sigma\, \alpha_\varkappa\psi_\varkappa\,, \tag{26.30}$$

where $\varphi_1 \neq 0$. It then follows from (26.27) and the linear nature of the $\mathbf{u}$ that all $\mathbf{u}\varphi_1$ are also linear combinations of the $\psi'_\varkappa$ and this applies also to all linear combinations of the $\mathbf{u}\varphi_1$. We shall represent all $\psi'_\varkappa$ as linear combinations of the $\mathbf{u}\varphi_1$. Then they will also be linear combinations of the $\psi_\varkappa$ so that it will follow that all $\psi'_\varkappa$ are linear combinations of the $\psi_\varkappa$ if one relation, such as (26.30), obtains between them.

In order to obtain all $\psi'_\varkappa$ as linear combinations of the $\mathbf{u}\varphi_1$, we transform $\bar{\mathbf{\Delta}}$ in such a way that φ_1 belong to its first row. This can be accomplished by a unitary transformation the first column of which is $\alpha'_1, \alpha'_2, \cdots, \alpha'_l$. Hence, the partners of φ_1 can be obtained as linear combinations of the $\mathbf{u}\varphi_1$ by (12.3a). From these, the $\psi'_\varkappa$ can be obtained by the reciprocal of the aforementioned unitary transformation. This concludes the proof of the lemma.

If the $\psi'_\varkappa$ are linear combinations of the $\psi_\varkappa$, it follows from the foregoing calculation, leading to (26.24) and (26.29a), that the $\mathbf{u}\psi_\varkappa$ and $\mathbf{a}\psi_\varkappa$ are also linear combinations of these functions. In this case the corepresentation is reduced to an l-dimensional and to an $(f - l)$-dimensional part. The $\mathbf{D}_{\lambda\mu}$ all vanish if $\mu \leq l$, $\lambda > l$ and the same holds if $\mu > l$, $\lambda \leq l$. This last statement holds because all $\mathbf{D}(\mathbf{u})$ and $\mathbf{D}(\mathbf{a})$ are unitary. As a result, $\mathbf{D}(\mathbf{u})^\dagger = \mathbf{D}(\mathbf{u}^{-1})$ and, according to (26.22), $\mathbf{D}(\mathbf{a})' = \mathbf{D}(\mathbf{a}^{-1})$. Since $\mathbf{D}(\mathbf{u}^{-1})_{\lambda\mu}$ and $\mathbf{D}(\mathbf{a}^{-1})_{\lambda\mu}$ have only zeros in the rectangle $\lambda > l$, $\mu \leq l$, the matrices $\mathbf{D}(\mathbf{u})_{\lambda\mu}$ and $\mathbf{D}(\mathbf{a})_{\lambda\mu}$ will have only zeros at $\mu > l$, $\lambda \leq l$.

If, on the other hand, the $\psi_\varkappa$ and $\psi'_\varkappa$ are all linearly independent, one can select an orthonormal set the first l members of which are the $\psi_\varkappa$, the next l members linear combinations of the $\psi_\varkappa$ and $\psi'_\varkappa$, and the rest of which is orthogonal to both the $\psi_\varkappa$ and $\psi'_\varkappa$. This can be done by applying the Gram-Schmidt procedure to the functions $\psi_1, \psi_2, \cdots, \psi_l$; $\psi'_1, \psi'_2, \cdots, \psi'_l$; $\psi_{l+1}, \psi_{l+2}, \cdots, \psi_f$. The $\psi_\varkappa$ and $\psi'_\varkappa$ will be, then, linear combinations of the first $2l$ members of this set. If either a $\mathbf{u}$ or an $\mathbf{a}$ is applied to one of the first $2l$ members of the set, the resulting function will be again a linear combination of the first $2l$ members. This again follows from the calculation which precedes this discussion and leads to (26.24), (26.27), (26.29a), and (26.29b). Hence, if $\mathbf{D}$ is assumed in the form as it applies to the orthonormal set just described, all $\mathbf{D}(\mathbf{u})_{\lambda\mu}$ and $\mathbf{D}(\mathbf{a})_{\lambda\mu}$ will vanish for which $\lambda \leq 2l$, $\mu > 2l$. It then follows as before that $\mathbf{D}$ decomposes into two parts, one $2l$-dimensional, the other $(f - 2l)$-dimensional. The first part contains only two irreducible representations of the unitary subgroup $\mathbf{\Delta}$ and $\bar{\mathbf{\Delta}}$.

The reduction of $\mathbf{D}$ can now be continued by applying the same procedure to the $(f - l)$- or $(f - 2l)$-dimensional second part which was applied above to the whole $\mathbf{D}$. As a result of this decomposition, every reduced part of the corepresentation will contain either only one irreducible representation of the unitary subgroup or only two such representations, $\mathbf{\Delta}(\mathbf{u})$ and $\bar{\mathbf{\Delta}}(\mathbf{u}) = \mathbf{\Delta}(\mathbf{a}_0^{-1}\mathbf{u}\mathbf{a}_0)^*$.

Determination of the Irreducible Corepresentations

The irreducible representations of the unitary subgroup $\boldsymbol{\Delta}$ and $\bar{\boldsymbol{\Delta}}$ can be either inequivalent or equivalent. The former of these two possibilities is simpler, and will be treated first.

1. If $\boldsymbol{\Delta}(\mathbf{u})$ and $\boldsymbol{\Delta}(\mathbf{a}_0^{-1}\mathbf{u}\mathbf{a}_0)^*$ are not equivalent, the wave functions $\psi_\varkappa$ and $\psi'_\varkappa = \mathbf{a}_0\psi_\varkappa$ are orthogonal because they belong to different representations of the unitary subgroup. Hence, the first $2l$ members of the orthonormal set defined in the last section will be the $\psi_\varkappa$ and $\psi'_\varkappa$ themselves and the matrices $\mathbf{D}(\mathbf{u})$ and $\mathbf{D}(\mathbf{a})$ are given by (26.24), (26.27), (26.29a), and (26.29b):

$$\mathbf{D}(\mathbf{u}) = \begin{pmatrix} \boldsymbol{\Delta}(\mathbf{u}) & 0 \\ 0 & \boldsymbol{\Delta}(\mathbf{a}_0^{-1}\mathbf{u}\mathbf{a}_0)^* \end{pmatrix} \tag{26.31}$$

$$\mathbf{D}(\mathbf{a}) = \begin{pmatrix} 0 & \boldsymbol{\Delta}(\mathbf{a}\mathbf{a}_0) \\ \boldsymbol{\Delta}(\mathbf{a}_0^{-1}\mathbf{a})^* & 0 \end{pmatrix}. \tag{26.31a}$$

Naturally, these matrices can be subjected to a similarity transformation. In particular, if one wishes to replace $\mathbf{a}_0$ by another group element $\mathbf{a}_1$, one has to transform $\mathbf{D}$ by

$$\boldsymbol{\alpha} = \begin{pmatrix} 1 & 0 \\ 0 & \boldsymbol{\Delta}(\mathbf{a}_0^{-1}\mathbf{a}_1)^* \end{pmatrix}.$$

The matrix system (26.31), (26.31a) is clearly irreducible if $\boldsymbol{\Delta}(\mathbf{u})$ and $\bar{\boldsymbol{\Delta}}(\mathbf{u}) = \boldsymbol{\Delta}(\mathbf{a}_0^{-1}\mathbf{u}\mathbf{a}_0)^*$ are inequivalent irreducible representations. The reader might convince himself that this does not depend on the choice of the antiunitary operator $\mathbf{a}_0$. Note that $\mathbf{D}(\mathbf{a})$ has to be transformed according to (26.23b).

2. In the alternative situation, the representations $\boldsymbol{\Delta}(\mathbf{u})$ and

$$\bar{\boldsymbol{\Delta}}(\mathbf{u}) = \boldsymbol{\Delta}(\mathbf{a}_0^{-1}\mathbf{u}\mathbf{a}_0)^* = \boldsymbol{\beta}^{-1}\,\boldsymbol{\Delta}(\mathbf{u})\boldsymbol{\beta} \tag{26.32}$$

are equivalent. There are two cases to be distinguished: the representation $\mathbf{D}$ may have as many rows and columns as $\boldsymbol{\Delta}$, or it may have twice as many rows and columns. In the former case the $\mathbf{D}(\mathbf{u})$ are already determined as

$$\mathbf{D}(\mathbf{u}) = \boldsymbol{\Delta}(\mathbf{u}). \tag{26.32a}$$

In the latter case $\mathbf{D}(\mathbf{u})$ can be assumed to have the form

$$\mathbf{D}(\mathbf{u}) = \begin{pmatrix} \boldsymbol{\Delta}(\mathbf{u}) & 0 \\ 0 & \boldsymbol{\Delta}(\mathbf{u}) \end{pmatrix}. \tag{26.32b}$$

The matrices which correspond to unitary operators are determined in both cases. In order to determine the $\mathbf{D}(\mathbf{a})$, we have to analyze the representation $\boldsymbol{\Delta}$ somewhat more closely.

Application of (26.32) to the unitary transformation $\mathbf{a}_0^{-1}\mathbf{u}\mathbf{a}_0$ gives

$$\boldsymbol{\Delta}(\mathbf{a}_0^{-2}\mathbf{u}\mathbf{a}_0^2)^* = \boldsymbol{\beta}^{-1}\,\boldsymbol{\Delta}(\mathbf{a}_0^{-1}\mathbf{u}\mathbf{a}_0)\boldsymbol{\beta} \tag{26.33}$$

and the conjugate complex of this, together with (26.32), yields, since $\mathbf{a}_0^{-2}$ and $\mathbf{a}_0^2$ are in the unitary subgroup,

$$\mathbf{\Delta}(\mathbf{a}_0^{-2})\,\mathbf{\Delta}(\mathbf{u})\,\mathbf{\Delta}(\mathbf{a}_0^2) = \mathbf{\Delta}(\mathbf{a}_0^{-2}\mathbf{u}\mathbf{a}_0^2) = \boldsymbol{\beta}^{*-1}\boldsymbol{\beta}^{-1}\,\mathbf{\Delta}(\mathbf{u})\boldsymbol{\beta}\boldsymbol{\beta}^*. \tag{26.33a}$$

It follows that the matrix $\boldsymbol{\beta}\boldsymbol{\beta}^*\mathbf{\Delta}(\mathbf{a}_0^{-2})$ commutes with all matrices $\mathbf{\Delta}(\mathbf{u})$ of an irreducible representation and is, therefore, a constant matrix $\omega\mathbf{1}$; thus,

$$\boldsymbol{\beta}\boldsymbol{\beta}^* = \omega\,\mathbf{\Delta}(\mathbf{a}_0^2). \tag{26.34}$$

Because of the unitary nature of all matrices in (26.34), one has $|\omega| = 1$. It will be shown, next, that $\omega = \pm 1$. We substitute, for this purpose, $\mathbf{u} = \mathbf{a}_0^2$ in (26.33) to give

$$\mathbf{\Delta}(\mathbf{a}_0^2)^* = \boldsymbol{\beta}^{-1}\,\mathbf{\Delta}(\mathbf{a}_0^2)\boldsymbol{\beta} \tag{26.34a}$$

and express $\mathbf{\Delta}(\mathbf{a}_0^2)$ by (26.34).

$$\omega\boldsymbol{\beta}^*\boldsymbol{\beta} = \boldsymbol{\beta}^{-1}(\omega^{-1}\boldsymbol{\beta}\boldsymbol{\beta}^*)\boldsymbol{\beta} = \omega^{-1}\boldsymbol{\beta}^*\boldsymbol{\beta}. \tag{26.34b}$$

Thus, $\omega^2 = 1$, $\omega = \pm 1$. Hence, either

$$\boldsymbol{\beta}\boldsymbol{\beta}^* = \mathbf{\Delta}(\mathbf{a}_0^2), \quad \boldsymbol{\beta} = \mathbf{\Delta}(\mathbf{a}_0^2)\boldsymbol{\beta}', \tag{26.35a}$$

or

$$\boldsymbol{\beta}\boldsymbol{\beta}^* = -\mathbf{\Delta}(\mathbf{a}_0^2), \qquad \boldsymbol{\beta} = -\mathbf{\Delta}(\mathbf{a}_0^2)\boldsymbol{\beta}'. \tag{26.35b}$$

The preceding analysis shows great similarity to that in Section 2 of Chapter 24. It shows a distinction between representations $\mathbf{\Delta}$, which are equivalent with the derived representation $\bar{\mathbf{\Delta}}$ of (26.27a), a distinction very similar to that between potentially real and pseudoreal representations for those representations which are equivalent with their complex conjugates. One may convince oneself that, for a given $\mathbf{\Delta}$, the same alternative, (26.35a) or (26.35b), applies independently of the choice of the antiunitary transformation $\mathbf{a}_0$.

Let us now return to the problem of determining the irreducible corepresentations. The problem can be simplified by noting that every $\mathbf{a}$ can be written as $\mathbf{u}\mathbf{a}_0$ with a fixed $\mathbf{a}_0$ but variable $\mathbf{u}$. According to the second equation (26.21),

$$\mathbf{D}(\mathbf{u}\mathbf{a}_0) = \mathbf{D}(\mathbf{u})\mathbf{D}(\mathbf{a}_0). \tag{26.36}$$

Introducing $\mathbf{u}\mathbf{a}_0$ for $\mathbf{a}$ in the two other equations (26.21), and replacing all $\mathbf{a}$ by the product of a unitary operator and $\mathbf{a}_0$, replaces these by

$$\mathbf{D}(\mathbf{u}\mathbf{a}_0)\mathbf{D}(\mathbf{u}_1)^* = \mathbf{D}(\mathbf{u}\mathbf{a}_0\mathbf{u}_1) = \mathbf{D}(\mathbf{u}\mathbf{a}_0\mathbf{u}_1\mathbf{a}_0^{-1}\cdot\mathbf{a}_0)$$

$$\mathbf{D}(\mathbf{u}_1\mathbf{a}_0)\mathbf{D}(\mathbf{u}_2\mathbf{a}_0)^* = \mathbf{D}(\mathbf{u}_1\mathbf{a}_0\mathbf{u}_2\mathbf{a}_0) = \mathbf{D}(\mathbf{u}_1\cdot\mathbf{a}_0\mathbf{u}_2\mathbf{a}_0^{-1}\cdot\mathbf{a}_0^2).$$

If (26.36) is substituted into these and if it is assumed that the $\mathbf{D}(\mathbf{u})$ form a representation of the unitary subgroup, these equations are replaced by

$$\mathbf{D}(\mathbf{u})\mathbf{D}(\mathbf{a}_0)\mathbf{D}(\mathbf{u}_1)^* = \mathbf{D}(\mathbf{u}\mathbf{a}_0\mathbf{u}_1\mathbf{a}_0^{-1})\mathbf{D}(\mathbf{a}_0) = \mathbf{D}(\mathbf{u})\mathbf{D}(\mathbf{a}_0\mathbf{u}_1\mathbf{a}_0^{-1})\mathbf{D}(\mathbf{a}_0) \tag{26.37}$$

$$\mathbf{D}(\mathbf{u}_1)\mathbf{D}(\mathbf{a}_0)\mathbf{D}(\mathbf{u}_2)^*\mathbf{D}(\mathbf{a}_0)^* = \mathbf{D}(\mathbf{u}_1)\mathbf{D}(\mathbf{a}_0\mathbf{u}_2\mathbf{a}_0^{-1})\mathbf{D}(\mathbf{a}_0^2). \tag{26.37a}$$

The first of these will be satisfied if

$$\mathbf{D}(\mathbf{u}_1)^* = \mathbf{D}(\mathbf{a}_0)^{-1}\mathbf{D}(\mathbf{a}_0\mathbf{u}_1\mathbf{a}_0^{-1})\mathbf{D}(\mathbf{a}_0)$$

is valid for every $\mathbf{u}_1$. In this expression, one can replace $\mathbf{u}_1$ by $\mathbf{a}_0^{-1}\mathbf{u}\mathbf{a}_0$ and obtain

$$\mathbf{D}(\mathbf{a}_0^{-1}\mathbf{u}\mathbf{a}_0)^* = \mathbf{D}(\mathbf{a}_0)^{-1}\mathbf{D}(\mathbf{u})\mathbf{D}(\mathbf{a}_0). \tag{26.38}$$

If this equation is satisfied for all $\mathbf{u}$, and if $\mathbf{D}(\mathbf{a})$ is defined by (26.36), the third equation (26.21) will be fulfilled. Assuming now (26.38) to be valid and introducing $\mathbf{a}_0^{-1}\mathbf{u}\mathbf{a}_0$ for $\mathbf{u}_2$ in (26.37a), this will be replaced by

$$\mathbf{D}(\mathbf{a}_0)\mathbf{D}(\mathbf{a}_0)^* = \mathbf{D}(\mathbf{a}_0^2). \tag{26.38a}$$

This is a special case of the last equation (26.21). The preceding analysis shows, however, that if $\mathbf{D}(\mathbf{a}_0)$ satisfies (26.38) and (26.38a), and if the other $\mathbf{D}(\mathbf{a})$ are defined by (26.36), they will satisfy all equations (26.21). This makes it much easier to determine the $\mathbf{D}(\mathbf{a})$ which, together with the $\mathbf{D}(\mathbf{u})$ of (26.32a) or (26.32b), form solutions of (26.21). It reduces this problem to solving (26.38) and (26.38a) which contain only $\mathbf{D}(\mathbf{a}_0)$.

Let us consider first the case (26.32a) in which $\mathbf{D}$ contains $\boldsymbol{\Delta}$ only once. Comparison of (26.32) with (26.38) shows that, apart from an unimportant factor (see the remark after (26.23) page 336),

$$\mathbf{D}(\mathbf{a}_0) = \boldsymbol{\beta}. \tag{26.39a}$$

Hence, (26.38a) will be satisfied if, and only if, the alternative (26.35a) applies to $\boldsymbol{\Delta}$ so that (26.32a) can hold only if (26.35a) is valid for $\boldsymbol{\Delta}$. Conversely, the $\boldsymbol{\Delta}$ to which (26.35a) applies can be completed to a corepresentation of the whole group by means of Eq. (26.36)

$$\mathbf{D}(\mathbf{a}) = \boldsymbol{\Delta}(\mathbf{a}\mathbf{a}_0^{-1})\boldsymbol{\beta}. \tag{26.40a}$$

If $\mathbf{D}$ contains $\boldsymbol{\Delta}$ twice, $\mathbf{D}(\mathbf{u})$ is given by (26.32b). This can also be written as the direct product $\mathbf{1} \times \boldsymbol{\Delta}(\mathbf{u})$, that is, the direct product of the two-dimensional unit matrix and $\boldsymbol{\Delta}(\mathbf{u})$. In this case, a particular solution of (26.38) is

$$\mathbf{D}(\mathbf{a}_0) = \begin{pmatrix} \boldsymbol{\beta} & \mathbf{0} \\ \mathbf{0} & \boldsymbol{\beta} \end{pmatrix} = \mathbf{1} \times \boldsymbol{\beta}. \tag{26.E.3}$$

The most general solution of (26.38) is then (26.E.3) multiplied on the left by a matrix

$$\begin{pmatrix} c_{11}\mathbf{1} & c_{12}\mathbf{1} \\ c_{21}\mathbf{1} & c_{22}\mathbf{1} \end{pmatrix} = \mathbf{c} \times \mathbf{1} \tag{26.E.4}$$

which commutes with all $\mathbf{D}(\mathbf{u})$ of (26.32b). This follows from Schur's lemma (Theorem 2, Chapter 9). The $\mathbf{c}$ on the right side of (26.E.4) is an arbitrary two-by-two matrix, and (26.E.4) is the direct product of such a matrix with the unit matrix of the same dimensionality as $\mathbf{\Delta}$. Hence, the general solution of (26.38) is in this case

$$\mathbf{D}(\mathbf{a}_0) = \begin{pmatrix} \mathbf{c}_{11}\boldsymbol{\beta} & \mathbf{c}_{12}\boldsymbol{\beta} \\ \mathbf{c}_{21}\boldsymbol{\beta} & \mathbf{c}_{22}\boldsymbol{\beta} \end{pmatrix} = \mathbf{c} \times \boldsymbol{\beta}. \tag{26.39b}$$

Since $\mathbf{D}(\mathbf{a}_0)$ shall be unitary, $\mathbf{c}$ must be unitary. The second condition (26.38a) for $\mathbf{D}(\mathbf{a}_0)$ gives

$$(\mathbf{c} \times \boldsymbol{\beta})(\mathbf{c}^* \times \boldsymbol{\beta}^*) = \mathbf{c}\mathbf{c}^* \times \boldsymbol{\beta}\boldsymbol{\beta}^* = \mathbf{D}(\mathbf{a}_0^2) = \mathbf{1} \times \mathbf{\Delta}(\mathbf{a}_0^2).$$

The $\mathbf{1}$ in this equation is the two-dimensional unit matrix. From $\boldsymbol{\beta}\boldsymbol{\beta}^* = \pm\mathbf{\Delta}(\mathbf{a}_0^2)$, it follows that $\mathbf{c}\mathbf{c}^* = \pm\mathbf{1}$. We shall assume that the *lower* sign holds in this case; it will be shown below that the representation is reducible if the upper sign (and hence (26.35a)) is valid. It then follows from the unitary condition $\mathbf{c}\mathbf{c}^\dagger = \mathbf{1}$ that $\mathbf{c}^* = -\mathbf{c}^\dagger = -\mathbf{c}^{*\prime}$, that is, that $\mathbf{c}$ is skew symmetric. Since a common factor in all $\mathbf{D}(\mathbf{a})$ remains arbitrary, we can set

$$\mathbf{c} = \begin{pmatrix} 0 & 1 \\ -1 & 0 \end{pmatrix},$$

and this gives, for the case when the alternative (26.35b) is valid for the representation $\mathbf{\Delta}$,

$$\mathbf{D}(\mathbf{a}) = \begin{pmatrix} \mathbf{0} & \mathbf{\Delta}(\mathbf{a}\mathbf{a}_0^{-1})\boldsymbol{\beta} \\ -\mathbf{\Delta}(\mathbf{a}\mathbf{a}_0^{-1})\boldsymbol{\beta} & \mathbf{0} \end{pmatrix}. \tag{26.40b}$$

Only the case $\mathbf{c}\mathbf{c}^* = \mathbf{1}$ has yet to be disposed of. In this case, $\mathbf{c}$ is a symmetric unitary matrix. According to (24.4b) it can be written in the form $\mathbf{r}^{-1}\boldsymbol{\omega}\mathbf{r}$, where $\mathbf{r}$ is a real orthogonal matrix and $\boldsymbol{\omega}$ a diagonal matrix. Hence, if $\mathbf{D}$ is transformed by

$$\boldsymbol{\alpha} = \mathbf{r}^{-1} \times \mathbf{1} \tag{26.41}$$

($\mathbf{r}$ is two-dimensional; $\mathbf{1}$ is l-dimensional), $\mathbf{D}(\mathbf{u}) = \mathbf{1} \times \mathbf{\Delta}$ remains unchanged, $\mathbf{D}(\mathbf{a}_0) = \mathbf{c} \times \boldsymbol{\beta}$ goes over into $(\mathbf{r} \times \mathbf{1})(\mathbf{r}^{-1}\boldsymbol{\omega}\mathbf{r} \times \boldsymbol{\beta})(\mathbf{r}^{-1} \times \mathbf{1}) = \boldsymbol{\omega} \times \boldsymbol{\beta}$. Hence the representation decomposes into two l-dimensional representations of the type (26.40a).

Summarizing, there are *three types of irreducible corepresentations*, that is, irreducible solutions of (26.21). The type which we considered first but which will be called *the third type contains two inequivalent irreducible representations of the unitary subgroup*, $\mathbf{\Delta}$ and

$$\bar{\mathbf{\Delta}}(\mathbf{u}) = \mathbf{\Delta}(\mathbf{a}^{-1}\mathbf{u}\mathbf{a})^*, \tag{26.27a}$$

where $\mathbf{a}$ is any antiunitary operator. Note that $\bar{\bar{\mathbf{\Delta}}}$ and $\mathbf{\Delta}$ are equivalent; the relation between the representations $\mathbf{\Delta}$ and $\bar{\mathbf{\Delta}}$ is reciprocal. *The corepresentations of the first type contain only one irreducible representation* $\mathbf{\Delta}$ *of the unitary subgroup. In this case*—which is the most frequent one—$\mathbf{\Delta}$ *and* $\bar{\mathbf{\Delta}}$ *are equivalent; the matrix* $\boldsymbol{\beta}$ *which transforms* $\mathbf{\Delta}$ *into* $\bar{\mathbf{\Delta}}$ *satisfies the equation* $\boldsymbol{\beta}\boldsymbol{\beta}^* = \mathbf{\Delta}(\mathbf{a}_0^2)$. The last type of corepresentation, which will be called *the* *second type, contains the same irreducible representation* $\mathbf{\Delta}$ *of the unitary subgroup twice. This* $\mathbf{\Delta}$ *is also equivalent to* $\bar{\mathbf{\Delta}}$ *but in this case* $\boldsymbol{\beta}\boldsymbol{\beta}^* = -\mathbf{\Delta}(\mathbf{a}_0^2)$ *holds for the matrix* $\boldsymbol{\beta}$ *which transforms* $\mathbf{\Delta}$ *into* $\bar{\mathbf{\Delta}}$. *In the third type of corepresentations,* $\mathbf{\Delta}$ *and* $\bar{\mathbf{\Delta}}$ *are inequivalent.* The three types of corepresentations are given by (26.32a), (26.40a), by (26.32b), (26.40b), and by (26.31), (26.31a). It follows from this enumeration that each irreducible representation of the unitary subgroup is contained in only one irreducible corepresentation. If $\mathbf{\Delta}$ and $\bar{\mathbf{\Delta}}$ are equivalent, $\mathbf{\Delta}$ is contained in the corepresentation only once if it satisfies (26.35a), it is contained twice if it satisfies (26.35b). It also follows that the irreducible parts of a corepresentation are completely determined by the irreducible parts of the matrices which correspond to the unitary subgroup, and hence by the character of the unitary subgroup. A corepresentation, just as a representation, cannot be broken up into irreducible parts in two essentially different ways. It follows, finally, that the antiunitary operators never lead to a further differentiation of types of eigenvalues (never lead to new quantum numbers) beyond the differentiation provided by the unitary subgroup.[4] They may be responsible for coincidences between eigenvalues. Thus, if $\mathbf{\Delta}$ and $\bar{\mathbf{\Delta}}$ are inequivalent, an eigenvalue with the representation $\mathbf{\Delta}$ always coincides with an eigenvalue with the representation $\bar{\mathbf{\Delta}}$. The antiunitary symmetry operators may also be responsible for the vanishing of matrix elements.

It may be worth the reader's time to verify that the same type of extension of a unitary representation to a corepresentation is obtained, no matter which antiunitary operator plays the role of $\mathbf{a}_0$ in the preceding calculation. This amounts to verifying that if in (26.32) $\mathbf{a}_0$ is replaced by another antiunitary operator $\mathbf{u}_0\mathbf{a}_0$, the corresponding $\bar{\mathbf{\Delta}}$ is equivalent with $\mathbf{\Delta}$ if the $\bar{\mathbf{\Delta}}$ of (26.32) is equivalent thereto. It turns out that if $\mathbf{a}_0$ is replaced by $\mathbf{u}_0\mathbf{a}_0$, the $\boldsymbol{\beta}$ of (26.32) has to be replaced by $\boldsymbol{\gamma} = \mathbf{\Delta}(\mathbf{u}_0)\boldsymbol{\beta}$. Second, depending on whether $\boldsymbol{\beta}$ satisfies (26.35a) or (26.35b), $\boldsymbol{\gamma}$ will satisfy the same equation with $\mathbf{a}_0$ replaced by $\mathbf{u}_0\mathbf{a}_0$. All this follows also from the foregoing theory since the type of the corepresentation which contains a certain $\mathbf{\Delta}$ cannot depend on the arbitrary choice of the operator $\mathbf{a}_0$.

Consequences of Invariance under Time Inversion

Let us consider the case first in which the *full rotational symmetry* is present. It seems natural to choose as $\mathbf{a}_0$ the operation of time inversion $\boldsymbol{\theta}$ itself. The

[4] This is not in conflict with the "types" in the theory of elementary particles. These differ in the group of symmetry operators which expresses the same physical symmetry. Thus, for type 1 and type 2 particles $\boldsymbol{\theta}^2 = (-1)^{2s}$, for type 3 and type 4 particles $\boldsymbol{\theta}^2 = -(-1)^{2s}$, where s is the spin of the particle. The group of operators has different multiplication laws for the different types; every set of multiplication law has only one corepresentation.

conclusions are, of course, independent of this choice. It follows from (26.17) and (26.32) that in this case $\bar{\mathbf{\Delta}} = \mathbf{\Delta}^*$ or, if we use our standard notation for the representations in this case

$$\bar{\mathfrak{D}}^{(J)} = \mathfrak{D}^{(J)*}. \tag{26.42}$$

The $\boldsymbol{\beta}$ which transforms $\mathfrak{D}^{(J)}$ into this form is the $\mathbf{C}^{-1} = \mathbf{C}^\dagger$ of (24.3). Hence $\boldsymbol{\beta\beta}^* = \mathbf{C}^{-1}\mathbf{C}^{\dagger *} = \mathbf{C}^{-1}\mathbf{C}'$ and since $\mathbf{C}' = \mathbf{C}$ for integral J, we have $\boldsymbol{\beta\beta}^* = \mathbf{1}$. We have seen that $\boldsymbol{\theta}^2 = \mathbf{1}$ in this case, which corresponds either to the simple Schrödinger theory which disregards spin, or to an even number of electrons. Hence (26.35a) is valid and the corepresentations are all of the first type. The same is true, if the number of electrons is odd. In this case J is odd and $\boldsymbol{\beta\beta}^* = \mathbf{C}^{-1}\mathbf{C}' - \mathbf{C}\mathbf{C}^\dagger = -\mathbf{1}$, since $\mathbf{C} = -\mathbf{C}'$ in this case. Since $\boldsymbol{\theta}^2 = -\mathbf{1}$ if the number of electrons is odd, again all corepresentations are of the first type. *In the case of full rotational symmetry, the time inversion does not lead to any additional degeneracy.*

The consideration of time inversion does lead, however, to significant results concerning the reality of the eigenfunctions. Since, according to (26.39a) or (26.40a), one has $\mathbf{D}(\mathbf{a}_0) = \mathbf{D}(\boldsymbol{\theta}) = \boldsymbol{\beta} = \mathbf{C}$ in this case, we can write in the simple Schrödinger theory

$$\boldsymbol{\theta}\psi_\mu^l = \psi_\mu^{l*} = \sum_{\mu'} \mathbf{C}_{\mu'\mu}\psi_{\mu'}^l = (-)^{l-\mu}\psi_{-\mu}^l. \tag{26.43}$$

The form of $\mathbf{C}$ given in (24.6) was substituted. It should be realized that (26.43) implies a definite choice of a phase factor; such a choice was made when $\mathbf{D}(\mathbf{a})$ was set equal to $\boldsymbol{\beta}$ rather than $\omega\boldsymbol{\beta}$ in (26.39a).[5] In the present case, ψ_μ^l and $\psi_{-\mu}^l$ are conjugate complex if $l - \mu$ is even, $-\psi_\mu^l$ and $\psi_{-\mu}^l$ are conjugate complex if $l - \mu$ is odd. In particular, ψ_0^l is real for even l, purely imaginary for odd l. The same result can be derived for the G_μ^l in the wave function (19.18) of the He atom. It then follows from (19.19) and (19.19a) that the G are all real for even states, all purely imaginary for odd states. It would be possible, of course, to change all reality characteristics by multiplying all wave functions which belong to the different rows of a representation by a common factor.

In the theory which takes the spin into account, (26.43) is replaced by

$$\begin{aligned}\boldsymbol{\theta}\Psi_M^{\kappa J}(\cdots, x_k, y_k, z_k, s_k, \cdots) &= i^{-s_1-s_2-\cdots-s_n}\Psi_M^{\kappa J}(\cdots, x_k, y_k, z_k, -s_k, \cdots)^* \\ &= \sum_{M'} \mathbf{C}_{M'M}\Psi_{M'}^{\kappa J}(\cdots, x_k, y_k, z_k, s_k, \cdots) = (-)^{J-M}\Psi_{-M}^{\kappa J}(\cdots, x_k, y_k, z_k, s_k, \cdots)\end{aligned} \tag{26.43a}$$

[5] This choice of phase differs from that used in the explicit wave functions of Chapter 15 by a factor i^l. The spherical harmonics are sometimes conveniently defined to include this factor. Cf. for instance L. C. Biedenharn, J. M. Blatt and M. E. Rose, *Rev. Mod. Phys.* **24,** 249 (1952).

In this case Ψ^J_M and Ψ^J_{-M} are related at opposite spin directions. Thus, for instance, if $M = 0$, the wave function is real if J and the Z-component of the spin angular momentum are both even, or both odd; Ψ^J_0 is purely imaginary if J is even and the Z-component of the spin angular momentum is odd, or vice versa.

The preceding consideration corresponds to that of Chapter 19 inasmuch as it provides information on the wave function. From this, inferences can be drawn on the magnitude of the matrix elements. Alternately, the matrix elements can be considered directly. This was done in Chapter 21 where the concept of irreducible tensor operators was introduced. Considerations similar to those of Chapter 21 can be carried out also by means of the antiunitary operators. Let us consider, for instance, a symmetric (that is, scalar) operator $\mathbf{p}$ which contains an odd power of the time, that is, for which (26.12) is valid. Such an operator is, for instance, the scalar product of the coordinate vector and of the spin (or orbital) angular momentum

$$x\mathbf{S}_x + y\mathbf{S}_y + z\mathbf{S}_z \quad \text{or} \quad x\mathbf{L}_x + y\mathbf{L}_y + z\mathbf{L}_z$$

for any of the particles, or the scalar product of coordinate and velocity, etc. The expectation value of such an operator is zero for any stationary state unless there is an accidental degeneracy. In fact, in

$$(\Sigma\, a_\mu \Psi^J_\mu, \mathbf{p}\, \Sigma\, a_\nu \Psi^J_\nu) \tag{26.E.5}$$

the mixed terms $\mu \neq \nu$ vanish because Ψ^J_μ and $\mathbf{p}\Psi^J_\nu$ belong to different rows of a representation. Moreover, the terms $\mu = \nu$ vanish. This can be seen from (26.8) and (26.43a) as follows:

$$\begin{aligned}(\Psi^J_\mu, \mathbf{p}\Psi^J_\mu) &= (\boldsymbol{\theta}\mathbf{p}\Psi^J_\mu, \boldsymbol{\theta}\Psi^J_\mu) = -(\mathbf{p}\boldsymbol{\theta}\Psi^J_\mu, \boldsymbol{\theta}\Psi^J_\mu) \\ &= -(-1)^{2J-2\mu}(\mathbf{p}\Psi^J_{-\mu}, \Psi^J_{-\mu}) = -(\Psi^J_{-\mu}, \mathbf{p}\Psi^J_{-\mu}).\end{aligned} \tag{26.44}$$

The last parts follow because $2J - 2\mu$ is always an even number and because $\mathbf{p}$, as a physical quantity, is Hermitian. According to (26.44), $(\Psi_\mu, \mathbf{p}\Psi_\mu)$ has opposite sign for μ and $-\mu$. Since Ψ_μ and $\Psi_{-\mu}$ are partners and since $\mathbf{p}$ is a symmetric operator, the two expressions must be equal. They vanish, therefore, and so does the expression (26.E.5). There are many similar examples, some of which lead to conclusions concerning the real or purely imaginary nature of matrix elements. Thus, for instance, if $\mathbf{p}$ satisfies the conditions enumerated above, but the two wave functions in

$$(\Psi^J_\mu, \mathbf{p}\Phi^J_\mu) \tag{26.E.6}$$

are not identical, the scalar product is purely imaginary. This presupposes that the phases of Ψ^J_μ and Φ^J_μ are so determined that the corepresentation has the same form for both, for instance that (26.43a) holds for both. If $\mathbf{p}$

is the Z-component of a vector operator, of similar nature with respect to time inversion, (26.E.6) is real. These results can be obtained by the argument contained in (26.44) and can be properly generalized to irreducible tensor operators of arbitrary rank.

Let us now consider the opposite case of *no spatial symmetry*. In this case the unitary subgroup reduces to the unit element and $\mathbf{\Delta} = (1)$. Hence, $\mathbf{\Delta}$ and $\bar{\mathbf{\Delta}}$ are identical and $\boldsymbol{\beta}$ is an arbitary number of modulus 1. Thus $\boldsymbol{\beta}\boldsymbol{\beta}^* = (1)$. On the other hand, $\boldsymbol{\theta}^2 = 1$ if the number of electrons is even but $\boldsymbol{\theta}^2 = -1$ if the number of electrons is odd. As a result, the corepresentation (there is only one) is of type one in the former case but of type two if the electron number is odd and the spin is taken into consideration. In this latter case, all characteristic values are doubly degenerate: if one chooses $\boldsymbol{\beta} = (1)$, the two wave functions ψ_1, ψ_2 transform under time inversion according to (26.40b)

$$\boldsymbol{\theta}\psi_1 = -\psi_2 \quad \boldsymbol{\theta}\psi_2 = \psi_1. \tag{26.45}$$

This is the Kramers' degeneracy in its original form. The fact of the degeneracy already follows from the fact that if $\boldsymbol{\theta}$ *is an antiunitary operator such that* $\boldsymbol{\theta}^2 = -\mathbf{1}$, *then* ψ *and* $\boldsymbol{\theta}\psi$ *are always orthogonal*. This follows from (26.8)

$$(\psi, \boldsymbol{\theta}\psi) = (\boldsymbol{\theta}\boldsymbol{\theta}\psi, \boldsymbol{\theta}\psi) = (-\psi, \boldsymbol{\theta}\psi). \tag{26.45a}$$

In the case of an even number of electrons, or in the simple Schrödinger theory, on the other hand, there is no degeneracy and

$$\boldsymbol{\theta}\psi = \psi \tag{26.46}$$

is valid for every stationary state with a properly chosen phase factor. The present case of no spatial symmetry, but invariance with respect to time inversion, is important for atoms in an asymmetric electric field as prevails, for instance, in a crystal of low symmetry.

As a last example, we consider the case of a homogeneous magnetic field in the Z-direction. The unitary subgroup was determined in Chapter 18; it consists of all rotations $\mathbf{O}_{\{\alpha,0,0\}}$ about Z and the products of these rotations with space inversion $\mathbf{O}_I$. The interesting point here is that time inversion as such is not a symmetry element but only the product of time inversion and an operation which reverses the direction of the magnetic field. A rotation by π about any axis in the XY-plane accomplishes this and so does a reflection in any plane through the Z-axis. The product $\boldsymbol{\theta}\mathbf{O}_{\{0,\pi,0\}}$ of time inversion and of a rotation by π about Y can be chosen as $\mathbf{a}_0$. Hence, and since $\boldsymbol{\theta}$ and $\mathbf{O}_R$ commute,

$$\mathbf{a}_0^{-1}\mathbf{O}_{\{\alpha,0,0\}}\mathbf{a}_0 = \mathbf{O}_{\{0,\pi,0\}}^{-1}\boldsymbol{\theta}^{-1}\mathbf{O}_{\{\alpha,0,0\}}\boldsymbol{\theta}\mathbf{O}_{\{0,\pi,0\}} = \mathbf{O}_{\{0,\pi,0\}}^{-1}\mathbf{O}_{\{\alpha,0,0\}}\mathbf{O}_{\{0,\pi,0\}} = \mathbf{O}_{\{-\alpha,0,0\}}.$$

Equation (26.32) defining $\boldsymbol{\beta}$ becomes

$$\boldsymbol{\Delta}(\{-\alpha, 0, 0\})^* = \boldsymbol{\beta}^{-1} \boldsymbol{\Delta}(\{\alpha, 0, 0\})\boldsymbol{\beta} \tag{26.47}$$

along with the equation involving space inversion which is, however, automatically satisfied. Since $\boldsymbol{\Delta}(\{\alpha, 0, 0\}) = (e^{im\alpha})$, Eq. (26.47) gives again $\boldsymbol{\beta} = (\omega)$ and all the corepresentations are of type one. As could have been anticipated, all eigenvalues are simple in the presence of a magnetic field. However, taking for $\boldsymbol{\beta}$ the unit matrix, Eq. (26.39a) states that

$$\boldsymbol{\theta}\mathbf{O}_{\{0,\pi,0\}}\psi_\mu = \psi_\mu, \tag{26.47a}$$

or, substituting from (26.15c) $(-i)^n\mathbf{Q}_{\{0,\pi,0\}}\mathbf{K}$ for $\boldsymbol{\theta}$, and $\mathbf{P}_{\{0,\pi,0\}}\mathbf{Q}_{\{0,\pi,0\}}$ for $\mathbf{O}_{\{0,\pi,0\}}$

$$(-i)^n\mathbf{Q}_{\{0,\pi,0\}}\mathbf{K}\mathbf{P}_{\{0,\pi,0\}}\mathbf{Q}_{\{0,\pi,0\}}\psi_\mu = \psi_\mu.$$

Since $\mathbf{P}$ and $\mathbf{Q}_{\{0,\pi,0\}}$ are real and since the square of the latter is $(-1)^n$, one obtains

$$i^n\mathbf{P}_{\{0,\pi,0\}}\psi_\mu^* = \psi_\mu, \tag{26.47b}$$

or

$$i^n\psi_\mu(-x_1, y_1, -z_1, s_1, \cdots, -x_n, y_n, -z_n, s_n)^*$$
$$= \psi_\mu(x_1, y_1, z_1, s_1, \cdots, x_n, y_n, z_n, s_n), \tag{26.47c}$$

which holds in the presence of an arbitrarily strong homogeneous magnetic field along the Z-axis. The choice of the phase factor implied by $\boldsymbol{\beta} = (1)$ is the same as implied by the choice of the phase factor for Ψ_M^J with $M = \mu$ in (26.43a) so that the equations (26.47) are valid for the Ψ_M^J also without a change in phase factor. They can be obtained from (26.43a) by applying $\mathbf{O}_{\{0,\pi,0\}}$ to it and using the transformation properties of the Ψ_M^J along with the explicit expression for $\mathfrak{D}^{(J)}(\{0, \pi, 0\})$.

27. Physical Interpretation and Classical Limits of Representation Coefficients, Three- and Six-j Symbols

The representation coefficients, the three-j symbols, and the Racah coefficients are all typically quantum mechanical quantities. As all quantum mechanical quantities, they can be interpreted as probability amplitudes. It is the first aim of the present chapter to spell this out in detail.

The value of the angular momentum[1] $j\hbar$ and its component in a given direction $\mu\hbar$ can be simultaneously specified for a state. The wave functions Ψ^j_μ represent states in which the angular momentum and its Z-component are so specified. It is not possible, however, to specify two components of the angular momentum simultaneously. The wave function of the state, for which the projection of the angular momentum in the direction Z' is $\mu\hbar$, is $\mathbf{O}_R\Psi^j_\mu$ where R is a rotation which carries Z' into Z. However, except in the case of $j = 0$, the Z-component of the angular momentum does not have a specified value in the state $\mathbf{O}_R\Psi^j_\mu$; in fact the equation

$$\mathbf{O}_R\Psi^j_\mu = \sum_{\mu'} \mathfrak{D}^{(j)}(R)_{\mu'\mu}\Psi^j_{\mu'} \tag{27.1}$$

shows that all possible values of the Z-component of the angular momentum have, in general, a finite probability. The probability for the value $\mu'\hbar$ is the absolute square of the expansion coefficient of $\Psi^j_{\mu'}$ in (27.1); that is, it is $|\mathfrak{D}^{(j)}(R)_{\mu'\mu}|^2$. This is the simplest physical interpretation of the representation coefficients. Similar interpretations of the three-j symbols and of the six-j symbols will be given later.

In the region of large quantum numbers, the classical concepts become increasingly valid. Hence, it will have to be possible to define states the angular momenta of which are confined to narrow ranges in all directions. This will be verified below. Similarly, the three-j symbols and the six-j symbols must have, in the limit of large quantum numbers, interpretations in terms of ordinary geometric concepts. Such interpretations should render the symmetry properties of these symbols evident. This will indeed be the case. However, the approach of the quantum mechanical quantities to their classical analogues is by no means simple: they approach the classical limits only if averaged over a reasonable range of at least one of their indices. Individually, they will show oscillations around the average in a manner to be described in somewhat more detail below.

[1] It would be more in keeping with the general principles of quantum mechanics to say that the square of the angular momentum is $j(j + 1)\hbar^2$.

Representation Coefficients

The interpretation of

$$|\mathfrak{D}^{(j)}(R)_{\mu'\mu}|^2 = [\boldsymbol{d}^{(j)}(\beta)_{\mu'\mu}]^2 \tag{27.E.1}$$

in terms of observations which can be carried out, at least in principle, is contained in the preceding section. Expression (27.E.1) gives the probability that the Z-component of the angular momentum be $\mu'\hbar$ if the Z'-component of this quantity is $\mu\hbar$ and the total angular momentum[1] $j\hbar$. The rotation R carries the direction Z' into the direction Z. The angle between Z and Z' is β and, indeed, (27.E.1) depends only on β, not on the other Euler angles of the rotation R. A similar interpretation for the transformation matrix of the spin of a single electron was given after (20.20); the interpretation of the representation coefficients implicit in (27.E.1) was particularly emphasized by Güttinger.[2]

Several relations follow from the preceding interpretation of the representation coefficients. The most obvious among these is that the expression (27.E.1) must be symmetric in μ' and μ. It is easy to verify that

$$\boldsymbol{d}^{(j)}(\beta)_{\mu'\mu} = (-)^{\mu-\mu'}\boldsymbol{d}^{(j)}(\beta)_{\mu\mu'}. \tag{27.2}$$

Other relations the *square* of which is implicit in the interpretation of (27.E.1) are (24.7) and (19.14).

Setting $\mu = j$ in (27.1) one obtains a state in which the angular momentum is parallel to Z'. Then, the probability that the Z-component of the angular momentum be $\mu\hbar$ is, by (27.2) and (15.27a)

$$P(\mu) = \binom{2j}{j-\mu} \cos^{2j+2\mu} \tfrac{1}{2}\beta \sin^{2j-2\mu} \tfrac{1}{2}\beta. \tag{27.3}$$

If j is large, this expression must be expected to have a maximum around $\mu_0 = j \cos \beta$—*the* value which μ would assume in classical theory. The probability $P(\mu)$ can be calculated in the neighborhood of μ_0 most easily if one assumes that $\mu_0 = j \cos \beta$ is an integer. Since j is large, this is no essential restriction. Then, if $\mu > \mu_0$

$$P(\mu) = \frac{(2j)!}{(j-\mu)!(j+\mu)!} \cos^{2j+2\mu} \tfrac{1}{2}\beta \sin^{2j-2\mu} \tfrac{1}{2}\beta$$

$$= \frac{(j-\mu_0)(j-\mu_0-1)\cdots(j-\mu+1)}{(j+\mu_0+1)(j+\mu_0+2)\cdots(j+\mu)} (\tan^2 \tfrac{1}{2}\beta)^{\mu_0-\mu} P(\mu_0),$$

or since

$$\tan^2 \tfrac{1}{2}\beta = \frac{1-\cos\beta}{1+\cos\beta} = \frac{j-\mu_0}{j+\mu_0},$$

[2] P. Güttinger, *Z. Physik.* **73**, 169 (1932).

$$P(\mu) = \frac{1\left(1-\frac{1}{j-\mu_0}\right)\left(1-\frac{2}{j-\mu_0}\right)\cdots\left(1-\frac{\mu-\mu_0-1}{j-\mu_0}\right)}{\left(1+\frac{1}{j+\mu_0}\right)\left(1+\frac{2}{j+\mu_0}\right)\cdots\left(1+\frac{\mu-\mu_0}{j+\mu_0}\right)} P(\mu_0).$$

If $\mu - \mu_0 \ll j \pm \mu_0$, this is very nearly equal to

$$P(\mu) \approx \frac{e^{-(\mu-\mu_0)^2/2(j-\mu_0)}}{e^{(\mu-\mu_0)^2/2(j+\mu_0)}} P(\mu_0)$$

$$= e^{-j(\mu-\mu_0)^2/(j^2-\mu_0^2)} P(\mu_0). \tag{27.4}$$

The same formula applies if $\mu < \mu_0$. In quantum theory, $P(\mu)$ shows a Gaussian distribution around the value μ_0 which would be *the* value of μ in classical theory. The result would not have been so simple if we had considered a state $\mathbf{O}_R\Psi^j_\mu$ with $\mu \neq j$ because the angular momentum of such a state can assume, even in classical theory, every direction which includes an angle ϑ with Z' where $\cos\vartheta = \mu/j$. Only if $\mu = \pm j$ is this direction unique; it then coincides with Z' and $-Z'$, respectively.

Vector Coupling Coefficients

The most direct physical interpretation of the three-j symbols or of the vector coupling coefficients is implied by (24.20) or the numerous equivalent relations. According to (24.20)

$$(2j+1)\begin{pmatrix} j & \varkappa & \lambda \\ m & j_1 & j_2 \end{pmatrix}^2 = (2j+1)\begin{pmatrix} j & j_1 & j_2 \\ -m & \varkappa & \lambda \end{pmatrix}^2 \tag{27.E.2}$$

is the probability that the Z-components of the vectors[3] $\mathbf{j}_1$ and $\mathbf{j}_2$ be $\varkappa$ and λ if these vectors add up to $\mathbf{j}$ and the direction of $\mathbf{j}$ is such that its Z-component is m. The relation of $\mathbf{j}$, $\mathbf{j}_1$, and $\mathbf{j}_2$ becomes more symmetric if $\mathbf{j}$ is replaced by $-\mathbf{j}$ so that the three vectors $\mathbf{j}_1, \mathbf{j}_2, \mathbf{j}$ add up to zero. The situation in classical theory is illustrated in Fig. 14. The vector $\mathbf{j}_1$ can be directed to any point of the circle, the vector $\mathbf{j}_2$ then starts from that point. Evidently, if the lengths j_1, j_2, j of the vectors $\mathbf{j}_1, \mathbf{j}_2, \mathbf{j}$ and the projections of these vectors on the Z-axis, $\varkappa$, λ, and m (where $\varkappa + \lambda + m = 0$) are given, the whole configuration of the vectors $\mathbf{j}_1, \mathbf{j}_2, \mathbf{j}$ is determined, except that the whole figure can be rotated about the Z-axis. The numbers $j_1, j_2, j, \varkappa, \lambda, m$ can therefore be characterized by geometrical properties of the figure which are invariant under rotations about Z.

[3] In this chapter we deviate from the convention followed in the early chapters (that vectors be set in German type) and use bold face type for vectors, since no confusion is likely to arise here between vectors and operators.

Arcs of the circle in Fig. 14 which have equal lengths are equally probable as end points of $\mathbf{j}_1$. Hence if one proceeds at a constant rate on the circle in such a way that one traverses it in unit time, the time spent between the planes $z = \varkappa$ and $z = \varkappa + 1$ will give the probability of the value $\varkappa$ for the projection of $\mathbf{j}_1$ on Z. At the point P on the plane $z = \varkappa$, the direction of the tangent to the circle is $\mathbf{j}_1 \times \mathbf{j}_2$, the unit vector in this direction is $(\mathbf{j}_1 \times \mathbf{j}_2)/|(\mathbf{j}_1 \times \mathbf{j}_2)|$. The projection of this in the Z-direction is $(\mathbf{j}_1 \times \mathbf{j}_2) \cdot \mathbf{e}_z/|(\mathbf{j}_1 \times \mathbf{j}_2)|$,

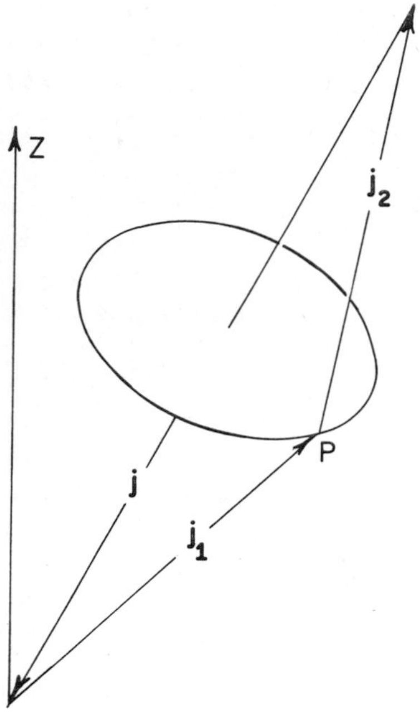

FIG. 14. Geometrical interpretation of the three-j symbol. The angular momenta $\mathbf{j}_1$ and $\mathbf{j}_2$ are coupled to a total angular momentum $\mathbf{j}$ with Z-component m. Under these circumstances, the probability that the Z-components of $\mathbf{j}_1$ and $\mathbf{j}_2$ are $\varkappa$ and $\lambda = m - \varkappa$, respectively, is given by (27.E.2). The asymptotic value of this probability is proportional to the total length of the arcs of the circle which lie between the planes $Z = \varkappa$ and $Z = \varkappa + 1$.

where $\mathbf{e}_z$ is the unit vector in the Z-direction. Hence if one proceeds with the velocity v on the circle, one proceeds in the Z-direction with the velocity

$$v \frac{(\mathbf{j}_1 \times \mathbf{j}_2) \cdot \mathbf{e}_z}{|(\mathbf{j}_1 \times \mathbf{j}_2)|},$$

and the time which one spends between the $z = \varkappa$ and $z = \varkappa + 1$ plane is the reciprocal of this quantity or, rather, twice the reciprocal because one passes through the interval $(\varkappa, \varkappa + 1)$ of z twice when traversing the circle. Since the circumference of the circle is $2\pi|(\mathbf{j}_1 \times \mathbf{j}_2)|/j$, this is also the velocity v. It follows that the probability for the Z-component of $\mathbf{j}_1$ to be between $\varkappa$ and $\varkappa + 1$ is

$$\frac{2|(\mathbf{j}_1 \times \mathbf{j}_2)|}{|(\mathbf{j}_1 \times \mathbf{j}_2) \cdot \mathbf{e}_z| v} = \frac{2|(\mathbf{j}_1 \times \mathbf{j}_2)|}{|(\mathbf{j}_1 \times \mathbf{j}_2) \cdot \mathbf{e}_z|} \frac{j}{2\pi|(\mathbf{j}_1 \times \mathbf{j}_2)|}. \tag{27.5}$$

Since this probability is also given by (27.E.2), with $-m$ replaced by m, the classical analogue of the square of the three-j symbol becomes

$$\begin{pmatrix} j & j_1 & j_2 \\ m & \varkappa & \lambda \end{pmatrix}^2 \approx \frac{\delta_{m+\varkappa+\lambda,0}}{2\pi|(\mathbf{j}_1 \times \mathbf{j}_2) \cdot \mathbf{e}_z|}. \tag{27.6}$$

The coefficient $j/(2j+1)$ was replaced by $\frac{1}{2}$. As was mentioned before, the numbers $j, j_1, j_2, m, \varkappa, \lambda$ determine the vectors $\mathbf{j}_1, \mathbf{j}_2, \mathbf{j}$ (where $\mathbf{j}_1 + \mathbf{j}_2 + \mathbf{j} = 0$), except that the figure of these vectors can be rotated about Z. However, the right side of (27.6) is evidently invariant under such a rotation. It is *the reciprocal of* 4π *times the projection of the area of the triangles formed by the vectors* $\mathbf{j}_1$, $\mathbf{j}_2$, $\mathbf{j}$ *on the* XY*-plane*. This last description also shows that (27.6) is invariant under interchanges of the vectors $\mathbf{j}_1, \mathbf{j}_2, \mathbf{j}$. Since $\mathbf{j}_1 + \mathbf{j}_2 + \mathbf{j} = 0$, this can be seen also from (27.6).

The explicit expression for the classical limit of the three-j symbol in terms of the indices contained therein is

$$4\pi \begin{pmatrix} j & j_1 & j_2 \\ m & m_1 & m_2 \end{pmatrix}^2 \approx \frac{\delta_{m_1+m_2+m,0}}{[A^2 + \frac{1}{4}(j^2 m_1 m_2 + j_1^2 m_2 m + j_2^2 m m_1)]^{1/2}} \tag{27.6a}$$

where A^2 is the square of the area of the triangle with the sides j, j_1, j_2.

$$16A^2 = -j^4 - j_1^4 - j_2^4 + 2j^2 j_1^2 + 2j^2 j_2^2 + 2j_1^2 j_2^2. \tag{27.6b}$$

As before, only the *square* of the quantum mechanical quantity, the three-j symbol, could be given a classical analogue. This is natural because the three-j symbols are *amplitudes* which, similar to ψ, have no direct classical analogue. For this reason (27.6) can be expected to be valid only if averaged over one of the indices over a reasonable range. It is possible, however, to use semiclassical concepts to interpret both $\mathfrak{D}$ and the vector coupling coefficients; the expressions so obtained[4,5] reproduce the sign of these quantities also. These semiclassical expressions are also valid only if all the quantum numbers are large but they show that the $\mathfrak{D}$ and the three-j symbols have an oscillatory character in the region in which our formulas are valid on the average. One would infer, from the interpretation of the three-j symbols here given, that these quantities vanish if m_1 assumes a value which lies either below the lowest point of the circle of Fig. 14, or above the highest point of this circle. The denominator of (27.6a) becomes imaginary in such a case. However, the semiclassical expressions show that the three-j symbol does not vanish for such m_1; it only decreases exponentially below and above the m_1 values which correspond to the lowest and highest point of the circle of Fig. 14.

[4] Cf. A. R. Edmonds, "Angular Momentum in Quantum Mechanics" Section 2.7 and Appendix 2. Princeton Univ. Press, Princeton, New Jersey, 1957.

[5] P. Brussard and J. H. Tolhoek, *Physica*, **23**, 955 (1957).

If $m = -j$, the vector $\mathbf{j}$ in Fig. 14 becomes antiparallel to Z, and $\varkappa$ and λ would be uniquely determined in classical theory. Their values will be denoted by $\varkappa_0$ and λ_0. Then

$$\varkappa_0 + \lambda_0 = j, \tag{27.7}$$

and the square of the altitude perpendicular to j is

$$j_1^2 - \varkappa_0^2 = j_2^2 - \lambda_0^2. \tag{27.7a}$$

These two equations determine $\varkappa_0$ and λ_0. In quantum theory, the probability that the projections of $\mathbf{j}_1$ and $\mathbf{j}_2$ assume the values $\varkappa$ and λ is given by (27.E.2). This probability will be denoted by $P(\varkappa, \lambda)$. The three-j symbol occurring in (27.E.2) for $m = -j$ is given by (17.27b) and (24.9a):

$$\begin{pmatrix} j & j_1 & j_2 \\ -j & \varkappa & \lambda \end{pmatrix} = \frac{(-)^{2j_1+j_2-\lambda}\delta_{\varkappa+\lambda,j}[(2j)!(j_1+j_2-j)!(j_1+\varkappa)!(j_2+\lambda)!]^{1/2}}{[(j+j_1+j_2+1)!(j-j_1+j_2)!(j+j_1-j_2)!(j_1-\varkappa)!(j_2-\lambda)!]^{1/2}} \tag{27.8}$$

Hence,

$$P(\varkappa, \lambda) = \text{const}\,\frac{(j_1+\varkappa)!(j_2+\lambda)!}{(j_1-\varkappa)!(j_2-\lambda)!} \tag{27.9}$$

where the constant is independent of $\varkappa$ and λ.

The following calculation is much simplified if one assumes that the classical values of $\varkappa$ and λ, that is $\varkappa_0$ and λ_0, are integers. Since the expression to be obtained for $P(\varkappa, \lambda)$ will be of interest only if all j and also $\varkappa$ and λ are large, this is not an essential assumption. If $\varkappa = \varkappa_0 + n$, $\lambda = \lambda_0 - n$, with a positive n, one has

$$\frac{P(\varkappa, \lambda)}{P(\varkappa_0, \lambda_0)} = \frac{(j_1+\varkappa_0+1)(j_1+\varkappa_0+2)\cdots(j_1+\varkappa_0+n)}{(j_2-\lambda_0+1)(j_2-\lambda_0+2)\cdots(j_2-\lambda_0+n)} \times \frac{(j_1-\varkappa_0)(j_1-\varkappa_0-1)\cdots(j_1-\varkappa_0-n+1)}{(j_2+\lambda_0)(j_2+\lambda_0-1)\cdots(j_2+\lambda_0-n+1)}. \tag{27.9a}$$

Because of (27.7a),

$$(j_1+\varkappa_0)(j_1-\varkappa_0) = (j_2-\lambda_0)(j_2+\lambda_0)$$

If one divides the numerator and denominator of (27.9a) by the nth power of this expression and assumes that n is small as compared with $j_1 \pm \varkappa$ and $j_2 \pm \lambda$, all factors in (27.9a) will differ very little from 1. Hence, (27.9a) can be evaluated by the formula

$$(1+h_1)(1+h_2)\cdots(1+h_n) = e^{h_1+h_2+\cdots+h_n}$$

and gives, by (27.7) and (27.7a),

$$\frac{P(\varkappa, \lambda)}{P(\varkappa_0, \lambda_0)} \approx \frac{\exp[-\varkappa_0 n^2/(j_1^2-\varkappa_0^2)]}{\exp[\lambda_0 n^2/(j_2^2-\lambda_0^2)]} = \exp(-jn^2/(j_1^2-\varkappa_0^2)). \tag{27.9b}$$

The same formula applies for negative n.

The last expression, for the probability of a deviation of $\varkappa$ from its classical value $\varkappa_0$ by the amount n, shows a great similarity to (27.4), the probability of a deviation of μ from its classical value μ_0. This probability is again largest for the value $\varkappa = \varkappa_0$ and shows, for large quantum numbers $j, j_1, j_2, \varkappa, \lambda$, a Gaussian distribution around $\varkappa_0$. In fact, there is for large quantum numbers a close similarity between the three-j symbols and the representation coefficients.[6] This is already apparent from Fig. 14 which becomes the figure underlying the interpretation of the representation coefficients if one omits therefrom the vector $\mathbf{j}_2$ and the part of $\mathbf{j}$ which extends above the plane of the circle.

Racah Coefficients

The physical interpretation of the six-j symbol is most apparent from the decomposition (24.22) of the wave function X_M^{jJ}—in which the combined angular momentum of particles 1 and 2 is j—into wave functions $\Phi_M^{j'J}$—in which the combined angular momentum of particles 1 and 3 is j':

$$X_M^{jJ} = \sum_{j'} \sqrt{2j+1}\,\sqrt{2j'+1}\,(-)^{2j_1} \begin{Bmatrix} J & j_2 & j' \\ j_1 & j_3 & j \end{Bmatrix} \Phi_M^{j'J}. \tag{27.10}$$

The $c(jJM;\ j'J'M') = \delta_{JJ'}\,\delta_{MM'}\,c^J(j;\ j')$ is expressed in (27.10) by means of the six-j symbol, as given in (24.23a). It follows that

$$(2j+1)(2j'+1) \begin{Bmatrix} J & j_2 & j' \\ j_1 & j_3 & j \end{Bmatrix}^2 \tag{27.E.3}$$

gives the probability that the sum of the angular momenta $\mathbf{j}_1$ and $\mathbf{j}_3$ has a length j'; provided the angular momenta $\mathbf{j}_1$ and $\mathbf{j}_2$ are coupled to a vector $\mathbf{j}$ of length j, and $\mathbf{j}_3$ is coupled with this vector to an angular momentum of length J. Figure 15 illustrates the relation of the six vectors; they form a (in general, irregular) tetrahedron.

If the length of the vectors $\mathbf{j}_1, \mathbf{j}_2, \mathbf{j}, \mathbf{j}_3, \mathbf{J}$ is fixed, the plane of the vectors $\mathbf{j}_1, \mathbf{j}_2, \mathbf{j}$ can yet rotate around $\mathbf{j}$. The point P of Fig. 15 then describes a circle, centered on a point on $\mathbf{j}$. Equal arcs of this circle have equal probabilities. The probability for a given value of j' can be calculated by the method used when we interpreted the three-j symbols. The unit vector tangent to the circle at P is $(\mathbf{j}_1 \times \mathbf{j}_2)/|(\mathbf{j}_1 \times \mathbf{j}_2)|$. The probability of unit range of j' is inversely proportional to the projection of this vector on j'; that is, it is proportional to

$$\frac{|(\mathbf{j}_1 \times \mathbf{j}_2)|}{(\mathbf{j}_1 \times \mathbf{j}_2)\cdot \mathbf{j}'/j'}.$$

[6] A. R. Edmonds, "Angular Momentum in Quantum Mechanics," Appendix 2. Princeton Univ. Press, Princeton, New Jersey, 1957.

The proportionality constant is the reciprocal of one half of the circumference of the circle, that is of $\pi|(\mathbf{j}_1 \times \mathbf{j}_2)|/j$. Hence, in the limit of large quantum numbers j, the expression (27.E.3) becomes

$$(2j+1)(2j'+1)\begin{Bmatrix} J & j_2 & j' \\ j_1 & j_3 & j \end{Bmatrix}^2 \approx \frac{|(\mathbf{j}_1 \times \mathbf{j}_2)|j'}{(\mathbf{j}_1 \times \mathbf{j}_2)\cdot\mathbf{j}'} \frac{j}{\pi|(\mathbf{j}_1 \times \mathbf{j}_2)|}. \quad (27.11)$$

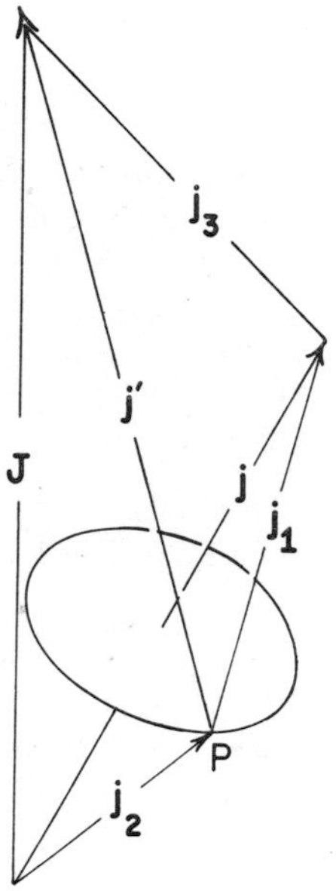

FIG. 15. Geometrical interpretation of the Racah coefficient. The angular momenta $\mathbf{j}_1$ and $\mathbf{j}_2$ are coupled to a combined angular momentum $\mathbf{j}$. This in turn is coupled with $\mathbf{j}_3$ to a total angular momentum $\mathbf{J}$. The probability that the angular momenta $\mathbf{j}_3$ and $\mathbf{j}_1$ are coupled to a combined angular momentum of magnitude j' is given in terms of the Racah coefficient by (27.E.3). The asymptotic value of this probability is proportional to the length of the arc of the circle the points of which have a distance between j' and $j' + 1$ from the end point of the vector $\mathbf{J}$.

Replacement of $j/(2j+1)$ and of $j'/(2j'+1)$ by $\frac{1}{2}$ gives

$$\begin{Bmatrix} J & j_2 & j' \\ j_1 & j_3 & j \end{Bmatrix}^2 \approx \frac{1}{4\pi(\mathbf{j}_1 \times \mathbf{j}_2)\cdot\mathbf{j}'}. \quad (27.12)$$

The square of the six-j symbol becomes asymptotically equal to the reciprocal of 24π *times the volume of the tetrahedron formed by the vectors contained in the symbol.* The approach to the asymptotic value is of the same character as in the case of the three-j symbols; only an average of the left side of (27.12), over at least one of the j can be expected to converge to the right side.

Appendix A.[1] Conventions

In this appendix we summarize the conventions for coordinates, rotations, and phases which have been adopted in this translation. These are identical with those of Rose[2] and have the advantage that they allow one to retain the wave functions of Condon and Shortley,[3] the representation coefficients of Wigner,[4] and the most widely used[3,4,5,6] convention for vector coupling coefficients, while making the change from the original left-handed coordinate system of Wigner to the more conventional right-handed system. Thus, any confusion which might arise from questions of convention in reference to the physical literature is minimized, while the disadvantage of the left-handed coordinates is eliminated.

A more complete summary of the relationships among the phases and notations used by various authors for representation coefficients, vector coupling coefficients, and recoupling coefficients is given by Edmonds.[6]

1. Coordinates

The coordinates used in this book are such that a (positive) rotation of the positive x-axis toward the (positive) y-axis would advance a right-handed screw along the positive z-axis. The spherical coordinates (r, ϑ, ϕ) are defined by the equations

$$
\begin{aligned}
r &= \sqrt{x^2 + y^2 + z^2}, \\
\vartheta &= \cos^{-1} \frac{z}{r}, \\
\phi &= \sin^{-1} y/\sqrt{x^2 + y^2}.
\end{aligned}
\tag{A.1}
$$

Figure 7, page 153, illustrates these definitions.

2. Rotations

A rotation R is specified by its Euler angles $\{\alpha, \beta, \gamma\}$. With each rotation is associated an operator $\mathbf{P}_R$ which (a) rotates the field about the z-axis by

[1] This appendix was added in translation.

[2] M. E. Rose, "Multipole Fields." Wiley, New York, 1955.

[3] E. U. Condon and G. H. Shortley, "The Theory of Atomic Spectra." Cambridge Univ. Press, London and New York, 1953.

[4] E. P. Wigner, "Gruppentheorie und ihre Andwendung auf die Quantenmechanik der Atomspektren." Vieweg, Braunschweig, 1931, of which this book is a translation.

[5] G. Racah, *Phys. Rev.* **62**, 438 (1942); **63**, 367 (1943).

[6] A. R. Edmonds, "Angular Momentum in Quantum Mechanics." Princeton Univ. Press, Princeton, New Jersey, 1957.

an angle α, (b) rotates the field about the y-axis by an angle β, and (c) rotates the field about the z-axis by an angle γ. The coordinate axes remain fixed in these rotations of the field. With each rotation is also associated a coordinate transformation, represented by a matrix $\mathbf{R}_R$, which effects (a) a rotation of the coordinates about the z-axis by an angle γ, (b) a rotation of the coordinates about the new y-axis by an angle β, and (c) a rotation of the coordinates about the new z-axis by an angle α. Thus[7]

$$\mathbf{R}_R = \mathbf{R}_{\{\alpha\beta\gamma\}} = \begin{pmatrix} \cos\alpha, & \sin\alpha, & 0 \\ -\sin\alpha, & \cos\alpha, & 0 \\ 0, & 0, & 1 \end{pmatrix} \begin{pmatrix} \cos\beta, & 0, & -\sin\beta \\ 0, & 1, & 0 \\ \sin\beta, & 0, & \cos\beta \end{pmatrix} \begin{pmatrix} \cos\gamma, & \sin\gamma, & 0 \\ -\sin\gamma, & \cos\gamma, & 0 \\ 0, & 0, & 1 \end{pmatrix} \tag{A.2}$$

A rotation of the coordinate system by means of $\mathbf{R}_{\{\alpha\beta\gamma\}}$ is entirely equivalent physically to an inverse rotation of the field by means of $\mathbf{P}_{\{\alpha\beta\gamma\}^{-1}} = \mathbf{P}_{\{\pi-\gamma,\beta,-\pi-\alpha\}}$; that is,

$$f(\mathbf{R}_R\mathfrak{r}) = (\mathbf{P}_{R^{-1}}f)(\mathfrak{r}) \tag{A.3}$$

where one writes $(\mathbf{P}_{R^{-1}}f)$ to emphasize the fact that the operator $\mathbf{P}$ gives a new function of the coordinates $\mathfrak{r}$. Let

$$\mathbf{P}_{R^{-1}}f(\mathfrak{r}) = g(\mathfrak{r}). \tag{A.4}$$

Then $f(\mathfrak{r}) = \mathbf{P}_R g(\mathfrak{r})$, and Eq. (A.3) becomes Eq. (11.19), which was used to define[8] the operator $\mathbf{P}_R$:

$$\left.\begin{aligned} \mathbf{P}_R g(\mathfrak{r}') &= g(\mathfrak{r}) \\ \mathfrak{r}' &= \mathbf{R}_R\mathfrak{r}. \end{aligned}\right\} \tag{A.5}$$

We note here for reference later that according to Eq. (A.2) the matrix $\mathbf{R}_{\{\alpha,\beta,\gamma\}}$ carries the point $(0, 0, z_1)$ with polar coordinates $(r = z_1, \vartheta = 0, \phi = 0)$ into the point (x', y', z') with polar coordinates $(r' = z_1, \vartheta' = \beta, \phi' = \pi - \alpha)$.

3. Representations of the Rotation Group and Spherical Harmonics

Equation (11.23) or (11.26) defines the representation matrix in terms of the operator $\mathbf{P}_R$ and the partner functions $\psi_\lambda(x_1, y_1, z_1, \cdots, x_n, y_n, z_n)$:

$$\mathbf{P}_R\psi_\nu(x_1, y_1, z_1, \cdots, x_n, y_n, z_n) = \sum_\varkappa \mathbf{D}(R)_{\varkappa\nu}\psi_\varkappa(x_1, y_1, z_1, \cdots, x_n, y_n, z_n) \tag{A.6}$$

[7] See Eqs. (15.14a) through (15.15).

[8] In evaluating products like $\mathbf{P}_S\mathbf{P}_R\,f(x)$, one must consider the operators in order from left to right, as discussed in Chapter 11. Only in this way can one insure that $\mathbf{P}_S\mathbf{P}_R = \mathbf{P}_{SR}$. See Chapter 11, page 106.

or, equivalently,

$$\psi_\nu(x_1', y_1', z_1', \cdots, x_n', y_n', z_n') = \sum_{\varkappa} \mathbf{D}(R)^*_{\nu\varkappa} \psi_\varkappa(x_1, y_1, z_1, \cdots, x_n, y_n, z_n), \quad (A.7)$$

where

$$\mathbf{r}_i' = \mathbf{R}_R \mathbf{r}_i.$$

For the case of the rotation group, the spherical harmonics $Y_{l,m}(\vartheta, \phi)$, $-l \leqslant m < +l$ are the partner functions, and the representation matrix is $\mathfrak{D}^{(l)}(R)_{km}$. Then by (A.6)

$$Y_{l,m}(\vartheta', \phi') = \sum_k \mathfrak{D}^{(l)}(R)^*_{mk} Y_{l,k}(\vartheta, \phi). \quad (A.8)$$

This equation defines the spherical harmonics for all ϑ' and ϕ' in terms of their values at $\vartheta = 0$, $\phi = 0$ and the $\mathfrak{D}^{(l)}_{km}$:

$$Y_{l,m}(\vartheta, \phi) = \sum_k \mathfrak{D}^{(l)}(R)^*_{mk} Y_{lk}(\vartheta = 0, \phi = 0). \quad (A.9)$$

Here R must be the rotation whose matrix $\mathbf{R}_R$ carries the point on the Z-axis at the distance r from the origin into the point with the polar coordinates r, ϑ, ϕ. As we have noted in the previous section, this rotation is $R = \{\pi - \phi, +\vartheta, +\gamma\}$. It was demonstrated in Chapter 15 that only $Y_{l,0}$ is nonzero at the point $\vartheta = \phi = 0$. Therefore, Eq. (A.9) is simply

$$Y_{l,m}(\vartheta, \phi) = \mathfrak{D}^{(l)}(\{\pi - \phi, +\vartheta, +\gamma\})^*_{m0} Y_{l0}(\vartheta = 0, \phi = 0). \quad (A.10)$$

In accordance with Condon and Shortley[3] we take $Y_{l0}(0, 0)$ to be real and positive; then

$$Y_{l,m}(\vartheta, \phi) = (\text{const}) \cdot (-1)^m e^{im\phi} \boldsymbol{d}^{(l)}(\vartheta)_{m0}. \quad (A.11)$$

This is the relationship stated in Eq. (19.8b) between the spherical harmonics and the representation coefficients. The spherical harmonics themselves are identical with those of Condon and Shortley.

4. Vector Coupling Coefficients

As was noted in Chapter 17, the matrix $\mathbf{S}^{(l,l)}_{Lm;\mu\nu} = s^{(l,l)}_{L,\mu,\nu}\, \delta_{m,\mu+\nu}$ is not uniquely specified by the requirement that it provides those linear combinations of products $\Psi'^{(l)}_\mu \Psi'^{(l)}_\nu$ which belong to the $(\mu + \nu)$th row of the representation $\mathfrak{D}^{(L)}$. Equation (17.21) states the choice made to specify the vector coupling coefficients uniquely:

$$s^{(l,l)}_{L,l,-l} = \left|s^{(l,l)}_{L,l,-l}\right| > 0. \quad (A.12)$$

Condon and Shortley[3] follow Wigner[4] in this choice, as do Racah[5], Rose,[2] and Edmonds.[6]

In terms of the vector coupling coefficients, one has for the 3-j symbols used in Chapter 24:

$$\begin{pmatrix} j_1 & j_2 & j_3 \\ m_1 & m_2 & m_3 \end{pmatrix} = \frac{(-1)^{j_1-j_2-m_3}}{\sqrt{2j_3+1}} s^{(j_1j_2)}_{j_3m_1m_2} \delta_{m_1+m_2+m_3,0} \,. \tag{A.13}$$

5. Racah Coefficients and Six-j Symbols

The recoupling coefficients, or six-j symbols, used in this text are related to Racah's W-coefficients as follows:

$$W(j_1j_2l_1l_2;\, j_3l_3) = (-1)^{j_1+j_2+l_1+l_2} \begin{Bmatrix} j_1 & j_2 & j_3 \\ l_1 & l_2 & l_3 \end{Bmatrix} \tag{A.14}$$

Appendix B. Summary of Formulas

Perturbation Theory

$$\mathbf{V}_{lk} = (\psi_l, \mathbf{V}\psi_k) \tag{5.8}$$

$$F_k = E_k + \lambda \mathbf{V}_{kk} + \lambda^2 \sum_{l\neq k} \frac{|\mathbf{V}_{lk}|^2}{E_k - E_l} \tag{5.10}$$

$$\varphi_k = \psi_k + \lambda \sum_{l\neq k} \frac{\mathbf{V}_{lk}}{E_k - E_l} \psi_l. \tag{5.11}$$

Group Theory

The symbol $\sum_R$ denotes a summation over all group elements for finite groups; for continuous groups, it implies the *Hurwitz* integral.

$$\sum_R J_R = \sum_R J_{SR}. \qquad (7.1), (10.5)$$

The orthogonality relationships of the unitary, irreducible representations of a group of order h are

$$\sum_R \mathbf{D}^{(j')}(R)^*_{\mu'\nu'} \mathbf{D}^{(j)}(R)_{\mu\nu} = \frac{h}{l_j} \delta_{j'j}\, \delta_{\mu'\mu}\delta_{\nu'\nu}, \tag{9.32}$$

where l_j is the dimension of $\mathbf{D}^{(j)}$. For the characters $\chi^{(j)}(R) = \sum_\mu \mathbf{D}^{(j)}(R)_{\mu\mu}$, one has

$$\sum_R \chi^{(j')}(R)^* \chi^{(j)}(R) = h\, \delta_{j'j}. \tag{9.33}$$

For continuous groups $h = \sum_R 1$ is replaced by $\int dR$ (Eqs. (10.12), (10.13)).

Representations and Eigenfunctions

From

$$\mathbf{P}_R f(x_1', x_2', \cdots, x_n') = f(x_1, x_2, \cdots, x_n), \tag{11.19}$$

where x_i and x_j' are related by the real, orthogonal transformation $\mathbf{R}$

$$x_j' = \sum_i \mathbf{R}_{ji} x_i \quad \text{or} \quad x_i = \sum_j \mathbf{R}_{ji} x_j', \tag{11.18}$$

it follows that

$$\mathbf{P}_{SR} = \mathbf{P}_S \mathbf{P}_R. \tag{11.20}$$

Also

$$\mathbf{P}_R \psi_\nu = \sum_\varkappa \mathbf{D}(R)_{\varkappa\nu} \psi_\varkappa \tag{11.23}$$

and $\mathbf{P}_S\mathbf{P}_R = \mathbf{P}_{SR}$ imply

$$\mathbf{D}(SR) = \mathbf{D}(S)\mathbf{D}(R). \tag{11.25}$$

Finally,

$$\mathbf{P}_R f_\varkappa^{(j)} = \sum_\lambda \mathbf{D}^{(j)}(R)_{\lambda\varkappa} f_\lambda^{(j)} \quad \text{and} \quad \mathbf{P}_R g_{\varkappa'}^{(j')} = \sum_{\lambda'} \mathbf{D}^{(j')}(R)_{\lambda'\varkappa'} g_{\lambda'}^{(j')}$$

imply

$$(f_\varkappa^{(j)}, g_{\varkappa'}^{(j')}) = \frac{h}{l_j}\,\delta_{jj'}\,\delta_{\varkappa\varkappa'} \sum_\lambda (f_\lambda^{(j)}, g_\lambda^{(j')}). \tag{12.8}$$

Irreducible Representations of the Three-Dimensional Rotation Group

$$\mathfrak{D}^{(j)}(\{\alpha\beta\gamma\})_{m'm} = e^{im'\alpha} \boldsymbol{d}^{(j)}(\beta)_{m'm} e^{im\gamma}. \tag{15.8}$$

$$\mathfrak{D}^{(\frac{1}{2})}(\{\alpha\beta\gamma\}) = \begin{pmatrix} e^{-\frac{1}{2}i\alpha}\cos\frac{1}{2}\beta e^{-\frac{1}{2}i\gamma} & -e^{-\frac{1}{2}i\alpha}\sin\frac{1}{2}\beta e^{\frac{1}{2}i\gamma} \\ e^{\frac{1}{2}i\alpha}\sin\frac{1}{2}\beta e^{-\frac{1}{2}i\gamma} & e^{\frac{1}{2}i\alpha}\cos\frac{1}{2}\beta e^{\frac{1}{2}i\gamma} \end{pmatrix}. \tag{15.16}$$

$$\mathfrak{D}^{(j)}(\{\alpha\beta\gamma\})_{j\mu} = \sqrt{\binom{2j}{j-\mu}}\, e^{ij\alpha} \cos^{j+\mu}\tfrac{1}{2}\beta \sin^{j-\mu}\tfrac{1}{2}\beta e^{i\mu\gamma}. \tag{15.27a}$$

$$\chi^{(j)}(\varphi) = \sum_{\mu=-j}^{j} e^{i\mu\varphi}. \tag{15.28}$$

The representation $\mathfrak{D}^{(l)} \times \mathfrak{D}^{(\bar{l})}$ contains exactly once each of the representations $\mathfrak{D}^{(L)}$, where

$$L = |l-\bar{l}|, |l-\bar{l}|+1, \cdots, l+\bar{l}-1, l+\bar{l}. \tag{17.14}$$

$$\mathfrak{D}^{(l)}(R)_{\mu'\mu}\mathfrak{D}^{(\bar{l})}(R)_{\nu'\nu} = \sum_{L=|l-\bar{l}|}^{l+\bar{l}} s_{L\mu'\nu'}^{(l\bar{l})}\mathfrak{D}^{(L)}(R)_{\mu'+\nu';\mu+\nu} s_{L\mu\nu}^{(l\bar{l})}, \tag{17.16b}$$

$$s_{L\mu L-\mu}^{(l\bar{l})} = \frac{(-1)^{l-\mu}\sqrt{(2L+1)!(l+\bar{l}-L)!}}{\sqrt{(L+l+\bar{l}+1)!(L+l-\bar{l})!(L-l+\bar{l})!}}, \times \sqrt{\frac{(l+\mu)!(\bar{l}+L-\mu)!}{(l-\mu)!(\bar{l}-L+\mu)!}} \tag{17.27b}$$

$$\begin{aligned} \sum_\mu s_{L,\mu,m-\mu}^{(l\bar{l})} s_{L',\mu m-\mu}^{(l\bar{l})} &= \delta_{LL'}, \\ \sum_L s_{L,\mu,m-\mu}^{(l\bar{l})} s_{L,\mu',m-\mu'}^{(l\bar{l})} &= \delta_{\mu\mu'}. \end{aligned} \tag{17.28}$$

Pauli's Theory of Spin

$$\begin{aligned} &\mathbf{Q}_R\Phi(x_1, y_1, z_1, s_1, \cdots x_n, y_n, z_n, s_n) \\ &= \sum_{t_1=\pm 1} \cdots \sum_{t=\pm 1} \mathfrak{D}^{(1/2)}(R)_{\frac{1}{2}s_1,\frac{1}{2}t_1} \cdots \mathfrak{D}^{(1/2)}(R)_{\frac{1}{2}s_n,\frac{1}{2}t_n} \\ &\qquad \Phi_{(x_1,y_1,z_1,t_1,\cdots x_n,y_n,z_n,t_n)} \end{aligned} \tag{21.6b}$$

$$\mathbf{O}_R = \mathbf{P}_R\mathbf{Q}_R = \mathbf{Q}_R\mathbf{P}_R. \tag{21.8}$$

Irreducible Tensors

$$\mathbf{O}_R^{-1}\mathbf{T}^{(\rho)}\mathbf{O}_R = \sum_{\sigma=-\omega}^{\omega} \mathfrak{D}^{(\omega)}(R)_{\rho\sigma}\mathbf{T}^{(\sigma)}, \tag{21.16b}$$

$$\mathbf{T}^{(\rho)}_{Nj\mu;N'j'\mu'} = (\Psi_{\mu}^{Nj}, \mathbf{T}^{(\rho)}\Psi_{\mu'}^{N'j'}) \tag{21.18}$$

$$= s^{(j\omega)}_{j'\mu\rho}\,\delta_{\mu+\rho,\mu'}T_{Nj;N'j'}. \tag{21.19}$$

$s^{(j\omega)}_{j'\mu\rho}$ here is zero if

$$|j-\omega| > j' \quad \text{or} \quad j' > j+\omega.$$

Infinitesimal Rotations

The operator for the infinitesimal rotation of the cartesian coordinates is:

$$\frac{1}{\hbar}\mathbf{L}_z\Psi = -i\frac{\partial}{\partial\alpha}\mathbf{P}_{\{\alpha 00\}}\Psi\Big|_{\alpha=0}; \tag{18.7}$$

of the spin coordinates

$$\tfrac{1}{2}(s_1+s_2+\cdots+s_n)\Psi = \frac{1}{\hbar}\mathbf{S}_z\Psi = -i\frac{\partial}{\partial\alpha}\mathbf{Q}_{\{\alpha 00\}}\Psi\Big|_{\alpha=0}; \tag{23.23a}$$

and of all coordinates simultaneously:

$$\frac{1}{\hbar}(\mathbf{L}_z+\mathbf{S}_z) = -i\frac{\partial}{\partial\alpha}\mathbf{O}_{\{\alpha 00\}}\Big|_{\alpha=0}. \tag{23.30a}$$

Three-*j* Symbols

1. Relationship between three-*j* symbols and vector coupling coefficients.

$$\begin{pmatrix} j_1 & j_2 & j_3 \\ m_1 & m_2 & m_3 \end{pmatrix} = \frac{(-1)^{j_1-j_2-m_3}}{\sqrt{2j_3+1}} s^{(j_1j_2)}_{j_3m_1m_2}\delta_{m_1+m_2+m_3,0} \tag{24.9a}$$

2. Symmetries of three-*j* symbols.

$$(-)^{j_1+j_2+j_3}\begin{pmatrix} j_1 & j_2 & j_3 \\ m_1 & m_2 & m_3 \end{pmatrix} = \begin{pmatrix} j_1 & j_3 & j_2 \\ m_1 & m_3 & m_2 \end{pmatrix} = \begin{pmatrix} j_3 & j_2 & j_1 \\ m_3 & m_2 & m_1 \end{pmatrix} = \begin{pmatrix} j_2 & j_1 & j_3 \\ m_2 & m_1 & m_3 \end{pmatrix} \tag{24.10}$$

$$\begin{pmatrix} j_1 & j_2 & j_3 \\ m_1 & m_2 & m_3 \end{pmatrix} = \begin{pmatrix} j_2 & j_3 & j_1 \\ m_2 & m_3 & m_1 \end{pmatrix} = \begin{pmatrix} j_3 & j_1 & j_2 \\ m_3 & m_1 & m_2 \end{pmatrix} \tag{24.10a}$$

$$\begin{pmatrix} j_1 & j_2 & j_3 \\ -m_1 & -m_2 & -m_3 \end{pmatrix} = (-1)^{j_1+j_2+j_3}\begin{pmatrix} j_1 & j_2 & j_3 \\ m_1 & m_2 & m_3 \end{pmatrix} \tag{24.10b}$$

Six-*j* Symbols

1. Relationships with three-*j* symbols.

$$(j_1\, l_2\, l^{\cdot})(l_1\, j_2\, l_{\cdot}) = (-)^{2l_1} \sum_j (2j+1) \begin{Bmatrix} j_1 & j_2 & j \\ l_1 & l_2 & l \end{Bmatrix} (j_1\, j_2\, j^{\cdot})(l_1\, l_2\, j_{\cdot}) \qquad (24.24a)$$

$$(j_1\, l_{2\cdot}\, l_3^{\cdot})(l_1^{\cdot}\, j_2\, l_{3\cdot})(l_{1\cdot}\, l_2^{\cdot}\, j_3) = \begin{Bmatrix} j_1 & j_2 & j_3 \\ l_1 & l_2 & l_3 \end{Bmatrix} (j_1\, j_2\, j_3) \qquad (24.24b)$$

(See Chapter 24 for covariant notation used above.)

2. Consider the σth component $\mathbf{T}^{\sigma}$ of an irreducible tensor of degree p with respect to the positional coordinates, and of degree 0 (scalar) with respect to the spin coordinates. The operator $\mathbf{T}^{\sigma}$ is then an irreducible tensor of rank $\omega = p$ with respect to the rotations of all coordinates. For such an operator, an alternative form of Eq. (21.19) is

$$(\Psi_{\mu}^{NJ}, \mathbf{T}^{\sigma}\Psi_{\mu'}^{N'J'}) = (J^{\mu}, p^{\sigma}, J'_{\mu'})T_{NJ;N'J'}. \qquad (24.27a)$$

The $T_{NJ;N'J'}$ in (24.27a) is $(-1)^{J-p-J'}\sqrt{2J'+1}$ times the $T_{NJ;N'J'}$ of (21.19). If LS coupling applies for both Ψ_{μ}^{NJ} and $\Psi_{\mu'}^{N'J'}$, then

$$T_{NJ;N'J'} = (-1)^{2J-L+S+J'+p} \begin{Bmatrix} J & p & J' \\ L' & S & L \end{Bmatrix} \sqrt{2J+1}\,\sqrt{2J'+1}\; T_{NSL;N'S'L'}. \qquad (24.30)$$

Antiunitary Operators

An operator $\boldsymbol{\theta}$ is antiunitary if for any two states Ψ and Φ

$$(\boldsymbol{\theta}\Phi, \boldsymbol{\theta}\Psi) = (\Phi, \Psi)^* = (\Psi, \Phi) \qquad (26.8)$$

and

$$\boldsymbol{\theta}(\alpha\Phi + \beta\Psi) = \alpha^*\boldsymbol{\theta}\Phi + \beta^*\boldsymbol{\theta}\Psi. \qquad (26.5)$$

The antiunitary time inversion operator is given by

$$\boldsymbol{\theta} = \mathbf{s}_{1y}\mathbf{s}_{2y}\cdots\mathbf{s}_{ny}\mathbf{K} \qquad (26.15a)$$

$$= (-i)^n \mathbf{Q}_{\{0,\pi,0\}}\mathbf{K}, \qquad (26.15c)$$

where $\mathbf{K}$ is the operator which replaces a quantity by its complex conjugate.

The multiplication laws for the matrices which correspond to antiunitary operators $\mathbf{a}$ and unitary operators $\mathbf{u}$ are

$$\mathbf{D}(\mathbf{u}_1)\mathbf{D}(\mathbf{u}_2) = \mathbf{D}(\mathbf{u}_1\mathbf{u}_2),$$

$$\mathbf{D}(\mathbf{a})\mathbf{D}(\mathbf{u})^* = \mathbf{D}(\mathbf{a}\mathbf{u}),$$

$$\mathbf{D}(\mathbf{u})\mathbf{D}(\mathbf{a}) = \mathbf{D}(\mathbf{u}\mathbf{a}),$$

$$\mathbf{D}(\mathbf{a}_1)\mathbf{D}(\mathbf{a}_2)^* = \mathbf{D}(\mathbf{a}_1\mathbf{a}_2). \qquad (26.21)$$

SUBJECT INDEX

D

E

F

U

V

W

Z